D1592345

Parasitic Diseases
Fifth Edition

Dickson D. Despommier, Robert W. Gwadz, Peter J. Hotez, Charles A. Knirsch

36 Life Cycles by
John Karapelou

Photographs by
Dickson D. Despommier

Parasitic Diseases
Fifth Edition

Foreword by James Jensen

With 417 illustrations in full color

1,869 references

Apple Trees Productions, LLC
P.O. Box 280, New York, New York 10032

Dickson D. Despommier, Ph.D. Professor of Public Health (Parasitology) and Microbiology, The Joseph L. Mailman School of Public Health, Columbia University in the City of New York. 10032

Robert W. Gwadz, Ph.D. Captain USPHS (ret) Assistant Chief, Laboratory of Malaria and Vector Research, National Institute of Allergy and Infectious Diseases.

Peter J. Hotez, M.D., Ph.D. F.A.A.P. Professor and Chairman, Department of Microbiology and Tropical Medicine, George Washington University Medical Center, Washington, DC 20037, Attending Pedia trician, Children's National Medical Center, Washington DC

Charles A. Knirsch, M.D., M.P.H. Assistant Clinical Professor, Division of Infectious Diseases, Department of Medicine, College of Physicians and Surgeons, Columbia University in the City of New York, New York, NY 10032; Therapeutic Head, Anti-infectives, Pfizer, Inc., New York. 10017.

John Karapelou. Biomedical Illustrations, Inc. 3739 Pendlestone Drive, Columbus, Ohio. 43230.

Cover Design: Dickson Despommier

Page layout and design: Steven X. Chen, Director of Productions, Apple Trees Productions, LLC. P.O. Box 280, New York, 10032.

Additional graphics and editing by Steven X. Chen

Library of Congress Cataloguing-in-Publication Data
Despommier, Dickson D.
    Parasitic Diseases / Dickson D. Despommier, Robert W. Gwadz, Peter J. Hotez, Charles A. Knirsch:
        - 5th edition
    p. cm.
    Includes bibliographical references and index.
    ISBN 0-9700027-7-7
    1. Parasitic diseases I. Gwadz, Robert W. II. Hotez., Peter J. III Knirsch, Charles A.
    IV. Title.

Printed on paper made of pulp from trees harvested in managed forests.

Production and design by Steven X. Chen
Cover design by Dickson Despommier
Printing was by Sentinel Printing, 250 North Highway 10, St. Cloud, MN 65302

We dedicate the 5th edition of Parasitic Diseases to Harold W. Brown, George B. Craig, Jr., Benjamin Kean, and Harry Most. Through their tireless devotion to educating students as to the importance of tropical infectious diseases, so have they have inspired us to continue their good work.

Acknowledgements:

We acknowledge the contribution of John Karapelou for his elegant life cycle drawings. Thanks to David Scharf for granting us use of his stunning scanning electron micrographs of the very things that attract of legions of new medical students to the field of tropical medicine. Thank you Rosemary D'Alesandro, and a special thanks to Molly Bloom for carefully going through the fourth edition with a sharp eye for gramatical correctness and syntax. Thanks to Steven Chen for working tirelessly on the formatting and layout (without your input, we would still be working on it). A special thanks to Dennis Dwyer for reviewing the chapters on leishmaniasis. We thank all our students for carefully reading our book and pointing out all the correctable things to us that will make this new edition so much better. Thanks to James Jensen, a good friend and excellent teacher of parasitic diseases, for writing the Foreword to the fifth edition; his insightful personal observations on the prevalence and incidence of parasitic infections give each reader a sense of their true medical relevance to the human condition. Finally, thanks to all the course directors of parasitic diseases and parasitology who choose our book as the one to help guide their students throught the complexities of life cycles, clincial presentations, etc. We hope that the fifth edition proves even more useful for you and your students in the coming years.

Foreword

The prevalence of diseases caused by eukaryotic parasites in a given region is an excellent indicator of the quality of human life there. Since most of them are transmitted by fecal contamination or by vectors, there is more incidence of them where personal and community hygiene is poor and where vector control is not possible for biological or economic reasons. As the world's population continues to expand, placing greater and greater stress on already limited resources, these diseases will most surely increase. What is particularly disturbing is the lack of understanding of parasites and their diseases within the medical community of more developed nations. I taught parasitology for a while at Cornell University's medical school, and one day another professor, whom I had not yet met, asked me what I did my research on. I told him that I worked on the malaria parasite. Looking somewhat puzzled, he remarked, "Is that still a problem?"

Over the next twenty years, I carried out many aspects of my research in Africa, Southeast Asia, and Central and South America. It was apparent to me that the principal health problems of the developing world were not heart disease, cancer, and diabetes, but rather malaria, leishmaniasis, intestinal helminths, schistosomes, and parasite-induced diarrheal disease. Despite the fact that these diseases were all around me, the amount of human suffering due to parasitic diseases was still difficult to accurately estimate. A case in point: while doing field-based research on malaria in the Sudanese village of Um Shoka ("Mother of Thorn"), our team had gathered some 200 villagers together. They were sitting around the clinic waiting for us to fix, stain, and read their blood films so that they could receive treatment, and were a bit put out with us because they all knew they had malaria—they didn't need a blood film to tell them that! The graduate student who was reading the slides called me over to look at one that had a 9% parasitemia, a genuine medical emergency. Trying to remain as calm as I could, I called out to the waiting crowd: "Ahmed Mohamed, Ahmed Mohamed," to which there was no answer. Eventually, a man replied, "I know him. He is not here." "But I need to see him," I answered. The man said to me, "I know where he lives, I'll take you there." As we drove through the village, he said to me, "he is only a young boy."

In Africa, as elsewhere, malaria is a childhood disease. As we approached the mud hut of the young boy, his father was just entering the gate with a shovel on his shoulder. This heart-rending experience was my first with malaria's unrelenting mortality rate. It was also clear that no one recorded the death of Ahmed Mohamed. How did he fit into the statistics?

In the village of Mypurajaya, deep in the forest of Irian Jaya, Indonesia, we were once again studying malaria. It was about 2:00 AM when a loud pounding on the door of our hut awoke us. We could barely see through the sheets of rain, but a large, bundled apparition stumbled across the threshhold and collapsed on the floor; it was a man with a large grass cloak over his shoulders. Under the cloak, we discovered two children strapped to his back. We carried them into our makeshift clinic while the man told us that he came from a village some fifteen miles away to seek help for his sons, who were suffering from malaria. He had tied them to his back and had walked for several hours in the rain to see us. It was with great sadness that we informed him that during the journey, his two sons had died of the disease. Again, who recorded these deaths?

These are indeed tragic stories, yet one might be tempted to dismiss them as not being relevant to our part of the world. Please reconsider; Sudan and New Guinea are not so far away. Modern transportation has shrunken the world, so that any place on earth is no more than an 18-hour plane ride away. Parasitic diseases are emerging in the western world due to immigration and travel at an alarming rate. A search of the infectious disease databases reveals more and more of these "exotic" diseases being regularly reported in the USA. Not only are there increasingly more cases of tropical diseases in the USA, Canada, and Europe in visitors and immigrants, but also among those native to those regions of the world. The number of Americans traveling to exotic lands is in the tens of millions. They return home, but not necessarily safe and sound; many of these travelers have acquired diseases along the way that puzzle the US medical community regarding their diagnosis and treatment.

Just five short years ago, President Clinton announced the Millennium Initiative, whose goal was to reduce the burden of infectious diseases in the developing world. In a State of the Union address, he stressed that infectious diseases, particularly malaria, tuberculosis and HIV/AIDS, cause almost half of all deaths worldwide of people under age 45, killing some 8 million children each year and orphaning millions more. Furthermore, parasitic infectious diseases impose a mounting social and economic burden on developing countries, and are a threat to American health as well. This book contains a valuable section, "Travel Medicine: Advice to the Clinician," a chapter every physician should be familiar with.

Notwithstanding the mortality rates due to malaria and a few other parasitic diseases, the real problem of parasites is their impact on human vitality. There is a long-recognized phenomenon, newly coined by the World Health Organization as DALY, meaning "disease-associated lost years." The concept is to underscore the loss of human energy, creativity, and productivity caused by the burden imposed by parasitic and other chronic diseases. No one disputes the view that solutions to future problems will come from the educated, creative minds of today's youth. I invite the students who are using this book as a study guide to imagine how much more difficult school would be if their efforts were hampered by persistent fevers, chronic diarrhea, hookworm, or malaria-associated anemia. Such is the situation in developing countries where nearly every young student is parasitized, often by several different species. This book provides excellent insights into both zoonotic and vector-borne diseases, common themes in parasitology and tropical infectious diseases. No one can predict where or how the next emerging scourge will come, but the odds are excellent that it will be vector-borne and probably a zoonosis.

What can be done to alleviate the stress on the human condition caused by these pathogens? We desperately need new drugs for malaria, schistosomiasis, leishmaniasis, Chagas' disease, the geohelminths, and hookworm. Vaccines are non-existent. It is of interest to note that recent efforts in molecular genetics have yielded complete genomes of several important parasites, including malaria and its vector mosquito species. Hopefully, this information will aid in developing new approaches of control of parasitic diseases, including the possibility for molecular-based vaccines. Genetic engineering holds great promise for solutions to infectious diseases in general and parasitic diseases in particular.

Most importantly, the education of a new generation of physicians, whose knowledge base includes a global view of infectious diseases, will insure the recruitment of some of them to our field of parasitic diseases. This is why *Parasitic Diseases* exists. I have used this book in one edition or another for many years, and each version has been a marked improvement over its predecessor. *Parasitic Diseases* bridges the gap between classroom and bedside. It is what college students call "a keeper."

James Jensen

Preface

Remarkable advancements in parasitic disease research have occurred over the past 5 years, and we have striven wherever possible to incorporate these findings into this 5th edition of Parasitic Diseases. This is reflected in the fact that we have used some 550 new references (2000 to 2005) to document these advances. Innovative work in the laboratory has provided the clinician/research scientist with a much clearer understanding of the mechanisms of pathogenesis, including those intricate strategies employed by parasites to evade host immune attack. The mode of action of a few important anti-parasitic drugs, and the description at the molecular level of complex pathways activated throughout the infection period as revealed by the now well-established technology of DNA microchips are subject areas in which much new progress has been made.

The Genome Project reached a high point several years back with the completion of the sequencing of the human genome. Now it is focused squarely on the genomes of significant pathogens and their vectors. Completion of the sequencing of genomes of several important parasites has been accomplished over the last two years (e.g., *Plasmodium falciparum* and *Toxoplasma gondii*). In addition, the genome of *Anopheles gambiae*, a significant mosquito vector of *P. falciparum* has also been completed. Other parasites whose entire genomes will soon be available include the schistosomes, *Entamoeba histolytica, Giardia lamblia, Leishmania tropica,* and the American and African trypanosomes. Results from these efforts hold great promise for the development of effective new vaccines and drugs based on identifying unique molecular pathways essential to each pathogen in question. These on-going projects serve as a living testament to the perseverance of a small, dedicated band of talented molecular parasitologists whose sole wish is to help stem the tide regarding the spread of these life-threatening diseases.

Political will and strong social mobilization have combined to severely limit the spread of some parasites without the use of vaccines or drugs. For example, dracunculosis has been brought under control in all but a few regions of Africa, and the southern cone initiative of South America has resulted in fewer and fewer cases of Chagas' Disease transmitted by the reduviid bug vectors. While there are no new classes of drugs for treating resistant malaria, artemesinin derivatives continue to be effective in reducing the mortality wherever that chemotherapeutic agent is available.

As encouraging and inspiring as these research efforts are, they are the only bright spots on an ever increasingly darkening picture of world health, revealing the lack of control of most species of eukaryotic parasites that significantly detract from our ability to live long and prosper. For example, geohelminths continue to exact their toll on the normal development of the children of the world who are forced, simply by where they live, to co-exist with them. In addition, diarrheal diseases caused by a veritable alphabet soup of infectious agents, including *Entamoeba histolytica, Giardia lamblia, Cryptosporidium parvum* and *Cyclospora cayatenensis*, round out the list of miseries to be dealt with by all those living in poverty in the less developed world. Regrettably, there is no end in sight for the control of these agents, despite the best efforts of WHO, numerous in-country and NGO health agencies. The simple act of safely sequestering feces and urine away from our drinking water and food supply remains high on the list of things to do for those countries in which these two human by-products serve as the only source of fertilizer. It as if the parasites themselves were in charge of the agricultural practices of the less developed world, insuring that they will succeed in infecting us!

Political instability of vast regions of Africa and the Middle East has led to the re-emergence of many infectious diseases, with malaria, leishmaniasis, and trypanosomiasis leading the parade. This has been largely due to environmental destruction, abandonment of control programs, and forced migration of tens of thousands of individuals from regions that were relatively safe in which to live to places that no one should have to occupy, no matter how short the duration. These difficult situations require more than vaccines and drugs to effect a "cure". Social equity, economic development, and long-term planning are the "drugs of choice". The impact of HIV/AIDS in resource constrained geographic areas has reduced overall life expectancy significantly. The interplay of the immunosuppression caused by this disease and the impact on other parasitic diseases is poorly understood and requires careful monitoring. As access to antiretroviral therapy improves due to the Global Fund and other entities, new clinical syndromes are likely to emerge due to parasites behaving differently in hosts with an ever changing immune status.

To counteract these negative trends, the United Nations member States combined forces, committing to a new initiative, The Millennium Development Goals (MDG's), which set targets for improvement of the human condition on a worldwide basis by the year 2015. The MDG's of reducing child mortality, improving maternal health and combating HIV/AIDS, malaria and other diseases are intricately linked to the subject matter that fleshes out the contents of our 5th Edition of Parasitic Diseases.

There has been increasing recognition from all organizations that deal with our subject that 10 parasitic diseases of great public health importance, namely African trypanosomiasis, Chagas' disease, leishmaniasis, hookworm, ascariasis, trichuriasis, dracunculiasis, onchocerciasis, and lymphatic filariasis, have been sorely neglected by the scientific and international health community. If the MDG's targets are addressed, the next five years should see the beginning of a new era, in which the burden of parasitic diseases need not be taken for granted when the fate of less developed countries are discussed.

Readers of this text will be armed with the basic knowledge of parasites and disease states to join an effort that has everything to do with the fitness and survival of the majority of the human species.

Dickson Despommier
Robert Gwadz
Peter Hotez
Charles Knirsch

Contents

III. Eukaryotic Parasites

Eukaryotic parasites encompass subsets of organisms within the protozoan and helminths groups. In addition, medically important arthropods have been included in discussions of eukaryotic parasites, since so many of these pathogens are transmitted to humans by arthropod vectors. Furthermore, some medically relevant arthropods cause disease on their own.

From a biological perspective, a phylogenetic presentation of eukaryotic parasitic organisms would undoubtedly satisfy those specialists who strictly adhere to the zoological literature, while most medical students and practicing clinicians would have little or no use for this information. The physician is more inclined to group them according to their syndromes, if they were to classify them at all. We have settled upon a compromise, in which they are encountered by the reader in a somewhat biologically correct order, together with an outline of their classification, realizing that physicians do not receive and treat patients from the waiting room in that way, nor do they conduct rounds each day in the wards in phylogenetic order of disease presentation. Nonetheless, it is in some sense intellectually satisfying to review parasitic organisms with a semblance of evolutionary precision, allowing each student to learn about them in a sequence that most experts in the field of parasitology have agreed upon, going from the single cell parasites to the worms and beyond. We present protozoans first, followed by the helminths, and finally round out the synopsis with medically-relevant arthropods.

The last half of the twentieth century has been a remarkable one for the community-based control of pathogenic organisms. New vaccines and antibiotics have also helped reduce the incidence of numerous pathogenic organisms. At the same time, it has also heralded the emergence and re-emergence of a wide spectrum of infectious agents: viruses (e.g., SARS, HIV, monkey pox, avian influenza), bacteria (e.g., *Legionella pneumophila*, *Borrelia burgdorferi*, *Escherichia coli* strain OH157, protozoa (e.g., *Cryptosporidium parvum*, *Cyclospora cayetanensis*), and helminths (eg., *Echinococcus multilocularis*, *Angiostrongylus cantonesis*, *Trichinella spiralis*). Viewed from an evolutionary perspective, humans represent a highly successful system of essential niches, of which an astonishingly wide variety of eukaryotes have been able to take advantage. The number of individuals infected with any given parasite rarely makes but little impression on even the most attentive medical student, especially when it is a very large number, as is the case for *Ascaris lumbricoides,* which infects hundreds of millions of people around the world. So when one hears for the first time that over 800 million people are infected with malaria each year, and over 1 million children per year die in Africa alone from this infection, these facts seem somehow coolly remote, even abstract. Yet, when a single child suffering from the cerebral form of this disease-causing entity is admitted into a modern hospital in critical condition, and, regardless of treatment, that young person dies, the health care community of that institution is put into collective shock. If the death occurred at a teaching hospital, a grand rounds is the usual outcome, perhaps motivated by some vague sense of guilt, in a futile attempt to see if anything could have been done to spare that life. But the truth is that the most lethal species of malaria, *Plasmodium falciparum*, is evolving more and more towards total resistance to synthetic derivatives of quinine (e.g., chloroquine and mefloquine), a family of drugs that not long ago freed us from its death grip. Perhaps nothing could have been done to save that person. This situation represents the ultimate fear of every physician.

Parasitic Protozoa

What is a protozoan? Which ones cause disease? How do those which are parasitic differ from their free living counter parts? What are the pathogenic mechanism(s) by which they cause disease? There are over 200,000 named species of single celled organisms that fall under the category protozoa, while many more, no doubt, await discovery. Only some small fraction of these are parasitic on the human host, yet some can cause great harm (e.g., malaria), especially when they are encountered for the first time.

Protozoans are single-cell organisms inside of which usually resides one membrane-bound nucleus, the only two exceptions being *Giardia lamblia* and *Dientamoeba fragilis*. Most protozoa have one type of organelle that aids in their movement (e.g., flagella, undulating membrane, cilia). Metabolic pathways also vary from group to group, with both anaerobic and aerobic energy metabolisms being represented among the parasites to be discussed. In the case of parasitic organisms, the host provides the energy source. There are a variety of drugs that take advantage of the dependence of parasites on host energy metabolism. When a specific drug with a known mode of action is recommended, we will present a detailed description of it.

The following section is organized in such a way as to enable the student or clinician easy access to a highly distilled body of information relating to the general schemes employed when these organisms interact with the human host to produce disease. Thus, only biological information essential to the understanding of clinical aspects of a given disease-causing organism will be emphasized.

The following topics are deemed medically relevant: (1) mechanisms of entry; (2) niche selection; (3) reproduction; (4) mechanisms of survival (i.e., virulence factors); and (5) mechanisms of pathogenesis. All single-cell organisms have complex biochemistries, often employing unique pathways that give some of them remarkable evolutionary advantages. These include the ability of a given population to vary their protein surfaces (e.g., the African trypanosomes, some species of Plasmodium, and *Giardia lamblia*), edit their mRNA transcripts, secrete peptides that prevent the fusion of lysosomal membranes to the parasitophorous vacuole, and give off substances that inhibit host protective immune responses. A plethora of unique molecular pathways have been described for this diverse group of parasites, but a comprehensive description of them is beyond the scope of this book. Some attention to both the biochemical and molecular biological findings for a given organism will be presented whenever they have relevance to the understanding of the mechanisms of pathogenesis or parasite survival strategies.

Mechanisms of Entry

Protozoans gain entry into their host in one of three ways: oral, sexual, and through the bites of blood-sucking vectors (e.g., tsetse flies, sandflies, and mosquitoes). Avoidance or prevention of infection requires an intimate knowledge of its transmission cycle, and knowing the route of entry into the host is one of the most important aspects in that regard. Many species of parasitic protozoa have evolved stages that facilitate their dispersal into the environment, increasing their chances of encountering a host. Som intestinal protozoa (e.g., *Entamoeba histolytica*, *Cryptosporidium parvum* and *Giardia lamblia)* produce a resistant cyst enabling them to lie dormant in the environment for long periods of time - months to years, in some cases. Others depend upon human activities for their dispersal, as in the case of *Trichomonas vaginalis*, which is sexually transmitted. Vector-borne organisms rely on the biology of blood sucking insects, for the most part. Mosquitoes transmit all species of malaria (*Plasmodium spp.*), tsetse flies transmit African Sleeping Sickness (*Trypanosoma brucei spp.*) and sandflies transmit all species of Leishmania. In these instances, the organism is injected directly into the host's blood stream or interstitial tissue fluids where they proceed to undergo complex developmental life cycles culminating in numerous cycles of asexual division once they achieve their essential niche.

A more complex strategy is employed by *Trypanosoma cruzi*, an organism transmitted by a large hemipteran with ferocious looking biting mouth parts. In this instance, the organisms are excreted along with the fecal exudate at the time of the second blood feeding. We unknowingly rub the organisms into the bite wound or into a mucous membrane after the insect withdraws its mouth parts and become infected.

Niche Selection

Each protozoan has been selected for life in a specific essential niche, which can only be defined by a comprehensive knowledge of the anatomical, physiological, and biochemical features of that site. To gain some measure of the difficulties associated with attempting to describe the essential niche, be it that of a parasite or any other organism, let us consider the intracellular milieu of the normal red blood cell. This site represents one of the best studied of all intracellular environments. Yet for the most part, we still do not understand precisely how that anucleate cell's membranes interact with vascular endothelial cells when the cell traverses the capillary and exchanges gases with the surrounding tissues. To make matters worse, a red blood cell that is infected with *Plasmodium falciparum* behaves quite differently from that of a normal one, failing to deform as it enters the capillary bed. This single aspect of the infection has serious pathological consequences for the host, as will be detailed in the section dealing with the clinical aspects of malaria. The internal molecular environment of the infected red cell must be considered as a "hybrid," consisting of both host and parasite elements. Proteins produced by the developing merozoite locate to the cytoplasm of the host cell, and some even integrate at the red cell membrane surface, forming complexes with host structural proteins such as spectrin and glycophoran. Others remain in the general region of the red cell cytoplasm. Over the entire period of the developmental cycle of the parasite, new proteins are produced that locate to specific regions of an ever-changing host cell environment. The infected red cell represents a very dynamic situation; even with the most sophisticated instrumentation, it has been impossible to fully appreciate the setting in which this important pathogen lives out its life. Finally, no two species of Plasmodium behave the same in their erythrocytic niche, due largely to dramatic genetic differences between the four major species infecting humans. Hence, it is likely that we will never gain a "full face-on" view of this or any other pathogen in order to sufficiently design new therapeutics that would prevent the organism from taking full advantage of its ecological setting. The complexities presented to the research parasitologist by just this single organism continue to challenge them to design innovative experiments that may allow us one day more than a glimpse into its secret life.

At the other end of the scale is *Toxoplasma gondii*, a protozoan capable of infecting virtually any mammalian cell and reproducing within it. *Toxoplasma gondii's* lack of host specificity makes it the most widely-distributed parasite on earth.

Migration to favorable sites within the host often requires an active role for the pathogen, but frequently they "hitch a ride" in our bloodstream or through our intestinal tract. Some are capable of infecting cells that under most circumstances would serve to protect us from these kinds of organisms. The macrophage is a permissive host cell for *Toxoplasma gondii* and for all species of Leishmania. In these infections, the very cell type we depend upon for innate protection against invaders turns out to be the culprit, aiding in their dispersal throughout the body.

Division and Reproduction

Multiplication within the human host is the rule for protozoans, in contrast to most helminth species, in which infection usually results in a single adult parasite. The definitive host is the one harboring the sexual stages of a given parasite. Hence, the human is not the definitive host for a wide range of protozan infections, including the Plasmodia and *Toxoplasma gondii*. Female anopheline mosquitoes are the definitive hosts for all malaria species infecting humans, while the domestic cat is the permissive host for the sexual stages of *T. gondii*. Humans are the definitive host for *Cryptosporidium parvum*. It should be emphasized, however, that not all parasitic protozoa have sexual cycles.

As pointed out, all protozoans reproduce asexually after gaining entrance into the human host. Pathological consequences result directly from their increasing numbers. During the height of the infection, they place ever-increasing demands upon their essential niches. The mechanisms by which protozoa divide asexually are numerous, with binary fission being the most common. Malarial parasites reproduce within the red cell by a process called schizogony, in which the organism undergoes nuclear division within a common cytoplasm (karyokinesis). Just before rupturing out of the hemoglobin-depleted red cell, the parasite's cytoplasm divides to accommodate each nucleus, leaving its toxic waste product, crystals of haemazoin, in the now empty red cell stroma.

Mechanisms of Survival

Each species of parasite has been selected for life within the human host by evolving strategies that (A) inhibit or divert our immune system; and (B) avoid or inhibit intracellular killing mechanisms; (C) infect regions of the body that are incapable of protective immune responses. For example, the African trypanosomes produce "smoke screens" of surface antigens whose sole purpose seems to be to keep the immune system busy, while a small select population changes its protein coat to a different antigenic variant, thus temporarily escaping the host's immune surveillance system. Certain stages of the malaria parasite and *Giardia lamblia* can also vary their surface proteins, presenting our immune system with a bewildering array of antigenic determinants to deal with as an infection progresses. *Toxoplasma gondii* inhibits the fusion of lysosomal vesicles with the parasitophorous vacuole, thus escaping the killing effects of acid hydrolases. *Cryptosporidium parvum* and all species of malaria occupy immunologically "silent" niches. *Trypanosoma cruzi* actually penetrates out of the parasitphorous vacuole into naked cytoplasm, escaping the ravages of lysosomal enzyme activity. There are numerous other examples and they will be discussed whenever relevant. Regardless of the mechanism employed by the protozoan parasite, the result is tissue damage, often severe.

Mechanisms of Pathogenesis

Regardless of the mechanism employed by the parasite to escape being killed, the usual consequence of infection from the perspective of the human host is tissue damage. The extent of cellular damage inflicted by a given parasite is related to the location of their essential niche, the metabolic requirements of the parasite, and their population density throughout the infection. Energy is derived from the host, thus placing a burden on infected hosts for providing this essential ingredient. The penchant of the parasite for killing the cell it invades, or eroding away the tissue it occupies while feeding on our cells, results in measurable pathological consequences that translate directly into clinical signs and symptoms. For example, when the malaria parasite exits from the red cell at the end of its division cycle, the rupture of the stroma results in the release of toxic waste products (haemazoin) that elicit fever. *E. histolytica*, as its name implies, attaches to, then ingests, living cells. It then digests them, using acid hydrolases to do so, and in the process induces bloody diarrhea (dysentery).

Infection with *T. gondii* results in lymphedema and

fever due to the death of large numbers of host cells throughout the body. The molecular basis for these pathological effects will be discussed in detail at the appropriate time. Suffice it to state here that we do not know any parasite's modus operandi completely, and the scientific literature will undoubtedly continue to bring with it new surprises and revelations in the near future.

Parasitic Helminths (worms)

Helminths belong to four phyla: Nematoda (roundworms), Platyhelminthes (flatworms), Acantho-cephala (spiny-headed worms), and Nematophora (hairworms). Only worms belonging to the former two are endoparasitic to humans. Both the Nematoda and Platyhelminthes have many free-living species as well. General descriptions of each major group precedes each section. What follows is a general description of their biology.

Mechanisms of Entry

Helminths have evolved multiple strategies for entering the host and establishing infection. Among the nematodes, infection is usually established by exposure to an environmentally resistant stage.

For many of the common intestinal nematodes such as *Ascaris lumbricoides* or *Trichuris trichiura*, this occurs via the ingestion of embryonated eggs in the soil, or on soil-contaminated fruits and vegetables. In many tropical countries helminth eggs have been isolated from nearly all environments. They have even been recovered from paper currency. For other nematodes, infection is established when larval stages, living in the soil, enter the host (e.g., *Necator americanus*, *Ancylostoma duodenale*, or *Strongyloides stercoralis*). Sometimes infection is strictly food-borne and occurs only when larvae are ingested in uncooked meat (e.g., *Trichinella spiralis*, or some juvenile tapeworm species). Many species of nematode are transmitted by arthropods, such as lymphatic filariasis (mosquito), loaiasis (midge), onchocherciasis (black fly) and guinea worm infection (copepods).

Trematodes spend a portion of their life cycle in a wide variety of snail intermediate hosts. After exiting the snail, the larval stage, known as a cercaria, typically attaches to a second intermediate host, such as a fish, a crab, or aquatic vegetation. For this reason, most trematode infections are food-borne. The exception are the schistosomes, which cause a spectrum of illnesses. The schistosome cercariae are able to penetrate skin via a hair shaft.

Cestodes are acquired via the oral route, regard-less of the stage that ends up causing the infection. Most adult tapeworm infections of humans result from the ingestion of inadequately cooked contaminated fish, beef, or pork. Two clinically significant juvenile tapeworm infections, cysticercosis and echinococcosis, result from accidental ingestion of the eggs.

Niche Selection

Unlike protozoans, most species of parasitic helminth occupy more than a single niche in their human host during their life cycle. For example, although hookworms live as adults in the small intestine, in order to arrive there, the infective larvae frequently must first pass through the skin and lymphatics before spending time in the bloodstream and lungs. Similarly, Ascaris eggs hatch in the intestine before the emerging larval stage enters the portal circulation; the larvae enter liver and lungs prior to re-entry into the gut. As adults, helminths have been recovered from almost every organ including liver, lungs, lymphatics, bloodstream, muscle, skin, subcutaneous tissues, and brain.

Many species of parasitic helminths (nematodes, cestodes, and trematodes) live as sexually mature adults in the gastrointestinal tract In many underdeveloped countries, it is usual to find school-aged children who harbor three or four different species of helminths in their intestine, with each species occupying a different portion of the gut track. Symptoms arising from heavy infection with a given helminth are associated with a particular region of the GI tract.

Reproduction

All helminths reproduce (mate and deposit eggs) within the human host. Parasitic nematodes have both males and females, but females, in most cases after mating, out-live the males - a reproductive strategy remarkably similar to humans. One exception is *Strongyloides stercoralis* for which there is no permanent parasitic male.

Except for the schistosomes, the trematodes (flukes) are all hermaphroditic. Despite this all-in-one reproductive arrangement, cross-fertilization between two trematodes of the same species is common.

In the cestodes, the situation is somewhat different compared to the trematodes. Each proglottid segment of the adult cestode tapeworm is hermaphroditic, and because there is usually only one adult worm present, the worm self-fertilizes adjacent segments.

Nematode parasites that live in the GI tract produce eggs or larvae that exit the host with the fecal mass. Nematodes living in blood or lymphatic vessels produce larvae that circulate in the bloodstream and must be ingested by the appropriate arthropod vector in order to exit the host.

Adult tapeworms shed segments into the lumen of the small intestine and they can exit the host under their own power. Other adult tapeworms produce segments that then disintegrate releasing their eggs into the fecal mass for export. Juvenile tapeworm infections remain as such and produce no diagnostic stage. These infections present real problems for the clinician seeking a definitive diagnosis for their patient.

Intestinal trematodes produce eggs that exit with the feces, as for example, with the eggs of *Heterophyes heterophyes*. Eggs of the lung fluke, *Paragonimus westermani*, exit the host either when they are coughed up in sputum or after they are swallowed, in which case they exit in the feces. Some helminths have evolved elaborate adaptations in order to ensure that their eggs leave the human host. For instance, schistosome eggs are deposited against the inside wall of a blood vessel. These eggs are equiped with sharp spines and a battery of lytic enzymes that allow them to traverse the vessel endothelium and gut wall. The eggs break through the serosal surface of either the intestine or bladder (depending upon the species), before entering the muscularis and then the lumen. Adult schistosomes and Paragonimus that locate to ectopic sites (e.g., nervous system) produce eggs that remain at the site of infection, often resulting in serious pathological consequences for the host.

Mechanisms of Survival

Like the protozoa, the helminths occupy habitats which most of us would consider highly inhospitable. The selective pressures that led to their elaborating mechanisms for survival in these environments are still poorly understood. Adult schistosomes live in the blood stream, a place where one might expect to encounter the constant bombardment of the immune system's slings and arrows of antibody molecules and leukocytes of various types. Yet, there the worms can remain for up to twenty years in that niche. The molecular basis by which this happens is not known, although a number of immune evasion and immunological masking mechanisms have been detected. Important for helminth's survival is their unique array of natural products elaborated and released into the host. Hookworms can freely ingest blood in the intestinal mucosa and submucosa because they produce peptides and eicasanoids that block host clotting, host platelet aggregation, and host inflammation. Many of these peptides themselves have proven to be useful as new potential therapeutic agents for human coronary artery disease, stroke and

autoimmune disorders. *Trichuris trichiura* releases a pore-forming protein that promotes cell fusion around the anterior end of the organism, allowing it to become embedded in epithelial tunnels. Indeed, the argument has been made that parasitic helminths are themselves equivalent to small biotechnology companies which, through research and development in the form of millions of years of evolutionary selection, now produce a wide array of pharmacologically active compounds which we may find useful, as well.

Mechanisms of Pathogenesis

Helminths injure their human host both through mechanical and chemical mechanisms. Large helminths, such as *Ascaris lumbricoides*, can cause physical obstruction of the intestine, or exert damage when they migrate into the biliary tree. As already noted, helminths release peptides and eicasanoids that down regulate host inflammatory processes. In some cases, helminths bias host immunity to produce Th-2 like responses, that may make the host less likely to eliminate the parasite. Immune regulation on the part of the parasite may also have consequences for the host regarding a wide variety of viral infections. There is some evidence to support the role of helminths as co-pathogens that promote susceptibility to HIV infection and AIDS. In many cases, some of the most important mechanisms of pathogenesis are still not known. Heavy infection with some intestinal nematodes (e.g., hookworm) are considered to be the major cause of stunted growth during childhood as well as inducing impaired cognitive behavior and intellectual development. While intuitively we might suspect that parasite-induced malnutrition plays an important role in this process, the true basis by which these processes occur is not known.

Host-mediated immunopathology accounts for a large measure of the damage that occurs during some helminth infections. This is particularly true for infection with the schistosomes. However, recent findings suggest that in the case of infection with a number of filarial worm species, an endosymbiont, *Wolbachia sp.* of bacteria, may be responsible for most of the pathological consequences of the infection. Brain parenchymal inflammation and seizures in cysticercosis is well documented.

As the genomes of many of these important pathogens become unraveled, new approaches to the clinical management of patients suffering from them will surely emerge from the laboratory and find their way to the bedside. At least that is the hoped for outcome of such research.

IV. The Protozoa

Over 200,000 species of protozoa have been described so far, of which more than half are represented in the fossil record. The repertoire of known living species (approximately 35,000) includes more than 10,000 that have been selected for life as parasites. Regardless of their lifestyle, all protozoans are eukaryotic single-cell organisms. Free-living species occupy every conceivable ecological niche, including marine trenches, rainforests, artesian and thermal springs, salt lakes, ice floes, glaciers, and many others, while parasitic protozoans infect a wide spectrum of vertebrate and invertebrate life.

Unlike the great majority of parasitic helminth species, protozoan parasites are able to replicate within a given host, often resulting in hundreds of thousands of new individuals within just a few days following initial infection. This single feature of their life cycle frequently has grave consequences for the host.

Parasitic protozoans have played a major role in the evolution of the human species, mainly due to lethal consequences of infection, or limiting where people can live by adversely affecting their livestock. These very same selection pressures continue to play out in many parts of the world today. For example, malaria in all its forms, African trypanosomiasis, and visceral Leishmaniasis infect millions of people and are responsible for untold numbers of deaths and debilitating chronic illnesses. Many others cause less severe disease (e.g., chronic diarrhea) that nonetheless results in lost time at work and school and loss of recreational activities we deem vital to living enriched, healthy, disease-free lives. This is due, in part, to the fact that some important species of parasitic protozoans are no longer susceptible to drugs that were once effective in limiting disease. There are no effective vaccines for the control of any protozoan infection in humans.

While the biology of parasitic protozoa varies widely from group to group, these organisms share many common features. They are bound by a unit membrane that functions in a similar fashion to all other eukaryotic cells. Nutrients may either be actively transported, phagocytosed, or moved into the cell by pinocytosis. Digestion of particulate material is by lysosomal enzymes within the phagolysosome. Protozoans excrete wastes either by diffusion or by exocytosis. Mechanisms of motility take advantage of the presence of one of a variety of structures (e.g., cilia, flagella, pseudopod). All species of protozoans can divide asexually, usually by binary fission. In some instances the process is more complex, and includes multiple nuclear divisions followed by cytokinesis. Those capable of sexual reproduction do so within the definitive host, resulting in the formation of a zygote.

In addition, their cytoplasm may contain subcellular organelles, including Golgi apparatus, lysosomes, mitochondria, rough and smooth endoplasmic reticulum, and a wide variety of secretory granules of specialized function (e.g., the hydrogenosome of *Trichomonas vaginalis*, and the glycosome of kinetoplastidae). Collectively, these cytoplasmic inclusions enable the organism to respire, digest food, generate energy, grow, and reproduce.

Some species have evolved elaborate surface coats consisting of materials derived from the host or secreted by the parasite that offer some protection from host immune responses, thereby extending their life within a given individual and resulting in great damage to the host as well.

The recent completion of the Human Genome Project has given way to many others, including those dealing with important disease-producing protozoans. *Plasmodium spp.*, *Leishmania spp.*, *Toxoplasma gondii*, and *Trypanosoma brucei* are among those genomes now being studied. Many will most likely have been completed before this edition is printed. It is hard to imagine that data from these projects would not be of immediate use to the development of specific molecular-based control strategies.

The field of immunoparasitology has also matured over the past several years. New understanding regarding the role(s) of cytokines and interleukins in the pathogenesis of disease has led to new clinical approaches for several important protozoan diseases. In addition, the details of protective host mechanisms that counter the invasion process have been described, giving hope for the development of a new generation of drugs and perhaps even the first of many effective vaccines.

The following chapters are but a thumbnail sketch of some of the excitement generated in the field of protozoan parasitology, as well as present to the medical student and physician alike; useful and practical information specific to the diagnosis, treatment, and management of infections caused by these infectious agents.

1. *Giardia lamblia* (Stiles 1915)

Introduction

Giardia lamblia is a flagellated protozoan that lacks a mitochondrion.[1] It is aerotolerant, but respires as an anaerobe, and lives in the small intestine. Other protozoa that share this metabolic strategy include *Entamoeba histolytica* (see page 84), and *Trichomonas vaginalis* (see page 46). It produces a cyst stage that is environmentally resistant. Giardia is acquired through the fecal-oral route, most commonly via contaminated drinking water.[2] *G. lamblia* is found throughout the world, and remains endemic in many regions. It is a common infection of children, especially those attending daycare centers.[3, 4] In 2002, The Centers for Disease Control and Prevention reported 21,300 cases of Giardia within the United States. It is highly likely that many more than that occurred there but went undiagnosed. Beavers are major reservoir hosts that are often responsible for contaminating public drinking water supplies. Giardia is the subject of much intensive research, including a complete sequence analysis of its genome.[5] A survey of its genome has revealed the presence of genes for meiosis, although a sexual stage for this protozoan has not yet been described.[6] An excellent review of the biology of *Giardia lamblia* was published by Adam. [7]

Historical Information

Antony Van Leeuwenhoek, the famous Dutch microscopist, in a letter written to Robert Hooke in 1681, described in detail the living trophozoite stage of Giardia, which he observed in a sample of his own stool: ". . . *animalcules a-moving very prettily. Their bodies were somewhat longer than broad, and their belly, which was flatlike, furnisht with sundry little paws. . . yet for all that they made but slow progress.*"[8]

Lambl described the main morphological fea-

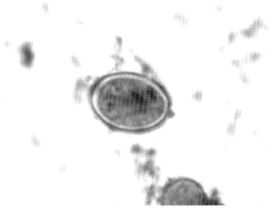

Figure 1.2. Cyst of *G. lamblia*. Two nuclei can be seen. 13 μm.

tures of the trophozoite stage in 1859,[9] that he obtained from the stools of various pediatric patients in Prague. His elegant scientific drawings remain impressive, even in today's world of sophisticated, technologically advanced light microscopy. Simon, in 1921,[10] completed the description of its morphology.

Life Cycle

Giardia lamblia exists in two forms: the trophozoite (Fig. 1.1) and the cyst (Fig. 1.2). The troph is pear-shaped and motile, measuring 10-20 μm long and 7-10 μm. in diameter. It possesses eight flagella and is binucleate. Both nuclei are transcriptionally active.[11] In addition, it contains two rigid structures, called median bodies, whose function is not known. *G. lamblia* has no mitochondria, peroxisomes, hydrogenosomes, or related subcellular organelles that might be associated with energy metabolism. Some strains of the parasite carry double-stranded RNA viruses, known as giardiaviruses,[12] whose function for the protozoan remains undefined. Apparently they are not linked with virulence of the infection. However, these viruses have facilitated the expression of foreign genes in Giardia, serving as shuttle vectors.[13]

Its anterior ventral region has a disc-like organelle that it uses for attachment to the surface of epithelial cells. The integrity of the disk is maintained by tubulin and giardins.[14] The latter are members of the class III, low affinity, calcium binding annexins.[15] Its surface is covered with cysteine-rich molecules.

Infection begins with ingestion of the quadrinucleate cyst, which must then excyst in response to physiological stimuli from the new host. Excystation involves a complex sequence of cellular events and molecular responses[16] to environmental cues received by the parasite. As the cyst passes through the stomach and into the small intestine, it is sequentially exposed to HCl[17] and pancreatic enzymes.[18]

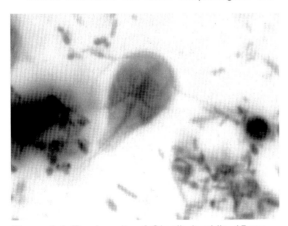

Figure 1.1. Trophozoite of *Giardia lamblia*. 15 μm.

Giardia lamblia

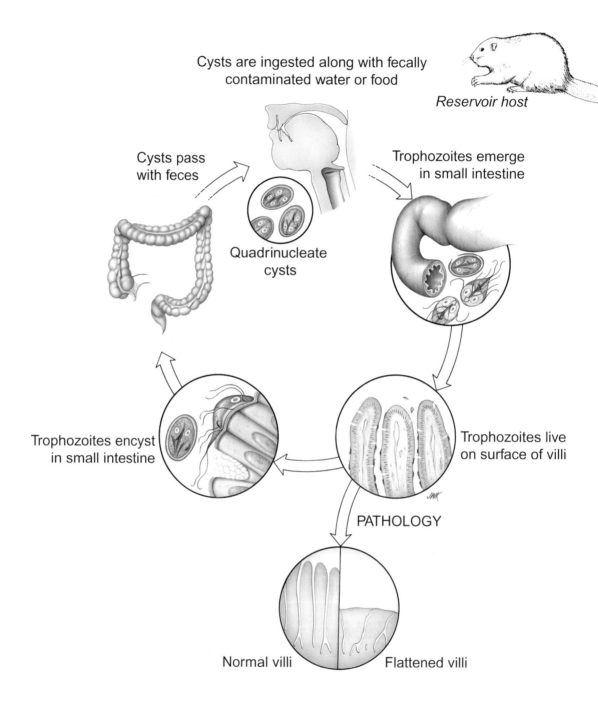

Cysts are ingested along with fecally contaminated water or food

Reservoir host

Cysts pass with feces

Quadrinucleate cysts

Trophozoites emerge in small intestine

Trophozoites live on surface of villi

Trophozoites encyst in small intestine

PATHOLOGY

Normal villi

Flattened villi

"Parasitic Diseases" 5ᵗʰ Ed. © Apple Trees Productions, LLC., Pub. P.O. Box 280, New York, NY 10032

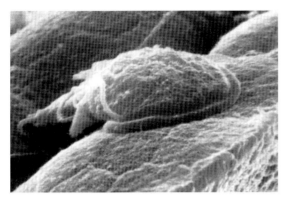

Figure 1.3. Scanning EM of a trophozoite of *G. muris* on epithelium of mouse small intestine. Courtesy R. Owen.

Excystation results in the emergence of two binucleate trophozoites that then attach to epithelial cells by their ventral disks (Fig. 1.3). The molecular mechanisms used to adhere to cells are not known, although carbohydrate binding lectins have been identified on the ventral disc's surface. Since the trophozoite can also adhere to an alcohol-cleaned glass surface, host molecules may not be necessary to the process. Once attached to epithelial cells, the binucleate organisms grow and divide by binary fission. Cysts are unable to replicate.

G. lamblia can be grown in vitro (Fig. 1.4). The nutritional needs of the trophozoite have yet to be fully determined, but some of its biochemical energy pathways are known.[19, 20] Glucose and arginine[21] appear to be its major sources of energy, and it may access a portion of its need for them through the breakdown of mucus.[22] Giardia is unable to synthesize nucleic acid bases *de novo*, employing salvage pathways.[23] Lipids are absorbed directly, likely facilitated by bile and bile salts,[24] and perhaps by endocytosis of lipoproteins.[25] *G. lamblia* is not considered an invasive or tissue parasite, but its ability to adhere closely to the columnar cells at the level of the microvilli, and its penchant for secreting proteins at the site, results in antibody production and, eventually, to protective immunity. To exit the host and survive, trophozoites must encyst, though the precise conditions governing this process are not fully defined.[26] Encystation in vitro is inducible by exposure of the trophozoite stage to bile and elevated pH, possibly by sequestering cholesterol.[27] Trophs take up and release conjugated bile salts,[28, 29] and these conditions may exist in its essential niche (Fig. 1.3). Apparently, a novel transglutaminase is also required for encystment.[30] Encysted parasites can endure for long periods of time outside the host if they remain moist. Both cysts and trophs pass out of the bowel with the fecal mass, but, as already stated, only the cyst stage survives. Cysts can withstand exposure to mild chemical treatments, such as chlorinated water. Even boiling water at high altitude may not kill cysts, and they do quite

well in cold water for weeks to months. Cysts can be killed by freezing or dessication. Production of cysts occurs throughout the infection, but the number produced each day varies greatly, depending upon a wide variety of conditions, including the development of acquired protective immunity.[31] Protective immunity appears to be directed against both surface antigens[32] and antigens that are secreted.[33]

Cellular and Molecular Pathogenesis

Steatorrhea[34] and malabsorption with flattening of the villi[35] (Fig. 1.5), often accompanied by rapid weight loss, are the dominant pathological consequences of chronic infection. Despite the fact that there are numerous related species of Giardia,[7] and that they can be manipulated in vivo and in vitro, surprisingly little is known regarding their biological effect(s) on the physiology and biochemistry of the small intestine. Hence, the molecular basis for these symptoms is as yet undefined.

Infection with *G. lamblia* induces numerous cellular[37] and humoral responses, some of which are protective in nature.[38] Particularly important is secretory IgA,[39] since it has been shown for nonsecretors that infection is easily established and not easily controlled. Physiological changes experienced during symptomatic infection could relate to these host-based responses, and might even be induced by mechanisms related to allergies,[37] such as those observed in wheat-gluten-sensitive individuals.[38]

Antigenic variation of surface components of the trophozoite is typical in the early phase of infection,[40, 41] and most likely aids the parasite in avoiding elimination by humoral responses (e.g., IgA antibodies)[39] directed at trophozoite surface proteins.[42] Switching of cysteine-rich variant surface proteins (VSPs) also occurs when the parasite is about to excyst,[43]

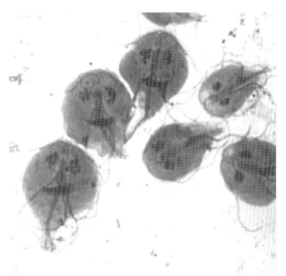

Figure 1.4. Trophozoites of *G. lamblia* in culture. Courtesy D. Lindmark.

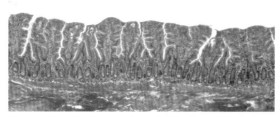

Figure 1.5. Flattened, fused villi of small intestine from a patient suffering from malabsorption syndrome due to *G. lamblia.*

allowing the parasite to evade immune elimination. Severe combined immune deficiency mice do not induce VSP switching, an indication that the overall process is under the control of B cell-mediated host responses. However, switching also occurs spontaneously or in response to physiological selection, but at a much slower pace than in immunocompetent hosts. Shuttle viral systems for transfecting *G. lamblia* have been developed.[44] Thus, genetic manipulation is now possible, which may lead to a more complete understanding of the molecular events governing pathogenesis.

Mother's milk is protective, because it contains antibodies of the IgA class.[45] Nonspecific defenses, such as lactoferrin or products of lipid hydrolysis of the milk in the normal digestive tract, may also play a role, as each is toxic to Giardia.[46, 47, 48] Nitric oxide, released lumenally by intestinal epithelial cells in response to infection, inhibits parasite growth and differentiation, although Giardia might be able to disarm this potential defense mechanism by competitively consuming the arginine needed by the host cells for NO synthesis.[49] In summary, the duration and severity of infection depends upon both immune and nonimmune host defenses, as well as the parasite's ability to evade them.

Clinical Disease

An excellent review of the clinical literature is available.[50] About half of all those who encounter *G. lamblia* and become infected fail to progress to a state of ill health. They may remain asymptomatic for long periods of time, even though they are still infected, and could become chronic carriers referred to as *cyst passers*. Of those who go on to develop disease, the most prominent symptom is protracted diarrhea.[22, 51] It can be mild and produce semisolid stools, or it can be acute with debilitating cramping when the stools become watery and voluminous. Untreated, this type of diarrhea may last weeks or months, although it usually varies in intensity. Children thus affected often fail to thrive.[52] Chronic infections are characterized by steatorrhea accompanied

by malabsorption syndrome associated with rapid, substantial weight loss, general debility, and consequent fatigue.[22] In addition, some people may complain of epigastric discomfort, anorexia, and even pain. Other symptoms may sometimes accompany giardiasis, such as allergic responses to certain food items,[53] but none of these have been proven to be caused by the parasite.

Certain patient groups are at greater risk for acquiring giardiasis and for developing chronic infection. In addition to those patients suffering from HIV/AIDS[54] and other immunocompromising conditions (e.g., hypogammaglobulinemia or cancer chemotherapies), cystic fibrosis patients[55] and children with underlying malnutrition[56] can have a protracted disease with more severe symptoms than other individuals generally contract.

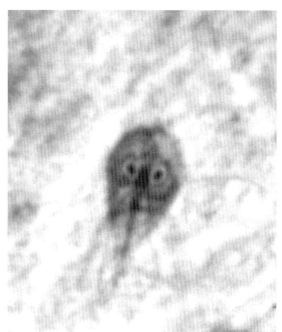

Figure 1.6a. *G. lamblia* trophozoite in stool sample.

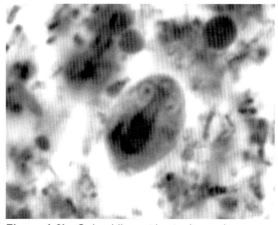

Figure 1.6b. *G. lamblia* cyst in stool sample.

Diagnosis

Definitive diagnosis depends upon: 1. direct observation of the parasites by microscopic examination of concentrated, stained stool sample in which either the trophozoite (Fig. 1.6a) or the cyst (Fig. 1.6b) is identified,[57] and 2. antigen-capture ELISA.[58] Both are comparable in specificity and sensitivity, as long as three or more stool samples per patient are sent to the diagnostic laboratory for microscopic examination. Antigen capture usually requires only one stool sample. While PCR is useful for detection of Giardia cysts in fresh water supplies,[59, 60] its application to routine laboratory diagnosis of *G. lamblia* infection[61] is not yet available due to cost constraints and lack of standardization. The string test[62] is useful if capture ELISA is not available or when organisms have not been found upon repeated stool examination, despite a strong suspicion of Giardia infection on the part of the clinician.

Treatment

All symptomatic patients infected with Giardia should be treated; Metronidazole is the primary drug of choice.[63] Either drug controls clinical symptoms of giardiasis in 80% of symptomatic cases; repetition of therapy after 1-2 weeks is usually effective if failure to cure is encountered. A reasonable definition of cure for patients with infection caused by *Giardia lamblia* is long term disappearance of symptoms after therapy and failure to detect organisms in three consecutive stool specimens. Recurrence of symptoms should be treated in the same manner as the original infection. Apparently, resistant strains of Giardia have been recently described in a few HIV/AIDS patients.[64] In those cases, nitazoxanide was used successfully.[65] Pediatricians who do prefer not to prescribe metronidazole for younger children have the alternative of furazolidone. This nitrofuran is available in liquid suspension and is usually well tolerated. However, long courses of up to 10 days are frequently necessary to achieve high levels of cure. Albendazole may soon be considered an alternative drug, based on positive findings from clinical trials in Turkey.[66]

Prevention and Control

Giardia lamblia is primarily a water-borne infection,[2, 67] although food handlers and infected children in daycare centers no doubt play important roles in transmission. Prevention strategies include proper disposal of human wastes, filtration of drinking water supplies, maintenance of buffer zones around watersheds when filtration is not practiced (e.g., in New York City), and maintaining the highest standards of hygiene in daycare centers and mental institutions, although this last recommendation is admittedly the most difficult one to achieve. No Giardia vaccines are likely to emerge from the research laboratory within the next several years.

References

1. Roger AJ. Svard SG. Tovar J. et al. A mitochondrial-like chaperonin 60 gene in *Giardia lamblia*: evidence that diplomonads once harbored an endosymbiont related to the progenitor of mitochondria. Proc Natl Acad Sci USA. 95(1):229-34, 1998.
2. Levy DA. Bens MS. Craun GF. Calderon RL. Herwaldt BL. Surveilance for waterborne-disease outbreaks – United States, 1995-1996. Mor Mortal Wkly Rep CDC Surveill Summ. 47(5):1-34, 1998.
3. Sagi EF. Shapiro M. Deckelbaum R. *Giardia lamblia*: prevalance, influence on growth, and symptomatology in healthy nursery children. Isr J Med Sci 19:815-817, 1983.
4. Pickering LK. Woodward WE. DuPont HL. et al. Occurrence of *Giardia lamblia* in children in daycare centers. J Pediatr 104:522-526, 1984.
5. Best AA, Morrison HG, et al. Evolution of eukaryotic transcription: insights from the genome of *Giardia lamblia*. Genome Res. 14:1537-47). 2004.
6. Ramesh MA, Malik SB, Logsdon JM Jr. A phylogenomic inventory of meiotic genes; evidence for sex in Giardia and an early eukaryotic origin of meiosis. Curr Biol. 15:185-91. 2005.
7. Adam RD. Biology of *Giardia lamblia*. Clin Micro rev 14:447-475. 2001.
8. Van Leenwenhoek A. Cited by Dobell C. In Antony van Leeuwen-hoek and His "Little Animals". Dover Publications, New York, p. 224, 1960.
9. Lambi VDF. Mikroskopische Untersuchungen der Darm-Excrete. Beitrag zur Pathologie des Darms und zur Diagnostik am Krankenbette; Vierteljahrschrift fur die Praktische Heilkunde. Med Fac Prague 1:1-58. 1859.
10. Simon CE. Giardia enterica, a parasitic intestinal flagellate of man. Am J Hyg 1:440-491, 1921.
11. Kabnick KS, and DA Peattie. *In situ* analyses reveal that the two nuclei of *Giardia lamblia* are equivalent. J Cell Sci 95:353-360. 1990.
12. Tai JH. Chang SC. Chou CF. Ong SJ. Separation and characterization of two related giardiaviruses in the parasitic protozoan *Giardia lamblia*. Virology. 216(1):124-32, 1996.
13. Liu Q, Zhang X, et al. *Giardia lamblia*: stable expression of green fluorescent protein mediated by giardiavirus. Exp Parasitol. 109:181-7. 2005.
14. Aggarwal A, Nash TE: Characterization of a 33-kilodalton structural protein of *Giardia lamblia* and localization to the ventral disk. Infect Immun 57:1305-1310, 1989.
15. Bauer B. Engelbrecht S. Bakker-Grunwald T. Scholze H. Functional identification of alpha 1-giardin as an annexin of *Giardia lamblia*. FEMS Microbiol Lett. 173(1):147-53, 1999.

16. Hetsko ML. McCaffery JM. Svard SG. et al. Cellular and transcriptional changes during excystation of *Giardia lamblia* in vitro. Exp Parasitol. 88(3):172-83, 1998.
17. Bingham AK. Meyer EA. Giardia excystation can be induced in vitro in acidic solutions. Nature 277:301, 1979.
18. Rice EW. Schaefer FW. Improved in vitro excystation procedure for *Giardia lamblia* cysts. J Clin Micrbiol 14:709, 1981.
19. Jarroll EL. Manning P. Berrada A. Hare D. Lindmark DG. Biochemistry and metabolism of Giardia J Protozool. 36(2):190-7, 1989.
20. Coombs GH. Muller M. Energy Metabolism in Anaerobic Protozoa. In: Biochemistry and Molecular Biology of Parasites (Marr J.J. and Muller M. eds). Academic Press, Pubs. London. pp. 109-131, 1995.
21. Edwards MR, Schofield PJ, O'Sullivan WJ, Costello M. Arginine metabolism during culture of Giardia intestinalis Mol Biochem Parasitol. 53(1-2):97-103, 1992.
22. Farthing MJG. *Giardia lamblia*. In: Infectious Disease, 2nd ed. (Gorbach SL. Bartlett JG. And Blacklow NR, eds) W,B.Saunders, Pubs. Philadelphia. pp. 2399-2406, 1998.
23. Wang, CC. Aldritt S. Purine salvage networks in *Giardia lamblia*. J Exp Med 158:1703, 1983.
24. Farthing MJG. Keusch GT. Carey MC. Effect of bile and bile salts on growth and membrane lipid uptake by *Giardia lamblia*: possible implications for pathogenesis of intestinal disease. J Clin Invest 76:1727, 1985.
25. Lujan HD. Mowatt MR. Nash TE. Lipid requirements and lipid up-take by *Giardia lamblia* trophozoites I culture. J Eukaryot Microbiol. 43(3):237-42, 1996
26. Lujan HD. Mowatt MR. Nash TE. Mechanisms of *Giardia lamblia* differentiation into cysts Microbio Mol Biol Rev. 61(3):294-304, 1997.
27. Lujan HD. Mowatt MR. Byrd LG. Nash TE. Cholesterol starvation induces differentiation of the intestinal parasite *Giardia lamblia*. Proc Natl Acad Sci U S A 93(15):7628-33, 1996.
28. Halliday CE. Inge PM. Farthing MJ. Characterization of bile salt uptake by *Giardia lamblia*. Int J Parasitol 25(9):1089-97, 1995.
29. Halliday CE. Clark C. Farthing MJ. Giardia-bile salt interactions in vitro and in vivo. Trans R Soc Trop Med Hyg. 82(3):428-32, 1988.
30. Davids BJ, Mehta K, Fesus L, McCaffery JM, Gillin FD. Dependence of *Giardia lamblia* encystation on novel transglutaminase activity. Mol Biochem Parasitol.136:173-80. 2004.
31. Farthing MJG. Goka AKJ. Immunology of giardiasis. Balleries Clinical Gastroenterology 1:589, 1987.
32. Nash TE. Antigenic variation in *Giardia lamblia* and the host's immune response. Philos Trans R Soc Lond B Biol Sci. 352(1359):1369-75, 1997.
33. Kaur H. Samra H. et al. Immune effector responses to an excretory-secretory product of *Giardia lamblia*. FEMS Immunol Med Microbiol 23(2):93-105, 1999.
34. Carroccio A. Montalto G. Iacono G. et al. Secondary Impairment of pancreatic function as a cause of severe malabsorption in intestinal giardiasis: a case report. Am J Trop Med Hyg. 56(6):599-602, 1997.
35. Gottstein B. Stocks NI. Shearer GM. Nash TE. Human cellular immune response to *Giardia lamblia*. Infection 19(6):421-6, 1991.
36. Rosales-Borjas DM. Diaz-Rivadeneyra J. et al. Secretory immune response to membrane antigens during *Giardia lamblia* infection in humans. Infect Immun. 66(2):756-9, 1998.
37. Di Prisco MC. Hagel I. Lynch NR. et al. Association between giardiasis and allergy. Ann Allergy Asthma Immun. 81(3):261-5, 1998.
38. Doe WF. An overview of intestinal immunity and malabsorption Am J Med. 67(6):1077-84, 1979.
39. Eckmann L. Mucosal defences against Giardia. Parasite Immunol. 25:259-70. 2003.
40. Nash TE. Antigenic variation in *Giardia lamblia* and the host's immune response. Philo Trans R Soc Lond B Biolo Sci 352:1369-1375. 1997.
41. Nash TE. Surface antigenic variation in *Giardia lamblia*. Mol Microbiol. 45:585-90. 2002.
42. Heyworth MF. Immunology of Giardia and Cryptosporidium infections. Journal of J Infect Dis. 166(3):465-72, 1992.
43. Svard SG. Meng TC. Hetsko ML. et al. Differentiation-associated surface antigen variation in the ancient eukaryote *Giardia lamblia*. Molecular Microbiology 30(5):979-89, 1998.
44. Singer SM. Yee J. Nash TE. Episomal and integrated maintenance of foreign DNA in *Giardia lamblia*. Mol Biochem Parasitol 92(1):59-69, 1998.
45. Nayak N. Ganguly NK. Walia BNS. et al. Specific secretory IgA in the milk of *Giardia lamblia*-infected and uninfected women. J Infect Dis 155: 724-727, 1987.
46. Gillin FD. Reiner DS. Gault MI. Cholate-dependent killing of *Giardia lamblia* by human milk. Infect Immun 47:619-622, 1985.
47. Hernell O. Ward H. Blackberg L. et al. Killing of *Giardia lamblia* by human milk lipases: an effect mediated by lipolysis of milk lipids. I Infect Dis 153:715-720, 1986.
48. Reiner DS. Wang CS. Gillin FS. Human milk kills *Giardia lamblia* by generating toxic lipolytic products. J Inf Dis 154:825-832, 1986.
49. Eckmann L. Laurent F. Langford TD. et al. Nitric oxide production by human intestinal epithelial cells and competition for arginine as potential determinants of host defense against the lumen-dwelling pathogen *Giardia lamblia*. J Immunol. 164:1478-1487, 2000.
50. Ali SA, Hill DR. *Giardia intestinalis*. Curr Opin Infect Dis.16:453-60. 2003.
51. Reinthaler FF. Feierl G. Stunzner D. Marth E. Diarrhea in returning Austrian tourists: epidemiology, etiology, and cost-analyses. J Travel Med 5(2):65-72, 1998.
52. Craft IC. Giardia and giardiasis in childhood. Pediatr Infect Dis 1:196-211, 1982.
53. Di Prisco MC. Hagel I. Lynch NR. et al. Association between giardiasis and allergy. Ann Allergy Asthma Immunol 81(3):261-5, 1998.
54. Moolasart P. *Giardia lamblia* in AIDS patients with diarrhea. J Med Assoc Thai. 82(7):654-9, 1999.
55. Roberts DM. Craft JC. Mather FJ. et at. Prevalence of giardiasis in patients with cystic fibrosis. I Pediatr 112:555-559, 1988.
56. Sullivan PB. Marsh MN. Phillips MB. et al. Prevalence and treatment of giardiasis in chronic diarrhoea and malnutrition. Arch Dis Child 65: 304-306, 1990.
57. Kabani A. Cadrain G. Trevenen C. Jadavji T. Church DL. Practice guidelines for ordering stool ova and parasite testing in a pediatric population. The Alberta Children's Hospital. Am J Clin Pathol 104(3):272-8, 1995.
58. Boone JH. Wilkins TD. Nash TE. et al. TechLab and alexon Giardia enzyme-linked immunosorbent assay kits detect cyst wall protein 1. J Clin Microbiol. 37(3):611-4, 1999.
59. Rochelle PA. De Leon R. Stewart MH. Wolfe RL. Comparison of primers and optimization of PCR conditions for detection of *Cryptosporidium parvum* and *Giardia lamblia* in water.Appl Environ Microbiol. 63(1):106-14, 1997.
60. Mayer CL. Palmer CJ. Evaluation of PCR, nested PCR, and fluorescent antibodies for detection of Giardia and Cryptosporidium species in wastewater. Appl Environ Microbiol 62(6):2081-5, 1996.
61. Ng CT, Gilchrist CA, Lane A, et al. Multiplex Real time PCR assay using Scorpion probes and DNA capture for genotype-specific detection of *Giardia lamblia* on fecal samples J Clin Microbiol. 43:1256-60. 2005.
62. Jones JE. The string test for diagnosing Giradia lamblia. Am Fam Physician 34(2):123-6, 1986.
63. Freeman CD. Klutman NE. Lamp KC. Metronidazole. A therapeutic review and update. Drugs 54(5):679-708, 1997.
64. Abboud P, Lemee V, et al. Successful treatment of metronidazole- and albendazole-resistant giardiasis with nitazoxanide in a patient with acquired immunodeficiency syndrome. Clin Infect Dis. 32:1792-4. 2001.
65. Fox LM, Saravolatz LD. Nitazoxanide: a new thiazolide antiparasitic agent Clin Infect Dis. 40:1173-80. 2005.
66. Yereli K, Balcioglu IC, et al. Albendazole as an alternative therapeutic agent for childhood giardiasis in Turkey. Clin Microbiol Infect.10:527-9. 2004.
67. Steiner TS. Thielman NM. Guerrant RL. Protozoal agents: what are the dangers for the public water supply? Annu Rev Med. 48:329-40, 1997.

2. Introduction to the Leishmania

The genus Leishmania comprises a genetically diverse group of vector-borne haemoflagellate parasites.[1, 2] *Leishmania spp.* are transmitted from host to host by the bite of sand flies (Fig. 2.1). *Phlebotomous spp.* are vectors of Old World Leishmaniasis, while sand flies in the genus Lutzomyia transmit Leishmaniasis throughout the Western Hemisphere.

Leishmania spp. are primarily zoonotic in nature,[3] infecting a wide range of vertebrates throughout the tropical and subtropical world. All possess a well-characterized kinetoplast and live as obligate intracellular parasites within macrophages and other phagocytic cells of the reticuolendothelial system. All species of Leishmania share many features of their genetics, mode of transmission, biochemistry, molecular biology, immunobiology, and susceptibility to drugs. Differences at all the above levels exist between the cutaneous and visceralizing species of Leishmania.

The number of humans suffering from Leishmaniasis is unknown, but a conservative guess is that the prevalence is several million. More than 350 million people live within an area of transmission (see www.who.org). Leishmaniasis occurs in 88 countries located in Southern Europe, Africa, Asia, South Asia, and South and Central America. The subgenus Leishmania is distributed throughout the Old and the New World, whereas the subgenus Viannia is only found in the New World. In the Western Hemisphere, no less than fifteen species regularly infect people: *Leishmania (Leishmania) amazonensis, Leishmania (Viannia) braziliensis, L. (V.) colombiensis, L. (L.) donovani, L. (L.) garnhami, L. (V.) guyanensis, L. (L.) infantum chagasi, L. (V.) lainsoni, L. (V.) lindenbergi, L. (L.) mexicana, L. (V.) naiffi, L. (V.) panamensis, L. (L.) pifanoi, L. (V.) shawi,* and *L. (L.) venezualensis.* In the Eastern Hemisphere, there are significantly fewer species that infect humans: *L. (L.) donovani, L. (L.) infantum,*

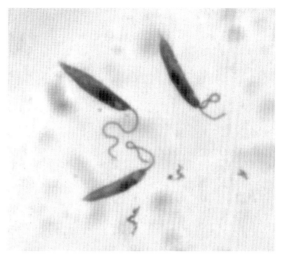

Figure 2.2. Promastigotes of *Leishmania spp.,* as seen in culture.

L. (L.) aethiopica, L. (L.) major, and *L. (L.) tropica.*

As might be expected, clinical conditions caused by *Leishmania spp.* vary greatly, depending upon the species of Leishmania and the immune status of the host. Disease can present as cutaneous lesions that resolve over time, or as systemic disease of the reticuloendothelial system often resulting in death of the host if left untreated. Fortunately, there are fewer clinical entities than the number of species of pathogens that cause them; cutaneous, muco-cutaneous, and visceral Leishmaniasis.

This introductory chapter will summarize the biology and molecular biology of the entire group, with the tacit assumption that they all behave similarly in their intracellular environment and within their sand fly vectors. Exceptions will be presented whenever they relate to a disease process applicable only to that species. The Leishmania Genome Project is based on the genome of *Leishmania major* and is essentially completed (see www.sanger.ac.uk/Projects/L_major/).

There are no commercially available vaccines

Figure 2.1. Sand fly taking a blood meal.

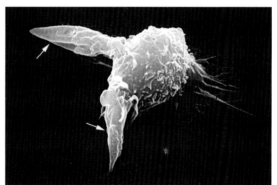

Figure 2.3. Scanning EM of macrophage ingesting two promastigotes (arrows). Photo by K-P Chang.

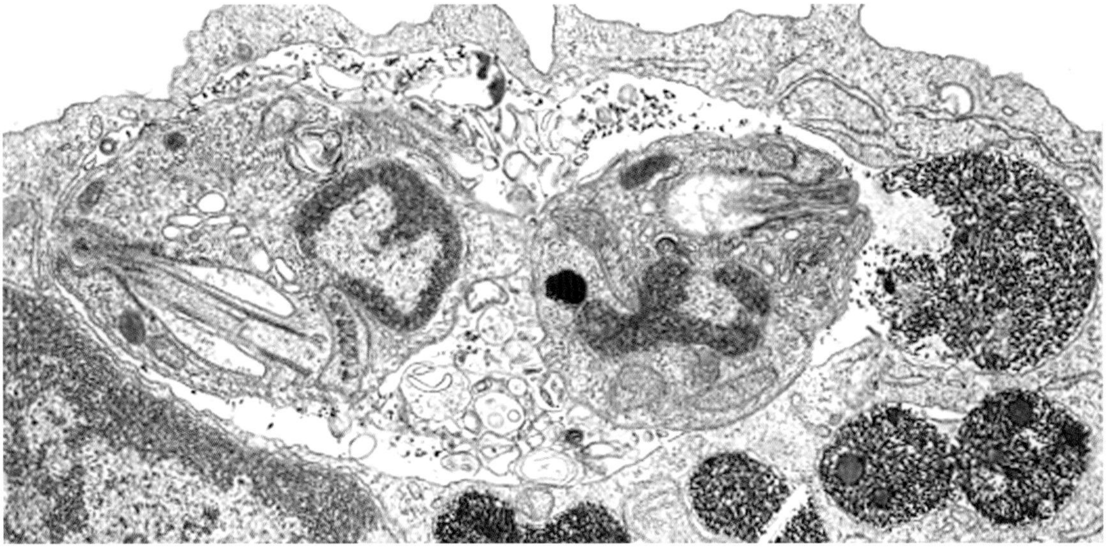

Figure 2.4. Electron micrograph of two amastigotes of *Leishmania spp.* Photo by K-P Chang.

as of yet, but infection with many of the species of Leishmania results in permanent immunity to reinfection with the same species.[4] Perhaps data derived from the genome project will hasten the development of an effective, cheap, easy-to-administer vaccine against the most dangerous forms of Leishmaniasis.

Life Cycle

The sand fly

Infection begins when the insect obtains blood from an infected mammal. As it does so it injects saliva containing numerous well-characterized bioactive components, many of which are peptides or proteins.[7, 8] One such protein, maxadilan, is a potent vasodilator,[9] a 7 kDa peptide believed essential to the taking of a blood meal by the fly. Maxadilan's primary mode of action is to reduce intracellular calcium in the host at the site of the bite wound through a cAMP-dependent mechanism, causing arterial dilation.[10, 11] Blood can then easily be drawn up by the sand fly. The receptor for maxadilan is the pituitary adenylate cyclase-activating polypeptide, a membrane-bound protein found on many cell types in the body, including smooth muscle cells and macrophages. During feeding, sand flies become maximally filled with blood and cannot regurgitate the excess, due to the inhibition of the emptying reflex by a parasite-specific peptide that interacts with myosin to prevent contraction of stomach muscle.[12] This enhances the chances for the sand fly to become infected and to remain so throughout the period that the parasite needs (i.e., 1-2 weeks) in order

to develop into the infectious stage for a mammalian host.

The parasite undergoes a complex series of developmental changes inside the gut tract of the sand fly,[13] and progresses to the flagellated metacyclic stage after about a week following ingestion. It first attaches to the wall of the gut tract by non-specific hydrophobic interactions between the surface of the parasite's flagella and the insect stomach cell membrane.[14] Attachment to other regions of the insect intestinal tract later on during the differentiation to the metacyclic promastigote stage is mediated, in part, by specific insect galectins (e.g., PpGalec),[15, 16] and the parasite cell surface multipurpose molecule, lipophosphoglycan. The release of infectious stage organisms, a necessary final step in their development, is mediated by arabinosyl capping of LPG sc-Gal residues upon differentiation to the metacyclic stage.[17] The leptomonad stage (heretofore unrecognized) locates to the anterior region of the gut and secretes a gel-like substance that blocks the digestive tract of the sand fly, causing the infected insect to regurgitate its complement of infectious metacyclic promastigotes into the host's subcutaneous tissues during feeding.[13] This is similar to a strategy employed by the plague bacillus while inside the rat flea.

The mammalian host

The flagellated metacyclic promastigote stage (Fig. 2.2) resides in the anterior midgut and thorax and is injected into the host along with the dipteran's salivary secretions. In addition to aiding the parasite to establish infection in the sand fly (see above), some of those same salivary proteins aid in Leishmania's ability to colonize the mammalian host.[5, 6] At least one salivary product interferes with production of IL-10.[18] Maxadilan induces negative effects on host immune cell function, including inhibition of the release of TNF-α, upregulation of IL-6 synthesis in macrophages, and stimulation of prostaglandin E2 production.[19] Presumably, some or all of these altered host responses play a role in aiding the parasite to establish itself in the host, although their precise mechanisms have not yet been determined.

The promastigotes deposited in the extracellular matrix at the site of the bite adhere there, aided by lipophosphoglycan and a surface membrane laminin receptor protein on their surface.[20] The promastigotes induce the production of antibodies and become opsonized. As the result, the C3 component of complement attaches to the parasite cell surface.[21] They are then able to attach to red cells or platelets and become engulfed by dendritic cells[22] or macrophages (Fig. 2.3). Many would-be pathogens are unable to survive this step and are digested by inclusion into phagolysosomal vacuoles. In contrast, Leishmania are able to avoid digestion and are free to differentiate into amastigotes to begin the intracellular phase of their life cycle.

It is at this point in the life cycle that differences between species of Leishmania become obvious. Those that cause only cutaneous lesions remain at the site throughout the infection, while those that cause visceral or mucocutaneous lesions somehow manage to find their way to the appropriate site in the body. The host and parasite factors resulting in these different biologies are still being sorted out in the research laboratory. For example, dendritic cells increase in number in the draining lymph nodes of experimentally infected mice infected with *L. (L.) tropica*, but infected dendritic cells do not appear to migrate to the lymph nodes.[23] How the parasites reach the draining lymphoid tissue remains to be demonstrated.

The mechanism of Leishmania survival inside the macrophage involves alteration of the phagolysosome, and comes about as the result of host cell interaction with lipophosphoglycan.[24] Infected phagocytes display abnormal maturation of the phagolysosome due to lipophosphoglycan's interference with F-actin, an essential component of the process of fusion of lysosomes with the phagocytic vacuole.[25] This lack of fusion, in part, enables the parasite to evade digestion. Amastigotes divide inside their host cells (Fig. 2.4) and can remain at the site of injection, resulting in the clinical condition known as a cutaneous Leishmaniasis. Alternatively, they can be carried by the phagocytes to mucocutaneous junctions, or to the reticuloendothelial tissues, resulting in mucocutaneous or visceral Leishmaniasis, respectively.

Leishmania spp. have salvage pathways[25, 28] for nucleic acid synthesis. The enzymes reside within the glycosome,[26] a specialized organelle unique to the kinetoplastidae. Cutaneous lesions form in most instances, allowing sand flies access to infected host cells at the raised margin. Circulating macrophages in blood-harboring amastigotes can also be taken up by the vector.

Cellular and Molecular Pathogenesis

Virulence factors and pathogenesis

The cell and molecular biology of *Leishmania spp.* has been reviewed.[27, 28] Most of what is known regarding the biology of Leishmania is derived from murine models and in vitro cell culture using various species of Leishmania.[29] The following summary of pathogenic mechanisms is derived from both types of experimental approaches. The turning-on of heat shock genes,[30] as well as cassettes of other developmentally regulated genes,[31] occurs as the parasite makes the transition from an environment dependent upon ambient temperature (sand fly) to the homeothermic essential niche inside the mammalian host cell. The amastigote downregulates IL-12, which delays the onset of cell-mediated protective immune responses.[32, 33] Amastigotes of *L. mexicana* interfere with antigen presentation by macrophages, employing cysteine protease B.[34] The amastigote stage also possesses potent cysteine protease inhibitors,[35] which it presumably uses to modify host cysteine protease activity during intracellular infection.

Replication of amastigotes is dependent upon host cyclophillins,[36] since division is inhibited by cyclosporin A.[37] The membrane of the promastigote contains a zinc protease, leishmanolysin,[38] a 63 kDa glycoprotein whose crystalline structure has been determined.[39] Current evidence favors a role for leishmanolysin in migration of parasites through the intracellular matrix by digestion of collagen type IV after their release from infected cells.[40] Induction of the chemokine MIP-1β by neutrophils harboring amastigotes attracts macrophages to the site of infection. Macrophages then engulf infected neutrophils, thus acquiring the infection.[41]

16 The Protozoa

Protective immune mechanism(s)

The mechanism(s) of protective immunity vary with clinical types of Leishmania.[42] The cutaneous forms typically induce well-defined Th-1 responses, which are T-cell-mediated, and play a critical role in controlling and finally eliminating the organism.[43] Permanent immunity to reinfection with cutaneous Leishmania causing organisms is the rule, and depends upon inducing high levels of CD4+ T-cell memory.[44] In addition, Langerhans cells are thought to play a major role in antigen presentation and in the induction of IL-12[45, 46] and IL-27.[47] The main effector mechanism involves CD4+ T cell-dependent macrophage activation and subsequent killing of amastigotes by nitric oxide.[48] Chemokines are also important for immunity,[49, 50] and include MIP-3beta and INF-δ.[50] Antibodies appear to play no role in immunity to cutaneous Leishmaniasis, and probably aid the parasite in gaining entrance into the macrophage.[51]

Protective immune mechanisms induced by infection with visceral Leishmaniasis (L. (L.) donovani and L. (L.) infantum), include IL-12 and INF-δ. Immunity is suppressed by IL-10 and TGF-β.[43]

To further complicate the clinical spectrum of diseases caused by Leishmania, one has to be reminded of the fact that Leishmania spp. have been around a long time, and have, within the last 165 million years, begun to diverge evolutionarily due to continental drift. Organisms in the New World must, by necessity, behave somewhat differently from their ancestor species that still continue to infect mammals in the Old World. The same is true for its hosts, including humans. Thus, when considering the type of disease and the immune responses to them, there exist many exceptions to the above summaries. For an excellent review on this aspect of the biology of Leishmania, see McMahon-Pratt and Alexander.[52]

References

1. Mauricio IL. Howard MK. Stothard JR. Miles MA. Genomic diversity in the Leishmania donovani complex. Parasitology 119:237-46, 1999.
2. Bates PA, Rogers ME. New insights into the developmental biology and transmission mechanisms of Leishmania. Curr Mol Med. 4:601-9.9. 2004.
3. Ashford RW. The Leishmaniases as model zoonoses. Ann Trop Med Parasitol. 91:693-701, 1997.
4. Handman E. Leishmaniasis: current status of vaccine development. Clin. Microbiol. Rev. 14:229–243. 2001.
5. Ribeiro, J. M. Blood-feeding arthropods: live syringes or invertebrate pharmacologists? Infect. Agents Dis. 4:143-152. 1995.
6. Nuttall, P. A., Paesen G. et al. Vector–host interactions in disease transmission. J. Mol. Microbiol. Biotechnol. 2, 381-386. 2000.
7. Valenzuela JG. Garfield M. Rowton ED, Pham VM Identification of the most abundant secreted proteins from the salivary glands of the sand fly Lutzomyia longipalpis, vector of Leishmania chagasi. J Exp Biol. 207:3717-29. 2004.
8. Dominguez M. Moreno I. Aizpurua C. Torano A. Early mechanisms of Leishmania infection in human blood. Microbes Infect. 5:507-13. 2003.
9. Jackson TS. Lerner E. Weisbrod RM. et al. Vasodilatory properties of recombinant maxadilan. Am J Physiol. 271(3 Pt 2): H924-30, 1996.
10. Moro O. Lerner EA. Maxadilan, the vasodilator from sand flies, is a specific pituitary adenylate cyclase activating peptide type I receptor agonist. J Biol Chem. 272(2):966-970, 1997.
11. Uchida D. Tatsuno I. et al. Maxadilan is a specific agonist and its deleted peptide (M65) is a specific antagonist for PACAP type 1 receptor. Ann N Y Acad Sci. 865:253-258, 1998.
12. Vaidyanathan R. Isolation of a myoinhibitory peptide from Leishmania major (Kinetoplastida: Trypanosomatidae) and its function in the vector sand fly Phlebotomus papatasi (Diptera Psychodidae). J Med Entomol. 42:142-52. 2005.
13. Bates PA, Rogers ME. New insights into the developmental biology and transmission mechanisms of Leishmania. Curr Mol Med. 4:601-9. 2004.
14. Wakid MH, Bates PA. Flagellar attachment of Leishmania promastigotes to plastic film in vitro. Exp Parasitol.106:173-8. 2004.
15. Kamhawi S. Ramalho-Ortigao M. et al. A role for insect galectins in parasite survival. Cell. 119:329-41. 2004.
16. Beverley SM, Dobson DE. Flypaper for parasites. Cell.119:311-2. 2004. 18.
17. Dobson DE. Mengeling BJ. et al. Identification of genes encoding arabinosyltransferases (SCA) mediating developmental modifications of lipophosphoglycan required for sand fly transmission of Leishmania major J. Biol. Chem. 278:28840-28848. 2003
18. Norsworthy NB. Sun J. et al. Sand fly saliva enhances Leishmania amazonensis infection by modulating interleukin-10 production. Infect Immun. 72:1240-7. 2004.
19. Soares MB. Titus RG. et al. The vasoactive peptide maxadilan from sand fly saliva inhibits TNF-alpha and induces IL-6 by mouse macrophages through interaction with the pituitary adenylate cyclase-activating polypeptide (PACAP) receptor. J Immunol 160(4):1811-6, 1998.
20. Ghosh A. Bandyopadhyay K. Kole L. Das PK. Isolation of a laminin-binding protein from the protozoan parasite Leishmania donovani that may mediate cell adhesion. Biochem J. 337 (Pt 3):551-8, 1999.
21. Antoine JC. Prina E. Courret N. Lang T. Leishmania spp.: on the interactions they establish with antigen-presenting cells of their mammalian hosts. Adv Parasitol. 58:1-68. 2004.
22. Steigerwald M. Moll H. Leishmania major modulates chemokine and chemokine receptor expression by dendritic cells and affects their migratory capacity. Infect Immun. 73:2564-7. 2005.
23. Baldwin T. Henri S. et al. Dendritic cell populations in Leishmania major-infected skin and draining lymph nodes. Infect Immun. 72:1991-2001. 2004.
24. Turco SJ. Descoteaux A. The lipophosphoglycan of Leishmania parasites, Annu. Rev. Microbiol. 46:65–94. 1992.
25. Lodge R, Descoteaux A. Modulation of phagolysosome biogenesis by the lipophosphoglycan of Leishmania. Clin Immunol. 114:256-65. 2005.
26. Moyersoen J. Choe J. et al. Biogenesis of peroxisomes and glycosomes: trypanosomatid glycosome assembly is a promising new

drug target. FEMS Microbiol Rev. 28:603-43. 2004.

27. Gull. K. The biology of kinetoplastid parasites: insights and challenges from genomics and post-genomics. Int J Parasitol. 31:443-52. 2001.

28. Olivier M. Gregory DJ. Forget G. Subversion mechanisms by which Leishmania parasites can escape the host immune response: a signaling point of view. Clin Microbiol Rev. 18:293-305. 2005.

29. Debrabant A. Joshi MB. Pimenta PF. Dwyer DM. Generation of *Leishmania donovani* axenic amastigotes: their growth and biological characteristics. Int J Parasitol. 34:205-17. 2004.

30. Bente M. Harder S. et al. Developmentally induced changes of the proteome in the protozoan parasite *Leishmania donovani*. Proteomics. 3:1811-29. 2003.

31. Duncan RC. Salotra P. et al. The application of gene expression microarray technology to kinetoplastid research. Curr Mol Med. 4:611-21. 2004.

32. Sutterwala FS. Mosser DM. The taming of IL-12: suppressing the production of proinflammatory cytokines. J Leukoc Biol 65(5): 543-51, 1999.

33. McDowell MA. Sacks DL. Inhibition of host cell signal transduction by Leishmania: observations relevant to the selective impairment of IL-12 responses. Current Opinion in Microbiology 2(4):438-43, 1999.

34. Buxbaum LU. Denise H. et al. Cysteine protease B of *Leishmania mexicana* inhibits host Th1 responses and protective immunity. J Immunol. 171:3711-7. 2003.

35. Besteiro S. Coombs GH. Mottram JC. A potential role for ICP, a Leishmanial inhibitor of cysteine peptidases, in the interaction between host and parasite. Mol Microbiol. 54:1224-36. 2004.

36. Hoerauf A. Rascher C. et al. Host-cell cyclophilin is important for the intracellular replication of *Leishmania major*. Mol Microbiol 24(2):421-9, 1997.

37. Meissner U. Juttner S. Rollinghoff M. Gessner A. Cyclosporin A-mediated killing of *Leishmania major* by macrophages is independent of reactive nitrogen and endogenous TNF-alpha and is not inhibited by IL-10 and 13. Parasitol Res. 89:221-7. 2002.

38. Chaudhuri G. Chaudhuri M. et al. Surface acid proteinase (gp63) of *Leishmania mexicana*. J. Biol. Chem. 264:7483–7489. 1989.

39. Schlagenhauf E. Etges R. Metcalf P. The crystal structure of the *Leishmania major* surface proteinase leishmanolysin (gp63). Structure. 6(8):1035-1046, 1998.

40. McGwire BS. Chang KP. Engman DM. Migration through the extracellular matrix by the parasitic protozoan Leishmania is enhanced by surface metalloprotease gp63. Infect Immun. 71:1008-10. 2003.

41. van Zandbergen G, Klinger M. et al. Cutting edge: neutrophil granulocyte serves as a vector for Leishmania entry into macrophages. J Immunol. 173:6521-5. 2004.

42. Wilson ME. Jeronimo SM. Pearson RD. Immunopathogenesis of infection with the visceralizing Leishmania specie. Microb Pathog. 38:147-60. 2005.

43. Scott P. Artis D. Uzonna J. Zaph C. The development of effector and memory T cells in cutaneous Leishmaniasis: the implications for vaccine development. Immunol Rev. 201:318-38. 2004.

44. Gabaglia CR. Sercarz EE. et al. Life-long systemic protection in mice vaccinated with *L. major* and adenovirus IL-12 vector requires active infection, macrophages and intact lymph nodes. Vaccine. 23:247-57. 2004.

45. Oliveira MA. Tadokoro CE. et al. Macrophages at intermediate stage of maturation produce high levels of IL-12 p40 upon stimulation with Leishmania. Microbes Infect. 7:213-23. 2005.

46. Simin M. Shahriar D. A quantitative study of epidermal Langerhans cells in cutaneous Leishmaniasis caused by *Leishmania tropica*. International Journal of Dermatology 43:819-823. 2004.

47. Hunter CA. Villarino A. Artis D. Scott P. The role of IL-27 in the development of T-cell responses during parasitic infections. Immunol Rev. 202:106-14. 2004. Sacks D. Noben-Trauth N. The immunology of susceptibility and resistance to *Leishmania major* in mice. Nat Rev Immunol 2002; **2**: 845858. 2002.

48. Awasthi A. Mathur RK. Saha B. Immune response to Leishmania infection. Indian J Med Res. 119:238-58. 2004.

49. Roychoudhury K, Roy S. Role of chemokines in Leishmania infection Curr Mol Med. 4:691-6. 2004.

50. Mitra R, Dharajiya N. et al. Migration of antigen presenting cells from periphery to the peritoneum during an inflammatory response: role of chemokines and cytokine. FASEB J. 18:1764-6. 2004.

51. Miles SA. Conrad SM. et al. A role for IgG immune complexes during infection with the intracellular pathogen Leishmania. J Exp Med. 201:747-54. 2005.

52. McMahon-Pratt D, Alexander J. Does the Leishmania major paradigm of pathogenesis and protection hold for New World cutaneous Leishmaniases or the visceral disease? Immunol Rev. 201:206-24. 2004.

3. Cutaneous Leishmaniasis:

Leishmania (L) major
(Yakimov and Schockov 1915)
Leishmania (L) tropica
(Wright 1903)
Leishmania (L) mexicana
(Biagi 1953)

Introduction

Cutaneous Leishmaniasis (CL) is caused by four species in the Old World: *Leishmania (Leishmania) aethiopica, L. (L.) major, L. (L.) tropica,* and *L. (L.) infantum.* Their vectors include sand flies of the following species: *Phlebotomous papatasi, P. sergenti, P. longipes, P. argentipes,* and *P. ariasi.* At least 15 species of Leishmania in the New World cause the same type of disease: *Leishmania (Leishmania) amazonensis, L. (V.) braziliensis, L. (L.) colombiensis, L. (L.) garnhami, L. (V.) guyanensis, L. (L.) infantum chagasi, L. (V.) lainsoni, L. (L.) lindenbergi, L. (L.) mexicana, L. (V.) naiffi, L. (V.) panamensis, L. (V.) peruviana, L. (L.) pifanoi, L. (L.) shawi, L. (L.) venezuelensis.* The principal vector species are *Lutzomyia olmeca olmeca, Lu. flaviscutellata,* and *Lu. trapidoi.* In some locales, *L. (L.) tropica* visceralizes,[1] suggesting that another strain of this species exists with quite different characteristics from the one that only causes cutaneous lesions.

Although accurate statistics regarding incidence rates and prevalence are not available, it is estimated

Figure 3.1. Old lesion on face due to *Leishmania major.*

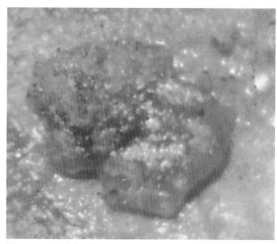

Figure 3.2. Healing lesion due to *Leishmania spp.*

that several million people throughout the world suffer from cutaneous Leishmaniasis each year. Rodents are a primary reservoir for human infection caused by *L. (L.) major,* while domestic dogs serve as reservoirs in many parts of the world for other species of Leishmania.

Historical Information

Russell, in 1856,[2] described the clinical aspects of cutaneous Leishmaniasis. Cunningham, while working in India in 1885,[3] accurately described the Leishmania organism he saw in a fixed histological section of a skin lesion. Sergent and coworkers, in 1921,[4] demonstrated that sand flies were the vectors responsible for transmitting Leishmania to humans; one species bears his name. Cosme Bueno, much earlier (1764) suspected the same was true for "uta," a cutaneous lesion, later shown to be caused by infection with Leishmania.

"Oriental sore" is common among people living in endemic areas of the Middle East, India, and Africa. A rudimentary kind of immunization referred to as "leishmanization" was practiced in the Middle East, where it was known that infection results in permanent immunity to reinfection.[5] Uninfected individuals were deliberately inoculated in areas other than the face with scrapings containing organisms from the margins of active lesions. This controlled the region of the body on which the scar developed.

Life Cycle

Infection begins with the bite of an infected sand fly. The promastigotes are introduced into the subcutaneous tissue, attach to the extracellular matrix and are then taken up by dendritic cells and macrophages. The promastigotes transform into the amastigote stage and begin to replicate. Infection progresses at the site of the bite only. Eventually, a large, painless craterform ulcer

Leishmania tropica

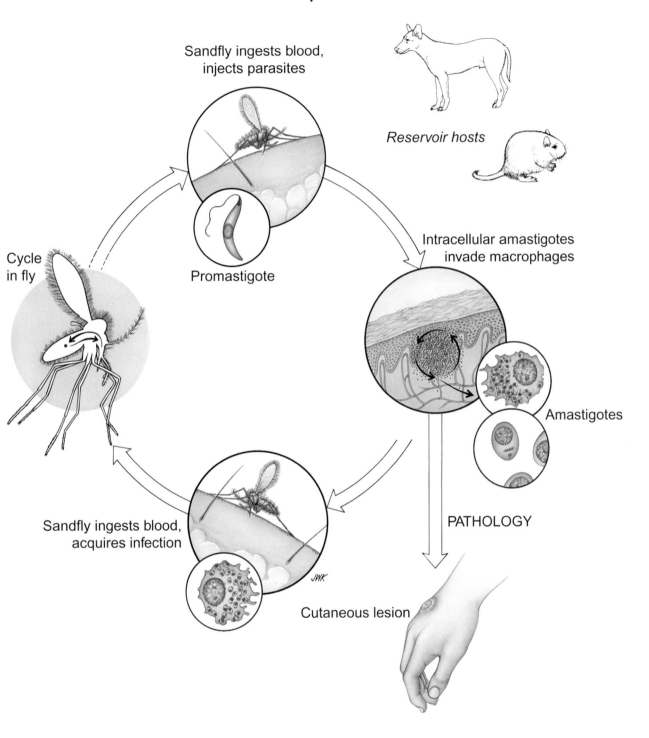

Sandfly ingests blood, injects parasites

Reservoir hosts

Cycle in fly

Promastigote

Intracellular amastigotes invade macrophages

Amastigotes

Sandfly ingests blood, acquires infection

PATHOLOGY

Cutaneous lesion

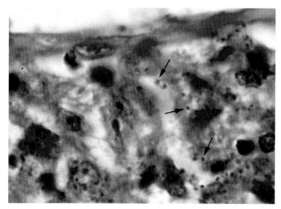

Figure 3.3. Histologic section of skin showing amastigotes (arrows) of *Leishmania spp.* in dendritic cells and macrophages.

forms as the result of extensive cell death. Sand flies acquire the infection by feeding on blood taken up at the margin of the ulcer.

Clinical Disease

Cutaneous Leishmaniasis (CL) is first recognized as a small red papule at the site of the bite wound approximately 2-8 weeks after injection of metacyclic promastigotes. The lesion progresses from a painless nodule, measuring approximately 1 cm in diameter, into a much larger one by the formation of satellite papules (Fig. 3.1). The area around the bite wound eventually ulcerates due to intense destruction of cells, and becomes depressed, then heals through scarring (Fig. 3.2). Organisms are found only in the living tissue at the raised margin, regardless of the age of the lesion (Fig. 3.3). Occasionally, more than one lesion is present (Fig. 3.4).

After the ulcer heals, which may take weeks to months, immunity to reinfection is permanent, and is also effective against other Leishmania species that cause only cutaneous lesions. In experimental infections in rodents, exposure to *L. (V.) braziliensis* confers protection against challenge with *L. (L.) major*,[6] suggesting that shared, cross-reacting antigens might be good candidates for a CL vaccine.[7]

Regardless of which species causes the lesion, it may vary in size and shape, sometimes confounding even the most experienced clinician. CL should always be suspected in travelers, or patients from endemic areas when any lesion that fails to heal is encountered. This is particularly true for CL in the western hemisphere.[8] Prolonged infection is the rule in a subset of patients that have an altered pattern of immunity. Chiclero's ulcer, on the pina of the ear (Fig. 3.5), is a good example of this exception.[9]

Occasionally, *L. (L.) tropica* visceralizes.[10] This occurred in Saudi Arabia and in other parts of the Middle

East among coalition forces stationed in that region during the Gulf War,[11, 12, 13] and again when troops were deployed to Afganistan.[14] Leishmaniasis was suspected as one of the causes of a postwar condition referred to as "Gulf War" syndrome,[15] but there is no evidence that this is the case, and the root cause of the syndrome remains unknown and somewhat controversial.[16] Onset of signs and symptoms is unpredictable, often taking months to manifest. Splenomegaly, double daily fever spikes, leucopenia and malaise were the most frequently encountered complaints. The fatality rate in untreated individuals is high.

Infection due to *L. (L.) aethiopica* is restricted to Ethiopia and Kenya,[17] and causes a wide spectrum of disease, including diffuse cutaneous Leishmaniasis (DCL),[18] characterized by involvement of the entire surface of the skin.[19] Other species of Leishmania (e.g., *L. (V.) braziliensis, L. (L.) amazonensis*) have also been diagnosed in patients suffering from DCL.[20] DCL begins as a single nodule on an exposed part of the skin,

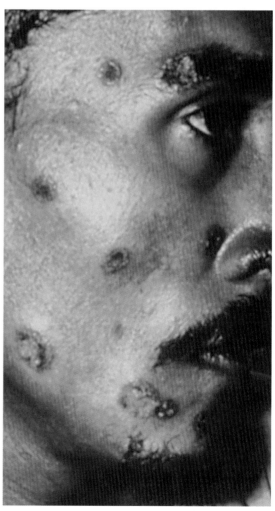

Figure 3.4. Multiple cutaneous lesions due to *Leishmania panamanensis*.

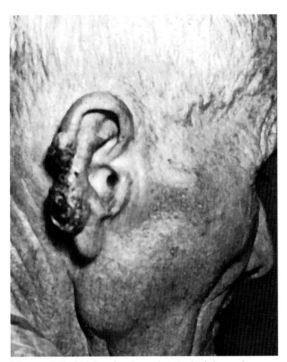

Figure 3.5. Chiclero's ulcer due to *Leishmania spp.*

then starts to grow and spread, eventually involving vast areas of the skin. Patients resemble those suffering from lepromatous leprosy. Nodules and plaques harbor large numbers of organisms.

Similarly, *L. (L.) mexicana, L (L.) amazonensis* and *L. (L.) venezuelensis* occasionally cause anergic disseminated cutaneous Leishmaniasis (ADCL), which is similar to DCL.[21] Nodules and large patches of involved skin, in which abundant amastigote-infected cells can be found, are typical and may remain so for many years. Chemotherapy is of little consequence to the outcome, which includes extensive scarring of all involved areas. However, one patient treated with 10% solution of zinc sulfate appeared to be cured of her infection.[22]

Leishmania (L.) infantum can cause cutaneous lesions,[23] but is more commonly associated with visceral disease in children throughout the Mediterranean basin.

Patients with HIV/AIDS may present with cutaneous lesions, only, or the infection can visceralize.[8] Co-infection with Leishmania and HIV are not common in the New World, but this lack of association is not due to the low number of individuals harboring either group of infectious agents.[24]

Diagnosis

Although most cutaneous lesions caused by Leishmania look similar (i.e., craterform with a raised edge), there are many other dermatological conditions that might be mistaken for CL. Therefore, diagnosis of all forms of CL due to Leishmania depends upon PCR,[25, 26] and has more than a 95% rate of positivity when organisms are present. Most PCR tests employ primer sequences based on mini circle DNA.[27] Histopathological examination of biopsy tissue is less successful in identifying organisms (10-20%).[28] Culture of needle aspiration samples in biphasic Medium-199 appears to be a viable alternative to PCR, but takes much longer (several days), due to the slow growth of the promastigotes at 20^0 C.[29]

Treatment

The drug of choice for all forms of cutaneous Leishmaniasis is sodium stibogluconate, an antimony-containing drug with many serious side effects,[30] including rash, headache, arthralgias and myalgias, pancreatitis, transaminitis, and hematologic suppression. Cure rates ranging from 85-95% are typical in the majority of cases. Re-treatment improves that figure to close to 100%. Ketoconizole, an anti-fungal agent, is an alternate drug with fewer side effects, but is not as effective as sodium stibogluconate. Other drugs, such as orally administered fluconazole, or topical paromomycin sulfate, show promise for replacing the standard treatment.[31, 32]

Prevention and Control

Eradication of sand fly breeding sites near suburban and urban centers, attaching pyrethroid-impregnated collars to domestic dogs, and sleeping under insecticide-impregnated bed netting are cost-effective control measures.[33] In many instances, transmission from person to person does not occur; rather, infection is from reservoir hosts (rodents and dogs), as is the case in many parts of the Middle East and South and Central America, and therefore, treating all infected individuals in a given community has little effect in reducing CL. Sand flies only bite at certain times of the day; mostly early in the morning and again late in the evening. Therefore, avoidance of outdoor activities during these times reduces the chance of being bitten. This is particularly good advice for travelers to endemic areas, who do not have to carry out their daily lives for long periods of time in areas of high transmission. Two additional ways of avoiding sand fly bites are using insect repellents and wearing clothing that covers most of the body.

Vaccines employing combinations of proven protection-inducing parasite proteins offer hope that a standard vaccine for use against CL and VL forms of Leishmaniasis may soon be available.[7]

References

1. Berman J. Recent Developments in Leishmaniasis: Epidemiology, Diagnosis, and Treatment. Curr Infect Dis Rep. 7:33-38. 2005.
2. Russell A: Of the mal d'Aleppo. In: Natural History of Aleppo and Parts Adjacent. (Millar A (ed) London, pp. 262-266, 1856.
3. Cunningham DD. On the presence of peculiar parasitic organisms in the tissue of a specimen of Delhi boil. Sci Mem Med Officers Army India 1: 21-31, 1885.
4. Theodorides J. Note historique sur la decouverte de la transmission de la leishmaniose cutanee par les phlebotomes. Bull Soc Pathol Exot 90:177-180, 1997.
5. Handman E. Leishmaniasis: current status of vaccine development, Clin. Microbiol. Rev. 14:229–243. 2001.
6. Lima HC. DeKrey GK. Titus RG. Resolution of an infection with *Leishmania braziliensis* confers complete protection to a subsequent challenge with *Leishmania major* in BALB/c mice. Mem Inst Oswaldo Cruz 94:71-6, 1999.
7. Coler RN, Reed SG. Second-generation vaccines against Leishmaniasis. Trends Parasitol. 21:244-9. 2005.
8. Lainson R. Shaw JJ. New World Leishmaniasis – The Neotropical Leishmania Species. In: Topley and Wilson's Microbiology and Microbial Infections. 10th ed. (Collier L, Balows A., Sussman M., eds.). Volume 5. Parasitology (Cox FEG. Despommier, DD. Kreier JP. Wakelin D., volume eds.). Arnold, Pub., London. 2005.
9. Lianson R. Strangeways-Dixon J. *Leishmania mexicana*: The epidemiology of dermal Leishmaniasis in British Honduras. Trasn Roy Soc Trop Med Hyg 57:242-265, 1963.
10. Berman J. Recent Developments in Leishmaniasis: Epidemiology, Diagnosis, and Treatment. Curr Infect Dis Rep. 7:33-38. 2005.
11. Kreutzer RD. Grogl M. et al. Identification and genetic comparison of Leishmanial parasites causing viscerotropic and cutaneous disease in soldiers returning from Operation Desert Storm. Am J Trop Med Hyg 49:357–363. 1993.
12. Magill AJ. Drogi M. et al. Visceral infection caused by *Leishmania tropica* in veteerans of Operation Desert Storm. N Engl J Med 328:1383-1387, 1993.
13. Hyams KC, Hanson K. et al. The impact of infectious diseases on the health of U.S. troops deployed to the Persian Gulf during operations Desert Shield and Desert Storm. Clin Infect Dis. 20:1497-504. 1995.
14. Halsey ES. Bryce LM. et al Visceral Leishmaniasis in a soldier returning from Operation Enduring Freedom. Mil Med. 169:699-701. 2004.
15. Oumeish OY, Oumeish I, Parish JL. Gulf War syndrome. Clin Dermatol. 20:401-12. 2002.
16. Dyer O. US and UK scientists disagree about causes of Gulf war syndrome. BMJ. 329:940. 2004.
17. Hailu A. The use of direct agglutination test (DAT) in serological diagnosis of Ethiopian cutaneous Leishmaniasis. Diagn Microbiol Infect Dis. 42:251-6. 2002.
18. Akuffo H, Maasho K. et al. *Leishmania aethiopica* derived from diffuse Leishmaniasis patients preferentially induce mRNA for interleukin-10 while those from localized Leishmaniasis patients induce interferon-gamma. J Infect Dis 175:73741.1997.
19. Bryceson ADM. Diffuse cutaneous Leishmaniasis in Ethiopia. I. The clinical and histological features of the disease. Trans Roy Soc Trop Med Hyg 63:708–737. 1969.
20. Turetz ML, Machado PR. Disseminated Leishmaniasis: a new and emerging form of Leishmaniasis observed in northeastern Brazil. J Infect Dis.186:1829-34. 2002.
21. Bonfante-Garrido R. Barroeta S. et al. Disseminated American cutaneous Leishmaniasis. Int J Dermatol 35(8):561-5, 1996.
22. Sharquie KE. Najim RA. Disseminated cutaneous Leishmaniasis. Saudi Med J. 25:951-4. 2004.
23. del Giudice P. Marty P. Lacour JP. et al. Cutaneous Leishmaniasis due to Leishmania infantum. Case reports and literature review Arch Dermatol 134(2):193-8, 1998.
24. Postigo C. Llamas R. Zarco C. et al. Cutaneous lesions in patients with visceral Leishmaniasis and HIV infection. J Infect 35(3):265-8, 1997.
25. Mimori T. Sasaki J. Nakata M. et al. Rapid identification of Leishmania species from formalin-fixed biopsy samples by polymorphism-specific polymerase chain reaction. Gene 210(2):179-86, 1998.
26. Gangneux JP. Menotti J. et al. Prospective value of PCR amplification and sequencing for diagnosis and typing of Old World Leishmania infections in an area of nonendemicity. J Clin Microbiol 41:1419-1422. 2003.
27. Rodriguez N B. Guzman B. et al. Diagnosis of cutaneous Leishmaniasis and species discrimination of parasites by PCR and hybridization. J. Clin. Microbiol. 32:2246-2252. 1994.
28. Faber WR. Oskam L. et al. Value of diagnostic techniques for cutaneous Leishmaniasis. J Am Acad Dermatol. 49:70-4. 2003.
29. Dey T. Afrin F. Anam K. Ali N. Infectivity and virulence of *Leishmania donovani* promastigotes: a role for media, source, and strain of parasite. J Eukaryot Microbiol. 49:270-4. 2002.
30. Aronson NE. Wortmann GW. et al. Safety and efficacy of intravenous sodium stibogluconate in the treatment of Leishmaniasis: recent U.S. military experience. Clin Infect Dis 27(6):1457-64, 1998.
31. Laffitte E. Genton B. Panizzon RG. Cutaneous Leishmaniasis caused by *Leishmania tropica*: treatment with oral fluconazole. Dermatology. 210:249-51. 2005.
32. Shazad B. Abbaszadeh B. Khamesipour A. Comparison of topical paromomycin sulfate (twice/day) with intralesional meglumine antimoniate for the treatment of cutaneous Leishmaniasis caused by *L. major*. Eur J Dermatol. 15:85-7. 2005.
33. Desjeux P. Leishmaniasis: current situation and new perspectives. Comp Immunol Microbiol Infect Dis. 27:305-18. 2004.

4. Mucocutaneous Leishmaniasis:

Leishmania (V) braziliensis
(Vianna 1911)

Introduction

Leishmania (V.) braziliensis is a zoonotic infection that typically causes cutaneous lesions. In rare instances (2-3% of all infections), infection metastasizes to mucocutaneous junctions (oral cavity, urogenital, and anal areas), where it erodes the soft tissues.[1] This often disfiguring condition is referred to as mucocutaneous Leishmaniasis (MCL). Infrequently, *L. (V.) guyanensis* and *L. (V.) panamensis* cause similar disease.[2] The vectors for MCL are sand flies in the genus Lutzomyia and Psychodopygus. MCL is widely distributed throughout Central and South America, with most of the cases occurring in Equator, Bolivia, and Northern Brazil. Reservoir hosts, both wild and domestic mammals, abound.

About 25% of the clinical cases of *L. (V.) braziliensis* and *L. (V.) guyanensis* are infected with a double-stranded RNA virus (leishmaniavirus [3, 4]). Its presence was not correlated with any stage of the infection, or with any clinical condition.[4]

Its role in the biology of Leishmania has yet to be determined.

Historical Information

Carini, in 1911,[5] identified patients suffering from mucocutaneous lesions as being different from those only demonstrating cutaneous lesions, thereby establishing MCL as a separate clinical entity. In the following year, Vianna[6] identified and named *L. (V.) braziliensis* as the causative agent. Kligler, in 1916,[7] and Noguchi, in 1929,[8] using serological and cultural methods succeeded in characterizing this parasite as a distinct species despite the lack of modern laboratory equipment.

Life Cycle

Infection begins when an infected sand fly takes a blood meal. Metacyclic promastigotes are injected into the subcutaneous tissue and adhere to the extracellular matrix. A primary lesion forms at the bite site as the result of infection in dendritic cells and macrophages (Fig. 2.3). The lesion evolves into an ulcer (Fig. 4.1), which can resemble that induced by any number of other species causing cutaneous Leishmaniasis. Amastigotes are transported to the mucocutaneous junction early on during infection, although lesions at this site are slow to appear, even if the patient goes on to develop MCL.[1] There, they divide within resident macrophages and erode the tissues. Infections typically "smolder" for long periods of time, usually months to years.

Person-to-person transmission probably does not occur. Rather, reservoir hosts (domestic dogs, rodents, and various rain forest mammals) serve as the source of infection.[9] The biology of *Leishmania (V.) braziliensis* in the sand fly closely resembles that of all other Leishmania species.

Clinical Disease

MCL lesions developing in the nasal passage (i.e., the most common mucocutanoeus site) are characterized by a necrotizing inflammation of mixed cell types (plasma cells, lymphocytes). Skin, mucous membranes, and cartilage can also be involved. Lesions of the oral cavity eventually result in the destruction of the soft palate and nasal septum, as well as invasion of the larynx.[10] When this occurs, the patient may die from infection that spreads to the lungs.[1] Parasites are seldom demonstrated in lesions, although they can be revealed by PCR.[11] The ulcers are replaced by fibrous granulomas that heal slowly, scar, and deform the tissues. The most advanced cases are known as "espundia" (Fig. 4.2).[12] MCL does not usually heal spontaneously, and secondary bacterial infections, including pneumonias, are common.

Patients coinfected with the HIV virus and *L. (V.) braziliensis* are rare. Multiple cutaneous lesions, as well as extensive mucocutaneous involvement are typical in HIV/AIDS patients.[13, 14] Due to enormous genetic variation among strains of *L. (V.) braziliensis*,[15, 16] and the variety of AIDS-related symptoms and signs manifested throughout the clinical course of HIV/AIDS, long

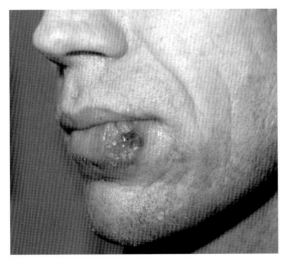

Figure 4.1. Cutaneous lesion on lower lip due to *Leishmania braziliensis*.

Leishmania braziliensis

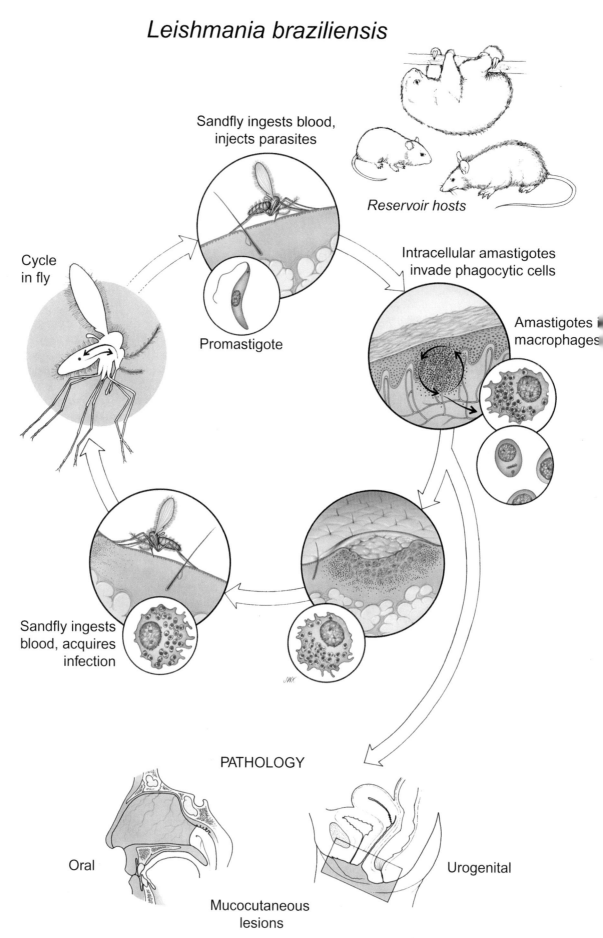

Sandfly ingests blood, injects parasites

Reservoir hosts

Cycle in fly

Promastigote

Intracellular amastigotes invade phagocytic cells

Amastigotes i macrophages

Sandfly ingests blood, acquires infection

PATHOLOGY

Oral

Mucocutaneous lesions

Urogenital

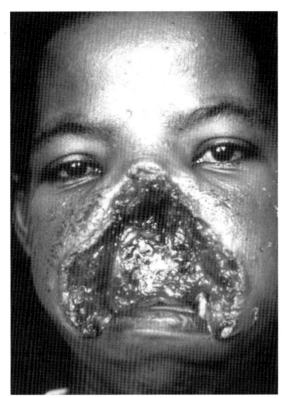

Figure 4.2. Espundia. This lesion resulted in the erosion of the soft palette. Most lesions do not advance this far before medical intervention.

term patterns of disease in rarely occurring infections such as MCL make for an exceedingly complex and difficult clinical picture.

Diagnosis

Definitive diagnosis is by PCR.[17] Organisms are difficult to identify in biopsy of infected palate and soft tissues of the oral cavity, so microscopy of histological sections is not an option for diagnosis. Culture of biopsy material is a possibility (see diagnosis for CL, page 21), but growth of promastigotes at room temperature is slow.

Treatment

The drug of choice for treating mucocutaneous Leishmaniasis is sodium stibogluconate. Persistence of infection beyond the treatment period is a possibility in longstanding infections, as judged by PCR on experimentally infected monkeys.[18] This suggests that organisms can survive in low numbers despite seemingly adequate treatment.[19] Liposomal amphotericin-B has been used successfully in difficult to treat cases.[20] Pentamidine is another drug with anti-Leishmanial activity.[21] Allopurinol is without additional efficacy.[22] Clearly, additional drugs are needed.[23]

Prevention and Control

Transmission of *L. (V.) braziliensis* and many other related species of Leishmania occurs through close contact of human populations with reservoir hosts (wild and domestic mammals). Deforestation of vast regions of rain forest for agriculture, mining, oil exploration, all of which leads to increased urbanization in South and Central America, has allowed large numbers of people access to the edges of the rain forest. Edges of natural systems are special ecologically defined areas termed ecotones.[24] These zones constitute the borders between ecosystems, and are further characterized by ecological stress on all plant and animal species in that zone due to intra and inter-specific competition for resources. Distribution of sand fly species is determined by the availability of natural habitat and of that created by human encroachment. Some species favor unaltered forest, while others thrive in ecologically disturbed situations.[24] It is unfortunately beyond the scope of this text to illustrate this concept with specific examples, but many could be given that would serve to reinforce the idea that when ecological change due to human settlement occurs, those living there are at greater risk from acquiring zoonotic infectious diseases (e.g., Yellow fever, Ebola virus, Marburg virus, Lassa fever virus). The number of new species of Leishmania now known to infect humans throughout South America alone[1] has increased dramatically since the last edition of this book (2000), and serves as a good indication that, before things improve, they will probably continue to get worse.

Avoidance of contact with vectors of MCL is too simple a recommendation to actually work, given the lack of awareness of their presence on the part of those living in close proximity to them. For those traveling to endemic areas wishing to avoid the bites of sand flies altogether, the following advice may be sufficient. Sand flies bite predominantly at night, so outdoor activities should be curtailed during this time. Some species of sand fly bite only during the rainy season.[25] Work schedules involving large numbers of people at ecotones where this is the case would do well to take this arthropod behavior into account.

The use of insecticide-impregnated clothing and bed netting has helped reduce disease transmission for malaria, particularly in Africa, and has now been proven effective in the reduction in transmission of Leishmania, as well. Maintaining wide buffer zones between settlements and the surrounding native forest appears to be the best environmentally based long-term solution to controlling the incidence of infection in endemic transmission zones, a recommendation originally made to those wishing to avoid becoming infected with the yellow fever virus. Curtailing this human imperative has, so far, been all but impossible to enforce.

Vaccines are still in the developmental stage.[26]

References

1. Lainson R. Shaw JJ. New World Leishmaniasis. In: Topley and Wilson's Microbiology and Microbial Infections. 10th ed. (Collier L. Balows A. Sussman M., eds.) Vol. Parasitology (Cox FEG. Despommier, DD. Krier JP. Wakelin D. volume eds.). Arnold, Pub. London. 2005 (in press).
2. Garcia AL. Kindt A. et al. American tegumentary Leishmaniasis: antigen-gene polymorphism, taxonomy and clinical pleomorphism. Infect Genet Evol. 5:109-16. 2005.
3. Chung IK. Armstrong TC. et al. Generation of the short RNA transcript in Leishmaniavirus correlates with the growth of its parasite host, Leishmania. Mol Cells. 8(1):54-61, 1998.
4. Ogg MM. Carrion R Jr,. Short report: quantification of Leishmaniavirus RNA in clinical samples and its possible role in pathogenesis. Am J Trop Med Hyg. 69:309-13. 2003.
5. Carini A. Leishmaniose de la muqucuse rhinobuccopharyngee. Bull Soc Pathol Exot 4:289-291, 1911.
6. Vianna G. Tratamento da leishmaniose tegumentar por injecoes intravenososas de tartaro emetico. Ann Congress Brasil Med Cirur 4:426-428, 1912.
7. Kligler IJ. The cultural and serological relationship of Leishmania. Trans R Soc Trop Med Hyg 19:330-335, 1916.
8. Noguchi H. Comparative studies on herpetomonads and Leishmaniasis. II. Differentiation of the organisms by serological reactions and fermentation tests. S Exp Med 44:305-314, 1929.
9. Alexander B. Lozano C. et al. Detection of *Leishmania (Viannia) braziliensis* complex in wild mammals from Colombian coffee plantations by PCR and DNA hybridization. Acta Trop 69:41-50, 1998.
10. Lohuis PJ. Lipovsky MM. et al. *Leishmania braziliensis* presenting as a granulomatous lesion of the nasal septum mucosa. J Laryngol Otol 111(10):973-5, 1997.
11. Belli A. Rodriguez B. Aviles H. Harris E. Simplified polymerase chain reaction detection of new world Leishmania in clinical specimens of cutaneous Leishmaniasis. Am J Trop Med Hyg 58:102-9, 1998.
12. Marsden PD. Mucosal Leishmaniasis ("espundia" Escomel, 1911). Trans R Soc Trop Med Hyg. 80:859-76. 1986.
13. Machado ES. Braga Mda P. et al. Disseminated American muco-cutaneous Leishmaniasis caused by *Leishmania braziliensis braziliensis* in a patient with AIDS: a case report. Mem Inst Oswaldo Cruz. 87:487-92. 1992.
14. Mattos M. Caiza A. Fernandes O. et al. American cutaneous Leishmaniasis associated with HIV infection: report of four cases J Eur Acad Dermatol Venereol 10(3):218-25, 1998.
15. Da-Cruz AM. Filgueiras DV. et al. Atypical mucocutaneous Leishmaniasis caused by *Leishmania (V.) braziliensis* in an acquired immunodeficiency syndrome patient: T-cell responses and remission of lesions associated with antigen immunotherapy. Mem Inst Oswaldo Cruz 94:537-42, 1999.
16. Chouicha N. Lanotte G. et al. Phylogenetic taxonomy of *Leishmania (Viannia) braziliensis* based on isoenzymatic study of 137 isolates. Parasitology 115:343-8, 1998.
17. Oliveira JG. Novais FO. Polymerase chain reaction (PCR) is highly sensitive for diagnosis of mucosal Leishmaniasis. Acta Trop. 94:55-9. 2005.
18. Teva A. Porrozzi R. et al. *Leishmania (Viannia) braziliensis*-induced chronic granulomatous cutaneous lesions affecting the nasal mucosa in the rhesus monkey (*Macaca mulatta*) model. Parasitology. 127:437-47. 2003.
19. Osman OF. Oskam L. et al. Use of the polymerase chain reaction to assess the success of visceral Leishmaniasis treatment. Trans R Soc Trop Med Hyg 92:397-400, 1998.
20. Sampaio RNR. Marsden PD. Mucosal leismaniasis unresponsive to glucantime therapy successfully treated with AmBisome™. Trans R Soc Trop Med Hyg 91:77
21. Berman JD. Human Leishmaniasis: clinical, diagnostic, and chemo- therapeutic developments in the last 10 years. Clin Infect Dis 24:684-703, 1997.
22. Franke E. Berman J. Modabber F. Marr J. Efficacy of sodium stibogluconate alone and in combination with allopurinol for treatment of mucocutaneous Leishmaniasis. Clin Infect Dis 25:677-84, 1997.
23. Azzouz S. Maache M. Garcia RG. Osuna A. Leishmanicidal activity of edelfosine, miltefosine and ilmofosine. Basic Clin Pharmacol Toxicol. 96:60-5. 2005.
24. Salomon OD. Rossi GC. Spinelli GR. Ecological aspects of phebotomine (Diptera, Psychodidae) in an endemic area of tegumentary Leishmaniasis in the northeastern Argentina, 1993-1998. Mem Inst Oswaldo Cruz. 97:163-8. 2002.
25. Souza NA. Andrade-Coelho CA. et al. Seasonality of *Lutzomyia intermedia* and *Lutzomyia whitmani* (Diptera: Psychodidae: Phlebotominae), occurring sympatrically in area of cutaneous Leishmaniasis in the State of Rio de Janeiro, Brazil. Mem Inst Oswaldo Cruz. 97:759-65. 2002.
26. Coler RN, Reed SG. Second-generation vaccines against Leishmaniasis. Trends Parasitol. 21:244-9. 2005.

5. Visceral Leishmaniasis:

Leishmania (L) donovani
(Ross 1903)

Leishmania (L) infantum
(Cunha and Chagas 1937)

Leishmania (L) infantum chagasi
(Cunha and Chagas 1937)

Introduction

Leishmania (Leishmania) donovani, *L. (L.) infantum* (Old World), and *L. (L.) infantum chagasi* (New World) routinely invade the reticuloendothelial tissues throughout the body and infect macrophages, causing a series of often fatal diseases collectively referred to as visceral Leishmaniasis (VL). *L. (L.) tropica* and *L. (L.) amazonensis* can also rarely visceralize.[1] The illness is characterized by hepatospenomegaly and high fever. VL is especially prevalent in children.[2, 3] It is not possible to get accurate statistics on the incidence and prevalence of VL. Even the World Health Organization and the Centers for Disease Control and Prevention do not list approximate figures, but certainly hundreds of millions are at risk from infection, worldwide. As with all other species of Leishmania, the vectors of VL are numerous species of sand flies. Humans are the primary

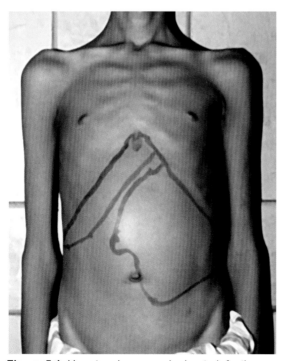

Figure 5.1. Hepatosplenomegaly due to infection with *Leishmania donovani*.

source of *L. (L.) donovani* infection, although domestic dogs are sometimes infected as well. A wide variety of reservoir hosts exist for the rest of the VL-causing agents, including the domestic dog and numerous rodent species.

L. (L.) infantum and *L. (L.) infantum chagasi* are closely related genetically, but current opinion is divided regarding whether or not they are both so closely related as to be considered the same species. One hypothesis favors *L. (L.) infantum chagasi* as being introduced into the New World at least several million years ago, since it is found in a fox species native to the remote inner Amazon River basin and causes no disease in that host.[4] This latter point is taken as evidence for its adaptation to that fox host species at reduced virulence. This would allow for the creation of at least a subspecies for *L. (L.) infantum chagasi*. The other view favors its introduction by the Spanish some 500 years ago and would eliminate the possibility that they might be different species.[5, 6] In either case, it is found in peridomestic habitats, infecting domestic dogs and humans. In addition, it occurs in a broad range of natural environments, where it infects a wide variety of wild mammals in dense forest areas, providing ample biological opportunities for eventual radiation into numerous new varieties and perhaps even new species. *L. (L.) donovani* does not appear to be closely related to any western hemisphere species of Leishmania, despite the fact that its mini circle DNA shows strong homology with New World species.[7]

Historical Information

Leishmania (Leishmania) donovani was described in 1903 by two physicians, Leishman[8] and Donovan,[9] while they were working in separate locations in India. Leishman was an officer in the British Army, and Donovan served as a physician in the Indian Medical Service. Ronald Ross, then the editor of the British Medical Journal, reviewed their separate manuscript submissions, recognized that they had observed the same disease, and named the genus and species after them in recognition of their landmark discovery. In 1908, Nicolle[10] discovered that other mammals, particularly the dog, could also become infected. Swaminath and colleagues, working in India in 1942,[11] using human volunteers, showed that the infection was transmitted by sand flies of the genus Phlebotomus.

A single example of what was most probably American visceral Leishmaniasis (AVL) was described by Migone in a patient in Rio de Janero in 1913. Cuhna and Chagas classified it and named it *Leishmania chagasi* in 1937.[12]

Leishmania donovani

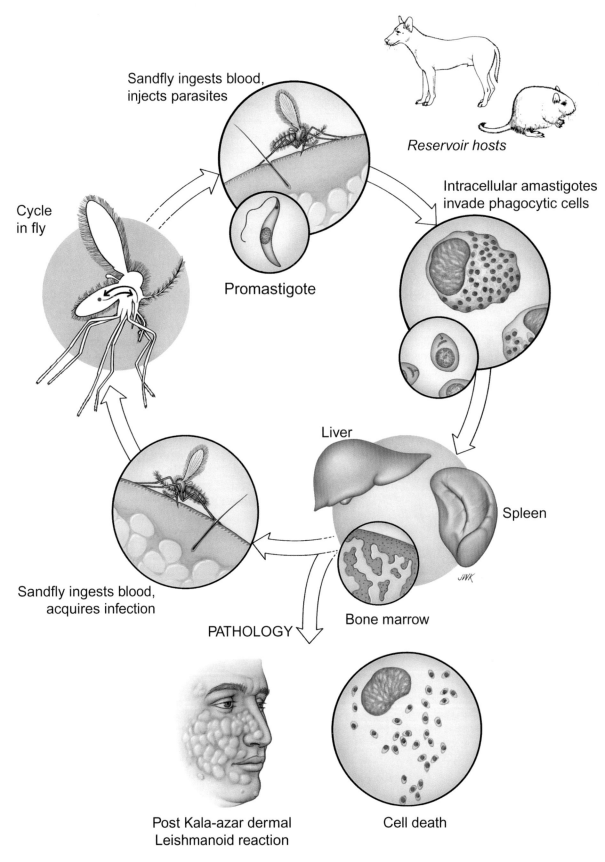

Sandfly ingests blood, injects parasites

Reservoir hosts

Cycle in fly

Promastigote

Intracellular amastigotes invade phagocytic cells

Liver

Spleen

Bone marrow

Sandfly ingests blood, acquires infection

PATHOLOGY

Post Kala-azar dermal Leishmanoid reaction

Cell death

Life Cycle

Infection begins with the bite of an infected sand fly (Fig. 2.1). The promastigotes enter the subcutaneous tissues, attach to the extracellular matrix, and are eventually taken up by dendritic cells[13] and macrophages (Fig. 2.3). The parasites transform into amastigotes and divide within these cells, eventually killing the host cell. The released amastigotes circulate or are carried by infected cells to new areas of the body, where macrophages again become infected. The ability of some *Leishmania spp.* to visceralize, in contrast to those species restricted to the skin, may relate to the VL type's ability to tolerate higher body temperatures.[14] In some mouse models, dendritic cells increase in lymphoid tissue and eventually become heavily infected, but do appear to be involved in transporting the organisms away from the site of the bite.[13]

The entire reticuloendothelial system eventually becomes involved, compromising the ability of the host to mount an effective immune attack against other invading microbes. The spleen, liver, and bone marrow are the most seriously affected organs (Fig. 5.1). Amastigotes have been observed in peripheral blood in greater densities at night than during daylight hours,[15] a biological phenomenon similar to that found in periodic filariasis (see *Wuchereria bancrofti*, page 143). Since sand flies bite more frequently at night, this diurnal rhythm makes the acquisition of parasites by the vector more likely.

The cycle is completed when an infected human is bitten by an uninfected sand fly, which ingests macrophages containing the amastigotes. The duration of the cycle within the fly is approximately 10 days. Rarely, *L. (L.) donovani* can be transmitted by organ transplantation.[16]

Immunity is dependent upon Th1 responses. T cells producing INF-δ, TNF-α, and IL-2 activate macrophages that kill intracellular parasites by nitric oxide synthesis.[17] Antibodies apparently play no role in protection, although high levels of specific IgG and IgE are generated during infection.[18]

Clinical Disease

Kala-azar (Old World VL)

Clinical aspects of infection with *Leishmania donovani* have been reviewed.[19] The term "Kala-azar" means "black fever" in Hindi, and characterizes the appearance of the patient's skin at the height of the infection. Most cases of Kala-azar have an incubation period of 3-6 months. With experimental disease in rodents, the incubation period varies between several days and

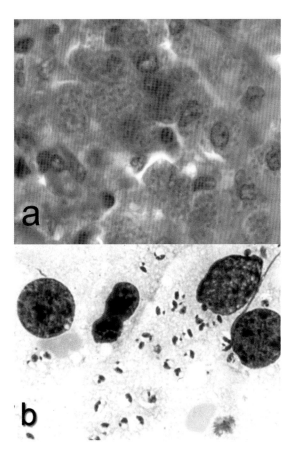

Figure 5.2a. Biopsy of liver positive for amastigotes of *L. donovani.*

Figure 5.2b. Bone marrow aspirate positive for amastigotes of *L. donovani.*

10 months. The onset can be gradual or sudden. In the former, the initial symptoms can be nonspecific, often relating to splenomegaly, which may eventually occupy most of the left side of the abdomen. The clinical diagnosis is often missed, or is discovered by accident when patients present with other acute illnesses, such as a respiratory or gastrointestinal infection.[20]

Onset of disease is accompanied by high fever, which may be irregular, often giving rise to a characteristic double daily spike. Fever is intermittent, subsiding for days or weeks only to return, and resembles the pattern seen in patients suffering from undulant fever.

The infected individual, though weak, does not feel ill, and is able to endure bouts of fever without complaint, distinguishing them from individuals with typhoid fever, tuberculosis, or malaria. Disease is frequently more obvious to the clinician than to the patient. Generalized lymphadenopathy, and later, hepatomegaly eventually develop. In light skinned patients, the skin darkens.

Disease is progressive and the individual eventually suffers the consequences of a compromised immune system. Many people die with Kala-azar rather than from it because of the acquisition of intercurrent infections, in particular HIV virus.[21]

Throughout this period, the patient becomes anemic and develops thrombocytopenia and hypersplenism, with leukocyte counts of 3000/cu[3] or lower. High concentrations of serum protein, approaching 10 g/dl, is due almost exclusively due to a rise in nonprotective IgG.[18] Patients infected with HIV/AIDS and VL due to *L. (L.) donovani* and *L. (L.) infantum* sometimes present with cutaneous lesions in which organisms can be demonstrated, in addition to involvement of the reticuloendothelial system.[23, 24]

Congenital Kala-azar

Infants born to mothers with Kala-azar can acquire the infection in utero.[25] Organisms are brought to the developing fetus by infected macrophages. The pathology and clinical presentation of congenital visceral Leishmaniasis in newborns is similar to the adult form.[26]

Post-Kala-azar Dermal Leishmaniasis

About 20% of treated patients develop a skin rash six months to several years later. This condition, known as post Kala-azar dermal Leishmaniasis (PKDL), is characterized by a hypopigmented or erythematous macular rash that eventually becomes papular and nodular.[27] They are particularly prominent on the face and the upper parts of the body, resembling lesions of lepromatous leprosy. The lesions are filled with histocytes containing amastigotes and serve as sources of infection for sand flies. There may be neurological damage.[28] Among African patients, only 2% of those who recover develop such skin lesions. Involvement of the eye is also common.[29] PKDL is strongly associated with an IL-10-driven (Th-2) cytokine pattern.[30, 31, 32]

Most people suffering from VL caused by infection with *L. (L.) infantum chagasi* resemble those exhibiting clinical disease caused *L. (L.) infantum* and *L. (L.) donovani*. Atypical cutaneous Leishmaniasis has also been described for infections caused by *L. (L.) infantum* and *L. (L.) infantum chagasi*; it may either be a form of PKDL following a subclinical infection, or a form of Kala-azar that presents with solely cutaneous manifestations.[33]

Diagnosis

Definitive diagnosis of VL depends upon PCR.[34–36] PKDL can also be diagnosed by PCR.[37] Culture of bone marrow aspirates in biphasic Medium 199 is effective at revealing the organisms, but it is takes three to four days for the parasites to grow to significant numbers. Parasites can also be seen on microscopy of sectioned or biopsied material (Figs. 5.2a, 5.2b).

Treatment

The drug of choice for all forms of VL is sodium stibogluconate. A 30-day course of treatment is recommended for Kala-azar patients,[38] since drug resistance has recently been reported[39] and may have been present for some time prior to that study.

PCR, as well as falling levels of amastigote membrane-specific immunoglobulin,[40] can be used to evaluate success of treatment. Negative PCR and falling levels of IgG1, IgG4, and IgE[23] all indicate that a cure has been achieved.

Prevention and Control

Infection due to *L. (L.) donovani* and *L. (L.) infantum* differ from one another regarding the source of infection. Reservoirs play no role in the epidemiology of *L. (L.) donovani*, while the domestic dog is a major source of infection for *L. (L.) infantum*. Political unrest forced migration due to wars (primarily in Africa and Afghanistan) and prolonged periods of drought (primarily in India) have triggered recent large epidemics of Kala-azar.[1, 41] These situations concentrate people into areas that favor high transmission rates. The unavailability of insecticides, insect repellents, and bed netting, as well as the general lack of proper attention to health care needs during times of high stress, often allow vector-borne diseases to "have their way" with refugees, and *Leishmania (L.) donovani* is no exception.

Attempts to control *L. (L.) infantum* transmission by controlling its spread in domestic dogs throughout the Mediterranean basin have met with a singular lack of success, as is also the case throughout South and Central America. Leishmaniasis in domestic and wild dogs has been recently described in the United States, due to *L. (L.) infantum*.[42] No human cases have been reported from this area of the world yet, but the proper vector species of sand flies are there, and perhaps it is just a matter of time before an outbreak occurs.

Vaccines may prove useful,[43] but have yet to come onto the market. Remote sensing efforts have identified rainfall and altitude as the two most important variables in predicting outbreaks of VL in Gedaref State, eastern Sudan.[44] It is hoped that future studies using this powerful new technology will result in even greater application of satellite data to the control of Leishmaniasis in other parts of the world as well.

References

1. Berman J. Recent Developments in Leishmaniasis: Epidemiology, Diagnosis, and Treatment. Curr Infect Dis Rep. 7:33-38. 2005.
2. Maltezou HC. Siafas C. et al. Visceral Leishmaniasis during childhood in southern Greece, Clin Infect Dis 31:1139–1143. 2000.
3. Haidar NA. Diab ABL. El-Sheikh AM. Visceral Leishmaniasis in children in the Yemen, Saudi Med J. 22:516–519. 2001.
4. Lainson R. Shaw JJ. New World Leishmaniasis – The Neotropical Leishmania Species. In: Topley and Wilson's Microbiology and Microbial Infections. 10th ed. (Collier L, Balows A., Sussman M., eds.). Volume 5. Parasitology (Cox FEG. Despommier, DD. Kreier JP. Wakelin D., volume eds.). Arnold, Pub., London. 2005.
5. Mauricio IL. Howard MK. Stothard JR. Miles MA. Genomic diversity in the *Leishmania donovani* complex, Parasitology 119:237–246. 1999.
6. IMauricio IL. Stothard JR. M.A. Miles. The strange case of *Leishmania chagasi*, Parasitol Today 16:188–189. 2000.
7. Singh N. Curran MD. Middleton D. Rastogi AK. Characterization of kinetoplast DNA minicircles of an Indian isolate of *Leishmania (Leishmania) donovani*. Acta Trop 73:313-9.1999.
8. Leishman WB. On the possibility of occurrence of trypanosomiasis in India. BMJ 1:1252-1254. 1903.
9. Donovan C. On the possibility of occurrence of trypanosomiasis in India. BMJ 2:79.1903.
10. Nicolle C. Nouvelles acquisitions sur kala-azar: cultures: inoculation au chien: etiologie. Hebdom Sci 146:498-499.1908.
11. Swaminath CS, Shortt HE, Anderson LAP: Transmission of Indian kala-azar to man by the bites of Phlebotomus argentipes. Ann Brun Indian J Med Res 30:473-477.1942.
12. Cunha AM. Chagas E. Nova especie de protozoario do genero Leishmania pathogenico para o homen. *Leishmania chagasi*, n. *spp.* Nota Previa.Hospital (Rio de Janerio) 11:3-9. 1937.
13. Baldwin T. Henri S. et al. Dendritic cell populations in *Leishmania major*-infected skin and draining lymph nodes. Infect Immun. 72:1991-2001. 2004.
14. Callahan HL. Portal IF. Bensinger SJ. Grogl M. *Leishmania spp*: temperature sensitivity of promastigotes in vitro as a model for tropism in vivo. Exp Parasitol. 84:40-9. 1996.
15. Saran R. Sharma MC. Gupta AK. Sinha SP. Kar SK. Diurnal periodicity of Leishmania amastigotes in peripheral blood of Indian Kala-azar patients. Acta Trop 68(3):357-60, 1997.
16. Hernandez-Perez J. Yebra-Bango M. et al. Visceral Leishmaniasis (kala-azar) in solid organ transplantation: report of five cases and review. Clin Infect Dis 29:918-21.1999.
17. Arora SK. Pal NS. Mujtaba S. *Leishmania donovani*: identification of novel vaccine candidates using human reactive sera and cell lines. Exp Parasitol. 109:163-70. 2005.
18. Ravindran R. Anam K. et al. Characterization of immunoglobulin G and its subclass response to Indian kala-azar infection before and after chemotherapy. Infect Immun. 72:863-70. 2004.
19. Herwaldt BL. Leishmaniasis. Lancet. 354:1191-9. 1999.
20. Badaro R. Jones TC. et al: New perspectives on a sub-clinical form of visceral Leishmaniasis. J Infect Dis 154: 1003-1011, 1986.
21. Ritmeijer K. Veeken H. Ethiopian visceral Leishmaniasis: generic and proprietary sodium stibogluconate are equivalent; HIV coinfected patients have a poor outcome. Trans R Soc Trop Med Hyg. 95:668-72. 2001.
22. Postigo C. Llamas R. et al. Cutaneous lesions in patients with visceral Leishmaniasis and HIV infection. J Infect 35:265-8.1997.
23. Alvar J. Canavate C. et al. Leishmania and human immunodeficiency virus coinfection: the first 10 years. Clin Microbiol Rev 10:298-319.1997.
24. Agostoni C. Dorigoni N. et al. Mediterranean Leishmaniasis in HIV-infected patients: epidemiological, clinical, and diagnostic features of 22 cases. Infection 26:93-9.1998.
25. Eltoum IA. Zijlstra EE. et al: Congenital kala-azar and Leishmaniasis in the placenta. Am J Trop Med Hyg 46:57-62.1992.
26. Meinecke CK. Schottelius J. Oskam L. Fleischer B. Congenital transmission of visceral Leishmaniasis (Kala Azar) from an asymptomatic mother to her child. Pediatrics 104:65.1999.
27. Beena KR. Ramesh V. Mukherjee A. Identification of parasite antigen, correlation of parasite density and inflammation in skin lesions of post kala-azar dermal Leishmaniasis. J Cutan Pathol. 30:616-20. 2003.
28. Khandpur S. Ramam M. et. al. Nerve involvement in Indian post kala-azar dermal Leishmaniasis. Acta Derm Venereol. 84:245-6. 2004.
29. el Hassan AM. Khalil EA. et. al. Post kala-azar ocular Leishmaniasis. Trans R Soc Trop Med Hyg 92:177-9. 1998.
30. Gasim S. Elhassan AM. et. al. High levels of plasma IL-10 and expression of IL-10 by keratinocytes during visceral Leishmaniasis predict subsequent development of post-kala-azar dermal Leishmaniasis Clin Exp Immunol 111:64-9.1998.
31. Kharazmi A. Kemp K. et al. T-cell response in human Leishmaniasis. Immunol Lett 65:105-8.1999.
32. Atta AM. D'Oliveira. C. et al. Anti-Leishmanial IgE antibodies: a marker of active disease in visceral Leishmaniasis. Am J Trop Med Hyg 59:426-30.1998.
33. Ponec C. Ponce E. et al: *Leishmania (Leishmania) donovani chagasi*: new clinical variant of cutaneous Leishmaniasis in Honduras. Lancet 337: 67-70.1991.
34. Andresen K. Gasim S. et al. Diagnosis of visceral Leishmaniasis by the polymerase chain reaction using blood, bone marrow and lymph node samples from patients from the Sudan. Trop Med Int Health 2:440-4.1997.
35. Minodier P. Piarroux R. et al. Pediatric visceral Leishmaniasis in southern France. Pediatr Infect Dis J 17:701-4.1998.

36. Sinha PK. Pandey K. Bhattacharya SK. Diagnosis & management of Leishmania/HIV co-infection Indian J Med Res.121:407-14. 2005.
37. Osman OF. Oskam L. et al. Use of PCR for diagnosis of post-kala-azar dermal Leishmaniasis. J Clin Microbiol 36:1621-1624. 1998.
38. Karki P. Koirala S. et al. A thirty day course of sodium stibogluconate for treatment of Kala-azar in Nepal. Southeast Asian J Trop Med Public Health 29:154-158.1998.
39. Lira R. Sundar S. et al. Evidence that the high incidence of treatment failures in Indian kala-azar is due to the emergence of antimony-resistant strains of *Leishmania (Leishmania) donovani*. J Infect Dis 180:564-567.1999.
40. Anam K. Afrin F. et al. Differential decline in Leishmania membrane antigen-specific immunoglobulin G (IgG), IgM, IgE, and IgG subclass antibodies in Indian kala-azar patients after chemotherapy. Infect Immun 67:6663-6669. 1999.
41. WHO: http://www.who.int/csr/don/2002_05_22/en/index.html
42. Alvar J, Canavate C. et al. Canine Leishmaniasis. Adv Parasitol. 57:1-88. 2004
43. Coler RN, Reed SG. Second-generation vaccines against Leishmaniasis. Trends Parasitol. 21:244-9. 2005.
44. Elnaiem D-E. Schorscher J. et al. Risk mapping of visceral Leishmaniasis: the role of local variation in rainfall and altitude on the presence and incidence of kala-azar in eastern sudan Am. J. Trop. Med. Hyg. 68:10-17. 2003.

6. African trypanosomiasis:

Trypanosoma brucei gambiense
(Dutton 1902)

Trypanosoma brucei rhodesiense
(Stephens and Fantham 1910)

Figure 6.2. Tsetse fly taking a blood meal.

Introduction

Trypanosoma brucei gambiense and *T. b. rhodesiense* are vector-borne flagellated protozoans found only in Africa. They live in the bloodstream of mammals and cause a disease in humans referred to as African sleeping sickness. Some 60 million people are at risk from both varieties of trypanosomes, and the disease has recently been classified as a re-emerging infection on that continent. 450,000 cases occurred in 2005 throughout sub-Saharan Africa according to the World Health Organization.[1] This was due mainly to extensive forced migration caused by civil turmoil leading to the breakdown of control measures against the vector. *T. brucei* and related species are part of a larger group of organisms characterized by the presence of a kinetoplast (a primitive mitochondrion), and are termed the kinetoplastidae (e.g., *Leishmania spp., T. cruzi*).

Tsetse flies of the genus *Glossina* transmit trypanosomes throughout a broad region of equatorial Africa, ecologically restricted to the boundaries of the Sahara desert to the north and the dryer temperate regions south of the equator. *T. b. gambiense* is found mainly in the western and central African countries of Cameroon,

Benin, Central African Republic, Gabon, Ghana, Guinea, Ivory Coast, Liberia, Nigeria, Senegal, The Gambia, Uganda, and the Democratic Republic of Congo. *T. b. rhodesiense* occurs mainly in Burundi, Botswana, Congo, Ethiopia, Kenya, Mozambique, Rwanda, Sudan, Tanzania, Uganda, Zambia, and Zimbabwe.

In West Africa, the domestic pig is considered the only important reservoir host for *T. b. gambiense*.[2] In contrast, many species of wild animals and domestic cattle of East Africa are reservoirs for *T. b. rhodesiense*. Trypanosomiasis is also a serious problem in animal husbandry because many species of the trypanosomes related to those infecting humans cause severe disease in cattle.[3,4] Its genome is currently under intensive investigation and a complete sequence should be forthcoming in the near future.[5]

Historical Information

Sleeping sickness has been known in Europe since the 1700s, when Atkins published his observations of the disease.[6] In 1895, Bruce[7] described the disease and its causative agent by showing that *nagana*, a disease of cattle, was caused by trypanosomes, and that tsetse flies were the vectors. Ford, in 1902,[8] working in West Africa, described a clinical condition in humans similar to that in cattle caused by *T. b. gambiense*. Stephens and Fantham, in 1910,[9] isolated and described *T. b. rhodesiense* from human cases in East Africa. The two organisms are morphologically identical. Kinghorn and Yorke, in 1912,[10] demonstrated that *T. b. rhodesiense* could be transmitted from humans to animals by tsetse flies. They also concluded that game animals, such as water buck, hartebeest, impala, and warthog, could serve as reservoir hosts for the East African trypanosome.

Life Cycle

The biology of *Trypanosoma brucei* has been reviewed.[11] Biological characteristics of the two subspecies are so similar that what follows applies to both. African trypanosomes live extracellularly, both in the

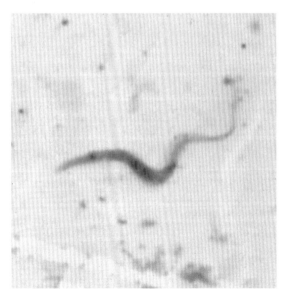

Figure 6.1. Metacyclic trypanomastigote from the tsetse fly. 20 μm. Courtesy I. Cunningham.

Trypanosoma brucei gambiense and *T. b. rhodesiense*

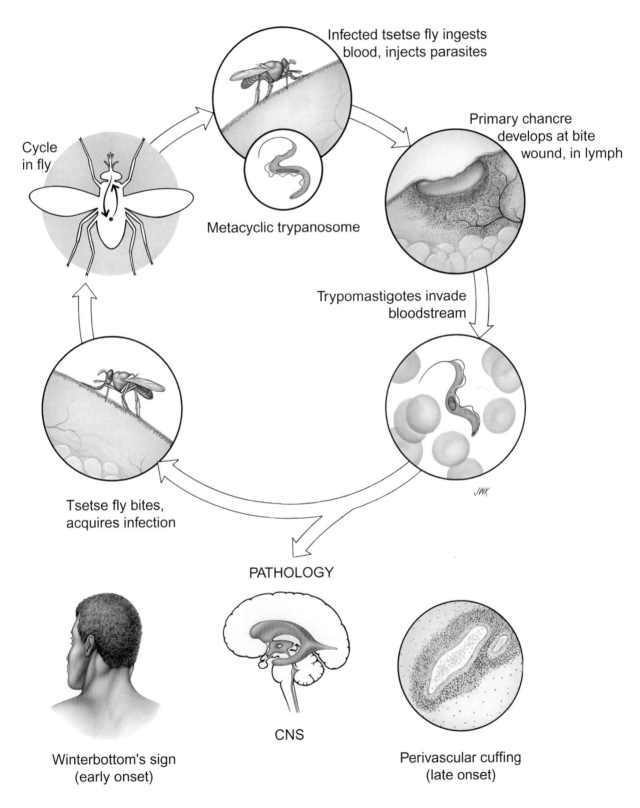

Infected tsetse fly ingests blood, injects parasites

Metacyclic trypanosome

Cycle in fly

Primary chancre develops at bite wound, in lymph

Trypomastigotes invade bloodstream

Tsetse fly bites, acquires infection

PATHOLOGY

Winterbottom's sign (early onset)

CNS

Perivascular cuffing (late onset)

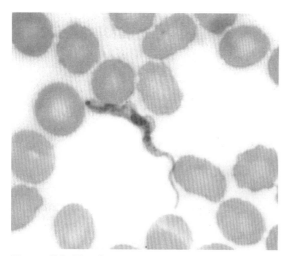

Figure 6.3. Bloodstream trypanomastigotes. 15 µm.

mammalian and insect host. The bloodstream form measures 25-40 µm in length (Fig. 6.1).

Infection in the human host begins when the infective metacyclic stage is injected by the tsetse fly intradermally (Fig. 6.2). The organisms immediately transform into bloodstream form trypomastigotes (long, slender forms) (Fig. 6.3), and divide by binary fission in the interstitial spaces at the site of the bite. As the result of repeated replication cycles, buildup of metabolic wastes and cell debris occurs, leading to extensive necrosis and the formation of a soft, painless chancre. Replication continues in the blood, resulting in millions of new trypomastigotes. During this time, they behave like anaerobes, processing glucose. Trypanosomes have several intracellular inclusions; the kinetoplast-mitochondrion,[12] the glycosome,[13, 14, 53] and a multiprotein aggregate termed the editosome.[46] One of its unusual features is that all of the DNA of the mitochondrion, which can be up to 25% of the total cell DNA, is localized in the kinetoplast, adjacent to the flagellar pocket. Kinetoplast DNA or kDNA exists in two forms: mini circles and maxi circles.[15] Mini circle DNA encodes guide RNAs that direct extensive editing of RNA transcripts post transcriptionally.[16–18] Maxi circle DNA contains sequences that, when edited, direct the translation of mitochondrial proteins.[19, 20]

In the vertebrate host, trypanosomes depend entirely upon glucose for energy and are highly aerobic, despite the fact that the kinetoplast-mitochondrion completely lacks cytochromes. Instead, mitochondrial oxygen consumption is based on an alternative oxidase that does not produce ATP. The parasite develops a conventional cytochrome chain and TCA cycle in the vector.[21]

The surface of the trypanosome has numerous membrane-associated transport proteins[22, 23] for ob-

taining nucleic acid bases, glucose, and other small molecular weight nutrients.[24] None of these proteins react well with antibodies, because although they lie in exposed regions of membrane, they are shielded by allosteric interference provided by the variant surface glycoprotein (VSG) coat proteins.[25]

This flagellated stage enters the bloodstream through the lymphatics and divides further, producing a patent parasitemia. The number of parasites in the blood is generally so low that diagnosis by microscopic examination is often negative. At some point, trypanosomes enter the central nervous system, with serious pathological consequences for humans. Some parasites transform into the non-dividing short, stumpy form, which has a biochemistry similar to those of the long, slender form and the form found in the insect vector.[26]

The tsetse fly becomes infected by ingesting a blood meal from an infected host.[27] These short, stumpy forms are pre-adapted to the vector, having a well-developed mitochondrion with a partial TCA cycle. In the insect vector, the trypanosomes develop into procyclic trypomastigotes in the midgut of the fly, and continue to divide for approximately 10 days. Here they gain a fully functional cytochrome system and TCA cycle. When the division cycles are completed, the organisms migrate to the salivary glands, and transform into epimastigotes. These forms, in turn, divide and transform further into metacyclic trypanosomes, the infective stage for humans and reservoir hosts. The cycle in the insect takes 25-50 days, depending upon the species of the fly, the strain of the trypanosome, and the ambient temperature.[27] If tsetse flies ingest more than one strain of trypanosome, there is the possibility of genetic exchange between the two strains, generating an increase in genetic diversity in an organism that may not have a sexual cycle.[28]

The vector remains infected for life (2-3 months).

Figure 6.4. Impala, one of many reservoirs for *Trypanosoma brucei rhodesiense*.

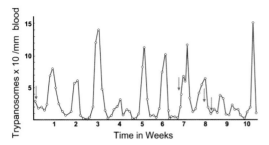

Figure 6.5. Parasitemia in a patient infected with *T. b. rhodesiense*. Each peak of parasitemia represents a new antigenic variant. Arrows indicate attempts at chemotherapy. Ultimately, the patient died of overwhelming infection.

Tsetse flies inject over 40,000 metacyclic trypanosomes when they feed. The minimum infective dose for most hosts is 300-500 organisms, although experimental animals have been infected with a single organism.

Infection can also be acquired by eating raw meat from an infected animal.[29] In East Africa, this mode of transmission may be important in maintaining the cycle in some reservoir hosts, such as lions, cheetahs, leopards, and scavengers (hyenas, dogs, etc.).

Cellular and Molecular Pathogenesis

African trypanosomes have evolved a balanced coexistence between themselves and their hosts, since none of the wild animals native to East Africa appear to be severely affected by this parasite (Fig. 6.4). In contrast, more recently evolved animals, such as humans, or the numerous mammalian species introduced into Africa from Europe, such as all non-African breeds of cattle, all suffer the pathological consequences of infection from this group of hemoflagellates.

Mechanisms of Escape from Host Immunity

African trypanosomes have evolved several molecular strategies enabling them to avoid elimination from the mammalian host: varying the antigenicity of its surface protein coat, destruction of compliment, and the ability to survive in elevated levels of interferon-γ.[30, 31] All infected mammals produce antibodies against a membrane-associated antigen of the trypanosome referred to as the variant surface glycoprotein (VSG).[32] Specific IgG antibodies destroy all clonal organisms sharing the same surface protein (e.g., VSG-1) by agglutination and lysis. However, a few trypanosomes can produce a second variety of surface protein (e.g., VSG-2), with a completely different antigenic signature, in addition to the original one. If some of these organisms shed VSG-1 prior to encountering antibody against it, and continue to synthesize VSG-2 exclusively, they es-

cape lysis,[33] and replace those that were destroyed.[34] A second IgG antibody with specificity to VSG-2 arises, killing all VSG-2 parasites but selecting for VSG-3 organisms, and so on. This antigen-antibody battle between parasite and host continues, until the infected individual is overcome by exhaustion due to glucose depletion and the buildup of metabolic wastes from the parasite (Fig. 6.5).

Antigenic variation depends upon trans-splicing of mRNAs encoded by genes that have been rearranged, duplicated,[35] and expressed at a unique site in the genome.[36] In experimental animal models, the repertoire of antigenic variants of the bloodstream trypomastigotes is large, numbering in the hundreds. In human disease, the maximum number of VSGs that can be produced remains unknown, although the genome codes for about 1000. Antigenic variation is the reason why vaccine development against this pathogen has not progressed.[37]

Neuropathology

Trypanosomes remain in the bloodstream and lymph nodes throughout the infection period, which can last weeks to years, depending upon the subspecies of parasite and the immune capabilities of the infected individual. All nodes become enlarged, but enlargement of the posterior cervical nodes is the most noticeable.[38] The invasion of the central nervous system induces a lethargic condition, leading eventually to coma and death.[39] Organisms enter the central nervous system much earlier in the infection with *T. b. rhodesiense* than with *T. b. gambiense*. Replication of the parasite in the CSF results in leptomeningitis, cerebral edema, and encephalopathy.[40] Dysregulated inflammation is the chief pathological correlate, with perivascular cuffing consisting of infiltrates of glial cells, lymphocytes, and plasma cells (Fig. 6.6). Astrocytes are induced to

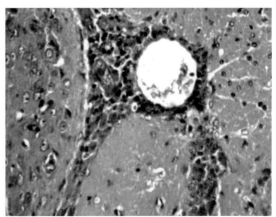

Figure 6.6. Perivascular cuffing around vein in brain of patient who died of sleeping sickness.

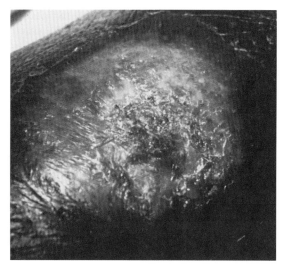

Figure 6.7. Chancre due to early infection with *T. b. gambiense*. Courtesy WHO.

release prostaglandin D2 (PGD2), a sleep regulating molecule.[41] Anti-inflammatory interleukins (IL-10 and TGF-β) are produced early on in the infection, but loose their effectiveness during the chronic and late phase.[42]

Clinical Disease

Both trypanosomes cause the same type of clinical disease; only the time scale of their evolution differs. Infection rapidly progresses on to disease with *T. b. rhodesiense*, with an incubation period of only 2-3 weeks, and a course of several weeks. Central nervous system involvement occurs some 3-4 weeks after infection. In contrast, *T. b. gambiense* has an incubation period of several weeks to months, and may not involve the brain for months or even years.

A painless chancre (Fig. 6.7) containing the dividing organisms develops at the site of the bite within 2-5 days and subsequently heals. Intermittent fever coincides with the organisms entering the bloodstream. Some patients develop rashes, particularly *erythema multiforme*. Lymphadenopathy of the posterior cervical nodes, referred to as Winterbottoms' sign,[38] is characteristic but not always present.

When trypanosomes invade the central nervous system, patients experience severe headache, stiff neck, periods of sleeplessness, and depression. Focal seizures, tremors, and palsies are also common. Coma eventually develops, and the patient dies, usually of associated causes such as pneumonia, inanition, or sepsis.

Anemia is a complication of infection with *T. b. rhodesiense*, but is not always seen due to the fulminating nature of this form of sleeping sickness.[43]

Diagnosis

Definitive diagnosis depends upon finding the organisms in blood smears stained with either Wright's stain or Giemsa stain (Fig. 6.3), or in the cerebrospinal fluid. Aspirates of lymph nodes may also contain organisms. Note that parasites are frequently very rare, even in a patient dying of the disease. Techniques to improve the sensitivity of diagnosis are to examine the buffy coat and the centrifuged sediment of the CSF and to make thick smears of samples stained without fixing, which loses erythrocytes but still reveals the characteristic morphology of the trypanosome.

Real time PCR will most likely become the laboratory method of choice for the rapid diagnosis of sleeping sickness,[44] since PCR has now replaced ELISA. In the field, testing cerebrospinal fluid for the presence of specific IgM antibodies shows promise.[45]

History of travel in an endemic area, recalling a painful fly bite, and the presence of a chancre can guide the clinician to the diagnosis. The differential diagnosis includes syphilis, Leishmaniasis, and malaria. Finding malarial parasites in the blood of a patient with trypanosomiasis is not unusual, and should not mislead the clinician, diverting their attention from the diagnosis of trypanosomiasis. Lymphoma must also be considered in any patients with protracted, unexplained fever.

Figure 6.8. Landsat photograph of African continent, colorized to show vegetation (in brown). Photo, NASA.

Treatment

The treatment of sleeping sickness has been reviewed.[47] Suramin can be used only for the early stages of the infection with *T. b. rhodesiense*,[47] since it does not cross the blood-brain barrier. The mode of action of suramin is not known, and is associated with possibly severe kidney dysfunction. Penatmidine is used for the early phase of infection with *T. b. gambiense*. When available, difluoromethylornithine (DFMO, eflornithine) is the recommended drug for all stages of *T. brucei gambiense* infection, but it is far less effective against *T. brucei rhodesiense*.[48] DMFO is a relatively nontoxic drug that irreversibly inhibits the enzyme ornithine decarboxylase, an enzyme essential for polyamine biosynthesis. Since it attacks only a single point in the metabolic pathway for polyamine biosynthesis, resistance is likely to develop, and has already been induced in experimental animals and even in certain instances when humans were receiving treatment. For infection with *T. brucei gambiense*, the cure rates are above 99%. Melarsoprol is often used and is more toxic. It is the only effective drug for treatment of *T. brucei rhodesiense* with CNS involvement, although the drug is associated with encephalopathy in about 3% of cases, and a high rate (>10%) of failure to cure in some instances.[49] A new drug, DB289, with characteristics of pentamidine but with reduced side effects, is in stage II drug trials and may one day soon replace pentamidine.[47]

Prevention and Control

Widespread political upheaval in many parts of Africa (Fig. 6.8) over the last five years has resulted in a dramatic increase in human cases of sleeping sickness.[50] A 2005 WHO report indicated at least 450,000 new cases that year, alone,[1] while prior to 1995, the estimate was fewer than 70,000. Military action and civil unrest in the Sudan, Ethiopia, Sierra Leone, Congo, and Liberia are responsible for forced migration of millions of individuals, placing them at high risk from a number of opportunistic patristic infections. At the same time, control programs for tsetse fly have disappeared in these same regions, exacerbating an already intractable situation. On top of all this turmoil, HIV/AIDS, and malaria have also increased in prevalence, complicating the picture and adding new, unwanted dimensions to the general problem of disease control. Limited resources in countries bordering conflicted areas cannot keep up with the need for vector control, due to large influxes of refugees. Tsetse flies and mosquitoes do not obey political boundaries, and thrive in certain disturbed environments.[51]

Work on vaccines based on VSG antigens has essentially stopped. Other protein antigens, particularly transporters on the membrane of the flagellar pocket and tubulin offer promise.[52] To learn more about the ecology of tsetse flies and control programs that take advantage of their biology, see www.medicalecology.org/diseases/d_african_trypano.htm.

References

1. World Health Organization estimates for 2005. See www.who.org
2. Schares G. Mehlitz D. Sleeping sickness in Democratic Republic of Congo: a nested polymerase chain reaction improves the identification of *Trypanosoma* (Trypanozoon) *brucei gambiense* by specific kinetoplast DNA probes. Trop Med Internat Health. 1:59-70, 1996.
3. Leak SG. Peregrine AS. et al. Use of insecticide-impregnated targets for the control of tsetse flies (*Glossina spp.*) and trypanosomiasis occurring in cattle in an area of south-west Ethiopia with a high prevalence of drug-resistant trypanosomes. Trop Med Internat Health. 1:599-609, 1996.
4. Katakura K. Lubinga C. Chitambo H. Tada Y. Detection of *Trypanosoma congolense* and *T. brucei* subspecies in cattle in Zambia by polymerase chain reaction from blood collected on a filter paper. Parasitol Res 83:241-5, 1997.
5. Ghedin E. Bringaud F. et al. Gene synteny and evolution of genome architecture in trypanosomatids. Mol Biochem Parasitol. 134:183-91. 2004.
6. Atkins J. The Navy Surgeon, or Practical System of Surgery with a Dissertation on Cold and Hot Mineral Springs and Physical Observations on the Coast of Guinea. J Hodges, London 1742.
7. Bruce D. Preliminary Report of the Tsetse Fly Disease or *Nagana* in Zululand. Bennet & Davis, Durban, 1895.
8. Forde RM. Some clinical notes on a European patient in whose blood a trypanosome was observed. J Trop Med 5:261-263, 1902.
9. Stephens JWW. Fantham HB. On the peculiar morphology of a trypanosome from a case of sleeping sickness and the possibility of its being a new species (*T. rhodesiense*). Proc R Soc Lond [Biol] 83:23-33, 1910.
10. Kinghorn A. Yorke W. On the transmission of human trypanosomes by *Glossina morsitans*, and on the occurrence of human trypanosomes in game. Ann Trop Med Parasitol 6:1-23, 1912.
11. Gull K. The cell biology of parasitism in *Trypanosoma brucei*: insights and drug targets from genomic approaches? Curr Pharm Des. 8:241-56. 2002.
12. Shlomai J. The structure and replication of kinetoplast DNA. Curr Mol Med. 4:623-47. 2004.
13. Opperdoes FR. Borst P. Localization of nine glycolytic enzymes in a microbody-like organelle in *Trypanosoma brucei*: the glycosome. FEBS Lett. 80:360–364. 1977.

14. Verlinde C. Glycolysis as a target for the design of new anti-trypanosome drugs. Drug Resist Updates 4:50-65. 2001.
15. Leon W. Frasch AC. et al. Maxi circles and mini circles in kinetoplast DNA from *Trypanosoma cruzi*. Biochim Biophys Acta. 607:221-31. 1980.
16. Feagin JE. Stuart K. Differential expression of mitochondrial genes between life cycle stages of *Trypanosoma brucei*. Proc Natl Acad Sci U S A. 82(10):3380-4, 1985.
17. Stuart K. Kable ML. Allen TE. Lawson S. Investigating the mechanism and machinery of RNA editing. Methods. 15(1):3-14, 1998.
18. Simpson L. Aphasizhev R. Gao G. Kang X. Mitochondrial proteins and complexes in Leishmania and Trypanosoma involved in U-insertion/deletion RNA editing. RNA.10:159-70. 2004.
19. Stuart K. Mitochondrial DNA of an African trypanosome. J Cell Biochem. 23(1-4):13-26, 1983.
20. Shapiro TA. Kinetoplast DNA maxicircles: networks within networks. Proc Natl Acad Sci U S A. 90(16):7809-13, 1993.
21. Walker R Jr. Saha L. Hill GC. Chaudhuri M. The effect of over-expression of the alternative oxidase in the procyclic forms of *Trypanosoma brucei*. Mol Biochem Parasitol. 139:153-62. 2005.
22. Borst P. Fairlamb AH. Surface receptors and transporters of *Trypanosoma brucei*. Annual Review of Microbiology. 52:745-78, 1998.
23. Sanchez MA. Ullman B. Landfear SM. Carter NS. Cloning and functional expression of a gene encoding a P1 type nucleoside transporter from *Trypanosoma brucei*. J Biol Chem 274:30244-30249, 1999.
24. Natto MJ. Wallace LJ. et al. *Trypanosoma brucei*: expression of multiple purine transporters prevents the development of allopurinol resistance. Exp Parasitol.109:80-6. 2005.
25. Donelson JE. Antigenic variation and the African trypanosome genome. Acta Trop. 85:391-404. 2003.
26. Kioy D. Jannin J. Mattock N. Human African trypanosomiasis. Nat Rev Microbiol. 2:186-7. 2004.
27. Vickerman K. Tetley L. Hendry KA. Turner CM. Biology of African trypanosomes in the tsetse fly. Biol Cell. 64:109-119. 1988.
28. Gibson W. Genetic exchange in trypanosomes. Bulletin et Memoires de l Academie Royale de Medecine de Belgique. 151(2): 203-210, 1996.
29. Betram BCR. Sleeping sickness survey in the Serengeti area (Tanzania) (1971). III. Discussion of the relevance of the trypanosome survey to the biology of large mammals in the Serengeti. Acta Trop (Basel) 30:36-48,1973.
30. Donelson JE. Hill KL. El-Sayed NM. Multiple mechanisms of immune evasion by African trypanosomes. Mol Biochem Parasitol. 91:51-66, 1998.
31. Barry JD. McCulloch R. Antigenic variation in trypanosomes: enhanced phenotypic variation in a eukaryotic parasite. Adv Parasitol. 49:1-70. 2001.
32. Cross GAM. Identification, purification and properties of clone-specific glycoprotein antigens constituting the surface coat of *T. brucei*. Parasitol 71:393-417, 1975.
33. Pays E. Vanhamme L. Berberof M. Genetic control for the expression of surface antigens in African trypanosomes. Ann Rev Micrbiol 48:28-52, 1994.
34. McCulloch R. Antigenic variation in African trypanosomes: monitoring progress. Trends Parasitol. 20:117-21. 2004.
35. Gray AR. Antigenic variation in a strain of *Trypanosoma brucei* transmitted by *Glossina morsitans* and *G. palpalis*. J Gen Microbiol 41:195-214, 1965.
36. Borst P. Bitter W. et al. Control of VSG gene expression sites in *Trypanosoma brucei*. Mol Biochem Parasitol. 91:67-76, 1998.
37. Barbour AG. Restrepo BI. Antigenic variation in vector-borne pathogens. Emerg Infect Dis. 6:449-57. 2000.
38. Winterbottom TM. An Account of the Native Africans in the Neighborhood of Sierra Leone (Vol 2). Hatchard & Mawman, London, 1803.
39. Mhlanga JD. Bentivoglio M. Kristensson K. Neurobiology of cerebral malaria and African sleeping sickness. Brain Res Bull 44:579-89, 1997.
40. Odiit M. Kansiime F. Enyaru JC. Duration of symptoms and case fatality of sleeping sickness caused by *Trypanosoma brucei*rhodesiense in Tororo, Uganda. East African Med J. 74:792-5, 1997.
41. Pentreath VW. Rees K. Owolabi OA. et al. The somnogenic T lymphocyte suppressor prostaglandin D2 is selectively elevated in cerebrospinal fluid of advanced sleeping sickness patients. Trans R Soc Trop Med Hyg 84:795-799, 1990.
42. Sternberg JM. Human African trypanosomiasis: clinical presentation and immune response. Parasite Immunol. 26:469-76. 2004.
43. Chisi JE. Misiri H. et al. Anaemia in human African trypanosomiasis caused by *Trypanosoma brucei rhodesiense*. East Afr Med J. 81:505-8. 2004.
44. Becker S, Franco JR, Simarro PP, Stich A, Abel PM, Steverding D. Real time PCR for detection of *Trypanosoma brucei* in human blood samples. Diagn Microbiol Infect Dis. 50:193-9. 2004.
45. Chappuis F. Loutan L. et al. Options for field diagnosis of human african trypanosomiasis. Clin Microbiol Rev. 18:133-46. 2005.
46. Panigrahi AK. Schnaufer A. et al. Identification of novel components of *Trypanosoma brucei* editosomes. RNA. 9:484-92. 2003.
47. Jannin J, Cattand P. Treatment and control of human African trypanosomiasis. Curr Opin Infect Dis. 17:565-71. 2004.
48. Bacchi CJ. McCann PP. Parasitic protozoa and polyamines. In: Inhibition of Polyamine Metabolism (McCann PP. Pegg AE. Sjoerdsma A., eds.). Academic Press, Pubs. New York, London. pp. 317-44, 1987.
49. Legros D. Fournier C. Gastellu Etchegorry M. et al. Echecs therapeutiques du melarsoprol parmi des patients traites au stade tardif de trypanosomose humaine africaine a T. b. gambiense en Ouganda. Bull Soc Pathol Exot. 92:171-172, 1999.
50. Chretien JP, Smoak BL. African Trypanosomiasis: Changing Epidemiology and Consequence. Curr Infect Dis Rep. 7:54-60. 2005.
51. Molyneux DH. Vector-borne parasitic diseases – an overview of recent changes. Internat J Parasitol 28(6):927-34, 1998.
52. Lubega GW, Byarugaba DK, Prichard RK. Immunization with a tubulin-rich preparation from *Trypanosoma brucei* confers broad protection against African trypanosomosis. Exp Parasitol.102:9-22. 2002.
53. Parsons M. Glycosomes: parasites and the divergence of peroxisomal purpose. Mol Microbiol. 53:717-24. 2004.

7. American Trypanosomiasis:

Trypanosoma cruzi
(Chagas 1909)

Introduction

Trypanosoma cruzi is the cause of American try-panosomiasis, also known as Chagas' Disease. It is an intracellular parasite for the majority of its life, in con-trast to its relatives, the African trypanosomes, that live in the blood and lymph. *T. cruzi* infects nearly all spe-cies of mammals native to South and Central America and is vector-borne. Insects in the order Hemiptera (true bugs), called "kissing bugs," are the only known vectors (see Fig. 38.29). Chronic infection with this parasite often leads to life threatening diseases of the hollow organs. It is one of the world's leading causes of cardiomyopathy. *T. cruzi* is found throughout Cen-tral and South America, and occasionally in the South-western portion of the United States.[1, 2] In contrast to most of South America, the incidence rate in Brazil and Chile is now under 1% in children under the age of 10. Transmission has been essentially eliminated in those two countries.[3] The disease has a case fatality rate of about 5% in its acute phase.[4]

Infection can be transmitted through blood trans-fusion,[5, 6] bone marrow transplants,[7] and organ trans-plants.[8, 9] *T. cruzi* can also infect the fetus across the placenta.[10] An outbreak in Santa Catarina, Brazil, of a particularly virulent strain of *T. cruzi* was initiated by drinking sugar cane extract that apparently was contaminated with "extract" of kissing bug. Some 30 people were infected, with a high degree of mortality. Apparently, the infected bug got into the processing ap-paratus by accident. Sugar cane extract is a popular drink on many of the beaches of Brazil. This is the first recorded epidemic of Chagas' disease in which trans-mission was by the oral route (see ProMed report on

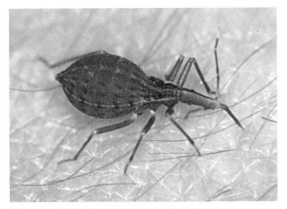

Figure 7.1. Kissing bug nymph, feeding.

Figure 7.2. Thatched roofed hut. Ideal breeding sites for kissing bugs.

04/01/05).

Rats, dogs, sloths, bats, and various non-human primates are important reservoir hosts, depending upon the region. Transmission takes place in both ru-ral and urban settings. Incidence is highest in children, with the notable exceptions of Brazil and Chile.[11]

Historical Information

Carlos Chagas, in 1909,[12,13] observed the infective stage of *T. cruzi* by chance while conducting a survey for vectors of malaria. He inoculated many species of mammals with the new agent and showed that they all became infected. He correctly speculated that humans were likely to be infected as well. He identified infected people in rural areas of Brazil. Chagas also described the major clinical features of the disease and the mor-phology of the trypomastigote stage of the parasite. All this work was accomplished within months after his ini-tial discovery. He named the organism after his beloved teacher and close friend, Oswaldo Cruz. Chagas went on to describe the essentials of the life cycle as well. Brumpt, in 1912,[14] completed the description of the life cycle of *T. cruzi*, while Vianna, in 1916,[15] published the details of the pathological consequences of infection with this important pathogenic protozoan.

Life Cycle

The biology, molecular biology, and epidemiology of American trypanosmiasis have been reviewed.[16–18] Organisms (metacyclic trypomastigote stage) are pres-ent in the fecal droppings of the infected reduviid bug. (Fig. 7.1) Transmission occurs usually by a person rub-bing the organisms into a mucous membrane or bite wound. Triatomid bugs are large, robust insects, and characteristically feed at night, biting the victim near the mouth or eyes while they are asleep. The bite itself is painless, hence the term "kissing bug." The vector ingests a large quantity of blood, and in order to make room for the new meal, it simultaneously defecates the remains of the last one, depositing it adjacent to the bite wound. The salivary secretions of the bug induce itching, causing the victim to rub the bug feces, laden with parasites, into the wound, or mucus membranes.

The infection can also occur without direct contact with the vector. Thatched roofs of rural houses can harbor large numbers of the bugs (Fig. 7.2), and their feces have the opportunity to fall onto people while they are sleeping. Individuals become infected simply by rubbing the parasites into their mucous membranes of the eye or oral cavity. The probability of infection by this route is high, because triatomids feed on many mammals, and rural peoples live in close proximity to their livestock and pets. Infection by transfusion, organ transplantation, or congenital transmission introduces the parasite directly into the host. For a somewhat gory account of what it's like to wake up covered with well-fed reduviid bugs, see Charles Darwin's description in his famous journal, *Voyage of The Beagle.* Because of this encounter, much speculation has centered around the possibility that Darwin actually contracted and suffered from chronic Chagas' disease. In fact, he most likely suffered from lactose intolerance masquerading as Chagas' disease![19]

Attachment to host cells is mediated through galectin-3 on the surface of host cells.[20] The parasite protein that binds to galactein-3 has yet to be identified. The trypomastigote can penetrate a wide variety of cells,[21] and the process is mediated by calcium ions and at least two parasite membrane proteins: a neuraminidase/trans-sialidase, which binds to sialic acid, and penetrin, which binds to heparin sulfate.[22] Another protein, gp82 might also be necessary for penetration into gastric epithelium if the metacyclic trypomastigote stage is swallowed,[23] as was the case in the recent outbreak in Santa Catarina, Brazil, involving the inges-

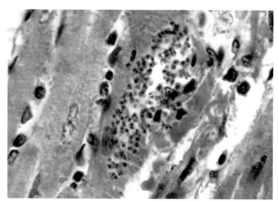

Figure 7.3. Histologic section of heart muscle infected with *Trypanosoma cruzi* amastigotes.

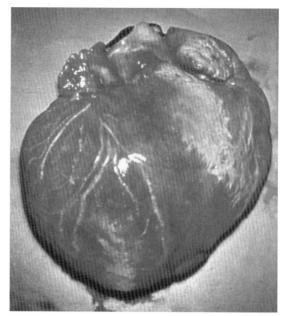

Figure 7.4. Enlarged heart of a patient who died of chronic Chagas' disease.

tion of sugar cane juice contaminated with at least one infected reduviid bug. Animals can become infected by ingesting infected reduviid bugs, and this might be the usual way for them to pick up the infection.[24]

After entering the parasitophorous vacuole, the trypomastigote enlists several escape mechanisms to aid in its survival there. It begins by neutralizing the pH of that intracellular space, thereby escaping the potentially damaging effects of exposure to the active forms of lysosomal enzymes.[22] The organism also produces a number of proteins which offer it additional advantages once inside the host cell. Chagasin is a cysteine protease inhibitor and is apparently necessary for avoiding lysosomal-derived cysteine protease activity and insures that the parasite has the time needed to differentiate into the amastigote stage.[25] Cruzipain is thought to play a major role in helping the parasite avoid being digested once inside the parasitophorous vacuole. Cruzipain also induces the upregulation of host-derived arginase-2, a known inhibitor of apoptosis.[26] Thus, the parasite may be engineering the longevity of its host cell, while at the same time, avoiding the ravages of lysosomal digestion.

The parasite then rapidly penetrates into the cytosol and differentiates into the amastigote stage. This is the dividing form of *T. cruzi* and the one that inflicts cell damage on the host. After several division cycles, some of the parasites transform back into trypomastigotes. The affected cells die, releasing the parasites that can now enter the bloodstream and become distributed throughout the body. They infect cells in many types of tissues, including the central nervous system,

Trypanosoma cruzi

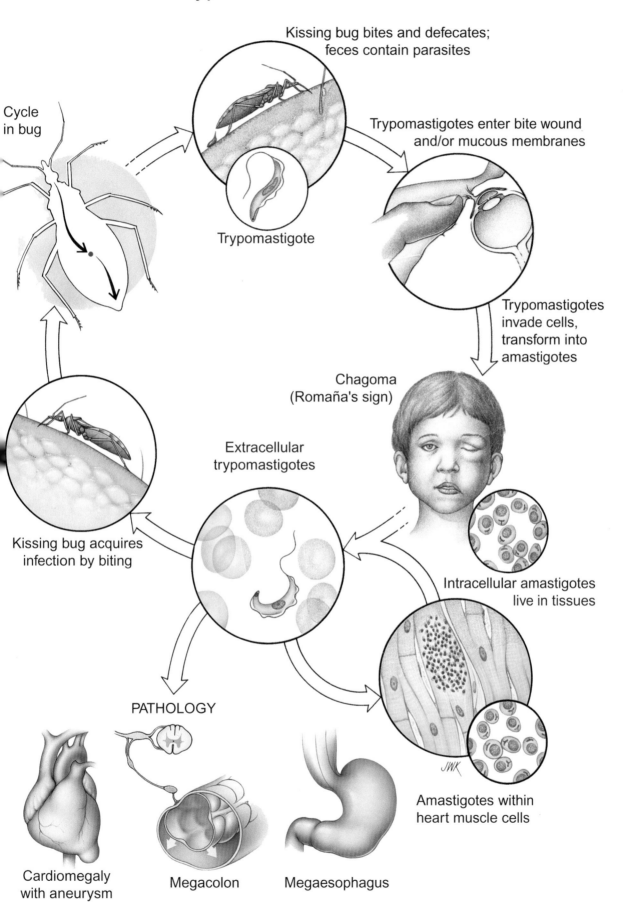

Kissing bug bites and defecates; feces contain parasites

Cycle in bug

Trypomastigote

Trypomastigotes enter bite wound and/or mucous membranes

Trypomastigotes invade cells, transform into amastigotes

Chagoma (Romaña's sign)

Extracellular trypomastigotes

Kissing bug acquires infection by biting

Intracellular amastigotes live in tissues

PATHOLOGY

Amastigotes within heart muscle cells

Cardiomegaly with aneurysm

Megacolon

Megaesophagus

heart muscle, the myenteric plexus, the urogenital tract, and the reticuloendothelial system.

Triatomids become infected by taking a blood meal from an infected individual.[27] The trypomastigote migrates to the midgut of the insect, where it transforms into the epimastigote, and then undergoes many divisions. Thousands of organisms are produced within one insect without apparently affecting it. The triatomids remain infected for life (i.e., 1-2 years). Epimastigotes maintain their place in the gut of the insect by specific receptor-ligand interactions involving at least one parasite surface glycoprotein and a carbohydrate lectin on the gut cells of the insect.[28] Ultimately, epimastigotes transform into metacyclic trypomastigotes and migrate to the hind gut, and from there they are excreted with feces following the taking of a blood meal.

Cellular and Molecular Pathogenesis

Infection with *Trypanosoma cruzi* results in partial immunosuppression[29, 30] that further aids the parasite in remaining inside the host cell for extended periods of time. For example, in vitro culture of human dendritic cells infected with *T. cruzi* resulted in a dramatic down regulation of synthesis of IL-6, IL-12, TNF-α, HLA-DR, and CD-40, and inhibited their maturation into antigen processing cells.[31] Parasite-derived calreticulin may also be important for amastigote survival in the intracellular environment, implicating a central role for calcium trafficking and storage in the life of the parasite.[32]

Release of trypomastigotes into the blood stream seemingly places them at risk for immune attack, since serum antibodies against them can be demonstrated at this time in the infected host. However, *T. cruzi* has an answer for this defense strategy. The surface coat of the free-swimming trypomastigote contains a specific compliment regulatory protein[33] that binds the C3b

Figure 7.5. Portion of enlarged heart of a patient who died of chronic Chagas' disease. Note thin wall of ventricle.

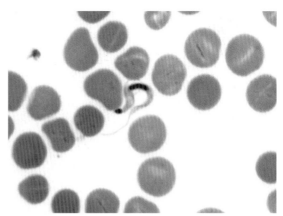

Figure 7.6. Trypomastigote of *T. cruzi*. 20μm x 3μm.

and C4b component, inhibiting the alternate pathway.

Host protection can develop, despite these highly evolved parasite evasion mechanisms. Immunity depends on CD1d antigen presentation and the upregulation of IL-12 for the production of natural killer cells, the protective arm of the immune system most effective against the amastigotes in the tissues.[34] Parasites are killed is by way of induction of nitric oxide synthase and the production of nitric oxide.[35] CD8+ T cells with specificities for parasite antigen are thought to be essential in maintaining some control of the infection throughout the chronic phase.[36]

Chagas' disease manifests in all hollow organs. Infected individuals remain so for life and most of the pathological consequences are those resulting from cell death (Fig. 7.3) Myenteric plexus damage results in loss of muscle tone and enlargement of the organ, particularly the digestive tract. Megacolon and megaesophagus are late onset sequelae to chronic infection. Heart damage is almost invariably associated with Chagas' disease in some regions of Central and South America,[37] and is detectable early on in infection.[38] Erosion of heart tissue is typical, and in many cases results in aneurysm and heart failure (Figs. 7.4, 7.5).

Current thinking regarding a dominant role for auto-antibodies inducing cardiomyopathy plays down this mechanism to account for heart damage during chronic infection.[38] This is because: 1. PCR has been able to demonstrate the presence of *T. cruzi* in heart tissue, even at times when biopsy material used in conventional histological mode could not reveal the presence of the parasite,[38] and: 2. disease progresses rapidly when parasites are abundant and not as fast when they are hard to demonstrate on biopsy.[39] Nonetheless, auto-antibodies have been detected in many individuals suffering from long term infection with *T. cruzi*.[40, 41] Meningoencephalitis occurs during the acute phase and is characterized by infiltrates of CD8+ T cells.[42]

Clinical Disease

Acute Chagas' Disease

A review of clinical aspects of Chagas' disease is available.[43] The incubation period for Chagas' disease is 4-12 days after introduction of the organisms. The acute stage is often asymptomatic, or the symptoms that develop are generalized and the disease is therefore misdiagnosed. A chagoma develops at the site of the bite within 2-4 days. If organisms are introduced into the body through mucous membranes by rubbing them into the eye, then the swelling associated with the chagoma is known as Romaña's sign. It occurs mostly as a unilateral swelling. The swollen eyelid is firm to the touch, and there may be associated conjunctivitis. If the bite occurs elsewhere, the adjacent area is erythematous, brawny, and firm to the touch. When the chagoma disappears after several weeks, it leaves an area of depigmentation. An associated neuropathy develops, and then disappears when the patient enters the chronic phase of the infection.

Systemic involvement includes fever, lymphadenopathy, hepatomegaly, splenomegaly, and myocarditis. The myocarditis of acute Chagas' disease presents with tachycardia, congestive heart failure, and cardiomegaly.

Chronic Chagas' Disease

Most patients survive the acute phase and become asymptomatic. The chronic phase can last the rest of their lives (i.e., 20-30 years). Infection persists, exacting its toll on all affected organs, particularly the heart. Cardiac involvement can be silent for some years after infection, and limited to ECG abnormalities consisting of conduction defects. A complete heart block with progressive destruction of the myocardium and conduction system leads to Chagas' cardiomyopathy. Ultrastructural studies showed that vinculin costameres in cardiomyocytes become disrupted during intracellular infection with the amastiogote stage, and this is thought to make a major contribution to the cardiomyopathy so typically seen in the chronic infection.[44]

Clinically, the patient experiences extrasystoles, right ventricular enlargement, and eventually heart failure. Right bundle branch block is typical, and eventually may lead to death.[45]

Gastrointestinal involvement includes development of megaesophagus, characterized by dysphagia and regurgitation, and megacolon,[46] leading to constipation and fecal retention.

Disease is not limited to the heart and gut. Rarely it leads also to megaureters, megabladder, megagallbladder, and bronchiectasis.

Patients suffering from HIV/AIDS exhibit signs and symptoms of the acute phase of infection, and if left untreated, usually die from overwhelming infection due to *T. cruzi*.[47]

Patients in the chronic phase of infection that acquire HIV can experience a reactivation of *T. cruzi* resembling the acute phase of the disease.[48]

Diagnosis

The use of PCR using primers based on kinetoplast DNA sequences[49, 50] has greatly facilitated definitive diagnosis in patients with chronic infection, and has essentially replaced ELISA-based immunological tests as the test of choice, next to microscopic identification (Fig. 7.3). Although PCR would also be considered practical for screening in blood banks, a chemiluminescent ELISA appears to offer more promise.[51] Parasites can also be identified microscopically from biopsy samples of infected tissue. Inoculating blood from suspected individuals into susceptible animals can reveal the organism, but this approach presents too many impracticalities for most diagnostic facilities. Xenodiagnosis, employing uninfected reduviid bugs, allowing them to feed on the patient, then dissecting the bugs some days later, can also reveal the presence of parasites in chronically infected individuals, but it is a special test requiring extensive laboratory infrastructure and technical assistance.

Treatment

The drugs of choice are nifurtimox[52] and benznidazole.[53] Neither drug is recommended without reservation; they are both associated with high toxicity and incomplete cure rates in adults, especially when they are used to treat the chronic phase of the infection.[53] Benznidazole is recommended for use in children who have either just acquired the disease (i.e., congenitally), or who are in the chronic phase of their infection.[54] Very little is known regarding the mode of action of either drug. Nifurtimox may exert its toxic effect by reacting with sulfhydryl compounds such as coenzyme A, glutathione, and cysteine.[55] Itraconizole and allopurinol[56] have also been tried with about a 40-50% cure rate. Newer drugs are being developed, some of which take advantage of known metabolic pathways.[57, 58]

Heart transplantation as a treatment modality for the cardiomyopathic aspects of Chagas' disease has been in vogue for as long as heart transplantation has been tried in humans.[59, 60] In fact, the fourth recipient ever to receive a heart transplant suffered from chronic *T. cruzi* infection. However, the use of cyclosporin-A for immunosuppression, in order to prevent rejection of the transplanted heart, allows *T. cruzi* to reproduce un-controlled, resulting in the death of the patient in most cases.

Prevention and Control

Control of Chagas' disease depends upon inter-fering with two major routes of transmission; vector-borne and transfusion. Control of vectors, by prudent use of insecticides (pyrethroids), has significantly re-duced transmission of *T. cruzi* in Brazil and Chile.[61, 62] Unfortunately, this trend has been slow to spread to neighboring countries. Prevalence remains at about 15 million throughout Central and South America. Trans-fusion-induced infection is still on the rise,[63] especially in countries where *T. cruzi* is not vector-borne, compli-cating the control of disease. Blood bank screening for *T. cruzi* should be mandatory in all countries experienc-ing high rates of immigration from South and Central America. Paid blood donors should be outlawed in all countries in which Chagas' disease is endemic.[63] A more permanent solution, and one that interfaces well with the concepts of medical ecology, is building better housing for the poor.[64, 65]

Houses constructed without a thatched roof, the slat board wood siding, or rough textured wall surfaces inside the house are relatively safe from reduviid bug colonization. Keeping pet dogs and pigs out of the house further reduces the chances of acquiring Cha-gas' disease.[66]

References

1. Schiffier RI. Mansur GP. et al. Indigenous Chagas' disease (American trypanosomiasis) in California. JAMA 251: 2983-2984, 1984.
2. Woody NC. Woody HB. Amercian trypanosomiasis (Chagas' disease): first indigenous case in the U.S.A. JAMA 159:676. 1955.
3. Reiche EM. Inouye MM. et al. Seropositivity for anti-*Trypanosoma cruzi* antibodies among blood donors of the "Hospital Universitario Regional do Norte do Parana", Londrina, Brazil. Rev Inst Med Trop Sao Paulo. 38:233-40. 1996.
4. Koberle F. Chagas' disease and Chagas' syndromes: pathology of American trypanosomiasis. Adv Parasitol 6:63-116. 1968.
5. Wendel S. Transfusion-transmitted Chagas' disease. Curr Opin Hematol. 5:406-11.1998.
6. Blejer JL. Saguier MC. Dinapoli RA. Salamone HJ. Prevalencia de anticuerpos anti-*Trypanosoma cruzi* en donantes de sangre. Medicina (B Aires). 59:129-32. 1999.
7. Dictar M. Sinagra A. et al. Recipients and donors of bone marrow transplants suffering from Chagas' disease: management and pre-emptive therapy of parasitemia. Bone Marrow Transplant. 21:391-3, 1998.
8. Carvalho MF. de Franco MF. Soares VA. Amastigotes forms of *Trypanosoma cruzi* detected in a renal allograft. Rev Inst Med Trop Sao Paulo. 39(4):223-6, 1997.
9. Altclas J. Jaimovich G. Milovic V. Klein F. Feldman L. Chagas' disease after bone marrow transplantation. Bone Marrow Transplant. 18:447-8. 1996.
10. Russomando G. de Tomassone MM. et al. Treatment of congenital Chagas' disease diagnosed and followed up by the polymerase chain reaction. Am J Trop Med Hyg. 59:487-91. 1998.
11. Chile and Brazil to be certified free of transmission of Chagas' Disease. Tropical Diseases Research News (WHO publication). No. 59 June. 1999.
12. Chagas C. Nova trypanozomiaze humana: estudos sobre a morfolojia e o ciclo evolutivo do Schizotrypanum cruzi n. gen, n. spec., ajente eti-olojico de nova entidade morbida de homem. Mem Inst Oswaldo Cruz 1:159-218, 1909.
13. Perleth M. The discovery of Chagas' disease and the formation of the early Chagas' disease concept. Hist Philos Life Sci.19:211-36. 1997.
14. Brumpt AJE. Le *Trypanosoma cruzi* evolue chez Conorhinus megistus. Cimex ectularius, Cimex boueti et Ornithodorus moubata: cycle evolutif de ce parasite. Bull Soc Pathol Exot 5:360-364, 1912.
15. Vianna G. Contribuicao para o estudo da anatomia patolojica da anatomia patolojica 'moletia de Carlos Chagas" (esquizotripanoze humana ou tireodite parazitaria). Mem Inst Oswaldo Cruz 3:276-294, 1916.
16. Gull K. The biology of kinetoplastid parasites: insights and challenges from genomics and post-genomics. Int J Parasitol. 31:443-52. 2001.
17. Miles MA, Feliciangeli MD, de Arias AR. American trypanosomiasis (Chagas' disease) and the role of molecular epidemiology in guid-ing control strategies. BMJ. 326:1444-8. 2003.
18. Mortara RA. Andreoli WK. et al. Mammalian cell invasion and intracellular trafficking by *Trypanosoma cruzi* infective forms. An Acad Bras Cienc. 77:77-94. 2005.
19. Campbell AK, Matthews SB. Darwin's illness revealed. Postgrad Med J. 81:248-51. 2005.
20. Kleshchenko YY. Moody TN. et al. Human galectin-3 promotes *Trypanosoma cruzi* adhesion to human coronary artery smooth muscle cells. Infect Immun. 72:6717-21. 2004.
21. Ortega-Barria E. Pereira EA. Entry of *Trypanosoma cruzi* into eukaryotic cells. Infect Agents Dis 1:136-145, 1992.
22. Herrera EM. Ming M. Ortega-Barria E. Pereira ME. Mediation of *Trypanosoma cruzi* invasion by heparan sulfate receptors on host cells and penetrin counter-receptors on the trypanosomes. Mol Biochem Parasitol. 65:73-83. 1994.
23. Neira I, Silva FA, Cortez M, Yoshida N. Involvement of *Trypanosoma cruzi* metacyclic trypomastigote surface molecule gp82 in adhe-sion to gastric mucin and invasion of epithelial cells. Infect Immun. 71:557-61. 2003.
24. Calvo Mendez ML, Nogueda Torres B, Alejandre Aguilar R. The oral route: an access port for *Trypanosoma cruzi*. Rev Latinoam Micro-biol. 34:39-42. 1992.
25. Santos CC. Sant'anna C. et al. Chagasin, the endogenous cysteine-protease inhibitor of *Trypanosoma cruzi*, modulates parasite dif-ferentiation and invasion of mammalian cells. J Cell Sci.118:901-15. 2005.
26. Aoki MP. Guinazu NL. et al. Cruzipain, a major *Trypanosoma cruzi* antigen, promotes arginase-2 expression and survival of neonatal mouse cardiomyocytes. Am J Physiol Cell Physiol. 286:C206-12. 2003.
27. Garcia ES. Azambuja P. Development and interactions of *Trypanosoma cruzi* within the insect vector. Parasitol Today. 7:240-4.1991.

28. Pereira ME. Loures MA. Villalta F. Andrade AF. Lectin receptors as markers for *Trypanosoma cruzi*. Developmental stages and a study of the interaction of wheat germ agglutinin with sialic acid residues on epimastigote cells. J Exp Med. 152:1375-92. 1980.

29. Sher A. Snary D. Specific inhibition of the morphogenesis of Trypanosoma cruzi by a monoclonal antibody. Nature (London). 300:639-640, 1985.

30. Majumder S. Kierszenbaum F. Mechanisms of *Trypanosoma cruzi*-induced down-regulation of lymphocyte function. Inhibition of transcription and expression of IL-2 receptor gamma (p64IL-2R) and beta (p70IL-2R) chain molecules in activated normal human lymphocytes. J Immunol. 156(10):3866-74, 1996.

31. Van Overtvelt L. Vanderheyde N. et al. *Trypanosoma cruzi* infects human dendritic cells and prevents their maturation: inhibition of cytokines, HLA-DR, and costimulatory molecules. Infect Immun. 67(8):4033-40, 1999.

32. Ferreira V. Molina MC. et al. Role of calreticulin from parasites in its interaction with vertebrate hosts. Mol Immunol. 40:1279-91. 2004.

33. Beucher M, Meira WS. et al. Expression and purification of functional, recombinant *Trypanosoma cruzi* complement regulatory protein. Protein Expr Purif. 27:19-26. 2003.

34. Duthie MS. Kahn M. et al. Both CD1d antigen presentation and interleukin-12 are required to activate natural killer T cells during *Trypanosoma cruzi* infection. Infect Immun. 73:1890-4. 2005.

35. Vespa GNR. Cunha FQ.Silva JS. Nitric oxide is involved in the control of *Trypanosoma cruzi* induced parasitaemia and directly kills parasite in vitro, Infect Immun 62:5177–5182. 1994.

36. Martin DL. Tarleton RL. Antigen-specific T cells maintain an effector memory phenotype during persistent *Trypanosoma cruzi* infection. J Immunol. 174:1594-601. 2005.

37. Parada H. Carrasco HA. et al. Cardiac involvement is a constant finding in acute Chagas' disease: a clinical, parasitological and histopathological study. Int J Cardiol. 60:49-54, 1997.

38. de Andrade AL. Zicker F. et al. Early electrocardiographic abnormalities in *Trypanosoma cruzi*-seropositive children. Am J Trop Med Hyg. 59:530-4, 1998.

39. Tarleton RL. Chagas' Disease: a role for autoimmunity? Trends Parasitol. 19:447-51. 2003.

40. Vermelho AB. de Meirelles M de N. et al. Heart muscle cells share common neutral glycosphingolipids with *Trypanosoma cruzi*. Acta Trop. 64:131-43, 1997.

41. Cunha-Neto E. Coelho V. et al. Identification of cardiac myosin-B13 *Trypanosoma cruzi* protein crossreactive T cell clones in heart lesions of a chronic Chagas' cardiomyopathy patient. J Clin Invest. 98:1709-12, 1996.

42. Roffe E. Silva AA. et al. Essential role of VLA-4/VCAM-1 pathway in the establishment of CD8+ T-cell-mediated *Trypanosoma cruzi*-elicited meningoencephalitis. J Neuroimmunol.142:17-30. 2003.

43. Anez N. Crisante G. Rojas A. Update on Chagas' Disease in Venezuela – a review. Mem Inst Oswaldo Cruz. 99:781-7. 2004.

44. Melo TG. Almeida DS. de Meirelles Mde N. Pereira MC. *Trypanosoma cruzi* infection disrupts vinculin costameres in cardiomyocytes. Eur J Cell Biol. 83:531-40. 2004.

45. Jorge MT. Macedo TA. et al. Types of arrhythmia among cases of American trypanosomiasis, compared with those in other cardiology patients. Ann Trop Med Parasitol. 97:139. 2003.

46. Meneghelli UG. Chagasic enteropathy. Rev Soc Bras Med Trop. 37:252-60. 2004.

47. Antunes AC. Cecchini FM. et al. Cerebral trypanosomiasis and AIDS. Arq Neuropsiquiatr. 60:730-3. 2002.

48. Harms G, Feldmeier H. The impact of HIV infection on tropical diseases. Infect Dis Clin North Am.19:121-35. 2005.

49. Britto C. Cardoso MA. et al. Polymerase chain reaction detection of *Trypanosoma cruzi* in human blood samples as a tool for diagnosis and treatment evaluation. Parasitology. 110:241-7, 1995.

50. Junqueira A.C. Chiari E. Wincker P. Comparison of the polymerase chain reaction with two classical parasitological methods for the diagnosis of Chagas' Disease in a endemic region of northeastern Brazil. Trans Roy Soc Trop Med Hyg 90:129–132. 1996.

51. Almeida IC. Covas DT. Soussumi LM. Travassos LR. A highly sensitive and specific chemiluminescent enzyme-linked immunosorbent assay for diagnosis of active *Trypanosoma cruzi* infection. Transfusion. 37(8):850-7, 1997.

52. Kirchhoff LV. Changing Epidemiology and Approaches to Therapy for Chagas' Disease. Curr Infect Dis Rep. 5:59-65. 2003.

53. Cerecetto H. Gonzalez M. Chemotherapy of Chagas' disease: status and new developments. Curr Top Med Chem. 2:1187-213. 2002.

54. Schenone H, Contreras M. et al. Nifurtimox treatment of chronic Chagasic infection in children. Rev Med Chil.131:1089-90. 2003.

55. Diaz EG. Montalto de Mecca M. Castro JA. Reactions of nifurtimox with critical sulfhydryl-containing biomolecules: their potential toxicological relevance. J Appl Toxicol. 24:189-95. 2004.

56. Apt W. Aguilera X. Arribada A. et al. Treatment of chronic Chagas' disease with itraconazole and allopurinol. Am J Trop Med Hyg 59(1):133-8, 1998.

57. Engel JC. Doyle PS. Hsieh I. McKerrow JH. Cysteine protease inhibitors cure an experimental *Trypanosoma cruzi* infection. J Exp Med. 188(4):725-34, 1998.

58. Choe Y. Brinen LS. et al. Development of alpha-keto-based inhibitors of cruzain, a cysteine protease implicated in Chagas' Disease. Bioorg Med Chem. 13:2141-56. 2005.

59. de Carvalho VB. Sousa EF. Vila JH. et al. Heart transplantation in Chagas' disease. 10 years after the initial experience Circulation. 94(8):1815-7, 1996.

60. Bocchi EA. Bellotti G. Mocelin AO. et al. Heart transplantation for chronic Chagas' heart disease. Ann Thorac Surg. 61(6): 1727-33, 1996.

61. Schofield CJ. Diaz JCP. The southern cone initiative against Chagas' Disease. In: Advances in Parasitology. (Baker JR. Muller R. Rollinson D. eds). Academic Press. Pubs. San Diego, London. pp. 2-30, 1999.

62. Moncayo A. Chagas' Disease: current epidemiological trends after the interruption of vectorial and transfusional transmission in the Southern Cone countries. Mem Inst Oswaldo Cruz. 98:577-91. 2003.

63. Schmunis GA, Cruz JR. Safety of the blood supply in Latin America. Clin Microbiol Rev.18:12-29. 2005.

64. Chaudhuri N. Interventions to improve children's health by improving the housing environment. Rev Environ Health.19:197-222. 2004.

65. Cecere MC. Gurtler RE. et al. Effects of partial housing improvement and insecticide spraying on the reinfestation dynamics of *Triatoma infestans* in rural northwestern Argentina. Acta Trop. 84:101-16. 2002.

66. Cohen JE. Gurtler RE. Modeling household transmission of American trypanosomiasis. Science. 293:694-8. 2001.

8. *Trichomonas vaginalis* (Donné 1836)

Introduction

Trichomonas vaginalis is a flagellated, anaerobic protozoan transmitted from person to person by sexual contact. Its distribution is worldwide. *T. vaginalis* infects both males and females. In males, infection is usually asymptomatic, but in females, it can induce clinical disease that includes vaginal itching, inflammation, and purulent discharge. While not life threatening, women infected with *T. vaginalis* typically experience periods of discomfort, and in its worst manifestations, longer periods of extreme discomfort and pain. It can also infect the newborn as it passes through the birth canal of an infected mother.[1] The infant may experience ectopic infection in the respiratory tract and other sites, as well. There are no reservoir hosts and exposure does not lead to permanent immunity, so reinfection after treatment is common. Drug resistant *T. vaginalis* exists,[2] but is still of low prevalence and incidence. The genome of *Trichomonas vaginalis* is currently being worked on and a summary of findings can be found at www.tigr.org/tdb/e2k1/tvg/. Reviews on all aspects of *T. vaginalis* are available.[3, 4]

Historical Information

Donné, in 1837,[5] described the infection but not the clinical aspects, citing Dujardin's unpublished morphologic description of this flagellate. Proof that *T. vaginalis* is indeed a pathogen came much later, in 1940, when Kessel and co-workers inoculated healthy volunteers with *T. vaginalis*. Many of these individuals developed majority of the signs and symptoms of the disease. The investigators were then able to match these with patients who were naturally infected.[6] This study also provided an accurate description of the pathologic findings of trichomoniasis. This research might have a rough time passing review by the Institutional Review Board of any accredited medical school if it were proposed today.

Life Cycle

T. vaginalis exists only the trophozoite stage (i.e., there is no known cyst stage), measuring 10-25 µm by 7-8 µm (Fig. 8.1). It is motile, and possesses four flagella, an undulating membrane, and a rigid axostyle. *T. vaginalis* has a simple, direct life cycle. Infection is initiated by sexual intercourse with an infected person. In order to infect, the trophozoites must be able to adhere to epithelial cells, and is facilitated by adhesions[7] and specific ligand-carbohydrate interactions. Mannose and N-acetyl-glucosamine are two parasite membrane-associated sugar residues that are used for attachment.[8, 9] Secretion of lysosomal hydrolases, such as acid phosphatase, occurs at the host cell-parasite interface[10] immediately following attachment. These parasite enzymes are cytotoxic,[11] causing the target cells to lyse, releasing their contents. The cell debris is then ingested by the parasite. The parasite uses carbohydrases, including N-acetyl glucosaminidase, and α-mannosidase,[12] to detach itself from the target cell membrane, which allows it to move on to the next cell.

T. vaginalis reproduces by binary fission. Trophozoites secrete molecular hydrogen as a by-product of energy metabolism. Despite its ability to induce clinical disease, *T. vaginalis* is quite a fragile organism. If organisms pass out of an infected individual, and the fluid they are in dries out, they die.

Cellular and Molecular Pathogenesis

The molecular biology of *Trichomonas vaginalis* has been reviewed.[13] *T. vaginalis* possesses an unusual organelle, the hydrogenosome, (Figs. 8.2, 8.3),[14, 15] a subcellular organelle derived from an ancient mitochondrion, but which functions in anaerobic metabolism.[16] It contains some of the necessary enzymes for processing glucose to acetate to molecular hydrogen,[17] and Putrescine biosynthesis.[18] The rest of the glycolytic cycle is cytosolic. Putrescine biosynthesis is essential for parasite growth. Inhibition of Putrescine synthesis by analogues of Putrescine kills the tropho-

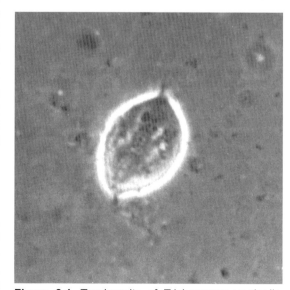

Figure 8.1. Trophozoite of *Trichomonas vaginalis*. Phase contrast. 20 µm x 10 µm.

Trichomonas vaginalis

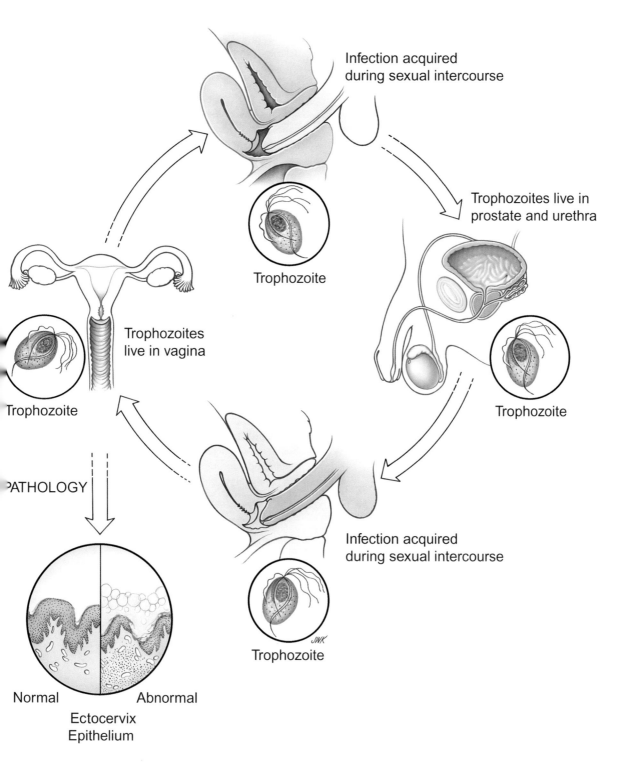

Infection acquired
during sexual intercourse

Trophozoite

Trophozoites live in
prostate and urethra

Trophozoite

Infection acquired
during sexual intercourse

Trophozoite

Trophozoites
live in vagina

Trophozoite

PATHOLOGY

Normal   Abnormal

Ectocervix
Epithelium

"Parasitic Diseases" 5ᵗʰ Ed. © Apple Trees Productions, LLC., Pub. P.O. Box 280, New York, NY 10032

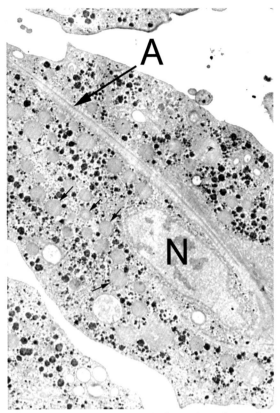

Figure 8.2. Transmission EM of a portion of a tropho-zoite of *T. vaginalis*. N=nucleus, A=axostyle. Arrows indicate hydrogenosomes. Courtesy H. Shio.

zoite.[19] Iron plays an important role in the attachment process.[7]Because *T. vaginalis* secretes proteases at the site of attachment,[10] cell death is the usual outcome. In heavy infection, sloughing of sheets of epithelium and intense inflammation of the infected area, elicited as repair mechanisms, attempt to compensate for the presence of the parasite. It is not known whether or not the release of molecular hydrogen into the vaginal tract has any pathological consequence other than produc-ing foul-smelling exudates. Isolates of *T. vaginalis* from patients suffering clinical manifestations showed dif-ferent capabilities with regards to their ability to induce damage in a mouse model,[20] but the molecular basis for this variation was not investigated.

Clinical Disease

The clinical aspects of trichomoniasis have been recently reviewed.[21] Approximately 20% of women in-fected are asymptomatic; the rest suffer from a wide range of symptoms,[22] from mild vaginal discomfort and dyspareunia, to incapacitating illness. Vaginal itching or burning associated with thick, yellow, blood-tinged discharge is typical in fulminating cases. Burning on urination and urethral discharge is also common in this

group of patients. Rarely, urticaria is a complication of heavy infection.[23]

On physical examination, women frequently pres-ent signs of colpitis macularis ("strawberry cervix") and vaginal and vulvar erythema.[24] All of these signs and symptoms are exacerbated during menstruation.

Infection with *T. gondii* is usually asymptomatic in men, making them the most common source of the infection for their partners, since most infected males are unaware of their infections. When the prostate be-comes infected, pain in the groin and upon urination are the most common complaints.[25] The infection in-creases the chances of transmission of HIV-1,[26, 27] due to erosion of the vaginal wall, allowing blood to escape into the vagina.

Infants born of mothers harboring the infection often acquire it upon passing through the birth canal.[1] Clinical consequences of infection in newborns include urinary tract infection (females only),[28] and rare involvement of the lung, resulting in a pneumonia-like syndrome.[29]

Diagnosis

Definitive diagnosis can be made by identifying the organism by microscopic observation (Fig. C.5., Ap-pendix C), or by use of PCR.[30, 31] Diagnosis by PCR is by far more sensitive than any other method, and is now the preferred method in most hospital parasitol-ogy diagnostic laboratories.[30]Alternatively, if PCR is not available, then anaerobic culture in thioglycolate medi-um is useful, especially when the infection is suspected based upon a constellation of signs and symptoms, in-cluding odoriferous exudate, and frothy appearance to the cervix (H_2 plus CO_2), at a time when no organisms can be found on microscopic examination.

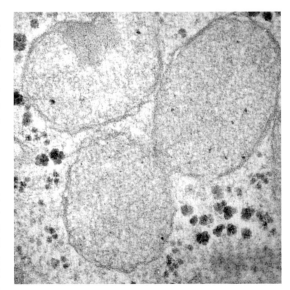

Figure 8.3. Higher magnification EM of hydrogeno-somes. Courtesy H. Shio.

Treatment

The drug of choice is metronidazole.[3] It can be given orally as a single dose, but is also available as a vaginal gel. However, its use as an intra-vaginal suppository is of little value, judging by most clinical trials.[3] The drug is typically well-tolerated, but metallic taste, and antabuse-like side effects are common. For a comprehensive review of metronidazole's pharmacokinetics, see Freeman.[32] Metronidazole is converted to active intermediates by hydrogenosome-associated pyruvate ferredoxin oxidoreductase and hydrogenase under anaerobic conditions. The parasite is inhibited from growing by exposure to those intermediates, but the precise biochemical mechanisms of the process are unknown. Resistant strains (approximately 2-5% of all infected individuals[3]) have inactive forms of pyruvate ferridoxin oxidoreductase and hydrogenase,[33] deriving all their energy from glucose by alternate pathways. Tinidazole, an alternate drug for treating resistant forms of the infection, is now available.[3]

Prevention and Control

Use of a condom during sexual intercourse for as long as either partner is infected is the recommended method of prevention. Treating both sexual partners with a single large dose of metronidazole can be effective in some cases, particularly when the number of new sexual partners for each infected individual is low. As in other sexually transmitted diseases, identification

References

1. Smith LM. Wang M. Zangwill K. Yeh S. *Trichomonas vaginalis* infection in a premature newborn. J Perinatol. 22:502-3. 2002.
2. Kulda J. Trichomonads, hydrogenosomes and drug resistance. Int J Parasitol. 29:199-212. 1999.
3. Schwebke JR, Burgess D. Trichomoniasis. Clin Microbiol Rev.17:794-803. 2004.
4. Lehker MW. Alderete JF. Biology of trichomonosis. Curr Opin Infect Dis.13:37-45. 2000.
5. Donne A. Animalcules observes dans la matieres purulentes et le produit des secretions des or-ganes genitaux de l'homme et da la femme. C R Hebdomad Seanc Acad Sci 3:385-386, 1837.
6. Kessel IF. Gafford JA. Observations on the pathology of *Trichomonas vaginitis* and on vaginal implants with *Trichomonas vaginalis* and *Trichomonas intestinalis*. Am J Obstet Gynecol 39:1005-1014, 1940.
7. Garcia AF. Chang TH. et al. Iron and contact with host cells induce expression of adhesins on surface of *Trichomonas vaginalis*. Mol Microbiol. 47:1207-24. 2003.
8. Mirhaghani A. Warton A. Involvement of *Trichomonas vaginalis* surface-associated glycoconjugates in the parasite/target cell interaction. A quantitative electron microscopy study. Parasitol Res 84(5):374-81, 1998.
9. Singh BN. Lucas JJ. et al. Adhesion of Tritrichomonas foetus to bovine vaginal epithelial cells. Infect Immun 67(8):3847-54, 1999.
10. Lockwood BC. North MJ. Coombs GH. The release of hydrolases from *Trichomonas vaginalis* and Tritrichomonas foetus. Mol Biochem Parasitol 30(2):135-42, 1988.
11. Chen W. Cai H. Chen J. et al. Study on ultrastructural cytochemistry and pathogenic mechanism of *Trichomonas vaginalis*. Chin Med J (Engl) 109(9):695-9, 1996.
12. Savoia D. Martinotti MG. Secretory hydrolases of Trichomonas vaginalis. Microbiologica 12(2):133-8, 1989.
13. Vanacova S. Liston DR. Tachezy J. Johnson PJ. Molecular biology of the amitochondriate parasites, *Giardia intestinalis, Entamoeba histolytica* and *Trichomonas vaginalis*. Int J Parasitol. 33:235-55. 2003.
14. PrDiaz JA. De Souza W. Purification and biochemical characterization of the hydrogenosomes of the flagellate protozoan *Tritrichomonas foetus*. Eur J Cell Biol 74(1):85-91, 1997.
15. Williams BA. Keeling PJ. Cryptic organelles in parasitic protists and fungi. Adv Parasitol. 54:9-68. 2003.
16. Embley TM. Giezen. M. et al. Hydrogenosomes and mitochondria are two forms of the same fundamental organelle. Phil Trans R Soc Lond 358: 191-201. 2002.
17. Wu G. Muller M. Glycogen phosphorylase sequences from the amitochondriate protists, *Trichomonas vaginalis, Mastigamoeba balamuthi, Entamoeba histolytica* and *Giardia intestinalis*. J Eukaryot Microbiol. 50:366-72. 2003.
18. North MJ. Lockwood BC. Bremner AF. Coombs GH. Polyamine biosynthesis in trichomonads. Mol Biochem Parasitol 19(3):241-9, 1986.
19. Reis IA. Martinez MP. Yarlett N. et al. Inhibition of polyamine synthesis arrests trichomonad growth and induces destruction of hydrogenosomes. Antimicrob Agents Chemother 43(8):1919-23, 1999.
20. Hussien EM. El-Sayed HZ. et al. Biological variability of *Trichomonas vaginalis* clinical isolates from symptomatic and asymptomatic patients. J Egypt Soc Parasitol. 34:979-88. 2004.
21. Deligeoroglou E. Salakos N. et al. Infections of the lower female genital tract during childhood and adolescence. Clin Exp Obstet Gynecol. 31:175-8. 2004.
22. Petrin D. Delgaty K. Bhatt R. Garber G. Clinical and microbiological aspects of *Trichomonas vaginalis* Clin Microbiol Rev 11(2):300-17, 1998.
23. Purello-D'Ambrosio F. Gangemi S. et al. Urticaria from *Trichomonas vaginalis* infection. J Investig Allergol Clin Immunol 9(2):123-5, 1999.
24. Wolner-Hanssen p. Krieger JN. Stevens CE, et al. Clinical manifestations of vaginal trichomoniasis. JAMA 261:571-576, 1989.
25. Krieger JN, Riley DE. Chronic prostatitis: charlottesville to Seattle J Urol.172:2557-60. 2004.
26. Mason PR. Fiori PL. et al. Seroepidemiology of *Trichomonas vaginalis* in rural women in Zimbabwe and patterns of association with HIV infection. Epidemiol Infect.133:315-23. 2005.
27. Moodley P. Wilkinson D. et al. *Trichomonas vaginalis* is associated with pelvic inflammatory disease in women infected with human immunodeficiency virus. Clin Infect Dis. 34:519-22. 2002.
28. Hoffman DJ. Brown GD. et al. Urinary tract infection with *Trichomonas vaginalis* in a premature newborn infant and the development of chronic lung disease. J Perinatol. 23:59-61. 2003.
29. Szarka K. Temesvari P. et al. Neonatal pneumonia caused by *Trichomonas vaginalis*. Acta Microbiol Immunol Hung. 49:15-9. 2002.
30. Negm AY, el-Haleem DA. Detection of trichomoniasis in vaginal specimens by both conventional and modern molecular tools. J Egypt Soc Parasitol. 34:589-600. 2004.
31. Ryu JS. Chung HL. Min DY. et al. Diagnosis of trichomoniasis by polymerase chain reaction. Yonsei Med J. 40(1):56-60, 1999.
32. Freeman CD. Klutman NE. Lamp KC. Metronidazole. A therapeutic review and update. Drugs 54(5):679-708, 1997.
33. Muller M. Lossick JG. in vitro susceptibility of *Trichomonas vaginalis* to metronidazole and treatment outcome in vaginal trichomoniasis. Sex Trans Dis 15:17-24, 1988.

9. The Malarias:

Plasmodium falciparum
(Welch 1898)

Plasmodium vivax
(Grassi and Filetti 1889)

Plasmodium ovale
(Stephens 1922)

Plasmodium malariae
(Laveran 1881)

Introduction

Malaria is a mosquito-borne (Fig. 9.1) infection caused by protozoa of the genus Plasmodium. Humans are commonly infected by four species of the parasite: *P. falciparum, P. vivax, P. ovale*, and *P. malariae*. Certain species of Plasmodium that usually have simian hosts may also infect humans.

Malaria remains the most important parasitic infection and one of the most prevalent infectious diseases. More than 800 million cases and at least one million consequent deaths are estimated to occur annually, and more than one-half of the world's population lives in areas where malaria is endemic.[1,2] Although formerly found throughout much of the world, with seasonal outbreaks extending well into temperate zones, malaria is now generally restricted to tropical and subtropical regions. However, travel and persistence of mosquito vectors in once-malarious areas continue to pose a threat of reintroduction of these parasites into non-immune populations.

Historical Information

Malaria most certainly afflicted man's ancestors. The earliest medical writers in China, Assyria, and India described malaria-like intermittent fevers, which they attributed to evil spirits. By the fifth century BC, Hippocrates was able to differentiate quotidian, tertian,

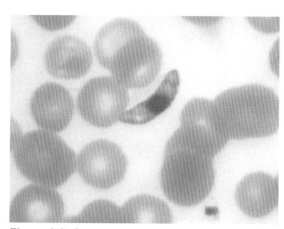

Figure 9.2. Gametocyte of *Plasmodium falciparum*.

and quartan fevers and the clinical symptoms of the disease.[3] At that time it was assumed that the disease was caused by vapors and mists arising from swamps and marshes. These theories persisted for more than 2,000 years and were reinforced by repeated observations that the draining of swamps led to a reduction in the number of cases of malaria. Indeed, the names for this disease, malaria (mal, bad; aria, air) and paludism (palus, marsh) reflect these beliefs.

All concepts of malaria changed within 20 years after Laveran's 1880 description of the crescent shaped sexual stage of *P. falciparum* and his observation of the dramatic release of the parasite's highly motile microgametes in the fresh blood of an infected soldier. Asexual development was described by Golgi in 1886, and the sexual cycle of the parasite was observed by MacCallum in 1897. In 1898 Ross, using a species of bird malaria, and Grassi and colleagues, working with human malaria, showed that the parasite developed in the mosquito and was transmitted by the bite of that insect. Ultimately, Ross and Laveran were awarded Nobel prizes for their contributions.[4,5]

Most of the basic features of the life cycle of the malarial parasite were understood by 1900. The scientific efforts then shifted to attempts to control the disease. Early strategies mainly sought to reduce the number of mosquitoes. Another 30 years passed before the exo-erythrocytic phase of the life cycle was described for a malaria of birds; it was 20 years later that the analogous stages were discovered in the simian and human livers.

Chemotherapy of malaria preceded the description of the parasite by nearly 300 years. The Peruvian bark of cinchona, or "fever tree", was first used during the early part of the seventeenth century, but the details of its discovery and its introduction into Europe are still a matter of discussion.[6-9] The alkaloids of the cinchona tree, quinine and cinchonine, were isolated in 1820 by Pelletier and Caventou. Synthetic antimalarial compounds effective against various stages of the parasite

Figure 9.1. Adult *Anopheles dirus* taking a blood meal from one of the authors (RWG).

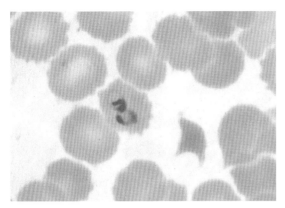

Figure 9.3. Signet ring stage of *Plasmodium spp.*

were later developed in Germany (pamaquine in 1924, mepacrine in 1930, chloroquine in 1934), in Britain (proguanil in 1944), and in the United States (pyrimethamine and primaquine in 1952).[9]

The Greeks and Romans practiced the earliest forms of malaria control, albeit inadvertently, by draining swamps and marshes. Their purpose was reclamation of land. These techniques were continued for centuries before the role of the mosquito as vector was discovered. Almost immediately, malarial control became synonymous with the control of mosquitoes. Destruction of breeding places by drainage and filling the swamps, killing the larvae by placing crude oil on the waters, and later by adding the larvicide Paris green, were typical early attempts. With the development of DDT, a residual insecticide, large-scale control programs became possible. They culminated in 1957 when the World Health Organization launched a worldwide eradication program.[12-15]

Plasmodium falciparum

Infection caused by *P. falciparum* (Fig. 9.2, 9.16) produces a form of malaria historically referred to as aestivoautumnal, malignant tertian, or simply falciparum malaria. It is the most pathogenic of the human malarias, and accounts for most of the mortality from the illness, and is the most prevalent of the human malarial infections. Falciparum malaria is now generally confined to tropical and subtropical regions and is the primary cause of malaria in sub-Saharan Africa.

Identification of *P. falciparum* is usually based on the presence of small ring-stage parasites on blood smears (Fig. 9.3). Infected erythrocytes are not enlarged, and multiple infections of a single erythrocyte are common. The rings often show two distinct chromatin dots. As trophozoites mature, they become sequestered in the capillaries of internal organs, such as the heart, brain, spleen, skeletal muscles, and placenta, where they complete their development. As a result

of sequestration, maturing parasites usually are not present in the peripheral circulation. The appearance of the mature asexual stages (larger trophozoites and schizonts) in the peripheral circulation indicates the increasing severity of the disease.

Gametocytogenesis also proceeds in sequestered erythrocytes and requires approximately ten days. The falciparum gametocytes are characteristically crescentic, or banana-shaped (Fig. 9.2). They remain infectious for mosquitoes for as long as four days.

Falciparum malaria does not relapse; that is, the erythrocytes do not become reinfected from a persistent infection in the liver once the parasites are cleared from the blood by drugs or by the immune response of the host. However, recrudescences (reappearance of erythrocytes infected by the blood stages of the organism when maintained at low levels) are common and can recur for about two years.

Plasmodium vivax

Plasmodium vivax infection is called benign tertian or vivax malaria. Red blood cells infected with *P. vivax* (Fig. 9.4, 9.17) are enlarged and, when properly stained with Giemsa, often show stippling on the erythrocyte membrane, known as Schüffner's dots. All stages of the parasite are present in the peripheral circulation. Single infections of invaded erythrocytes are characteristic. Gametocytes appear simultaneously with the first asexual parasites. The duration of the viability of the sexual stages appears to be less than 12 hours. *Plasmodium vivax* produces the classic relapsing malaria, initiated from hypnozoites in the liver that have resumed development after a period of latency. Relapses can occur at periods ranging from every few weeks to a few months for up to five years after the initial infection. The specific periodicity of the relapses is a characteristic of the geographic strain of the parasite. Vivax malaria also has recrudescences due to persistent circulating erythrocytic parasites.

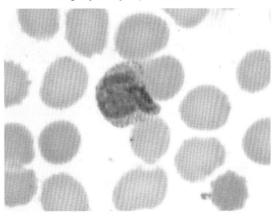

Figure 9.4. Trophozoite of *P. vivax*. Note Schüffner's dots in the parasite, and surrounding red cells that are smaller than the infected one.

Mosquito Cycle (Sporogany)

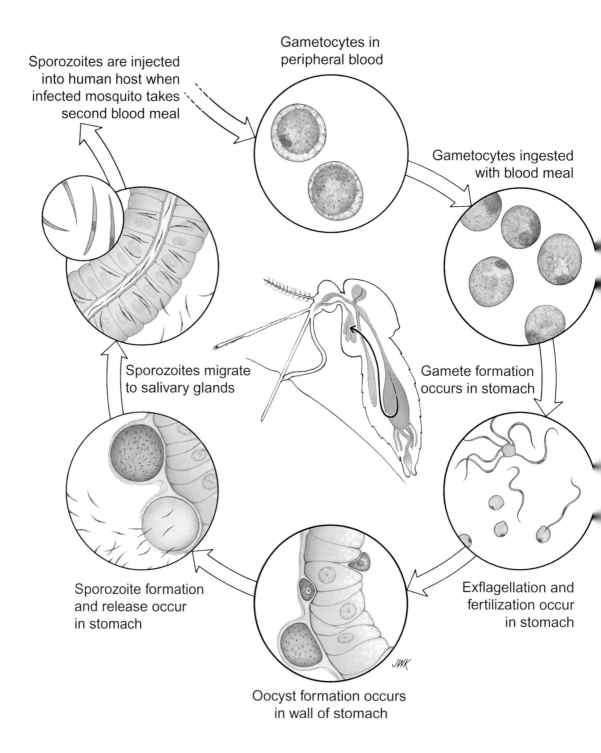

Gametocytes in peripheral blood

Sporozoites are injected into human host when infected mosquito takes second blood meal

Gametocytes ingested with blood meal

Sporozoites migrate to salivary glands

Gamete formation occurs in stomach

Sporozoite formation and release occur in stomach

Exflagellation and fertilization occur in stomach

Oocyst formation occurs in wall of stomach

JWK

"Parasitic Diseases" 5th Ed. © Apple Trees Productions, LLC., Pub. P.O. Box 280, New York, NY 10032

Plasmodium ovale

Plasmodium ovale (Fig. 9.5, 19.19) is the most recently described species of human malaria. Its distribution is limited to tropical Africa and to discrete areas of the Western Pacific. Ovale malaria produces a tertian fever clinically similar to that of vivax malaria but somewhat less severe. It exhibits relapses for the same duration as is seen with vivax malaria.

Plasmodium malariae

The disease caused by *P. malariae* is known as quartan malaria. *P. malariae* has a wide but spotty distribution throughout the world. Development in the mosquito is slow, and infection in humans is not as intense as those caused by the other Plasmodium species. Most current evidence indicates that *P. malariae* does not relapse. It does have recrudescences originating from chronic erythrocytic infections and can persist as a low level infection in the human host for decades.[10, 11] Erythrocytes infected with *P. malariae* remain the same size throughout schizozony (Fig. 9.6, 9.7, 9.18).

Simian Malarias That Infect Humans

Some species of Plasmodium that are parasites of chimpanzees and monkeys occasionally infect humans.[5] The disease they cause is relatively mild. Most notable is the quotidian fever (24-hour cycle) caused by *P. knowlesi* and the vivax-like malaria caused by *P. cynomolgi*.[12] Reports of human infection with malaria parasites from monkeys are becoming common with the ability to differentiate otherwise morphologically similar human and simian parasites at the molecular level. [13-15]

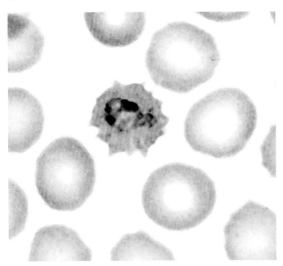

Figure 9.5. Trophozoite of *P. ovale*. Note "crenated" appearance of infected red cell. Courtesy M. Guelpe.

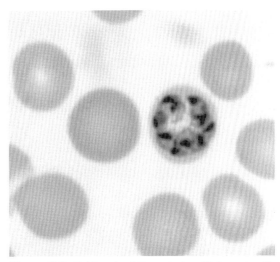

Figure 9.6. Schizont of *P. malariae*. Note red cells are the same size as the infected cell.

Life Cycles

The biology of the four species of Plasmodium is generally similar and consists of two discrete phases: sexual and asexual. The asexual stages develop in humans; first in the liver and then in the circulating erythrocytes. The sexual stages develop in the mosquito.

Asexual Stages

When the infected female Anopheles mosquito takes a blood meal (Fig. 9.1), she injects salivary fluids into the wound. These fluids contain sporozoites (Fig. 9.8), small (10-15 μm long), spindle-shaped, motile forms of the parasite, which initiate the infection. They are cleared from the circulation within an hour and eventually reach parenchymal cells of the liver. The route sporozoites follow to the liver has not been definitely established, and the hypotheses are subjects of controversy.[16-18] Once inside the liver cell, the parasites undergo asexual division (exoerythrocytic schizogony) (Fig. 9.9). The length of this exoerythrocytic phase and

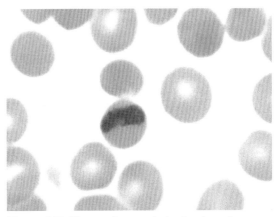

Figure 9.7. *Plasmodium malariae* trophozoite

Plasmodium falciparum

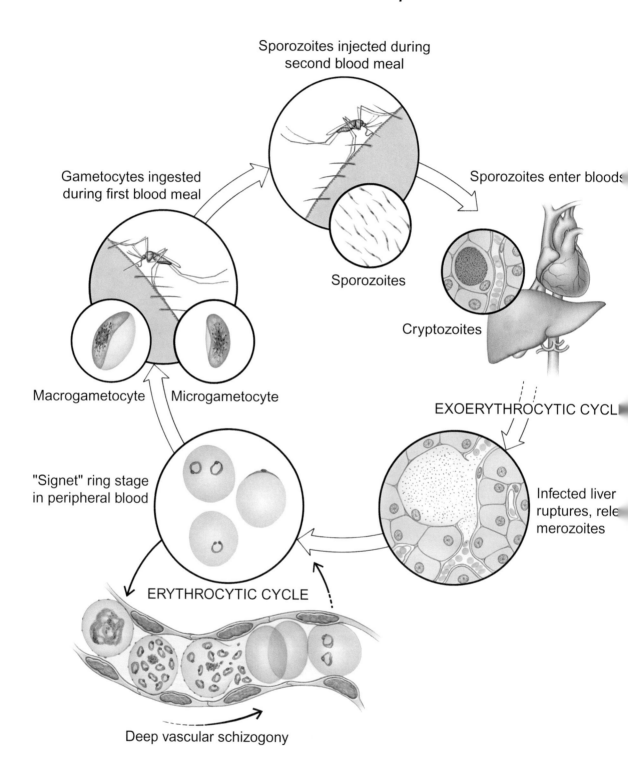

Sporozoites injected during second blood meal

Sporozoites enter bloods

Sporozoites

Cryptozoites

Gametocytes ingested during first blood meal

Macrogametocyte   Microgametocyte

EXOERYTHROCYTIC CYCL

Infected liver ruptures, rele merozoites

"Signet" ring stage in peripheral blood

ERYTHROCYTIC CYCLE

Deep vascular schizogony

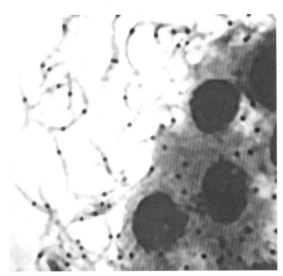

Figure 9.8. Sporozoites of malaria in infected mosquito stomach preparation.

the number of progeny (merozoites) produced within each infected cell is a characteristic of the individual species of Plasmodium. *P. vivax* can mature within 6-8 days, and each of its sporozoites produces about 10,000 daughter parasites. For *P. ovale*, these values are 9 days and 15,000 merozoites; for *P. malariae*, 12-16 days and 2000 merozoites; and for *P. falciparum*, 5-7 days and 40,000 merozoites.

The phenomenon of relapse in certain malarias (*P. vivax, P. ovale, P. cynomolgi*) has not been fully explained. By definition, a parasitologic malarial relapse is the reappearance of parasitemia in sporozoite-induced infection, following adequate blood schizonticidal therapy.[19] It has been long accepted that the exoerythrocytic forms of relapsing malaria persist in the liver as a result of cyclic development (rupture of infected cells and invasion of new cells).[20] However, experimental evidence has lent support to a different hypothesis for the mechanisms of relapse. It holds that some sporozoites fail to initiate immediate exoerythrocytic development in the liver and remain latent as the so-called hypnozoites capable of delayed development and initiation of relapse.[21] Several patterns of relapse have been described, often related to the geographic origin of the parasite; temperate strains of *P. vivax* may show delayed primary attacks and relapses, whereas more tropical forms emerge from the liver within weeks of infection. In vivax and ovale malarias, eradication of parasites from the peripheral circulation with drugs aborts the acute infection. Subsequently a fresh wave of exoerythrocytic merozoites from the liver can reinitiate the infection. The dormant parasites, or hypnozoites can remain quiescent in the liver for as long as five years. To achieve radical cure, it is necessary to destroy not only the circulating parasites but also the hypnozoites.

Plasmodium falciparum and *P. malariae* do not develop hypnozoites, and therefore lack the capacity to relapse. Untreated *P. falciparum* can recrudesce for 1-2 years through the continuation of the erythrocytic cycle, which for periods of time remains at a subclinical, asymptomatic level; *P. malariae* can do so for 30 years or more.[10] For both infections radical cure can be achieved by drugs that need only to eradicate the parasites in the peripheral circulation.

Erythrocytic Phase

When merozoites are released from the liver schizonts, they invade red blood cells (Fig. 9.10) and initiate the erythrocytic phase of infection. Invasion of the erythrocytes consists of a complex sequence of events beginning with contact between a free-floating merozoite and the red blood cell.[22] Attachment of the merozoite to the erythrocyte membrane involves interaction with specific receptor sites. Thereafter the erythrocyte undergoes rapid and marked deformation. The parasite enters by a localized endocytic invagination of the red blood cell membrane, utilizing a moving junction between the parasite and the host cell membrane.[23]

Once within the cell, the parasite begins to grow, first forming the ring-like early trophozoite, and eventually enlarging to fill the cell. The organism then undergoes asexual division and becomes a schizont composed of merozoites. The parasites are nourished by the hemoglobin within the erythrocytes and produce a characteristic pigment called hemazoin. The erythrocytic cycle is completed when the red blood cell ruptures and releases merozoites that proceed to invade other erythrocytes.[24]

The asexual cycle is characteristically synchronous and periodic. *Plasmodium falciparum, P. vivax*, and *P. ovale* complete the development from invasion by merozoites to rupture of the erythrocyte within 48 hours, exhibiting "tertian" periodicity. *Plasmodium malariae*, which produces "quartan" malaria, requires 72 hours for completion of the cycle.

Infection with erythrocytic phase merozoites can

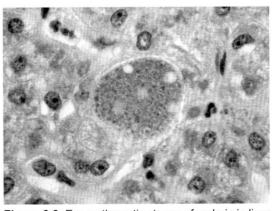

Figure 9.9. Exoerythrocytic stages of malaria in liver parenchymal cell.

Plasmodium vivax

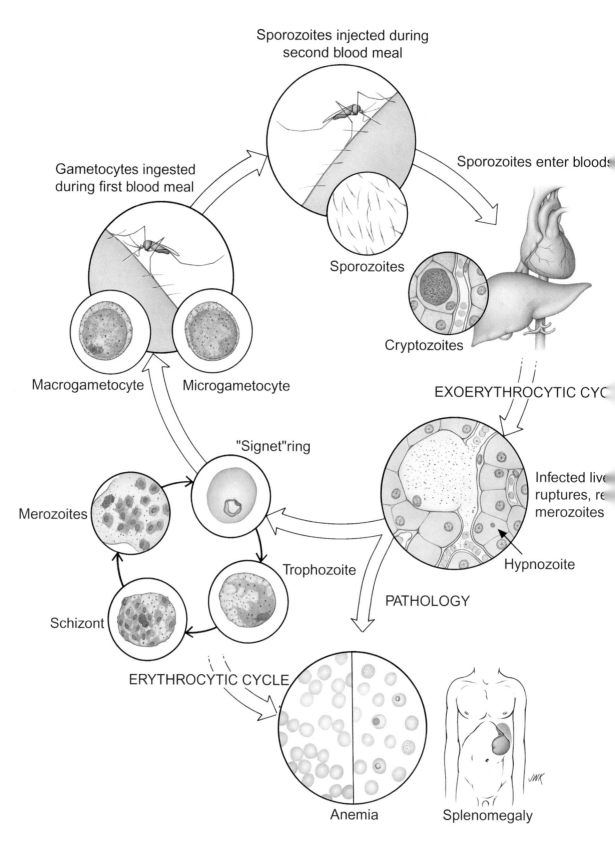

Sporozoites injected during second blood meal

Gametocytes ingested during first blood meal

Sporozoites enter bloods

Sporozoites

Cryptozoites

Macrogametocyte   Microgametocyte

EXOERYTHROCYTIC CYC

"Signet"ring

Infected live
ruptures, re
merozoites

Merozoites

Trophozoite

Hypnozoite

Schizont

PATHOLOGY

ERYTHROCYTIC CYCLE

Anemia   Splenomegaly

"Parasitic Diseases" 5th Ed. © Apple Trees Productions, LLC., Pub. P.O. Box 280, New York, NY 10032

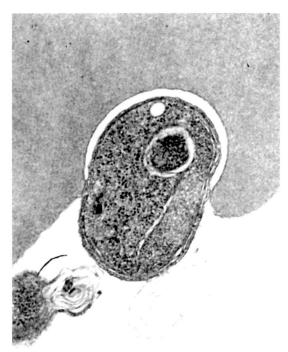

Figure 9.10. Transmission EM of a merozoite entering a red cell. Note points of attachment. Courtesy S. Langreth.

also occur as a result of blood transfusion from an infected donor or via a contaminated needle shared among drug addicts. Malaria acquired in this manner is referred to as "induced" malaria.[25] Congenital malaria as a result of transplacental infection rarely occurs.[26]

Sexual Stages

Not all merozoites develop asexually. Some differentiate into the sexual forms – macrogametocytes (female) and microgametocytes (males) – which can complete their development only within the gut of an appropriate mosquito vector. On ingestion by the mosquito in the blood meal, the gametocytes shed their protective erythrocyte membrane in the gut of the vector. Male gametocytes initiate exflagellation (Fig. 9.11), a rapid process that produces up to eight active, sperm-like microgametes, each of which can eventually fertilize the macrogametes. The resulting zygotes elongate into diploid vermiform ookinetes, which penetrate the gut wall and come to lie under the basement membrane (Fig. 9.12). The parasites then transform into oocysts within 24 hours of ingestion of the blood meal. Development of sporozoites follows, leading to the production of more than 1,000 of these now-haploid forms in each oocyst. They mature within 10–14 days, escape from the oocyst, and invade the salivary glands. When the mosquito bites another human host, a new cycle begins.

Although the four species have marked physiologic differences and some major differences in the patho-

logic course they pursue, they are most simply differentiated on the basis of their morphology. Thus, the blood smear, typically fixed and stained with Giemsa or Wright solution, is the basis of the fundamental diagnostic test, although alternatives are available. Commercially available methods for malaria parasite detection and characterization are becoming increasingly sensitive, and may eventually supplant microscopy in more advanced laboratories (see Diagnosis).[27]

Cellular and Molecular Pathogenesis

The rupture of infected erythrocytes and release of pyrogens are accompanied by fever and the consequent chills and sweating associated with malaria. The pathogenesis of general malaise, myalgia, and headache is not clear. The characteristic periodicity of the fever, based on synchronous infections, is not invariable; the early phases of all infections are often not synchronous. Some infections may be due to two or more broods of parasites, with the periodicity of one independent of that of the others. With severe falciparum malaria, the patient may be febrile continuously

Cerebral malaria is the most consequential manifestation of severe falciparum infection.[29] It is caused by blockage of the cerebral capillaries with infected erythrocytes, which adhere to the endothelium.[30] The mechanism of cytoadherence is related to the presence of "knobs" on the surface of the infected red blood cells and their subsequent attachment to appropriate receptors on the host endothelium (Fig. 9.13, 9.14). Although not essential for cytoadherence, the knobs seem to enhance binding.[31] They are produced by the parasite and host and consist of part of a histidine-rich protein.[32, 33] Binding to endothelial cells involves several host cell receptors, including CD36, thrombospondin,

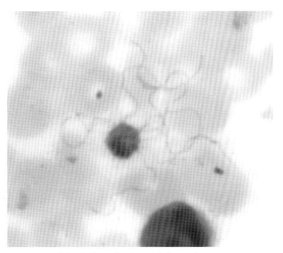

Figure 9.11. Exflagellation of the microgametocyte of a malaria parasite. Each "flagella" is actually a male gamete.

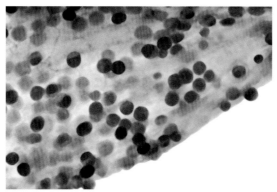

Figure 9.12. Portion of an infected mosquito stomach. Note numerous oocysts on outer wall.

Figure 9.14. Atomic force microscopy of normal (left) and *Plasmodium falciparum*-infected (right) red cells. Courtesy J. Dvorak.

intercellular adhesion molecule 1 (ICAM1), and others. Cytoadherance in the placentae of women in their first preganacies involves parasite binding to chondroitin sulfate A (CSA) and does not appear to involve the erythrocyte knobs.[34, 35] Sequestration of malaria parasites in the placentae of primagravid females is a major cause of death, fetal mortality, fetal wastage and low birth weight.[35-37] With falciparum malaria, anemia caused by hemolysis can be severe. Damage to the erythrocytes by intravascular hemolysis often is greater than that caused by rupture of the infected cells alone. Even uninfected cells have an increased osmotic fragility. Also present is bone marrow depression, which contributes to the anemia. Disseminated intravascular coagulopathy occurs in severely infected individuals.

The spleen plays a major role in host defense against malaria (Fig. 9.15). Parasitized cells accumulate in its capillaries and sinusoids, causing general congestion. Malarial pigment becomes concentrated in the spleen and is responsible for the darkening of this organ. Chronic infection, particularly with *P. malariae*, often causes persistent splenomegaly and is responsible for "big spleen disease," or tropical splenomegaly

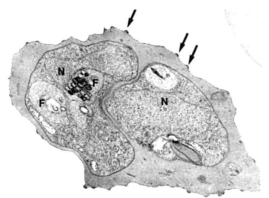

Figure 9.13. Transmission EM of red cell infected with *P. falciparum*. Arrows indicate points of attachment to host endothelial cells. N=nucleus, F=food vacuole. Courtesy S. Langreth.

syndrome,[38] consisting of hepatomegaly, portal hypertension, anemia, leukopenia, and thrombocytopenia. With vivax malaria, the spleen can become acutely enlarged and is susceptible to rupture. The liver is darkened by the accumulated malarial pigment and shows degeneration and necrosis of the centrilobular regions. The gastrointestinal tract is also affected. There are focal hemorrhages, edema, and consequent malabsorption. The kidneys, particularly with severe falciparum malaria, show punctate hemorrhages and even tubular necrosis. Accumulation of hemoglobin in the tubules is responsible for hemoglobinuria, or blackwater fever[39], which occurs after repeated attacks of falciparum malaria and is complicated by therapy with quinine. It is a consequence of severe hemolysis exacerbated by the host immune response against the intracellular parasites.

Chronic infections with *P. malariae* can lead to nephrotic syndrome, characterized by focal hyalinization of the tufts of glomeruli and by endothelial proliferation, apparently caused by the deposition of immune complexes. In addition, evidence suggests that an autoimmune process develops against glomerular basement membrane.

Congenital malaria can develop with any of the species of Plasmodium, although the incidence of this complication is relatively low. The mechanism by which the fetus becomes infected is uncertain. Some investigators have postulated damage to the placenta as a prerequisite to congenital malaria, but it is also possible that the parasites can infect the fetus through an intact placenta or at the time of birth. Malarial infections tend to suppress cell-mediated immune responses. It has been suggested that Burkitt's lymphoma is caused by infection with the Epstein-Barr virus under the influence of immunosuppression by chronic falciparum malaria.[40]

HIV and Malaria

The relationship between infection with malaria and the human immunodeficiency virus is a subject of great interest and intense scrutiny. In Africa, these two agents overlap in their geographic ranges and the populations they infect. Both are significant infections of children and young mothers. Indeed, it is fair to assume that most individuals infected with HIV were already infected with malaria. There is new evidence to suggest a relationship between HIV-induced reduction of CD4 cell counts and a rise in incidence of malaria.[41-45]

Clinical Disease

The most pronounced clinical manifestations of adult-onset malaria are periodic chills and fever, usually accompanied by frontal headache and myalgia.[27] Fever may persist for several days before the typical periodicity develops. In contrast, young children often present with non-specific symptoms, including fever, cough, vomiting, and diarrhea. Symptoms of malaria usually first appear 10-15 days after the bite of the infected mosquito, although delays of several months in the onset of symptoms and the appearance of parasites in peripheral blood are common, particularly for some strains of *P. vivax* found in temperate zones. Patients undergoing chemoprophylaxis may not develop any symptoms until they stop taking the drug. The classic pattern of clinical disease consists of paroxysms of chills and fever, reaching 41°C and lasting six hours, followed by sweating and defervescence. There are exceptions to this pattern, however, as noted under the pathogenesis section.

Additional symptoms for all malarias include malaise, nausea, anorexia, and abdominal pain. Vomiting can also develop and may be intense. Initially, there

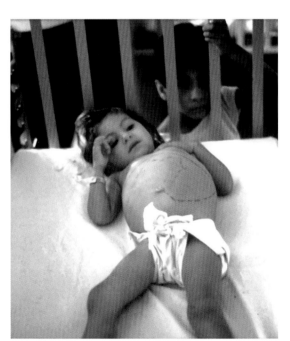

Figure 9.15. Child infected with malaria, probably *P. malariae*. Note enlarged spleen.

can be mild anemia with an elevation of the reticulocyte count. The leukocyte count tends to be normal or even low; there is no eosinophilia.

All forms of untreated malaria tend to become chronic. Repeated attacks are caused by recrudescence or relapses. The development of immunity eventually leads to spontaneous cure of falciparum malaria within two years and of vivax and ovale malarias within five years, although individuals are susceptible to reinfection during and after this period (Fig. 9.20). Infection with the quartan parasite can persist 30 years or more. Untreated falciparum malaria can be fatal during the initial attack, an especially likely event in young children (Fig. 9.20).

Unexplained fever in patients who have received transfusions or who are drug addicts may signal the presence of induced malaria. An infant who develops fever during the neonatal period should be suspected of malaria if the mother had been exposed to this infection. Diagnostic tests for induced or congenital malaria are the same as for the conventional forms of the disease. It must be remembered that neither induced nor congenital malaria has an exoerythrocytic cycle in the liver; hence, therapy directed against the liver cycle is inappropriate.Innate resistance to malaria is mediated by factors other than immune mechanisms. *Plasmodium vivax* and *P. ovale* preferentially invade reticulocytes. With these infections, usually only about 2% of red blood cells are parasitized, and the clinical disease is relatively mild. In contrast, *P. malariae* tends to invade older erythrocytes, again limiting maximum parasitemia. Finally, *P. falciparum* attacks erythrocytes of all ages, permitting high levels of parasitemia.

There are a number of genetic factors in human populations which confer varying levels of resistance to malaria.[46-48] Individuals carrying the gene for sickle-cell hemoglobin receive some protection against falciparum malaria. Those with sickle-cell trait (A and S hemoglobins) have a selective advantage over those with the hemoglobin AA genotype because the heterozygotes are protected against the severity of malaria. The hemoglobin SS individuals are also protected, but their sickle-cell disease leads to early death.[46-48] In areas of Africa with the highest frequency of this gene, it is estimated that the death rate due to malaria needed to have fixed this gene frequency may have exceeded 25%.[49] This situation is an example of balanced polymorphism.

The precise mechanism for the protection afforded by sickle hemoglobin S remains obscure, although it appears that both physiologic and immunologic factors may play a role. At the same time, hemoglobin AS individuals with *P. falciparum* infection may have lower cellular activation and higher cellular reactivity in response to malarial antigens.[50, 51]Hemoglobin C mutations appear to provide similar protection against falciparum

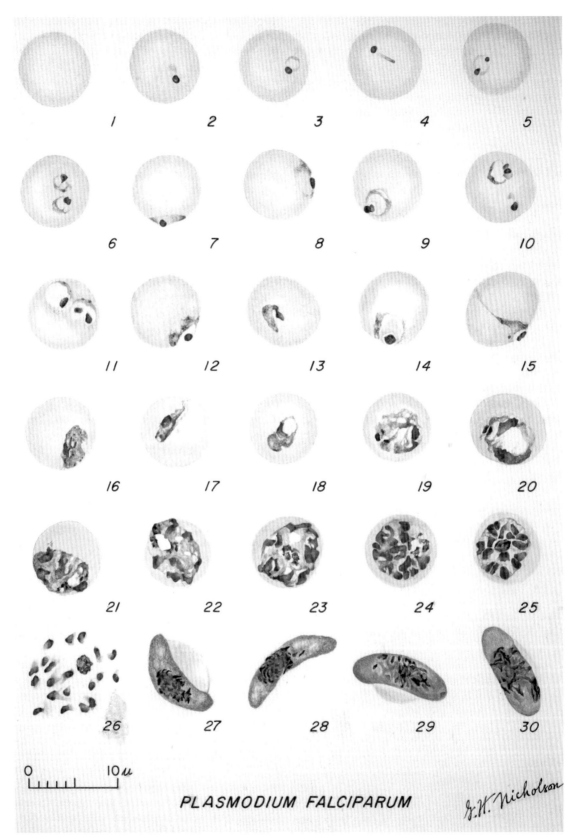

Figure 9.16.

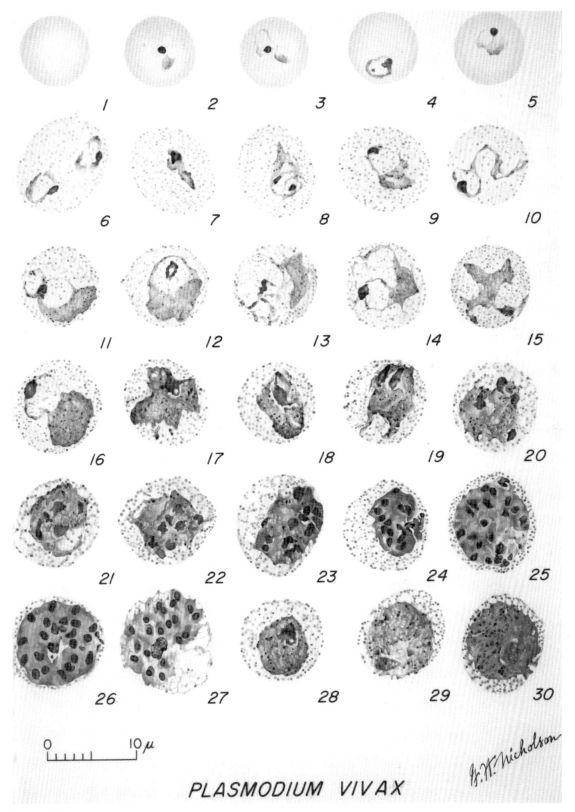

1

2

3

4

5

6

7

8

9

10

11

12

13

14

15

16

17

18

19

20

21

22

23

24

25

26

27

28

29

30

0   10 μ

PLASMODIUM VIVAX

Figure 9.17.

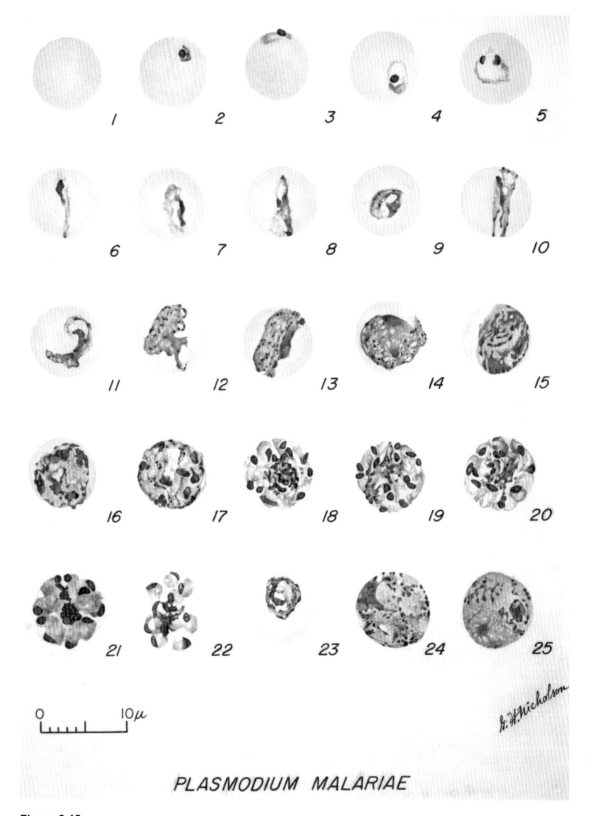

PLASMODIUM MALARIAE

Figure 9.18.

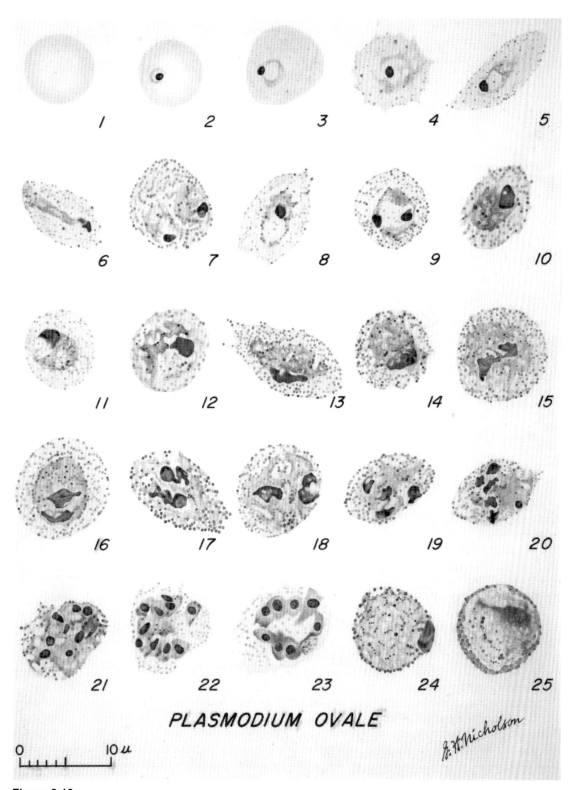

PLASMODIUM OVALE

0 |⌐⊥⊥⊥⊥| 10 μ

Figure 9.19.

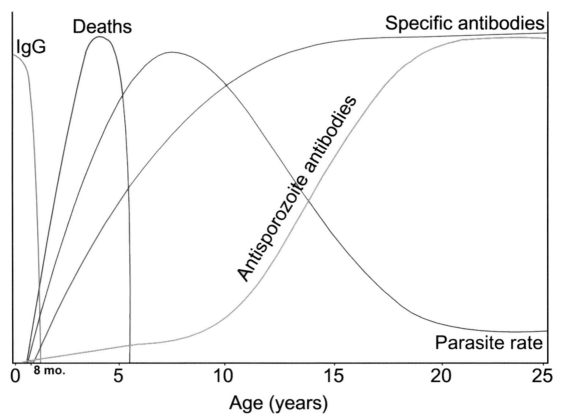

Figure 9.20. Graph indicating relationships between age of patient, susceptibility to infection, production of antibodies against different stages of parasite, and lethality of infection.

malaria in certain ethnic groups. [52,53]

Glucose-6-phosphate dehydrogenase deficiency, β-thalassemia, and ovalocytosis, the latter common in Southeast Asia,[54] have been implicated as mediators of innate resistance against *P. falciparum* infection. It has been suggested that the protective effect of thalassemia may be related to enhanced immune recognition and clearance of parasitized erythrocytes.[55]

Duffy blood type determinants are associated with receptor sites for *P. vivax* merozoites on the erythrocytes. While it is doubtful that the blood group carbohydrate itself is the actual receptor, most West Africans are negative for the Duffy blood type and are not susceptible to infection with *P. vivax*.[56]

Acquired immunity to malaria develops after long exposure and is characterized by low levels of parasitemia. Immune individuals have intermittent parasitemia with only mild symptoms. This state has been referred to as premunition, in contrast with classic immunity, which prevents any degree of infection.

Diagnosis

For over a century a definitive diagnosis of malaria has depended on the microscopic identification of the parasite on Giemsa-stained blood smears (see Appendices B and C). This procedure permits not only the confirmation of the presence of the parasite, but makes possible the identification of the species of malaria and an indication of the level of parasitemia in the infected host. Under normal conditions, both thick and thin smears should be examined. When malaria is suspected, the clinician should take a thorough travel history. Should the initial blood smears prove to be negative, new specimens should be examined at 6-hour intervals.

Identification of malaria on thick and thin blood smears requires an experienced microscopist who is well trained in parasite morphology. A British study indicated that at least 10% of positive slides are not identified.[57] To facilitate diagnosis, a number of techniques have been introduced, particularly for use in clinical laboratories. Microscopy enhanced with fluorescent stains, dipstick antigen detection, PCR assays, and the use of specialized blood cell analyzers are available and are constantly being improved. All can increase the probability of correct diagnosis, but still require microscopic confirmation.

In endemic areas, examination of stained blood films remains the standard. The application of more sophisticated detection methods to endemic areas may be premature. Most of the newer methods require specialized reagents or equipment and are prohibitively expensive. At the same time, in endemic areas, even microscopic techniques are often not used; most fevers as assumed to be malarial and are recorded as such in clinic or hospital records.

The identification of parasite genes conferring resistance to antimalarial drugs has permitted the development of mutation-specific PCR primers that can readily identify resistant parasites. Such detection systems are available and in use in the field for pyrimethamine, sulfadoxine, cycloguanil and chloroquine.[58-60] Epidemiologic studies requiring information on sporozoite inoculation rates by mosquito vectors have been facilitated by ELISA systems using species-specific monoclonal antibodies directed against the predominant surface antigens of the sporozoites.[61] The capacity for rapidly determining the proportion of mosquito populations coming to feed that have infectious sporozoites in their salivary glands allows accurate prediction of risk of infection or assessment of the effects of intervention strategies in the control of malaria.

Treatment

Recommendations for malarial prophylaxis and treatment are in a constant state of flux. The long reliance on chloroquine to treat *P. falciparum* is no longer tenable, due to the worldwide spread of resistance.[62] Alternative drugs may be indicated on a region-by-region basis.[63] Fansidar, a pyrimethamine-sulfadoxine combination, has already lost effectiveness as a replacement for chloroquine in East African countries.[64] Malarone (atovaquone-proguanil) is now a recommended prophylactic drug for travelers to most areas where *P. falciparum* is resistant to chloroquine; side effects and resistance have been reported.

In cases of infection with chloroquine-resistant *P. falciparum* or with a parasite whose resistance cannot be determined, the treatment consists of quinine sulfate and a second agent that often includes pyrimethamine-sulfadoxine, tetracycline or clindamycin. Strains resistant to all of these drugs have been reported.[65]

Artemisinin derivates are now recommended as primary therapy in areas of high drug resistance and must be used in combination with a second agent to prevent recrudescence. [66, 67] If a patient has *P. falciparum* infection and is from anywhere in Central America, chloroquine can be used, as there is little resistance to the drug there. In the rest of the world, resistance to chloroquine is so frequently reported that every patient must be assumed to have this form of *P. falciparum*. If the origin of infection is unknown, as may be the case with induced malaria, one must treat the infection as if the organisms were resistant. For patients who are too ill to take drugs orally, chloroquine hydrochloride must be administered intramuscularly. For resistant falciparum malaria, intravenous quinidine or quinine dihydrochloride must be used. Intravenous administration of quinine is dangerous because the drug can cause fatal arrhythmias. It is mandatory to administer it slowly over a period of one hour and to monitor the patient's vital signs. Intravenous preparations of artemisinins have been studied and in pilot studies appear safe and effective although use in routine clinical practice will depend on larger controlled studies and a reliable production source.[68]

Relapses due to *P. vivax* infections can be prevented by a course of primaquine to eradicate the hypnozoite liver stage of this species. It need not be started immediately but can be deferred until the patient has recovered from the acute attack. Primaquine tends to cause hemolysis in individuals deficient in glucose-6-phosphate dehydrogenase; therefore, the drug should not be administered until the proper test for this enzyme has been performed. Patients who are deficient should be given an option of chloroquine prophylaxis for five years or treatment of each acute attack during the five years within which the infection is expected to relapse.

Prevention and Control

There are more than 300 species of Anopheles mosquitoes, but only about 60 species are considered important vectors of malaria. Some of the factors that influence the efficiency of the insect are their feeding habits (most importantly, a preference for human blood), longevity, and susceptibility to infection with the malarial parasite, and the size of the mosquito population.

The variability of the parasite plays an important role in the pathogenicity of the disease. For example, geographic strains of *P. vivax* show markedly different incubation periods and patterns of relapses, and *P. falciparum* shows considerable variability in its responses to anti-malarial drugs. The susceptibility of geographic strains of vector mosquitoes may be highly variable.

Malaria in the United States since the 1960s has been of the imported variety. The wars in Korea and Vietnam increased the numbers of these imported cases because of the returning service personnel. Refugees or immigrants from endemic areas constitute the largest number of imported cases. In addition, there is a steady incidence of malaria among travelers returning from endemic areas. Autochthonous infections are rare in the United States, despite large, persistent populations of the anopheline vectors, *Ann. quadrimaculatus* in the East and *An. freeborni* in the West. Outbreaks of *P. vivax* in southern California have been associated with a new vector species, *An. hermsi*.[69] There are regular reports of malaria transmission in the U.S., usually limited to one or two cases transmitted by local anopheline mosquitoes.

Travelers to endemic areas and short-term residents of such areas should follow the Centers for Disease Control and Prevention (CDC) guidelines. Prophylactic drugs must be taken prior to departure, during the stay in the endemic area, and for several weeks thereafter, the regimen being dictated by the choice of drug. As a primary precaution, travelers should avoid or minimize contact with mosquitoes. Since most anophelines bite at night, sleeping under netting and, if possible, in rooms fitted with window screens is effective. Clothing that covers much of skin and insect repellents, particularly those containing diethyltoluamide (DEET), are useful adjuncts to transmission prevention.

Differential diagnosis of a febrile illness in travelers to endemic zones after they have returned home should include malaria. Delays in diagnosis, particularly of falciparum malaria, have resulted in death. Similarly, fevers in individuals who have received blood transfusions or who are drug addicts must also be evaluated for the possibility of malaria.

The development of *P. falciparum* resistance to chloroquine has had serious effects on the general prevention and treatment of this disease. Multiple drug resistance is common in Southeast Asia, and is rapidly spreading in the Asian subcontinent, South America, and Africa. Reports of chloroquine, primaquine, and pyrimethamine resistance in *P. vivax* in South Asia raises the possibility that these drugs may eventually be lost as weapons in the fight against this important parasite.[70]

Controlling the mosquito vector remains the most practical method for wide-scale control of malaria. A reduction in the number of mosquitoes through drainage or modification of breeding sites has been accomplished in some areas. Insecticides still offer the best but increasingly less-acceptable method for reducing populations of mosquitoes or of interrupting transmission by targeting only those infected mosquitoes coming to feed in houses. However, the rising costs of these insecticides and the development of resistance by the insects have severely limited their application and usefulness. Insecticide-impregnated bed nets have been shown to have a significant impact on the morbidity and mortality of infection due to *P. falciparum* and *P. vivax* in China,[71] and to *P. falciparum* in Africa.[72] Malaria control schemes based on genetic modification of the capacity of vector mosquitoes to transmit the parasite have been suggested.[73] Before such strategies are implemented, a better understanding of the mosquito-parasite relationship is required. In addition, the development of more efficient methods for introducing advantageous genes into the mosquito genome need to be developed, as well as methods for replacing vector populations in the field with populations of mos-

quitoes unable to transmit the parasite.[74]

The World Health Organization now recommends drug treatment of the sick child as the primary mechanism to reduce malaria related mortality.[75] A malaria vaccine remains the "holy grail" of control strategies. For over 50 years, researchers have been attempting to find antigens which could prevent infection or at least reduce morbidity and mortality. After years of sporadic advances, vaccine research was reinvigorated by the persistent work of the Nussensweigs and their colleagues, demonstrating that animals could develop immunity to infection with sporozoites, and stimulated by the development of methods for the in vitro cultivation of the asexual and sexual stages of *P. falciparum* by Trager and Jensen. The revolution of molecular biology made possible the identification of specific genes coding for specific antigens and sub-unit vaccines became possible.

There are three phases of the malaria life cycle which have been targeted by the vaccine hunters.[76,77] Vaccines directed against the pre-erythrocytic stages of the parasite are intended to prevent infection by blocking the invasion or development of sporozoites freshly injected by a feeding mosquito or the development of the parasite in the liver. Secondarily it has been suggested that even partial efficacy (the blockage of most pre-erythrocytic development) could reduce the intensity of the primary infection and be useful in concert with antigens directed against other stages. Because such vaccines may have short-term efficacy, the target population for pre-erythrocytic stage vaccines has usually been considered to be non-immune individuals moving through malarious areas, including tourists and military personnel. Even with a short life, such vaccines could be useful in areas of low transmission or in children and pregnant women in areas of high transmission.[78]

Vaccines directed against the erythrocytic (blood) stages of the parasite are not expected to induce sterile immunity and totally prevent infection. Rather, it is expected that a successful vaccine could reduce the parasite burden, eliminate most deaths and reduce morbidity. The primary target for blood stage vaccines are children and pregnant women in areas of intense transmission.[79]

Vaccines directed against the mosquito (sexual) stages of the parasite are designed to block the development of the parasite in the mosquito vector. An effective vaccine could interrupt transmission to additional victims. In combination with other antigens, a transmission-blocking component could prevent the spread of parasites resistant to other vaccines. A transmission-blocking vaccine could be used in an eradication scheme or to prevent epidemics in areas of unstable malaria transmission.[80]

An extraordinary array of candidate antigens are under investigation in animal models and field trials of several vaccine candidates are underway. The use of molecular approaches and the technology of subunit vaccines has opened the way. Expression systems, delivery systems, adjuvants and the juggling of antigen cocktails are all receiving critical examination. A virtual "antigen of the month" scenario will become even more exciting as the *Plasmodium falciparum* genome project identifies the genetic structure of more possible candidates.

Despite often tantalizing experimental successes, a malaria vaccine available for wide application is still many years away. Over the years, the parasite has shown an extraordinary capacity to evade the human immune system, and there is no doubt it will work with equal efficiency in evading many vaccine attacks. In the meantime, integrated control strategies including reduction of vector populations, reduction of human-vector contact, and chemotherapy remain the primary method for reducing the malaria burden. However, the effectiveness of these methods cannot be expected to last indefinitely, because of the development of resistance to chemicals directed against the vector and drugs aimed at the parasite. Novel approaches and new weapons are needed to prevent further deterioration of our ability to control malaria.

References

1. Greenwood BM, Bojang K et al. Malaria. Lancet 365: 1487-1498, 2005
2. Carter R, Mendes KN. Evolutionary and Historical aspects of the burden of malaria. Clin Microbiol Rev. 15: 564-594, 2002
3. Hippocrates. The Epidemics. Book 1. In: The genuine works of Hippocrates. Adams F, trans. New York: William Wood, 1886.
4. Harrison G. Mosquitoes, Malaria, and Man. E.P. Dutton, New York, 1978.
5. Bruce-Chwat LJ. History of malaria from pre-history to eradication. In: Malaria, Principles and Practice of Malariology (Wernsdorfer WH, McGregor SI., eds). Churchill Livingstone, Edinburgh, pp. 1-59, 1988.
6. Haggis AW. Fundamental errors in the early history of cinchona. Bull Hist Med 10:567-568, 1941.
7. Meshnick SR. From quinine to Qinghaosu: Historical perspectives. In: Malaria: Parasite Biology, Pathogenesis, and Protection (Sherman IW., ed.). ASM Press, Washington, D.C. pp 341-353, 1998.
8. Honigsbaum M. The Fever Trail: In search of the cure for malaria. Farrar, Strauss and Giroux, New York, 2001.
9. Rocco F. Quinine: Malaria and the quest for a cure that changed the world. Harper Collins, New York, 2003
10. Vinetz JM. Li J. McCutchan TF. Kaslow DC. *Plasmodium malariae* infection in an asymptomatic 74-year-old Greek woman with splenomegaly. New Engl J Med 338:367-371, 1998.
11. Garnham PCC. Malaria parasites of man: life cycles and morphology (excluding ultrastructure). In: Malaria, Principles and Practice of Malariology (Wernsdorfer WH, McGregor SI., eds.). Churchill Livingstone, Edinburgh. pp. 61-96, 1988.
12. Coatney GR. Collins WE. Warren M. et al: The Primate Malarias. US Department of Health, Education and Welfare, Bethesda, 1971.
13. White NJ. Sharing malarias. Lancet. 363: 1006, 2004.
14. Abegunde AT. Monkey malaria in man. Lancet 364: 1217, 2004.
15. Singh B, Sung LK, et al. A large focus of naturally acquired *Plasmodium knowlesi* infections in human beings. Lancet 363: 1017-1024, 2004.
16. Meis JEGM. Verhave JP: Exoerythrocytic development of malaria parasites. Adv Parasitol 27:1-61, 1988.
17. Hollingdale MR. Biology and immunology of sporozoite invasion of liver cells and exoerythrocytic development of malaria parasites. Prog. Allergy 41:15-48, 1988.
18. Frevert U. Crisanti A. Invasion of vertebrate cells: Hepatocytes. In: Malaria: Parasite Biology, Pathogenesis, and Protection (Sherman IW., ed.). ASM Press, Washington, D.C. pp. 73-91,1998.
19. Coatney GR: Relapse in malaria-an enigma. J Parasit 62:3- 9, 1976.
20. Schmidt LH. Compatibility of relapse patterns of *Plasmodium cynomolgi* infections in rhesus monkeys with continuous cyclical development and hypnozoite concepts of relapse. Am J Trop Med Hyg 35:1077-1099, 1986.
21. Krotoski WA. Discovery of the hypnozoite and a new theory of malarial relapse. Trans R Soc Trop Med Hyg 79:1-11, 1985.
22. Dvorak JSA. Miller LH. Whitehouse WC. et al. Invasion of erythrocytes by malaria merozoites. Science 187:748-750, 1975.
23. Aikawa M. Miller LH. Johnson J. et al. Erythrocyte entry by malaria parasites, a moving junction between erythrocyte and parasite. J Cell Biol 77:72-82, 1978.
24. Barnwell JW. Galinski MR. Invasion of vertebrate cells: Erythrocytes. In: Malaria:Parasite Biology, Pathogenesis and Protection (Sherman IW., ed.). ASM Press, Washington, D.C. pp. 93-120, 1998.
25. Garvey G. Neu HC. Katz M. Transfusion-induced malaria after open heart surgery. NY State J Med 75:602-603, 1975.
26. Covell G. Congenital malaria. Trop Dis Bull 47:1147-1167, 1950.
27. Hanscheid T. Diagnosis of malaria: A review of alternatives to conventional microscopy. Clin Lab Haem 21:235-245, 1999.
28. Marsh K. Clinical features of malaria. In: Malaria: Molecular and Clinical Aspects (Wahlgren M, Perlmann P., eds.). Harwood Academic Publishers, Amsterdam pp. 87-117, 1999.
29. World Health Organization: Severe and complicated malaria. Trans R Soc Trop Med Hyg 80(Suppl): 1-50, 1986.
30. Wahlgren M. Treutiger CJ. Gysin J. Cytoahherence and rosetting in the pathogenesis of severe malaria. In: Malaria: Molecular and Clinical Aspects (Wahlgren M and Perlmann P., eds.). Harwood Academic Publishers, Amsterdam, pp. 289-327, 1999.
31. Ruangjirachuporn W. Afzelius BA. Paulie S, et al: Cytoadherence of knobby and knobless *Plasmodium falciparum*. Parasitology 102:325-334, 1991.
32. Udeinya I. Schmidt JA. Aikawa M. et al. Falciparum malaria-infected erythrocytes bind to cultured human endothelial cells. Science 213: 555-557, 1981.
33. Chisti AH. Andrabi KI. Derick LM. et al. Isolation of skeleton-associated knobs from human blood cells infected with the malaria parasite *Plasmodium falciparum*. Mol Biochem Parasit 52:293-297, 1992.
34. Miller LH. Good MF. Milon G. Malaria pathogenesis. Science 264: 1878-1883, 1994.
35. Duffy PE, Fried M. Antibodies that inhibit *Plasmodium falciparum* adhesion to chondroitin sulfate A are associated with increased birth weight and gestational age of newborns. Infect Immun 71: 6620-6623, 2003.

36. Miller LH. Smith JD. Motherhood and malaria. Nature Medicine 4:1244-1245, 1998.
37. Duffy PE, Fried M. *Plasmodium falciparum* adhesion in the placenta. Curr Opin Microbiol 6: 371-376, 2003.
38. Looareesuwan S. Ho M. Wattanagoon Y. et al. Dynamic alteration in splenic function during acute falciparum malaria. N Engl J Med 317: 675-679, 1987.
39. Bruneel F, Gachot b. Blackwater fever. Presse Med 31: 1329-1334, 2002.
40. Ernberg I. Burkitt's lymphoma and malaria. In: Malaria: Molecular and Clinical Aspects (Wahlgren M, Perlmann P., eds.). Harwood Academic Publishers, Amsterdam. pp. 370-399, 1999.
41. Grimwadw k, French N et al. HIV infection as a cofactor for severe falciparum malaria in adults living in a region of unstable malaria transmission in South Africa. AIDS 18: 547-554, 2004.
42. Mount AM, Mwapasa V et al. Impairment of humoral immunity to *Plasmodium falciparum* malaria in pregnancy by HIV infection. Lancet 363: 1860-1867.
43. Kublin JG, Patnaik P et al. Effect of *Plasmodium falciparum* malaria on concentration of HIV-1-RNA in blood of adults in rural Malawi: a prospective cohort study. Lancet 365: 233-240, 2005.
44. Whitworth JAG, Hewitt KA. Effect of malaria on HIV-1 progression and transmission. Lancet 365: 196-197, 2005.
45. Chirenda J, Murugasampillay S. Malaria and HIV co-infection: available evidence, gaps and possible interventions. Cent Afr J Med 49: 66-71, 2003.
46. Hill AVS. Weatherall DJ. Host genetic factors in resistance to malaria. In: Malaria: Parasite Biology, Pathogenesis and Protection (Sherman IW., ed.). ASM Press, Washington, D.C. pp. 445-455, 1998.
47. Allison AC. Protection afforded by sickle-cell trait against subtertian malarial infection. BMJ 1: 290-294,1954.
48. Roberts DJ, Williams TN. Hemoglobinopathies and resistance to malaria. Redox Report 8:304-310, 2003.
49. Miller LH. The challenge of malaria. Science 257:36-37, 1992.
50. Hebbel RP. Sickle hemoglobin instability: a mechanism for malarial protection. Redox Rep 8: 2380240, 2003.
51. Cabrera G, Cot M et al. The sickle cell trait is associated with enhanced immunoglobin G antibody rersponses to *Plasmodium falciparum* variant surface antigens. J Infect Dis 191:1631-1638, 2005.
52. Diallo DA, Doumbo OK et al. A comparison of anemia in hemoglobin C and normal hemoglobin A children with *Plasmodium falciparum* malaria. Act Trop 90: 295-299, 2004.
53. Arie T, Fairhurst RM, et al. Hemoglobin C modulates the surface topography of *Plasmodium falciparum*-infected erythrocytes. J Struct Biol 150:163-169, 2005.
54. Jarolim P. Palek J. Amato D. et al. Deletion in erythrocyte band 3 gene in malaria-resistant Southeast Asian ovalocytosis. Proc Natl Acad Sci USA 88:11022-11026, 1991.
55. Luzzi GA. Merry AH. Newbold CI. et al. Surface antigen expression on *Plasmodium falciparum* infected erythrocytes is modified in alpha- and beta-thalassemia. J Exp Med 173:785-791, 1991.
56. Miller LH, Mason SJ. The resistance factor to *Plasmodium vivax* in Blacks: Duffy blood group genotype. NEJM 295:302-304, 1976.
57. Milne LM. Kyi MS. Chiodini PLL. Warhurst DC. Accuracy of routine laboratory diagnosis of malaria in the United Kingdom. J Clin Path 47:740-742, 1994.
58. Plowe CV. Cortese JF. Djimde. et al. Mutations in *Plasmodium falciparum* dihydrofolate reductase and dihyropteroate synthase and epidemiologic patterns of pyrimethamine-sulfadoxine use and resistance. J Infec Dis 176:1590-1596, 1997.
59. Plowe CV. Kublin JG. Doumbo OK. Plasmodiun falciparum dihydrofolate reductase and dihydropterase mutations: epidemiology and role in clinical resistance to antifolates. Drug Resistance Updates 1: 389-396, 1998.
60. Sidhu AB, Verdier-Pinard D, Fidock DA. Chloroquine resistance in *Plasmodium falciparum* malaria parasites conferred by pfert mutations. Science 298: 74-75, 2002.
61. BeierJC. Perkins PV. Wirtz RA. et al. Field evaluation of an enzyme-linked immunosorbent assay (ELISA) for *Plasmodium falciparum* sporozoite detection in anopheline mosquitoes from Kenya. Am J Trop Med Hyg 36:459-468, 1987.
62. Baird JK. Effectiveness of antimalarial drugs. NEJM 352: 1565-1577, 2005.
63. Medical Letter on Drugs and Therapeutics. Handbook of Antimicrobial Therapies. 2005.
64. Miller KD. Lobel HO. Satriale RF. et al. Severe cutaneous reactions among American travelers using pyrimethamine-sulfadoxine (Fansidar R) for malaria prophylaxis. Am J Trop Med Hyg 35: 451-458,1986.
65. Su X. Wellems. TE. Genome discovery and malaria research. In: Malaria: Parasite Biology, Pathogenesis and Protection (Sherman IW. ed.). ASM Press, Washington, D.C., pp. 253-266, 1998.
66. Smithuis F, Shahmanesh M, Kyaw MK, Savran O, Lwin S, White NJ. Comparison of chloroquine, sulfadoxine/pyrimethamine, mefloquine and mefloquine-artesunate for the treatment of falciparum malaria in Kachin State, North Myanmar. Trop Med Int Health. 2004 Nov;9(11):1184-90
67. Staedke SG, Mpimbaza A, Kamya MR, Nzarubara BK, Dorsey G, Rosenthal PJ. Combination treatments for uncomplicated falciparum malaria in Kampala, Uganda: randomised clinical trial. Lancet. 2004 Nov 27;364(9449):1950-7.
68. Krudsood S, Wilairatana P, et al. Clinical experience with intravenous quinine, intramuscular artemether and intravenous artesunate for the treatment of severe malaria in Thailand. Southeast Asian J Trop Med Public Health. 2003 Mar;34(1):54-61.
69. Porter CH. Collins FH. Susceptibility of Anopheles hermsi to *Plasmodium vivax*. Am J Trop Med Hyg 42:414-416, 1990.
70. White NJ. Drug resistance in malaria. Br Med Bull 54:703-715, 1998.
71. Lin LB. Bednets treated with pyrethroids for malaria control. In: Malaria: Waiting for the Vaccine (Target GAL., ed.). Wiley, Chichester, pp. 67-82, 1991.
72. The western Kenya insecticide-treated bed net trial. Am J Trop Med Hyg 68: 1-173, 2003.
73. James AA. Mosquito molecular genetics: the hands that feed bite back. Science 257:37-38, 1992.
74. Gwadz RW. Genetic approaches to malaria control: how long the road? Am J Trop Med Hyg Suppl. 116-125, 1994.
75. Sudre P. Breman JG. McFarland D. Koplan JP. Treatment of chloroquine-resistant malaria in African children: a cost-effectiveness analysis. Am J Epidemiol 21:146-154, 1992.
76. Hoffmann SL (ed): Malaria Vaccine Development: A Multi-Immune Response Approach. ASM Press, Washington, D.C. 1996.
77. Miller LH. Hoffman SL. Research toward vaccines against malaria. Nature Med Vaccine Suppl 4:520-524, 1998.
78. Narden E. Synthetic peptides as malaria vaccines. In: Malaria: Molecular and Clinical Aspects (Wahlgren M, Perlmann P., eds.). Harwood Academic Publishers, Amsterdam. pp. 495-540, 1999.
79. Narden E. Zavala F. Acquired immunity to malaria. In: Malaria: Parasite Biology, Pathogenesis and Protection (Sherman IW., ed.). ASM Press, Washington, D.C. pp. 495-512, 1998.
80. Druilhe PL. Renia L. Fidock DA. Immunity to liver stages. In: Malaria: Parasite Biology, Pathogenesis and Protection (Sherman IW., ed.). ASM Press, Washington, D.C. pp. 513-544, 1998.

10. *Cryptosporidium parvum*
(Tyzzer, 1929)

Introduction

The genus Cryptosporidium comprises a very large group of closely related obligate intracellular parasites that cause transient diarrheal disease in most mammal species throughout the world, including humans. All are transmitted through fecally contaminated food and water.[1,2,3] Most species have broad host ranges. Eight species have been shown to infect humans on a regular basis: *C. parvum*, *C. hominis*, *C. meleagridis*, *C. felis*, *C. canis*, *C. muris*, and *Cryptosporidium* pig and cervine species. [4-10] The majority of human infections are caused by *C. parvum* (sometimes referred to as *C. hominis*), which also infects sheep, cattle, birds, rodents, and non-human primates. This chapter will concentrate on *C. parvum,* with the assumption that disease in humans caused by other related species gives a similar clinical picture. In 1993, the city of Milwaukee, Wisconsin experienced the largest waterborne outbreak of diarrheal disease ever documented in the United States. Over 400,000 people suffered from infection with *C. parvum*.[11] In immunocompetent infected individuals, the most serious manifestation of infection is diarrhea of short duration, although sometimes severe. In contrast, infants, non-AIDS immunocompromised adults, and people suffering from HIV/AIDS often experience severe, protracted diarrhea, sometimes resulting in death.[12] *C. parvum* can be grown axenically in vitro, using monolayers of epithelial cells.[13, 14] The genome of *Cryptosporidum hominis (parvum)* has been determined.[15, 16]

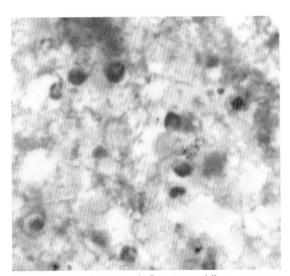

Figure 10.1. Oocyst of *Cryptosporidium parvum.* Cold acid fast stain. 5 μm.

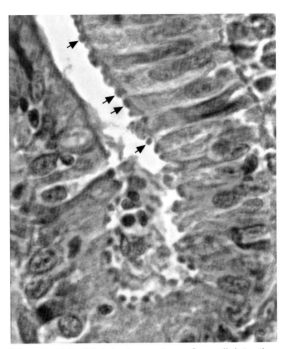

Figure 10.2. Histologic section of small intestine of patient suffering from HIV/AIDS, infected with *C. parvum* (arrows). Courtesy J. Lefkowitch.

Historical Information

Tyzzer, in 1907,[17] provided a description of Cryptosporidium based on histologic sections of mouse intestine, in which the parasites were observed attached to the epithelial cells. The pathogenic characteristics of Cryptosporidium were not recognized until much later, when Slavin, in 1955,[18] established that this protozoan caused diarrhea in turkeys. Nime and coworkers, in 1976,[19] described human diarrheal disease due to Cryptosporidium, and Meisel and colleagues, in 1976,[20] were the first to report it in immunocompromised human hosts.

Life Cycle

A comprehensive review of the biology of *C. parvum* is available.[21] Infection begins when the host ingests thick-walled sporulated oocysts (Fig. 10.1), each of which contains four sporozoites. A minimum of 30 oocysts are necessary to initiate infection,[22] while the calculated ID50 for healthy volunteers was 132 oocysts.[23]

The sporozoites excyst when the oocyst enters the small intestine. Little is known regarding excystment in vivo. A protein-plugged suture in the cyst wall blocks the escape route for sporozoites.[24] in vitro, excystment occurs after exposure to 37° C or by pretreatment of purified oocysts with either sodium taurocholate and trypsin,[25] or with sodium hypochlorite (bleach) alone, followed by introduction into culture medium. Oocysts treated with bleach can be inhibited from excysting by exposure to human α-1-anti-trypsin inhibitor[26] or inhibitors of arginine aminopeptidase.[27] Like other enteric parasites with resistant outer structures (e.g., eggs of helminths and cysts of Giardia and Entamoeba), alteration of the outer surface may be a prerequisite for the organism to receive environmental cues, triggering the synthesis of enzymes of parasite origin required for emergence.

Sporozoites attach to the surface of epithelial cells (Fig. 10.2), most likely aided by numerous proteins secreted from their rhoptries and micronemes. A monoclonal antibody, designated 3E2, binds solely to the apical complex of the organism (the region where microneme- and rhoptre-specific proteins exit from the parasite), and inhibits invasion in vitro.[28] On Western Blot analysis, this antibody recognizes numerous epitopes, ranging from 46 kDa to 1300 kDa. Furthermore, a purified microneme-specific mucin-like 900 kDa glycoprotein can prevent invading parasites from attaching to their target cells when employed in competitive inhibition studies.[29]

After the sporozoite attaches to the cell surface, microvilli in the area immediately adjacent to the parasite fuse and elongate, enveloping the parasite to cre-

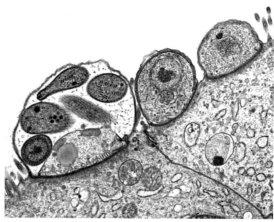

Figure 10.4. Transmission EM of *C. parvum* meronts. Courtesy M. Belosevic.

ate a unique intracellular environment (Fig. 10.3). This event may also be triggered by apical end-associated secreted proteins. A specialized membrane structure develops at the interface between the parasite and the host cell. Nutrients are thought to pass through this region, since parasite-specific ABC transporters have been identified there by means of immunofluorescent monoclonal antibodies.[30] The sporozoite differentiates into the type I meront (Fig. 10.4) and division ensues, producing four haploid merozoites. The merozoites are released and attach to new epithelial cells, now differentiating into Type II meronts. Macrogamonts and microgamonts (pre-sex cells analogous to the gametocytes of plasmodia) are produced inside these new meronts. Following their release, microgamonts fuse with macrogamonts, forming thick-walled zygotes termed oocysts. This stage sporulates within the large intestine, and four haploid sporozoites are produced. Oocysts can also be thin-walled. In this case, they sporulate and excyst within the same host, producing an autoinfection that may endure for months to years. Even in these cases, however, thick-walled oocysts are produced as well.

Thick-walled oocysts pass out in feces, and can infect another host. This type of oocyst is environmentally resistant, and can remain viable for months to years in soil, given optimum moisture conditions.[31]

Cellular and Molecular Pathogenesis

Until recently,[32] one of the most perplexing and frustrating aspects of the biology of *C. parvum* was its ability to avoid being affected by a wide variety of drugs.[33, 34] The altered microvillus-derived membrane complex that surrounds the parasites while they are attached to epithelial cells has proven highly impermeable to all chemotherapeutic agents, with the one possible ex-

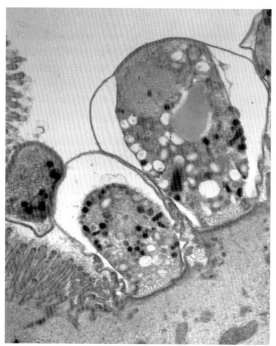

Figure 10.3. Transmission EM of *C. parvum*. Note microvillus-derived membranes encasing parasites (arrows). Courtesy J. Lefkowitch.

Cryptosporidium parvum

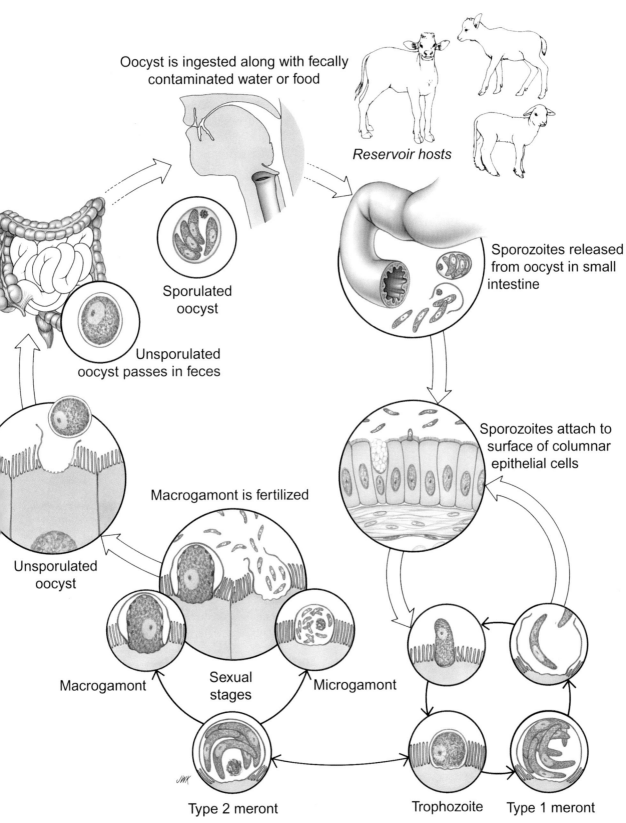

Oocyst is ingested along with fecally contaminated water or food

Reservoir hosts

Sporulated oocyst

Unsporulated oocyst passes in feces

Sporozoites released from oocyst in small intestine

Sporozoites attach to surface of columnar epithelial cells

Macrogamont is fertilized

Unsporulated oocyst

Macrogamont

Sexual stages

Microgamont

Type 2 meront

Trophozoite

Type 1 meront

"Parasitic Diseases" 5ᵗʰ Ed. © Apple Trees Productions, LLC., Pub. P.O. Box 280, New York, NY 10032

ception, nitazoxanide. That is why speculation favors the entry of nutrients through the attachment zone between the parasite and the surface of the host cell. The fact that ABC transporters have been identified in this region[30] is further indirect evidence in support of this hypothesis. Cellular or molecular events that result in the alteration of microvilli at the site of attachment have attracted the attention of some research groups.[35] Apparently, Cdc42 (a GTPase) and actin are recruited to the site of attachment early on in the process.[36] Actin then aggregates, forming a kind of platform on top of which the organism then elaborates its complex of membranes. Much more needs to be learned about the mechanism(s) of nutrient acquisition by *C. parvum* before rational drug design aimed at interference with this process can evolve.

Protection against the primary infection develops in individuals whose immune systems are not compromised. At least two classes of antibodies, IgA[37] and IgG,[23] and several cellular-based immune mechanisms are thought to play important roles in the elimination of the parasite from the gut tract, although the precise mechanisms responsible for this have yet to be determined.[38] Healthy human volunteers whose anti-*C. parvum* IgG levels were already present (exposed, immune), required a higher dose of oocysts to become infected, and developed fewer symptoms than their non-exposed (non-immune) counterparts.[23] Studies carried out in experimental infections employing various strains of inbred mice have shown that IL-12,[39] gamma interferon,[38] and perhaps β-defensins,[40, 41] peptides chemically related to magainins,[42, 43] act in conjunction to protect against a challenge infection. Calves fed irradiated oocysts of *C. parvum* were protected from a challenge infection,[44] implying that protection-inducing antigens are present in this stage of the infection. Patients suffering from AIDS do not develop protective immunity. In underserved regions of the tropics, many children born with the HIV virus and who went on to develop AIDS are dying from this opportunistic infection.[45]

Clinical Disease

Two excellent reviews on the clinical aspects of cryptosporidiosis have been published.[46, 47] In immunocompetent individuals disease can vary from a mild to profuse watery diarrhea. Upper abdominal cramps, anorexia, nausea, weight loss, and vomiting are common features of the acute stage of the infection. In those who have already experienced clinical disease and recovered, a second infecting dose of oocysts may be asymptomatic, or they may have only a mild, transient diarrhea. Cryptosporidiosis is self-limited, lasting from several days to one month.

Children are the most severely affected group,[48] as the diarrhea lasts longer, and there is usually some weight loss. Those undergoing cancer chemotherapies suffer worse yet, with protracted, life-threatening diarrhea accompanied by significant weight loss.[49]

Cryptosporidiosis in patients suffering from AIDS is chronic, lasting months and even years, during which patients can lose more than three liters of fluid each day, and are in significant danger of dying; the case fatality rate is 50%. However, death is usually a result of associated conditions, such as malnutrition or superinfection with other pathogens. Extraintestinal infection in the bile duct can cause acalculous biliary disease.

Diagnosis

Definitive diagnosis depends upon two approaches: identification of acid fast-stained oocysts (Fig. 10.1) by microscopy of stool samples[50] and PCR.[51] The latter test can identify cryptosporidium down to the species level. Oocysts are easily isolated from stool by flotation in sugar solution,[52] then stained by acid-fast methods, or used in the IFA test.

Treatment

Nitazoxanide is the drug of choice.[32, 53] Although use of this drug has been limited, so far it appears to be not effective when used to treat infections in HIV/AIDS patients.

Prevention and Control

Without knowledge as to the source of a given outbreak, control and prevention of infection due to *C. parvum* is not possible. In the case of waterborne epidemics,[11] management of watersheds[54] is the long-term solution in situations where the water supply is not filtered. Filtering drinking water is usually effective, but deterioration of filtration equipment and/or lack of proper maintenance can erode any progress made in controlling waterborne infections.[55] Chlorination of water supplies is ineffective against the oocyst, but ozonation kills this stage.[56, 57] In agricultural settings, creation of vegetative barriers to curtail the spread of oocycts is effective.[58] Surveillance is key to keeping public water supplies free of pathogens with environmentally resistant stages (e.g., *Giardia lamblia, Entamoeba histolytica, Cryptosporidium parvum*). In this regard, PCR-based testing now allows for the possibility of continuous monitoring of water supplies for *C. parvum*.[59] Urban and suburban pet stores and petting zoos for children are other sources of infection that until very recently have received little attention.

References

1. Laberge I. Griffiths MW. Griffiths MW. Prevalence, detection and control of *Cryptosporidium parvum* in food. Int J Food Microbiol. 32:1-26, 1996.

2. Keusch GT. Hamer D. Joe A. Kelley M. Griffiths J. Ward H. Cryptosporidia – who is at risk?. Schweiz Med Wochenschr. 125:899-908, 1995.

3. Guerrant RL. Cryptosporidiosis: an emerging, highly infectious threat. Emerg Infect Dis. 3:51-57, 1997.

4. Katsumata, T., D. Hosea, I. G. et al. Short report: possible *Cryptosporidium muris* infection in humans. Am. J. Trop. Med. Hyg. 62:70-72. 2000.

5. Ong, C. S., D. L. Eisler, A. et al. Novel *Cryptosporidium* genotypes in sporadic cryptosporidiosis cases: first report of human infections with a cervine genotype. Emerg. Infect. Dis. 8:263-268. 2002.

6. Pedraza-Diaz, S., C. Amar, and J. McLauchlin. The identification and characterisation of an unusual genotype of *Cryptosporidium* from human faeces as *Cryptosporidium meleagridis*. FEMS Microbiol. Lett. 189:189-194. 2000.

7. Pedraza-Diaz, S., C. Amar. et al. Unusual *Cryptosporidium* species recovered from human faeces: first description of *Cryptosporidium felis* and *Cryptosporidium* 'dog type' from patients in England. J. Med. Microbiol. 50:293-296. 2001.

8. Pieniazek, N. J., F. J. Bornay-Llinares. et al. New *Cryptosporidium* genotypes in HIV-infected persons. Emerg. Infect. Dis. 5:444-449. 1999.

9. Xiao, L., C. Bern. et al. Identification of the *Cryptosporidium* pig genotype in a human patient. J. Infect. Dis. 185:1846-1848. 2002.

10. Xiao, L., C. Bern. et al. Identification of 5 types of *Cryptosporidium* parasites in children in Lima, Peru. J. Infect. Dis. 183:492-497. 2001.

11. Kramer MH. Herwaldt BL. Craun GF. Calderon RL. Juranek DD. Surveillance for waterborne-disease outbreaks – United States, 1993-1994. Mor Mortal Wkly Rep CDC Surveill Summ. 45:1-33, 1996.

12. Farthing MJ. Kelly MP. Veitch AM. Recently recognised microbial enteropathies and HIV infection. J Antimicrob Chemother. 37 Suppl B:61-70, 1996.

13. Current WL. Reese NC. A comparisoin of endogenous development of three isolates of Cryptosporidium in suckling mice. J Protozol 33:98-108, 1986.

14. Meloni BP. Thompson RC. Simplified methods for obtaining purified oocysts from mice and for growing *Cryptosporidium parvum* in vitro. J Parasitol. 82(5):757-762, 1996.

15. Xu P, Widmer G. et al. The genome of *Cryptosporidium hominis*. Nature. 431:1107-12. 2004.

16. Abrahamsen MS, Templeton TJ. et al. Complete genome sequence of the apicomplexan, *Cryptosporidium parvum*. Science. 304:441-5. 2004.

17. Tyzzer EE. A sporozoan found in the peptic glands of the common mouse. Proc Soc Exp Biol Med 5;12-13, 1907.

18. Slavin D. Cryptosporidium meleagridis (sp. nov.) J Comp Pathol 65:262-266, 1955.

19. Nime FA. Burek JD. Page DL. et al: Acute enterocolitis in a human being infected with the protozoan Cryptosporidium. Gastroenterology 70:592-598, 1976.

20. Meisel JE. Perera DR. Meloigro C. et al: Overwhelming watery diarrhea associated with Cryptosporidium in an immunosuppressed patient. Gastroenterology 70:1156-1160, 1976.

21. Fayer R. Cryptosporidium: a water-borne zoonotic parasite Vet Parasitol.126:37-56. 2004.

22. DuPont HL. Chappell CL. Sterling CR. et al. The infectivity of Cryptosporidium *parvum* in healthy volunteers. N Engl J Med. 332(13): 855-859, 1995.

23. Chappell CL. Okhuysen PC. Sterling CR. et al. Infectivity of Cryptosporidium *parvum* in healthy adults with pre-existing anti-*C. parvum* serum immunoglobulin G. Am J Trop Med Hyg. 60(1): 157-164, 1999.

24. Neuman NF. Gyurek LL. Finch GR. Belosevic M. Intact Cryptosporidium *parvum* oocysts isolated after in vitro excystation are infectious to neonatal mice. FEMS Micrbiol. Letters 183:331-336, 2000.

25. Forney JR. Yang S. Healey MC. Antagonistic effect of human alpha-1-antitrypsin on excystation of *Cryptosporidium parvum* oocysts. J Parasitol. 83(4):771-774, 1997.

26. Okhuysen PC. Chappell CL. Kettner C. Sterling CR. *Cryptosporidium parvum* metalloaminopeptidase inhibitors prevent in vitro excystation. Antimicrob Agents Chemother. 40(12):2781-2784, 1996.

27. Langer RC. Riggs MW. *Cryptosporidium parvum* apical complex glycoprotein CSL contains a sporozoite ligand for intestinal epithelial cells. Infect Immun. 67(10):5282-5291, 1999.

28. Riggs MW. Stone AL. Yount PA et al. Protective monoclonal antibody defines a circumsporozoite-like glycoprotein exoantigen of *Cryptosporidium parvum* sporozoites and merozoites. J Immunol 158:1787-1795. 1997.

29. Barnes DA. Bonnin A. Huang JX. et al. A novel multi-domain mucin-like glycoprotein of *Cryptosporidium parvum* mediates invasion. Mol Biochem Parasitol. 96(1-2):93-110, 1998.

30. Zapata F, Perkins ME. et al The *Cryptosporidium parvum* ABC protein family Mol Biochem Parasitol.120:157-61. 2002

31. Brasseur P. Uguen C. Moreno-Sabater A. Favennec L. Ballet JJ. Viability of *Cryptosporidium parvum* oocysts in natural waters. Folia Parasitol (Praha). 45(2):113-116, 1998.

32. Smith HV, Corcoran GD. New drugs and treatment for cryptosporidiosis. Curr Opin Infect Dis.17:557-64. 2004

33. Blagburn BL. Soave R. Prophylaxis and chemotherapy: Human and animal. In: Cryptosporidium and Cryptosporidosis. (Fayer. R. ed.), CRC Press, Boca Raton, Fl. pp. 113-130, 1997.

34. Clark DP. New insights into human cryptosporidiosis. Clin Microbiol Rev. 12(4):554-563, 1999.

35. Huang BQ, Chen XM, LaRusso NF. *Cryptosporidium parvum* attachment to and internalization by human biliary epithelia in vitro: a morphologic study J Parasitol. 90:212-21. 2004

36. Chen XM, Huang BQ. et al. Cdc42 and the actin-related protein/neural Wiskott-Aldrich syndrome protein network mediate cellular inva-

sion by *Cryptosporidium parvum*. Infect Immun. 72:3011-21. 2004.

37. Jenkins MC. O'Brien C. Trout J. Guidry A. Fayer R. Hyperimmune bovine colostrum specific for recombinant *Cryptosporidium parvum* antigen confers partial protection against cryptosporidiosis in immunosuppressed adult mice. Vaccine. 17(19):2453-2460, 1999.

38. McDonald V. Host cell-mediated responses to infection with Cryptosporidium. Parasite Immunol. 22:597-604. 2000

39. Urban JF IL-12 protects immunocompetent and immunodeficient neonatal mice against infection with *Cryptosporidium parvum*. J Immunol 156(1):263-268, 1998.

40. Tarver AP. Clark DP. Diamond G. et al. Enteric beta-defensin: molecular cloning and characterization of a gene with inducible intestinal epithelial cell expression associated with *Cryptosporidium parvum* infection Infect Immun. 66(3):1045-1056, 1998.

41. Giacometti A. Cirioni O. Barchiesi F. et al. In-vitro activity of polycationic peptides against *Cryptosporidium parvum, Pneumocystis carinii* and yeast clinical isolates. J Antimicrob Chemother. 44(3):403-6, 1999.

42. Ludtke SJ. He K. Heller WT. et al. Membrane pores induced by magainin. Biochemistry. 35(43):13723-8, 1996

43. Huang HW. Peptide-lipid interactions and mechanisms of antimicrobial peptides. Novartis Found Symp. 225:188-200; discussion 200-6, 1999.

44. Jenkins M. Higgins J. et al. Protection of calves against cryptosporiosis by oral inoculation with gamma-irradiated *Cryptosporidium parvum* oocysts. J Parasitol. 90:1178-80. 2004.

45. Guarino A, Bruzzese E, De Marco G, Buccigrossi V. Paediatr Drugs. 2004;6(6):347-62. Management of gastrointestinal disorders in children with HIV infection.

46. Cryptosporidosis (Cryptosporidium spp.) – a CDC review. J Environ Health. 67:52. 2004.

47. Farthing MJ. Clinical aspects of human cryptosporidiosis. Contrib Microbiol 6:50-74. 2000.

48. Cicirello HG. Kehl KS. Addiss DG. et al. Cryptosporidiosis in children during a massive waterborne outbreak in Milwaukee, Wisconsin: clinical, laboratory and epidemiologic findings. Epidemiol Infect. 119(1):53-60, 1997.

49. Burgner D. Pikos N. Eagles G. McCarthy A. Stevens M. Epidemiology of *Cryptosporidium parvum* in symptomatic paediatric oncology patients. J Paediatr Child Health. 35(3):300-2, 1999.

50. Blackman E. Binder S. Gaultier C. Benveniste R. Cecilio M. Cryptosporidiosis in HIV-infected patients: diagnostic sensitivity of stool examination, based on number of specimens submitted. Am J Gastroenterol. 92(3):451-3, 1997.

51. Coupe S. Sarfati C. Hamane S. Derouin F. Detection of cryptosporidium and identification to the species level by nested PCR and restriction fragment length polymorphism. J Clin Microbiol. 43:1017-23. 2005.

52. Ignatius R. Eisenblatter M. Regnath T. et al. Efficacy of different methods for detection of low *Cryptosporidium parvum* oocyst numbers or antigen concentrations in stool specimens. Eur J

53. Fox LM, Saravolatz LD. Nitazoxanide: a new thiazolide antiparasitic agent. Clin Infect Dis. 40:1173-80. 2005.

54. Steiner TS. Thielman NM. Guerrant RL. Protozoal agents: what are the dangers for the public water supply?. Annu Rev Med. 48:329-40, 1997.

55. Watershed Management of Potable Water Supply. Assessing the New York City Strategy. National Research Council Publication, (O'Melia C, Committee Chair), National Academy Press, pp. 549. 2000.

56. Clancy JL. Hargy TM. Marshall MM and Dykesen JE. UV light inactivation of Cryptosporidium oocysts. J Am Water Works Assoc 90:92-102. 1998.

57. Gyurek LL. Li H. Belosevic M. and Finch GR. Ozone inactivation kinetics of *Cryptosporidium parvum* in phosphate buffer. J Enviro Engine 125:913-924. 2000.

58. Tate KW, Pereira MD, Atwill ER. Efficacy of vegetated buffer strips for retaining *Cryptosporidium parvum*. J Environ Qual. 33:2243-51. 2004.

59. Hallier-Soulier S. Guillot E. An immunomagnetic separartion polymerase chain reaction asay for rapid and ultra-sensitive detection of *Cryptopsoridium parvum* in drinking water. FEMS Microbiol Lett. 176:285-289. 1999.

11. *Toxoplasma gondii*
(Nicolle and Manceaux 1908)

Introduction

Toxoplasma gondii is an obligate intracellular parasite and has a worldwide distribution. It infects all species of mammals and has been isolated from every tissue in experimentally infected rodents, making this organism one of the most successful parasites on earth, even when one takes into account all the viruses and bacteria that infect this large group of vertebrates. It has emerged as a serious pathogen of some marine mammals (e.g., sea otters).[1] It can remain alive as a dormant infection for the life of the host. When immunity breaks down, it can reactivate, often with clinical consequences. In this regard, Toxoplasma behaves similarly to other infectious agents whose reproduction is held in check by host acquired protective immune responses (e.g., herpes simplex virus, *Mycobacterium tuberculosis*).

Toxoplasma gondii is easily cultured and can be experimentally transfected,[2] facilitating studies on its genetics, cell, and molecular biology.[3] Its genome is currently being worked on by several groups, and a complete DNA sequence should be forthcoming within the next year or two.[4] Toxoplasma is usually acquired through the ingestion of infected, raw, or undercooked meats,[5] but several recent outbreaks were traced back to drinking water supplies contaminated with the oocyst stage.[6] The domestic cat and other feline species serve as the definitive host, harboring the sexual stages of the parasite.

In immunocompetent humans, infection rarely leads to serious illness. In contrast, when *T. gondii* infects immunocompromised individuals, or when a previously acquired infection is reactivated, the clinical disease that follows can often be life-threatening. Congenital infection also occurs and can occasionally lead to devastating pathological consequences for the developing fetus.

Historical Information

Nicolle and Manceaux, in 1908,[7] described the organism which they isolated from *Ctenodactylus gondii*, the gondi, a gerbil-like desert inhabiting mammal. In the same year, Splendore,[8] working in Brazil, described the identical parasite, which he identified in the tissues of rabbits. They published their results at the same time, but in different publications, so neither was aware of the other's findings. Janku, in 1923,[9] described the congenital manifestations of the infection, which he accurately characterized as causing hydrocephalus and chorioretinitis. He was unable to isolate the organism from the brains of its victims. Wolf and colleagues, in 1939,[10] confirmed Janku's clinical description, and went on to experimentally transfer the infection from infected brain tissue to mice and rabbits. Pinkerton and Henderson,[11] and Sabin[12] independently described cases of adult acquired toxoplasmosis in 1941. Frenkel and colleagues, in 1970,[13] identified the sexual stages of the life cycle working in cats, as did Hutchinson and co-workers in that same year.[14]

Life Cycle

Definitive Host Cycle

The biology of *Toxoplasma gondii* has been reviewed.[2]

Felidae are the definitive host for *T. gondii*. Domestic cats acquire the infection in one of three ways: 1. ingesting oocysts in contaminated cat feces (Fig. 11.1), 2. ingesting the tissue cysts (Fig. 11.2) harbored by infected prey (e.g., mice, rats, rabbits, squirrels), 3. ingesting tissue cysts fed to them by their unwitting owners in the form of left-over bits of ground meats (particularly pork and lamb) purchased at supermarkets. Rodents acquire the asexual tissue cyst stage of the parasite by ingesting cat feces contaminated with oocysts.

The tissue cyst contains hundreds of infectious units, termed bradyzoites. When the cat eats this stage, the cyst wall becomes partially digested in the stomach and fully ruptures in the small intestine, releasing its complement of bradyzoites. This stage invades epithelial cells, developing into merozoites. The intracellular merozoite undergoes multiple cycles of division by a process termed endodyogeny. Finally, sheer numbers of parasites overwhelms the cell and they are released into the lumen of the small intestine. Each merozoite can infect other epithelial cells, continuing the infection. Alternatively, merozoites can develop into gametocytes (male and female). The molecular switch(s) that regulates differentiation into the sexual stages is not known. The two sexual forms fuse, forming an oocyst that passes out with the fecal mass. Oocysts sporulate outside the host, producing haploid sporozoites, the infectious stage for the intermediate host, or for another

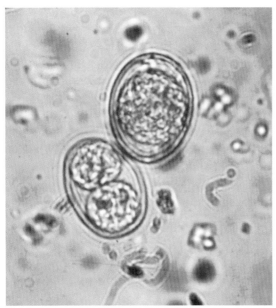

Figure 11.1. Sporulated oocysts of *Toxoplasma gondii*. 12 µm.

cat.Cats do not develop a high enough level of protective immunity after exposure to a primary infection to prevent reinfection with the oocyst stage. Long-term, full protection can be induced in experimental situations, giving hope for the eventual development of an effective vaccine, but progress has been slow.[15]

Domestic and semi-wild cats are implicated as the host most commonly responsible for transmission of the infection to farm animals (e.g., cattle, pigs, sheep, dogs, etc.). In addition, as will be described in full under clinical aspects, house cats may be considered a health hazard to pregnant women.

Intermediate Host Cycle

The oocyst stage contains the infectious sporozoites. Ingestion of this stage leads to infection in all species of mammal. Sporozoites are released by exposure of the oocyst to digestive enzymes in the small intestine. The freed parasites then penetrate the intestinal wall, and are taken up by macrophages. Once inside a cell (Fig. 11.3), the organisms are referred to as tachyzoites. The tachyzoite resides in its own membrane-bound parasitophorous vacuole.[16] Infected cells cannot destroy tachyzoites, due to the fact that *T. gondii* inhibits the process of fusion between the lysosomal vessels and this specialized intracellular niche (Fig. 11.4, 11.5).[17] Replication occurs inside the macrophages and parasites are passively carried to all parts of the body. About 10 to 20 tachyzoites are pro-

duced inside each infected cell. Macrophages eventually succumb to the infection, releasing tachyzoites into the surrounding tissues. Freed parasites are taken up by cells adjacent to the site of release (e.g., glial cells, astrocytes, hepatocytes, neutrophils, cardiac muscle). *T. gondii* undergoes another round of replication until acquired protective immune responses are elicited. As the result, extensive tissue damage can be incurred, often accompanied by a constellation of clinical correlates. Immunity, in the form of interleukin-12 and IFN-γ, limits the rate of parasite division. Antibodies are thought not to play a role in controlling this phase of the infection. Apparently, protective immunity does not result in the death of the parasite. Rather, in response to host defense mechanisms, tachyzoites are forced to differentiate into a second asexual stage known as the bradyzoite. This form divides both by endodyogeny and endopolygeny, then organizes into a tissue cyst.[18] Interferon-γ-dependent, nitric oxide-mediated effector mechanisms maintain this state of latency by eliminating any parasites emerging from the cysts.[19] Bradyzoites lie dormant in the tissues for as long as host defenses remain active. Although all tissues can harbor tissue cysts, the brain is a favored site for the long-term survival of the tissue cyst.

Intermediate hosts, in addition to ingesting oocysts, can also be infected by ingesting tissue cysts contained in the flesh of another intermediate host species. This route of transmission is most common among carnivores and scavengers.

In humans, infection is usually acquired by ingestion of infected raw or insufficiently cooked meat. Lamb[20] and pork [21, 22] are the most common meats implicated in transmission worldwide.

Congenital transmission occurs during infection of the mother, when tachyzoites cross the placenta. The

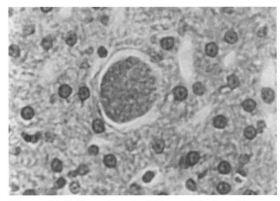

Figure 11.2. Pseudocyst of *T. gondii* in liver biopsy.

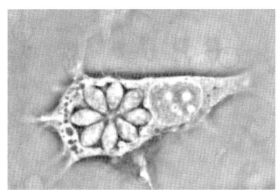

Figure 11.3. Tachyzoites of *T. gondii* in parasitophorous vacuoles of infected fibroblast.

role of specific antibodies in limiting infection to the mother and not the fetus has yet to be defined, while INFγ and CD8+ T cells appear to be necessary in preventing congenital infection in mouse models.[23]

Cellular and Molecular Pathogenesis

Since Toxoplasma infection is not restricted by cell type, entry does not depend upon tissue-specific receptor molecules. The process is nevertheless complex,[24] and involves the coordinated, sequential deployment of a set of specialized subcellular organelles: micronemes, rhoptries (lysosome-like granules), dense granules,[24] and the newly-described glideosome.[26] As the result of the biological activities unleashed upon the host cell by these organelles, the tachyzoite is able to assume its intracellular life without hindrance from host defense mechanisms related to phagocytosis. Rhoptries,[27, 30] located at the apical end of the tachyzoite, and micronemes[31] both secrete adhesin-like molecules.[25, 26] Parasite-specific secreted serine and cysteine proteases are absolutely required for the engineering of the parasitophorous vacuole in which the tachyzoite lives and reproduces.[27–29] They apparently emanate from one or more of the above mentioned organelles, enabling the parasite to deform the cell membrane of the target cell and to re-model the inner membrane of the vacuole. Inhibition of these two proteases prevents *T. gondii* from entering the cell.[27, 28] A few cDNA-encoding proteins from these organelles have been cloned and sequenced, and their amino acid sequences deduced.[32 – 34]

The parasite affects the arrangement of host cell organelles, including the mitochondria, which aggregate around the parasitophorous vacuole.[35] Division depends upon the ability of the parasite to inhibit lyso-

somal fusion with and inhibition of acidification[36] of the parasitophorous vacuole. Congenital toxoplasmosis is characterized by lesions of the central nervous system, which lead to various states of clinical disease.[37, 38] Inflammatory lesions become necrotic and eventually calcify. Retinochoroiditis is frequently associated with congenital toxoplasmosis.[39] The retina is inflamed and becomes necrotic, and the pigmented layer becomes disrupted by infiltration of inflammatory cells. Eventually, granulation tissue forms, and invades the vitreous humor. Calcification of brain tissue (Fig. 11.6) is common when the fetus acquires infection during the first trimester. Hydrocephalus may result. Learning deficits in children who became infected in the second or third trimesters have been documented, but are less common for those whose infection occurred in the third trimester. In adult-acquired toxoplasmosis, lesions are less intense, giving rise to foci of inflammation around tachyzoites in muscle and other tissues, such as spleen, liver, and lymph nodes. Interstitial pneumonitis may also accompany infection.[40, 41] Adult patients with AIDS who harbor latent infection with *T. gondii* suffer the most from reactivation of the infection.[42] This is due largely to the fact that the HIV virus down regulates IL-12 reproduction and reduces the number of parasite-specific CD4+ and CD8+ cells.[44 – 46] This reduces

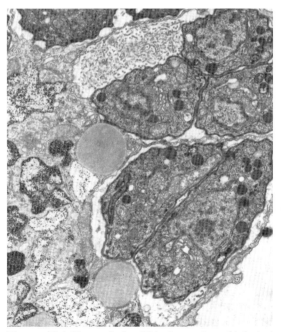

Figure 11.4. Transmission EM of a portion of infected macrophage. Note numerous tachyzoites (T). All parasites are alive; thus, the fusion of lysosomes with the parasitophorous vacuole is inhibited. Courtesy T. Jones.

Table 11.1. Congenital toxoplasmosis following maternal infection during first and second trimester*

Not Infected	73%
Subclinical Infection	13%
Mild Infection	7%
Severe Infection	6%

*From Desmonts and Couvier, NEJM 290:1110, 1974

dramatically or eliminates entirely the INF-γ dependent inhibition of parasite multiplication. Bradyzoites resume replication within tissue cysts, and eventually rupture into the tissues, initiating infection in neighboring cells. Toxoplasma encephalitis results when reactivation occurs in the brain.[47] Reactivation can also occur in the lung, gastrointestinal tract, heart, eye, and liver. However, with the introduction of effective chemoprophylaxis for toxoplasmosis and HAART for HIV, the incidence of clinical toxoplasmosis has been markedly reduced in recent years.

Clinical Disease

Several reviews summarize the current status of the clinical aspects of infection with *T. gondii*.[48, 49]

Congenital Toxoplasmosis

Congenital infection (Table 11.1)[50] varies from asymptomatic to severe damage to the central nervous system (CNS) and stillbirth. Fetal damage is most acute when infection occurs during the second to sixth month of gestation. At birth, most affected children are asymptomatic, but may show the pathological consequences

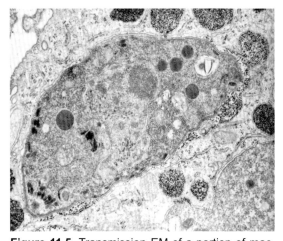

Figure 11.5. Transmission EM of a portion of macrophage that ingested a heat-killed tachyzoite. Note fusion of lysosomes with the parasitophorous vacuole (arrows). T = tachyzoite, Courtesy T. Jones.

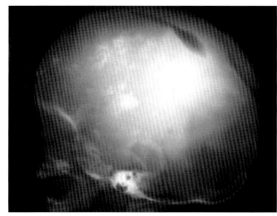

Figure 11.6. X-ray of the skull of an infant born with congenital toxoplasmosis. Infection was acquired most likely during the first or second trimester. Note calcifications.

of infection several months to years later. Nearly 40% of the time, mothers who were infected during pregnancy give birth to infected newborns. Of these infants, about 15% have severe clinical manifestations.[37] Retinochoroiditis leading to blindness, cerebral calcifications, and learning disabilities are the most frequent consequences.[51] Severely affected infants may have hepatosplenomegaly, liver failure, thrombocytopenia, convulsions, and hydrocephalus.[52] Furthermore, in these individuals, new lesions continue to develop, increasing the likelihood that severe impairment to the CNS will occur.[53]

Acquired Toxoplasmosis

Most acquired infections are asymptomatic. Those that are clinically apparent usually present as mild disease. This form of toxoplasmosis is characterized by generalized lymphadenopathy, with predominant enlargement of the cervical nodes, sometimes associated with a low-grade fever (Table 11.2). The disease mimics infectious mononucleosis and, to a lesser extent, Hodgkin's-type lymphomas. Rarely, adult-acquired toxoplasmosis is severe, involving major vital organs and systems. These patients may suffer myocarditis[54] and encephalitis.[55] In addition, some patients develop space-occupying lesions of the CNS, consisting of necrotic masses. Retinochoroiditis in acquired toxoplasmosis is rare. An unusual form of acquired toxoplasmosis has been described in sero-negative recipients of organ transplants from *T. gondii*-infected donors. Heart transplant recipients are particularly at risk, and develop a myocarditis or disseminated infection.[56]

Toxoplasma gondii

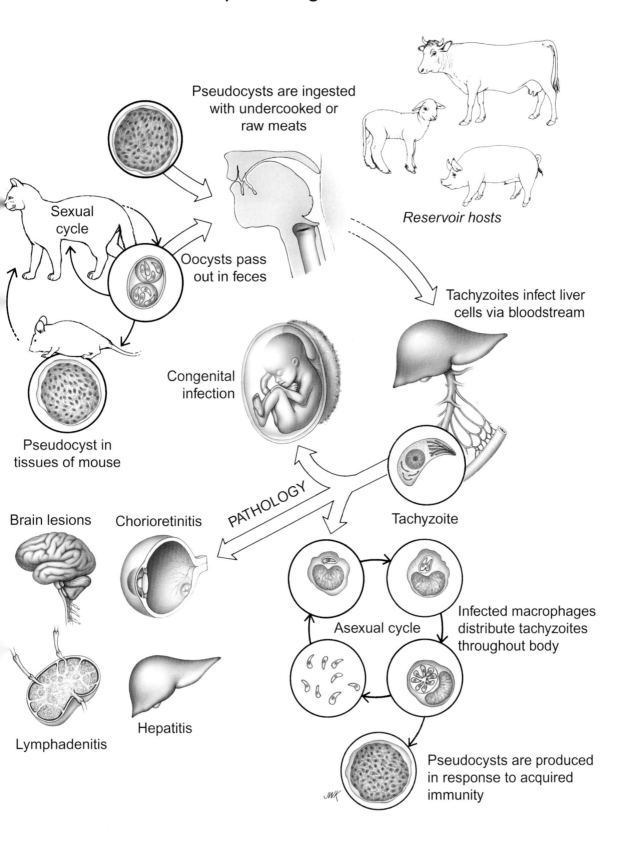

Pseudocysts are ingested with undercooked or raw meats

Reservoir hosts

Sexual cycle

Oocysts pass out in feces

Tachyzoites infect liver cells via bloodstream

Pseudocyst in tissues of mouse

Congenital infection

PATHOLOGY

Brain lesions

Chorioretinitis

Tachyzoite

Asexual cycle

Infected macrophages distribute tachyzoites throughout body

Hepatitis

Lymphadenitis

Pseudocysts are produced in response to acquired immunity

Table 11.2. Differential diagnosis of lymphadenopathy

	Toxoplasmosis	Inf. Mono	Lymphoma
Lymphadenopathy without other symptoms	+++	+	+++
Pharyngitis	+	+++	+
Monocytosis, eosinophilia	+++	+	+++
Atypical lymphocytes	+	++++	+++
Anemia	0	+	+++
Positive heterophil	0	++++	0
Altered liver function	0	++++	++
Hilar lymphadenopathy	+	+	+++
Lymph node pathology	Reticulum cells	Germinal cells	Bizarre cells

Recrudescent Toxoplasmosis

Encephalitis due to *T. gondii* is one of the most common causes of CNS disease in patients with AIDS.[47, 57, 58] The parasite commonly localizes to the brainstem, leading to ataxia and cranial nerve palsies. Meningeal involvement is rare. The lung is the next most common organ involved in reactivated toxoplasmosis, often manifesting as an interstitial pneumonitis.[40, 41] The gastrointestinal tract, liver, and heart may also be involved. Cutaneous toxoplasmosis presents as a prominent macular and papular rash on the palms and soles.[59] Severe recrudescent toxoplasmosis has also been described in patients undergoing immune suppression during bone marrow transplantation.[59, 60]

Diagnosis

Definitive diagnosis is made by demonstrating the organism in histological sections or by using PCR.[61, 62, 63, 64] Polymerase chain reaction tests are especially useful in identifying organisms in ocular, amniotic, or CSF fluids. Unfortunately, PCR for any eukaryotic parasite, including *T. gondii*, is not available in most hospital diagnostic settings. Isolation of viable organisms involves removal of lymph node material, macerating it in physiological saline, and injecting aliquots intraperitoneally into immunosuppressed mice. Smears of peritoneal fluid or brain tissue of the mice obtained 3-5 weeks later may reveal toxoplasma; this test is laborious and is carried out in only a few laboratories. Identification of tachyzoites in tissue sections without the aid of antibody-based staining methods is next to impossible, even for a seasoned histopathologist. Indirect evidence of infection includes the application of a wide variety of commercially available serological tests of several modalities (Fig. 11.7).[65] These tests depend on the identification of specific immunoglobulins - IgG and IgM. A wide variety of laboratory-based methods take advantage of these host responses to insure an accurate diagnosis of both active and inactive infection.[66]

In most infections among otherwise healthy adults, IgM antibodies appear within five days to two weeks after infection, and usually reach titers of 1:80 or more during the first 2-3 months after infection. They return to normal shortly thereafter. IgG antibody titers rise 2-3 weeks after infection, and usually achieve levels above 1:1024. Specific IgG antibodies are detectable for life. Accurate, careful interpretation of serologic tests is fun-

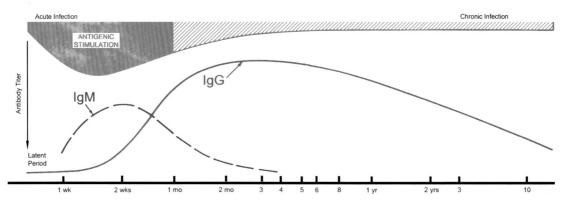

Figure 11.7. Relationship between antigenic stimulation, antibody production, and stages of infection (latent period, acute, and chronic infection). Redrawn after Remington.

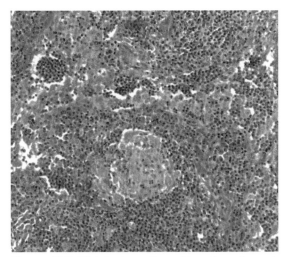

Figure 11.8. Histologic section of lymph node positive for macrophages infected with *T. gondii*. These cells are referred to as Piringa-Kuchenka cells.

damental to confirming the diagnosis. Significant rises in titers of IgG antibodies between acute and convalescent serum specimens are highly correlated with acute infection. A single elevated IgM titer early in the infection is also diagnostic. When a woman becomes pregnant, TORCH tests (*Toxoplasma gondii*, other, rubella virus, cytomegalovirus, herpes virus)[67] should be carried out every month during pregnancy. Seroconversion during pregnancy can then be documented early on in infection and closely monitored. Congenital infection has occurred when specific IgM antibodies are detected in the infant's serum. About 25% of newborns with congenital toxoplasmosis have IgM antibodies. In contrast, infants with IgG antibodies pose a problem to the clinician in deciding whether or not the fetus was ever infected. The presence of IgG antibodies may indicate that the newborn is experiencing an active infection or simply that it received maternal antibodies. Careful clinical and serological follow-up of the child is indicated to determine whether intrauterine infection has occurred.[67]Diagnosing toxoplasmosis in patients with AIDS is problematic.[68] IgM antibodies are not present in more than 10% of patients with reactivated toxoplasmosis. Other classes of immunoglobulin are equally low. Detecting *T. gondii* antigenemia appears to be a promising strategy for making the diagnosis in HIV/AIDS patients in the absence of reliable immunoglobulin responses.[68] PCR-based methods for detecting disseminated toxoplasmosis are also gaining acceptance.[69] Histologic examination of lymph node tissue (Fig. 11.8) obtained at biopsy may show abnormal histiocytes, but this evidence is not pathognomonic for toxoplasmosis.

Treatment

Pyrimethamine and sulfadiazine are the drugs of choice.[70] However, therapeutic effect can be difficult to evaluate because of the rapid acquisition of protective immunity in most immunocompetent patients. Neonates suffering from congenital toxoplasmosis, adults with severe acquired toxoplasmosis, and recrudescent infection in HIV/AIDS patients must be treated. Mild infection requires no therapy. If only pyrimethamine is given, then the patient's blood count must be monitored for lymphocytopenia and thrombocytopenia, since this compound is a folic acid antagonist. Administering folinic acid eliminates the requirement for monitoring. Pregnant women should be treated only with spiramycin or sulfadiazine, since pyrimethamine is teratogenic in animal models. Pyrimethamine and clindamycin is an acceptable alternate for patients who cannot tolerate pyrimethamine and sulfadiazine. In this case, other drugs, including azithromycin, spiramycin, clarithromycin, atovaquone, and roxithromycin are also effective.[71]

Prevention and Control

Most adult-acquired infections can be avoided by eating only cooked meats. This preventive measure often fails because of cultural or individual cuisine preferences. In France, where the rate of infection is over 85% among those over the age of 50, the most common source of infection is raw lamb served as "steak" tartar. Many other western cultures also have numerous recipes calling for undercooked or raw meat as a main ingredient. The majority of Eskimos still eat all their meat raw, and are therefore at the mercy of the pathogens lurking inside each carcass.[72] Prevention of infection from oocysts requires care when handling cat feces,[73] especially when cleaning litter boxes. This activity must be proscribed for pregnant women. Rarely, toxoplasmosis is acquired as the result of inhaling dust, or drinking contaminated water containing oocysts.[74] Vaccines offer another set of strategies for controlling this infection, but progress has been slow.[75]

The combination of trimethoprim-sulfamethoxazole, used for the prevention of P. carinii pneumonia is probably effective for preventing toxoplasma encephalitis.[76]

References

1. Miller MA, Grigg ME, et al. An unusual genotype of *Toxoplasma gondii* is common in California sea otters (*Enhydra lutris nereis*) and is a cause of mortality. Int J Parasitol. 34:275-84. 2004.

2. Kim K, Weiss LM. *Toxoplasma gondii*: the model apicomplexan. Int J Parasitol. 34:423-32. 2004.

3. Gubbels MJ, Striepen B. Studying the cell biology of apicomplexan parasites using fluorescent proteins. Microsc Microanal. 10:568-79. 2004.

4. Kissinger JC, Gajria B. et al. ToxoDB: accessing the *Toxoplasma gondii* genome. Nucleic Acids Res. 31:234-236. 2003.

5. Pozio E. Foodborne and waterborne parasites. Acta Microbiol Pol. 52 Suppl:83-96. 2003.

6. Dubey JP. Toxoplasmosis - a waterborne zoonosis. Vet Parasitol.126:57-72. 2004.

7. Nicolle C. Manceaux LH. Sur une infection a coyes de Leishman (ou organismes voisins) du gondi. C R Hebdomad Seance Acad Sci 147:763-766,1908.

8. Splendore A. Un nuovo protozoa parassita dei conigli: incontrato nelle lesioni anatomiche d'ua maittia che ricorda in molti punti ii Kala-azar dell'uomo. Rev Soc Sci Sao Paulo 3:109-112, 1908.

9. Janku J. Pathogenesis and pathologic anatomy of the "congenital coloboma" of the maculalutea in an eye of normal size, with microscopic detection of parasites in the retina. J Czech Phys 62:1021-1027,1923.

10. Wolf A. Cowen D. Paige BH. Human toxoplasmosis: occurrence in infants as encephalomyelitis: verification by transmission to animals. Science 89:226-227, 1939.

11. Pinkerton H. Henderson RG. Adult toxoplasmosis: a previously unrecognized disease entity simulating the typhus-spotted fever group. JAMA 116:807-814, 1941.

12. Sabin AB. Toxoplasmic encephalitis in children. JAMA 116:801-807, 1941.

13. Frenkel JK. Dubey JP. Miller NL. *Toxoplasma gondii* in cats: fecal stages identified as coccidian oocysts. Science 167:893-896, 1970.

14. Hutchinson WM. Dunachie JF. Sim JC. et al. Coccidian-like nature of *Toxoplasma gondii*. BMJ 1:142-144, 1970.

15. GM Bhopale, Development of a vaccine for toxoplasmosis: current status, *Microbes Infect* 5:457–462. 2003.

16. Jones TC. Hirsch JG. The interaction between *Toxoplasma gondii* and mammalian cells. II. The absence of lysosomal fusion with phagocytic vacuoles containing living parasites. J Exp Med 136(5):1173-94, 1972.

17. Dlugonska H. Molecular modifications of host cells by *Toxoplasma gondii*. Pol J Microbiol. 53:45-54. 2004.

18. Dzierszinski F, Nishi M, Ouko L, Roos DS. Dynamics of *Toxoplasma gondii* differentiation. Eukaryot Cell. 3:992-1003. 2004.

19. Scharton-Kersten TM. Yap G. Magram J. Sher A. Inducible nitric oxide is essential for host control of persistent but not acute infection with the intracellular pathogen *Toxoplasma gondii*. J Exp Med. 185(7):1261-73, 1997.

20. Williams RH. Morley EK. et al. High levels of congenital transmission of *Toxoplasma gondii* in longitudinal and cross-sectional studies on sheep farms provides evidence of vertical transmission in ovine hosts. Parasitology.130:301-7. 2005.

21. Dubey JP. Beattie CP. Toxoplasmosis of Animal and Man, CRC Press, Boca Ratón, FL (1988).

22. Dubey JP. Gamble HR. High prevalence of viable *Toxoplasma gondii* infection in market weight pigs from a farm in Massachusetts, J Parasitol 88:1234–1238. 2002.

23. Abou-Bacar A, Pfaff AW. et al. Role of gamma interferon and T cells in congenital Toxoplasma transmission. Parasite Immunol. 26:315-8. 2004.

24. Carruthers VB, Blackman MJ. A new release on life: emerging concepts in proteolysis and parasite invasion. Mol Microbiol. 55:1617-30. 2005.

25. Huynh MH, Rabenau KE, Harper JM, Beatty WL, Sibley LD, Carruthers VB. Rapid invasion of host cells by Toxoplasma requires secretion of the MIC2M2AP adhesive protein complex. EMBO J. 22: 2082-2090. 2003.

26. Keeley A, Soldati D. The glideosome: a molecular machine powering motility and host-cell invasion by Apicomplexa. Trends Cell Biol.14:528-32. 2004.

27. Que X, Ngo H. et al. The cathepsin B of *Toxoplasma gondii*, toxopain-1, is critical for parasite invasion and rhoptry protein processing. J Biol Chem 277: 25791-25797. 2002.

28. Conseil V, Soete M, Dubremetz JF. Serine protease inhibitors block invasion of host cells by *Toxoplasma gondii*. Antimicrob Agents Chemother 43: 13581361. 1999.

29. Kim K. Role of proteases in host cell invasion by *Toxoplasma gondii* and other Apicomplexa. Acta Trop 91:6981. 2004.

30. Ngo HM, Yang M, Joiner KA. Are rhoptries in Apicomplexan parasites secretory granules or secretory lysosomal granules?Mol Microbiol. 52:1531-41. 2004.

31. Carruthers VB. Giddings OK. Sibley DL. Secretion of micronemal proteins is associated with toxoplasma invasion of host cells. Cell Microbiol 1:1462-5822.1999.

32. Ajioka JW. Boothroyd JC. et al. Gene discovery by EST sequencing in *Toxoplasma gondii* reveals sequences restricted to the Apicomplexa. Genome Res. 8(1):18-28, 1998.

33. Yahiaoui B. Dzierszinski F. et al. Isolation and characterization of a subtractive library enriched for developmentally regulated transcripts expressed during encystation of *Toxoplasma gondii*. Mol Biochem Parasitol. 99(2):223-35, 1999.

34. Bradley PJ, Li N, Boothroyd JC. A GFP-based motif-trap reveals a novel mechanism of targeting for the Toxoplasma ROP4 protein. Mol Biochem Parasitol 137:111-120. 2004.

35. Lindsay DS. Mitschler RR. Toivio-Kinnucan MA. et al. Associa-tion of host cell mitochondria with developing *Toxoplasma gondii* tissue cysts. Am J Vet Res. 54(10):1663-7, 1993.

36. Shaw MK, Roos DS, Tilney LG. Acidic compartments and rhoptry formation in *Toxoplasma gondii*. Parasitology 117:435-443. 1998.

37. Remington JS. McLeod R. Desmonts G. Toxoplasmosis. In: Infec-tious Dsieases of the Fetus and Newborn Infeant, 4th ed. (Remington JS Klein JO. eds). W.B. Saunders, Pubs. Philadelphia. pp. 140-267, 1995.

38. Remington JS. McLeod R. Toxoplasmosis. In: Infectious Diseases, 2nd. ed. (Gorbach SL. Bartlett JG. Blacklow NR, eds). W.B. Saun-

ders, Pub. Philadelphia. pp. 1620-1640, 1998.

39. Mets MB. Holfels E. Boyer KM. Swisher CN. Roizen N. Stein L. Stein. Eye manifestations of congenital toxoplasmosis. Am J Ophthal 123(1):1-16, 1997.

40. Campagna AC. Pulmonary toxoplasmosis. Semin Respir Infect 12(2):98-105, 1997.

41. Mariuz P. Bosler EM. Luft BJ. Toxoplasma pneumonia. Semin Respir Infect 12(1):40-3, 1997.

42. Kaplan JE. Diagnosis, treatment, and prevention of selected common HIV-related opportunistic infections in the Caribbean region.Top HIV Med. 12:136-41. 2005.

43. Smed-Sorensen A. Lore K. HIV-1-infected dendritic cells up-regulate cell surface markers but fail to produce IL-12 p70 in response to CD40 ligand stimulation. Blood. 104:2810-7. 2004.

44. Vanham G. Penne L. Devalck J. et al. Decreased CD40 ligand induction in CD4 T cells and dysregulated IL-12 production during HIV infection. Clin Exp Immunol. 117(2):335-42, 1999.

45. Sartori A. Ma X. Gri G. et al. Interleukin-12: an immunoregulatory cytokine produced by B cells and antigen-presenting cells. Methods. 11(1):116-27, 1997.

46. Alonso K. Pontiggia P. Medenica R. Rizzo S. Cytokine patterns in adults with AIDS. Immunol Invest 26(3):341-50, 1997.

47. Luft BJ. Remington JS. Toxoplasmic encephalitis in AIDS. Clin Infect Dis 15: 211-222, 1992.

48. Hill D, Dubey JP. *Toxoplasma gondii*: transmission, diagnosis and prevention. Clin Microbiol Infect. 8:634-40. 2002

49. Montoya JG, Liesenfeld O Toxoplasmosis.Lancet. 363:1965-76. 2004., 43-45

50. Desmont G. Couvrer J. Congenital toxoplasmosis: a prospecstudy of 378 pregnancies. N Engl J Med 290:1110-1116, 1974.

51. Kravetz JD, Federman DG. Toxoplasmosis in pregnancy. Am J Med.118:212-216. 2005.

52. Koppe JG. Loewer-Sieger DH. Roever-Bonnet H. Results of 20-yearfollow-up of congenital toxoplasmosis. Lancet 1:254-256, 1986.

53. Bhopale GM. Pathogenesis of toxoplasmosis. Comp Immunol Microbiol Infect Dis. 26:213-22. 2003.

54. Kirchhoff LV. Weiss LM. Wittner M. Tanowitz HB. Parasitic diseases of the heart Front Biosci. 9:706-23. 2004.

55. Wilson EH, Hunter CA. The role of astrocytes in the immunopathogenesis of toxoplasmic encephalitis. Int J Parasitol. 34:543-8. 2004. Hermanns B. Brunn A. et al. Fulminant toxoplasmosis in a heart transplant recipient. Pathol Res Pract.197:211-5. 2001.

56. Sell M, Sander B, Klingebiel R. Ventriculitis and hydrocephalus as the primary manifestation of cerebral toxoplasmosis associated with AIDS. J Neurol. 252:234-236. 2005.

57. Nath A, Sinai AP. Cerebral Toxoplasmosis. Curr Treat Options Neurol. 5:3-12. 2003.

58. Leyva WH. Santa Cruz DJ. Cutaneous toxoplasmosis. J Am Acad Dermatol. 14:600-5. 1986.

59. Janitschke K. Held T. et al. Diagnostic value of tests for *Toxoplasma gondii*-specific antibodies in patients undergoing bone marrow transplantation. Clin Lab. 49:239-42. 2003.

60. Fricker-Hidalgo H. Pelloux H. Racinet C. et al. Detection of *Toxoplasma gondii* in 94 placentae from infected women by polymerase chain reaction, in vivo, and in vitro cultures. Placenta. 19(7):545-9, 1998.

61. Bergstrom T. Ricksten A. Nenonen N. et al. Congenital *Toxoplasma gondii* infection diagnosed by PCR amplification of peripheral mononuclear blood cells from a child and mother. Scand J Infect Dis 30(2):202-4, 1998.

62. Danise A. Cinque P. Vergani S. et al. Use of polymerase chain reaction assays of aqueous humor in the differential diagnosis of retinitis in patients infected with human immunodeficiency virus. Clin Infect Dis 24(6):1100-6, 1997.

63. Nimri L. Pelloux H. Elkhatib L. Detection of *Toxoplasma gondii* DNA and specific antibodies in high-risk pregnant women. Am J Trop Med Hyg. 71:831-5. 2004.

64. Wilson M. Remington JS. Clavet C. et al. Evaluation of six commercial kits for detection of human immunoglobulin M antibodies to *Toxoplasma gondii*. The FDA Toxoplasmosis Ad Hoc Working Group. J Clin Microbiol 35(12):3112-5, 1997.

65. Petersen E. Borobio MV. et al European Multicenter Study of the LIAISON Automated Diagnostic System for Determination of *Toxoplasma gondii*-Specific Immunoglobulin G (IgG) and IgM and the IgG Avidity Index. J Clin Microbiol. 43:1570-4. 2005.

66. Franca CM, Mugayar LR. Intrauterine infections: a literature review. Spec Care Dentist. 24:250-3. 2004.

67. Malla N, Sengupta C. et al. Antigenaemia and antibody response to *Toxoplasma gondii* in human immunodeficiency virus-infected patients. Br J Biomed Sci. 62:19-23. 2005.

68. K. Switaj A. Master M. Skrzypczak M. Zaborowski P. Recent trends in molecular diagnostics for *Toxoplasma gondii* infections. Clin Microbiol Infect. 11:3 170. 2005.

69. Dantas-Leite L. Urbina JA. et al. Selective anti-*Toxoplasma gondii* activities of azasterols. Int J Antimicrob Agents. 23:620-6. 2004.

70. Petersen E. Schmidt DR. Sulfadiazine and pyrimethamine in the postnatal treatment of congenital toxoplasmosis: what are the options? Expert Rev Anti Infect Ther.1:175-82. 2003.

71. Curtis MA Rau ME. et al. Parasitic zoonoses in relation to fish and wildlife harvesting by Inuit communities in northern Quebec, Canada. Arctic Med Res. 47:693-6. 1988.

72. Boyer KM, Holfels E. et al. Risk factors for *Toxoplasma gondii* infection in mothers of infants with congenital toxoplasmosis: Implications for prenatal management and screening.Toxoplasmosis Study Group. Am J Obstet Gynecol. 192:564-71. 2005.

73. Teutsch SM. Juranek DD. Sulzer A. Dubey JP. Sikes RK. Epidemic toxoplasmosis associated with infected cats. N E J Med 300(13):695-9, 1979.

74. Isaac-Renton J. Bowie WR. King A. et al. Detection of *Toxoplasma gondii* oocysts in drinking water. Applied Environ Microbiol 64(6):2278-80, 1998.

75. Beghetto E, Nielsen HV. A combination of antigenic regions of *Toxoplasma gondii* microneme proteins induces protective immunity against oral infection with parasite cysts. J Infect Dis. 191:637-45. 2005

76. Feinberg J. Prophylaxis for toxoplasmosis. AIDS Clin Care 5: 11-16. 1993.

12. *Entamoeba histolytica*
(Schaudinn 1903)

Introduction

Entamoeba histolytica is transmitted from person to person via the fecal-oral route, taking up residence in the wall of the large intestine. It is one of the leading causes of diarrheal disease throughout the world. Protracted infection can progress from watery diarrhea to dysentery (bloody diarrhea) that may prove fatal if left untreated. In addition, *E. histolytica* can spread to extra-intestinal sites causing serious disease wherever it locates. *E. histolytica* lives as a trophozoite in the tissues of the host and as a resistant cyst in the outside environment. Sanitation programs designed to limit exposure to food and water-borne diarrheal disease agents are effective in limiting infection with *E. histolytica*. Some animals (non-human primates and domestic dogs) can become infected with *E. histolytica*, but none serve as important reservoirs for human infection.

Entamoeba dispar is a morphologically identical, non-pathogenic amoeba, and is often misidentified as *E. histolytica* during microscopic examination of fecal samples.[1] Monoclonal antibodies are commercially available that identify only *E. histolytica*, distinguishing it from all other intestinal protozoans.[2] For reviews of the basic science and clinical information, see Reed and Ravdin[3] and Martinez-Palomo.[4] The full length of the genome of *Entamoeba histolytica* has been sequenced.[5]

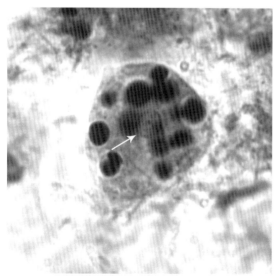

Figure 12.1. Trophozoite of *Entamoeba histolytica*. Note nucleus (arrow) and numerous ingested red cells. 35 µm.

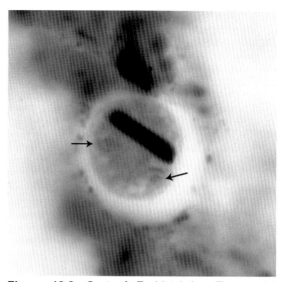

Figure 12.2. Cyst of *E. histolytica*. Two nuclei (arrows) and a smooth-ended chromatoidal bar can be seen. 15 µm.

Historical Information

Losch, in 1875,[6] described clinical features of infection with *E. histolytica* and reproduced some aspects of the disease in experimentally infected dogs. Quincke and Roos, in 1893,[7] distinguished *E. histolytica* from *Entamoeba coli*, a non-pathogenic amoeba acquired by the oral-fecal route and often found in the stool of asymptomatic individuals. Schaudinn, in 1903,[8] described the trophozoites and cysts of *E. histolytica*. He died at the age of 35 of overwhelming Amoebiasis, a tragic outcome of self-experimentation. Councilman and Lafleur, in 1891,[9] described the main features of the intestinal pathogenesis caused by *E. histolytica*. Boeck, in 1925,[10] was the first to culture *E. histolytica*, while Dobell, in 1928,[11] fully elucidated its life cycle.

Life Cycle

The trophozoite (Fig. 12.1) is a facultative anaerobe metabolizing glucose as its main source of energy.[12] The trophozoite measures 20-30 µm in diameter, and the cytoplasm contains a single nucleus with a centrally located nucleolus, often termed the karyosome. In addition, lysosomes, and a remnant mitochondrion called a "crypton,"[13] or mitosome, are present.[14] The latter organelle contains several mitochondrial genes encoding for proteins associated with heat-shock responses.[15] Discovery of a calreticulin-like molecule of 51 kDa may indicate the presence of a rough endoplasmic reticulum and Golgi apparatus,[16] although neither is visible on electron microscopy. The cyst

(Fig. 12.2) is smaller than the trophozoite (10-15 μm in diameter), and at full maturity contains four typically round *E. histolytica* nuclei. Each nucleus ultimately will give rise to an individual trophozoite. Immature cysts may contain a single, smooth-ended chromatoidal bar, a crystalline-like condensation of ribosomes, and any number of nuclei up to four.

Ingestion of a single cyst is all that is necessary to initiate infection, making this organism one of the most efficient pathogenic protozoa known to infect humans.[17] Each cyst undergoes excystation in the small intestine. The details of the cellular and molecular events leading to excystation have yet to be discovered. It is known that the cyst must receive certain specific environmental cues from the host, including sequential exposure to an acidic and a basic pH environment, in order for the four trophozoites contained within to breach the cyst wall and enter the small intestine. The newly emerged trophozoites then divide, and the eight parasites are carried by peristalsis to the large intestine.

There the trophozoite penetrates the perimucosal space and attaches to epithelial cells using lectin-carbohydrate interactions. This event is cytotoxic. They engulf and kill only the living cells encountered there (Fig. 12.3). The trophozoite divides by binary fission[11], occupying increasingly larger areas of tissue as it does so. This activity eventually causes flask-shaped ulcers to develop (Fig. 12.4). Hematogenous or lymphatic spread is then possible, but this aspect does not play a role in the life cycle.

Some trophozoites, instead of dividing, encyst in the lumen of the ulcer. Little is known regarding the environmental cues or cellular and molecular events that lead to cyst formation. Apparently, Amoebic proteasome activity is necessary for the process, since treating cultures with lactacystin caused marked inhibition of cyst formation.[18] Despite the fact that we have

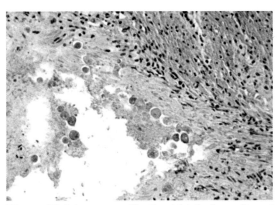

Figure 12.4. Low-magnification histologic section of Amoebic ulcer in small intestine. Organisms can be seen at living margin of ulcer.

known how to culture *E. histolytica* for over 70 years, encystment in vitro has never been achieved, although related species have been successfully induced to do so.[19] During infection in the GI tract, cysts may be continuously produced and exit the host in feces. This stage can survive in warm, moist conditions for weeks without losing infectivity.

Cellular and Molecular Pathogenesis

Reviews dealing with the detailed aspects of its molecular biology and mechanisms of pathogenesis are available. [4, 5, 20–23]

Amoebae must attach to host tissues as a necessary prerequisite for parasite-mediated cytotoxicity. Attachment is dependent upon interactions between epithelial cell membrane-bound N-acetyl-glucosamine and N-acetyl-galactosamine and at least two surface lectin proteins. The genes for both of the parasite lectins have been cloned and their cDNAs sequenced. One lectin is a 260 kDa protein,[24] while the other is 220 kDa. The heavy subunit of the 260 kDa lectin has a single transmembrane–spanning domain and a cytoplasmic domain related to β-2-integrins,[25, 26] which may also participate in the attachment process. These surface lectins apparently also facilitate the parasite's evasion of the complement membrane attack complex,[27] although the mechanism(s) is not yet known. in vitro, *E. histolytica* can be inhibited from attaching to its target cells simply by adding free galactose to the medium (Fig. 12.5).[28] In this situation, cells and trophozoites coexist. Attachment leads to cell death, which, at least in vitro, is calcium-dependent.[29] Several possible mechanisms for the actual killing of host cells have been proposed, all of which involve enzymes.[30]

The trophozoite's surface membrane contains phospholipase A, neuraminidase, and a metallocollagenase.[31] In addition, it secretes a minimum of four

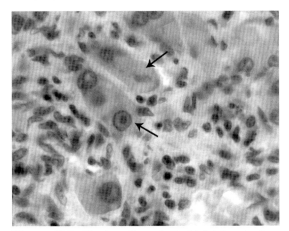

Figure 12.3. Trophozoites of *E. histolytica* in liver abcess (arrows). Note ingested host cells inside parasites.

Entamoeba histolytica

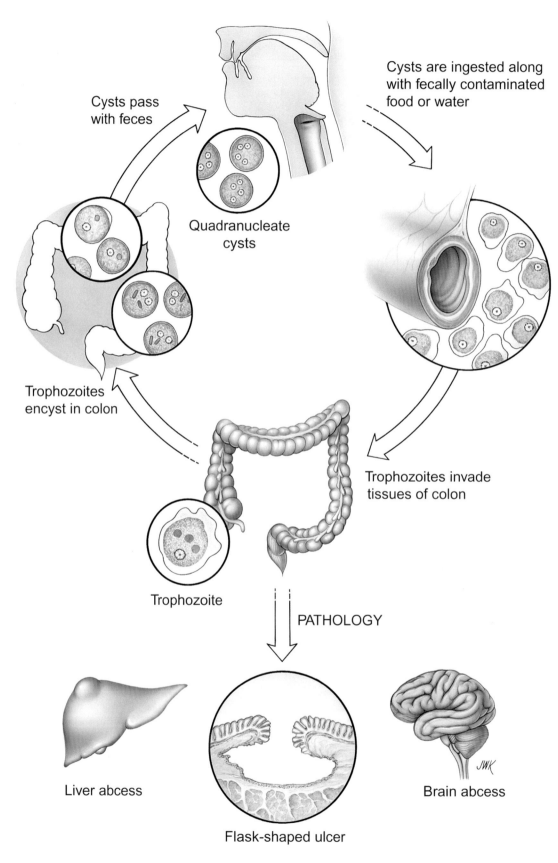

Cysts pass with feces

Quadranucleate cysts

Cysts are ingested along with fecally contaminated food or water

Trophozoites encyst in colon

Trophozoites invade tissues of colon

Trophozoite

PATHOLOGY

Liver abcess

Flask-shaped ulcer

Brain abcess

"Parasitic Diseases" 5ᵗʰ Ed. © Apple Trees Productions, LLC., Pub. P.O. Box 280, New York, NY 10032

CONTROL

GALACTOSE

CHO CELLS

CHO CELLS

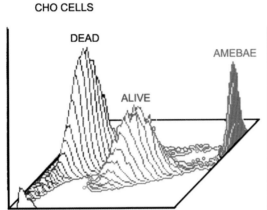

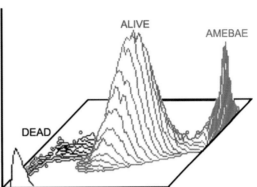

Figure 12.5. in vitro experiment showing that galactose-containing surface proteins are important for parasite cytotoxicity. Free galactose prevents attachment of amoebae to their target cells. CHO cells=Chinese hamster ovary cells. Redrawn after J. I. Ravdin.

cysteine proteases.[32] These enzymes may also aid the parasite in moving through the extracellular matrix. Attachment elicits the secretion of a pore-forming peptide[33] that is biochemically related both in structure and function to saposins.[34] The pore-forming protein presumably plays a central role in lysing the host cell membrane. During attachment, the intracellular calcium levels of the target cell increase by 20 fold.[35] One intriguing finding is that the trophozoite may actually "lure in" new target cells, in this case lymphocytes, to the site of infection by upregulating the lymphotactic interleukin IL-8 in the surrounding colonic epithelial cells, while simultaneously inhibiting the upregulation of other cytokines known to play a role in inflammation.[36, 37]

Protective immune mechanisms are short-lived and depend on the development of sIgA antibodies directed against parasite surface proteins involved in adherence to target cells.[38–42]

In addition, cell-mediated killing of parasites can occur by induction of nitric oxide by the 220 kDa lectin, which up-regulates interferon-γ.[43, 44] In experimental infections, polyclonal and monoclonal antibodies have been shown to be effective in protecting the host when they are directed against carbohydrate-binding lectins of the parasite,[45, 46] emphasizing the central role these parasite proteins play in the pathogenesis of disease.

Clinical Disease

A comprehensive summary of all aspects of clinical disease is presented by Petri [47]and Wells and Arguedas.[48]

Intestinal Amoebiasis

Many infected individuals are asymptomatic, and some go on to become carriers. Those who are symptomatic may experience a wide range of clinical manifestations. The most common consequence in symptomatic individuals is diarrhea, lasting more than a few days. Involvement of the entire bowel is usually associated with colicky pain, flatulence, alteration in the pattern of bowel movements, bloody stools, and eventually dysentery, indistinguishable from ulcerative colitis.

Generalized abdominal tenderness, with particular accentuation in the iliac fossae is frequently encountered on physical examination. Dysentery can either worsen, possibly resulting in a life-threatening situation, or resolve into a chronic state of ill health characterized by bouts of diarrhea, abdominal cramping, and abdominal discomfort. In the chronic condition, Amoeboma (large granuloma consisting of eosinophils, amoebae,

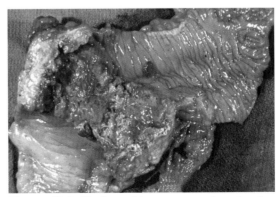

Figure 12.6. Portion of transverse colon showing extensive ulceration due to intestinal infection with *E. histolytica*.

and necrotic colonic tissue) are possible, presenting as palpable masses, and often misdiagnosed on barium enema as malignancies. If disease progresses, the colon may become atonic and may perforate at one or several points of ulceration (Fig. 12.6). If perforation occurs, symptoms and signs of peritonitis may develop. Acute colitis occurs more frequently in children.[47]

The perforated, inflamed bowel may adhere to the abdominal wall, and the perforation may extend to the skin, causing cutaneous Amoebiasis, which can progress rapidly.[49] This situation may also occur in the perianal area as the result of invasion of the skin by the trophozoites emerging from the rectum.

Extraintestinal Amoebiasis

Amoebae can erode the wall of the large intestine until the circulation of the submucosa is breached. In that case, parasites disseminate throughout the body. The most common extraintestinal site is the liver,[48, 50] occasionally presenting as a medical emergency. Invasion of liver tissue may occur after symptomatic intestinal Amoebiasis, or in cases where the colonic infection is asymptomatic. Nearly half of all patients with Amoebic liver abscess do not have a history suggestive of Amoebic colitis.

Hepatic Amoebiasis is a slowly progressive, insidious disease that typically begins as a nonspecific febrile illness, with pain and tenderness in the right upper quadrant of the abdomen. There is frequently referred shoulder pain. Examination at that time may reveal only a slightly enlarged, tender liver, or it may reveal a mass. Most patients with hepatic Amoebiasis have involvement of the right hepatic lobe, but the left lobe of the liver can also be infected; the enlargement and tenderness can be central or even left-sided.

The lungs are the next most common extraintestinal sites of infection.[51,52] The major pleuropulmonary findings include effusion, pleurisy, empyema, or lung abscess. Occasionally, an hepatobronchial fistula is formed, resulting in a productive cough, with large amounts of amoebae-containing necrotic material. Embolism is rare. Rupture into the pericardium is usually fatal.

Cerebral Amoebiasis rarely occurs. The onset is usually abrupt and is associated with a high mortality rate unless diagnosed early on in the infection.[53]

There is growing evidence suggesting that infection with HIV places those individuals at greater risk for developing extraintestinal Amoebiasis with more serious pathological consequences than those without HIV infection.[68]

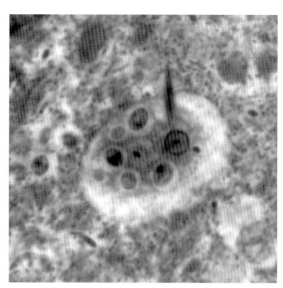

Figure 12.7. Trophozoite of *E. histolytica* in stool of patient suffering from Amoebic dysentery. Note Charcot-Leyden crystal "pointing" to nucleus. Also note numerous red cells in parasite cytoplasm. 30 µm.

Diagnosis

Definitive diagnosis depends upon two approaches: detection of antigens in stool[2] or PCR on stool or tissue samples.[54] Either of these two modalities will most likely replace microscopy, based on their sensitivity, specificity, rapidity, ease of execution, and cost. An ELISA-based test is now in common use that is both rapid and specific for distinguishing these two organisms.[2] Unfortunately, only fresh or frozen fecal samples can be examined by these two methods.[68]

Microscopy is still the only diagnostic modality in many facilities. If red blood cells are seen in the cytoplasm of a suspected trophozoite (Fig. 12.7), then a positive diagnosis of *Entamoeba histolytica* can be made. Without this telltale marker, misdiagnoses in favor of *Entamoeba dispar* will still be commonplace.

The presence of Charcot-Leyden crystals (Fig. 12.8) in stool are frequently seen when patients are suffering from disease caused by *E. histolytica*, but they are also seen with heavy infection caused by *Trichuris trichiura*, and therefore are not pathognomonic for Amoebiasis. PCR can also be useful for diagnosis of liver disease when used on aspirates derived from the abscess.[55]

Since infection with *E. histolytica* invariably leads to long-lasting antibody production, antibody-based tests[56] are sometimes difficult to interpret, especially when done during chronic infection. The IHA and IFA tests are used together to rule in the possibility of extraintestinal disease, but are not definitive proof of infec-

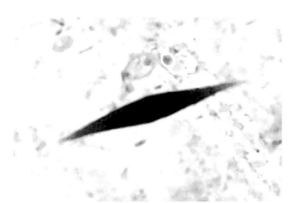

Figure 12.8. Charcot-Leyden crystal in stool of patient suffering from Amoebic dysentery. These crystals can also be found in patients infected with *Trichuris trichiuria* and *Strongyloides stercoralis*.

tion. Intestinal Amoebiasis must always be considered in any patient with protracted diarrhea and in all patients with dysentery. The diagnosis must also be considered in patients presenting with intraluminal colonic masses, because of the development of Amoebomas that resemble carcinoma of the colon. In extraintestinal Amoebiasis, identification of the lesion by the various modalities and the presence of a travel history compatible with Amoebiasis, in parallel with identification of amoebae in the colon, points to the diagnosis.

The erythrocyte sedimentation rate is typically increased, and the total PMN count may be low during active infection. Radiography of the abdomen may show enlargement of the liver and a fixed, raised diaphragm. In cases of perforation of the diaphragm, there may be evidence of consolidation of the left lower lobe of the lung or its lower segment, and a pleural effusion. A radionuclide or a CT scan often reveals the abscess; it may also show additional abscesses, which are rare. On ultrasonography, an Amoebic liver abscess usually appears as a round hypodense area that is contiguous to the liver capsule, usually without significant wall echoes.[47] Direct extension to the right pleural space and the lung is the most common form of intrathoracic Amoebiasis, but hematogenous spread may cause metastatic Amoebiasis in other portions of the lung and the pleura, as well as in other organs, notably the brain. Amoebic pericarditis can occur in the same manner.[57]

Treatment

Metronidazole is the drug of choice[58] for the intestinal and extraintestinal infection. It can be given in equivalent doses orally or intravenously. Apparently, there are no naturally occurring metronidazole-resistant strains

of *E. histolytica*,[59] but they can be easily induced under laboratory conditions.[60] It is probably only a matter of time before they appear in human populations. Liver abscesses resolve slowly, despite treatment with the recommended high doses of metronidazole. This drug also has a few limitations and some adverse side effects. Use of alcohol is prohibited during treatment, as it induces a side effect similar to that caused by disulfiram therapy. Furthermore, it does not affect the cyst stage. Therefore, a cysticidal agent is also indicated. In fact, the latter alone may be adequate for treating asymptomatic cyst passers and those with non-dysenteric Amoebic colitis. Diloxanide furoate and iodoquinol (diidohydroxyquin)[61] both are effective at killing cysts. Iodoquinol is a relatively nontoxic drug.

There are few reports of patients surviving Amoebic abscess of the brain,[53] since, unfortunately, they are typically diagnosed too late. In the case of infection involving the pleural cavity, quick aspiration of an expanding pericardial effusion, combined with aggressive anti-Amoebic therapy, has saved lives of most of those suffering from this rare manifestation of the infection.[62]

An Amoebic liver abscess[48] should be aspirated in the following circumstances: (1) if there is no clinical improvement within 48-72 hours despite appropriate medical therapy; (2) for abscesses greater than 10 cm in diameter; (3) when there is marked elevation of the diaphragm; (4) for abscesses in the left lobe; and (5) when there is negative serology, which might raise suspicion of a pyogenic abscess.[63, 64]

Prevention and Control

Good public health practice, starting with ensuring the safety of drinking water supplies, and in some cases, watershed management, are the best long-term approaches to controlling most waterborne diarrheal disease agents. Thorough screening of food handlers by periodic stool examinations can identify carriers whose occupations would place the general public at risk. Recurrent outbreaks of Amoebiasis in mental institutions can be prevented by strictly adhering to appropriate sanitary practices, coupled with routine stool examinations of the patients. All infected individuals should receive treatment.

Vaccines against both the intestinal and extraintestinal infection may soon become available, based on recent encouraging progress made in the laboratory.[65–68] Its primary use would be to vaccinate children living in hyper-endemic zones.

References

1. Tannich E. Royal Society of Tropical Medicine and Hygiene Meeting at Manson House, London, 19 February 1998. Amoebic disease. *Entamoeba histolytica* and *E. dispar*: comparison of molecules considered important for host tissue destruction.Trans R Soc Trop Med Hyg. 92(6):593-6, 1998.

2. Anane S, Khaled *Entamoeba histolytica* and *Entamoeba dispar*: differentiation methods and implications. S Ann Biol Clin (Paris). 63:7-13. 2005.

3. Reed S, Ravdin JI. Amoebiasis In: Infections of the Gastrointestinal Tract 2nd ed. (Blazer MJ. Smith PD. Ravdin JI. Greenberg HB, Guerrant RL, eds). Raven Press New York. pp 961-978. 2002.

4. Martinez-Paloma A. Espinoza Cantellano M. Intestinal Amoebiasis In: Topley and Wilson's Microbiology and Microbial Infections 9th ed. (Collier L. Balows A. Sussman M. eds). Vol. 5 Parasitology (Cox FEG. Kreier JP. Wakelin D, volume eds.) pp. 157-177. 1998.

5. Loftus B, Anderson I, et al. The genome of the protist parasite *Entamoeba histolytica*. Nature. 433:865-8. 2005.

6. Losch FA. Massenhafte Entwicklung von Amoben in Dickdarm. Arch Pathol Anat Phys KIm Med Virchow 65:196-211, 1875.

7. Quincke HI. Roos E. Uber Amoben-enteritis. Berl KIm Wochen-schr 30:1089-1094, 1893.

8. Schaudinn F. Untersuchungen uber Fortpflanzung einiger Rhizopoden (vorlaufige Mitteilung). Arb Kaiserlichen Ges 19:547–576, 1903.

9. Councilman WT. Lafleur HA. Amoebic dysentery. Johns Hopkins Hosp Rep 2:395-548, 1891.

10. Boeck WC. Cultivation of *Entamoeba histolytica*. Am J Hyg 5:371-407, 1925.

11. Dobell C. Researches on the intestinal protozoa of monkeys and man. Parasitology 20:357-412, 1928.

12. Saavedra E, Encalada R, et al. Glycolysis in *Entamoeba histolytica*. FEBS J. 272:1767-83. 2005.

13. Mai Z. Ghosh S. Frisardi M. et al. Hsp60 is targeted to a cryptic mitochondrion-derived organelle ("crypton") in the microaerophilic protozoan parasite *Entamoeba histolytica*. Mol Cell Biol. 19(3):2198-205, 1999.

14. Tovar J. Fischer A. Clark CG. The mitosome, a novel organelle related to mitochondria in the amitochondrial parasite *Entamoeba histolytica*. Mol Microbiol. 32(5):1013-21, 1999.

15. Bakatselou C, Beste D, et al. Analysis of genes of mitochondrial origin in the genus Entamoeba. J Eukaryot Microbiol. 50:210-4. 2003.

16. Gozalez E, Rico G et al. Calreticulin-like molecule in trophozoites of *Entamoeba histolytica*. Am J Trop Med Hyg 67:636-639. 2002.

17. Walker EL. Sellards AW. Experimental entAmoebic dysentery. Phillipine J Sci B Triop Med 8:253-330. 1913.

18. Makioka A, Kumagai M, et al. Effect of proteasome inhibitors on the growth, encystation, and excystation of *Entamoeba histolytica* and *Entamoeba invadens* Parasitol Res. 88:454-9. 2002

19. Eichinger D. Encystation of Entamoeba parasites. Bioessays 19:633-9. 1997

20. Carrero JC. Laclette JP. Molecular biology of *Entamoeba histolytica*: a review. Archives of Medical Research. 27(3):403-12, 1996.

21. Lohia A. The cell cycle of *Entamoeba histolytica*. Mol Cell Biochem. 253:217-22. 2003.

22. Petri WA Jr. Pathogenesis of Amoebiasis. Curr Opin Microbiol. 5:443-7. 2002

23. Stauffer W, Ravdin JI. *Entamoeba histolytica*: an update. Curr Opin Infect Dis. Oct;16(5):479-85. 2003.

24. Dodson JM. Lenkowski PW Jr. et al. Infection and immunity mediated by the carbohydrate recognition domain of the *Entamoeba histolytica* Gal/GalNAc lectin. J Infect Dis. 179(2):460-6, 1999.

25. Rosales-Encina JL. Meza I et al., Isolation of a 220 kDa protein with lectin properties from a virulent strain of *Entamoeba histolytica*. J Infect Dis 156:790-7. 1987.

26. Vines RR. Ramakrishnan G. et al. Regulation of adherence and virulence by the *Entamoeba histolytica* lectin cytoplasmic domain, which contains a beta2 integrin motif. Mol Biol Cell. 9(8):2069-79, 1998.

27. Braga LL. Ninomiya H. et al. Inhibition of the complement membrane attack complex by the galactose-specific adhesin of *Entamoeba histolytica*. J Clin Invest 90:1131-7. 1992.

28. Kain KC. Ravdin JI. Galactose-specific adhesion mechanisms of *Entamoeba histolytica*: model for study of enteric pathogens. Methods Enzymol 253:424-39, 1995.

29. Arias-Negrete S. Munoz M de L. Murillo-Jasso F. Evaluation of in vitro virulence by *Entamoeba histolytica*: effect of calmodulin inhibitors. APMIS. 107(9):875-81, 1999.

30. McKerrow JH. Sun E. Rosenthal PJ. Bouvier J. The proteases and pathogenicity of parasitic protozoa. Annu Rev Microbiol. 47:821-53, 1993.

31. Reed SL. Ember JA. Herdman DS. et al. The extracellular neutral cysteine proteinase of *Entamoeba histolytica* degrades anaphylatoxins C3a and C5a. J Immunol. 155(1):266-74, 1995.

32. Franco E. de Araujo Soares RM. Meza I. Specific and reversible inhibition of *Entamoeba histolytica* cysteine-proteinase activities by Zn2+: implications for adhesion and cell damage. Arch Med Res. 30(2):82-8, 1999.

33. Leippe M. Muller-Eberhard HJ. The pore-forming peptide of *Entamoeba histolytica*, the protozoan parasite causing human amoebiasis. Toxicology. 87(1-3):5-18, 1994.

34. Vaccaro AM. Salvioli R. Tatti M. Ciaffoni F. Saposins and their interaction with lipids. Neurochem Res. 24(2):307-14, 1999.

35. Ravdin JI, Moreau F. et al. The relationship of free intracellular calcium ions to the cytolytic activity of *Entamoeba histolytica*. Infect Immun 56:1505-1512. 1988.

36. Yu Y. Chadee K. Secreted *Entamoeba histolytica* proteins stimulate interleukin-8 mRNA expression and protein production in human colonic epithelial cells. Arch Med Res. 28 Spec No:223-4, 1997.

37. Utrera-Barillas D, Velazquez JR, et al. An anti-inflammatory oligopeptide produced by *Entamoeba histolytica* down-regulates the expression of pro-inflammatory chemokines. Parasite Immunol. 25:475-82. 2003.

38. Choudhuri G. Prakash. V. et al. Protective immunity to *Entamoeba histolytica* infection in subjects with antiAmoebic antibodies residing in a hyperendemic zone. Scand J Infect Dis. 23(6):771-6, 1991.

39. Lotter H. Zhang T. et al. Identification of an epitope on the *Entamoeba histolytica* 170-kD lectin conferring antibody-mediated protection against invasive Amoebiasis. J Exp Med. 185(10):1793-801, 1997.

40. Ravdin JI. Kelsall BL. Role of mucosal secretory immunity in the development of an Amoebiasis vaccine. Am J Trop Med Hyg. 50(5 Suppl):36-41, 1994.

41. Abou-el-Magd I. Soong CJ. et al. Humoral and mucosal IgA antibody response to a recombinant 52-kDa cysteine-rich portion of the *Entamoeba histolytica* galactose-inhibitable lectin correlates with detection of native 170-kDa lectin antigen in serum of patients with Amoebic colitis. J Infect Dis. 174(1):157-62, 1996.

42. Stanley SL Jr. Protective immunity to Amoebiasis: new insights and new challenges. J Infect Dis.184:504-6. 2001.

43. Ghadirian E. Denis M. In vivo activation of macrophages by IFN-gamma to kill *Entamoeba histolytica* trophozoites in vitro. Parasite Immunol. 14(4):397-404, 1992.

44. Seguin R. Mann BJ. Keller K. Chadee K. The tumor necrosis factor alpha-stimulating region of galactose-inhibitable lectin of *Entamoeba histolytica* activates gamma interferon-primed macrophages for Amoebicidal activity mediated by nitric oxide. Infect Immun. 65(7):2522-7, 1997.

45. Ravdin JI. Shain DC. Kelsall BL. Antigenicity, immunogenicity and vaccine efficacy of the galactose-specific adherence protein of *Entamoeba histolytica*. Vaccine. 11(2):241-6, 1993.

46. Marinets A. Zhang T. Guillen N. et al. Protection against invasive Amoebiasis by a single monoclonal antibody directed against a lipophosphoglycan antigen localized on the surface of *Entamoeba histolytica*. J Exp Med 186(9):1557-65, 1997.

47. Petri WA Jr. Pathogenesis of Amoebiasis. Curr Opin Microbiol. 5:443-7. 2002.

48. Wells CD, Arguedas M. Amoebic liver abscess. South Med J. 97:673-82. 2004

49. Parshad S, Grover PS, et al. Primary cutaneous amoebiasis: case report with review of the literature. Int J Dermatol. 41:676-80. 2002.

50. Hoffner RJ. Kilaghbian T. Esekogwu VI. Henderson SO. Common presentations of Amoebic liver abscess. Ann Emerg Med. 34(3):351-5, 1999.

51. Lyche KD. Jensen WA. Pleuropulmonary Amoebiasis. Semin Respir Infect. 12(2):106-12, 1997.

52. Mbaye PS. Koffi N. Camara P. et al. Manifestations pleuropulmonaires de l'amibiase. Rev Pneumol Clin. 54(6):346-52, 1998.

53. Sundaram C, Prasad BC, et al. Brain abscess due to *Entamoeba histolytica*. Assoc Physicians India. 52:251-2. 2004.

54. Mirelman D. Nuchamowitz Y. Stolarsky T. Comparison of use of enzyme-linked immunosorbent assay-based kits and PCR amplification of rRNA genes for simultaneous detection of *Entamoeba histolytica* and *E. dispar*. J Clin Microbiol. 35:2405-7, 1997.

55. Zengzhu G. Bracha R. et al. Analysis by enzyme-linked immunosorbent assay and PCR of human liver abscess aspirates from patients in China for *Entamoeba histolytica*. J Clin Microbiol. 37:3034-6, 1999.

56. Lotter H. Jackson TF. Tannich E. Evaluation of three serological tests for the detection of antiAmoebic antibodies applied to sera of patients from an area endemic for Amoebiasis Trop Med Parasitol. 46:180-2, 1995.

57. Shamsuzzaman SM. Hashiguchi Y. Thoracic Amoebiasis. Clin Chest Med. 23:479-92. 2002.

58. Rosenblatt JE. Antiparasitic agents. Mayo Clin Proc. 67: 276-87, 1992.

59. Bansal D. Sehgal R. et al. in vitro activity of antiAmoebic drugs against clinical isolates of *Entamoeba histolytica* and *Entamoeba dispar*. Ann Clin Microbiol Antimicrob. 3:27. 2004.

60. Upcroft P. Upcroft JA. Drug targets and mechanisms of resistance in the anaerobic protozoa. Clin Microbiol Rev. 14:150-64. 2001.

61. Mcauley JB. Herwaldt BL. et al. Diloxanide furoate for treating asymptomatic *Entamoeba histolytica* cyst passers: 14 years' experience in the United States. Clin Infect Dis 15:464-468, 1992.

62. Kirchhoff LV, Weiss LM, et al. Parasitic diseases of the heart. Front Biosci Jan. 9:706-23. 2004.

63. Gibney EI. Amoebic liver abscess. Br I Surg 77:843-844, 1990.

64. De la Rey Nell. Simjec AE. Patel A. Indications for aspiration of Amoebic liver abscess. S Afr Med J 75:373-376, 1989.

65. Zhang T. Stanley SL Jr. Oral immunization with an attenuated vaccine strain of *Salmonella typhimurium* expressing the serine-rich *Entamoeba histolytica* protein induces an antiAmoebic immune response and protects gerbils from Amoebic liver abscess. Infect Immun. 64:1526-31, 1996.

66. Houpt E. Barroso L. et al. Prevention of intestinal Amoebiasis by vaccination with the *Entamoeba histolytica* Gal/GalNac lectin. Vaccine. 22:611-7. 2004.

67. Lotter H. Russmann H. et al. Oral vaccination with recombinant *Yersinia enterocolitica* expressing hybrid type III proteins protects gerbils from Amoebic liver abscess. Infect Immun. 72:7318-21. 2004.

68. Hung CC, Deng HY, et al. Invasive Amoebiasis as an emerging parasitic disease in patients with human immunodeficiency virus type 1 infection in Taiwan. Arch Intern Med.165:409-15. 2005.

13. *Balantidium coli*
(Malmsten 1857)

Introduction

Balantidium coli is the only ciliated protozoan that routinely infects humans. Balantidiasis occurs throughout the world, but the prevalence of human infection is not known. It is endemic in Japan,[1] New Guinea, Micronesia, Seychelles Islands, Thailand,[2, 3] South Africa,[4] Central and South America, and Europe.[2, 5, 6] Sporadic epidemics have occurred in institutionalized populations. *B. coli* locates to the large intestine, where it causes dysentery, occasionally leading to fatalities. It has many reservoir hosts,[1] including both domestic and wild mammals (non-human primates, guinea pigs, horses, cattle, pigs, wild boars, and rats). When patients suffering from HIV encounter *B. coli*, the infection can locate to sites other than the GI tract.[7]

Historical Information

In 1857, Malmsten[8] observed and described in detail *B. coli* organisms in two patients from Stockholm, Sweden, suffering from acute diarrheal disease. One patient went on to recover, while the other succumbed to the infection.

Life Cycle

There are two stages produced by *Balantidium coli*; the trophozoite (Fig. 13.1), and the cyst (Fig. 13.2). The invasive stage is the trophozoite. *B. coli* resides in the tissues of the large intestine (Fig. 13.3), in a similar habitat to that of *Entamoeba histolytica* (see Fig. 12.4, 12.6) from which it must be clinically distinguished. The

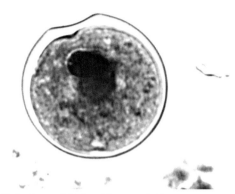

Figure 13.2. Cyst of *Balantidium coli*. Note macronucleus. 65 µm.

trophozoite of *B. coli* ingests living cells and causes ulcerations to develop at the site of infection. The cyst stage is found in the fecal mass, and measures 55 µm in diameter.

Infection begins by ingestion of the cyst, usually along with fecally-contaminated food or water. The trophozoite excysts in the small intestine, then relocates to the large intestine. The preferred site of infection is the epithelium of the transverse and descending colon. *B. coli* is usually limited to the bowel, although a case involving liver abscess has been reported,[9] as well as infection in the lungs and heart.[7, 10] The trophozoite divides by simple binary fission within the host, but in culture, it behaves like all other free-living ciliates, undergoing syngamy, a specialized type of sexual reproduction similar to conjugation.[11]

The trophozoites cause extensive destruction to the surrounding tissue (Fig. 13.4). During prolonged infection, some trophozoites enter the lumen of the colon, where they secrete an impervious, hyaline, acellular layer resulting in the formation of the cyst stage. The cyst exits from the host in the fecal mass and is immediately infectious. In many ecological settings, pigs are the presumed reservoirs, since infection is common where pigs live in close association with human habitats. Guinea pigs are thought to harbor *B. coli* as a commensal and have been the source of some human infections.[6]

Pathogenesis

Little is known about the nutritional requirements of *Balantidium coli*. The trophozoite possesses a hyaluronidase which is presumed to facilitate lysis of cells.[12] Proteases, most likely lysosomal in origin, released within food vacuoles (phagolysosomes), participate in the process of digestion of cell debris that enters through the peristome (mouth-like opening).

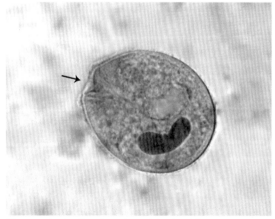

Figure 13.1. Trophozoite of *Balantidium coli*. Note large macronucleus and cytostome (arrow). 150 µm.

Balantidium coli

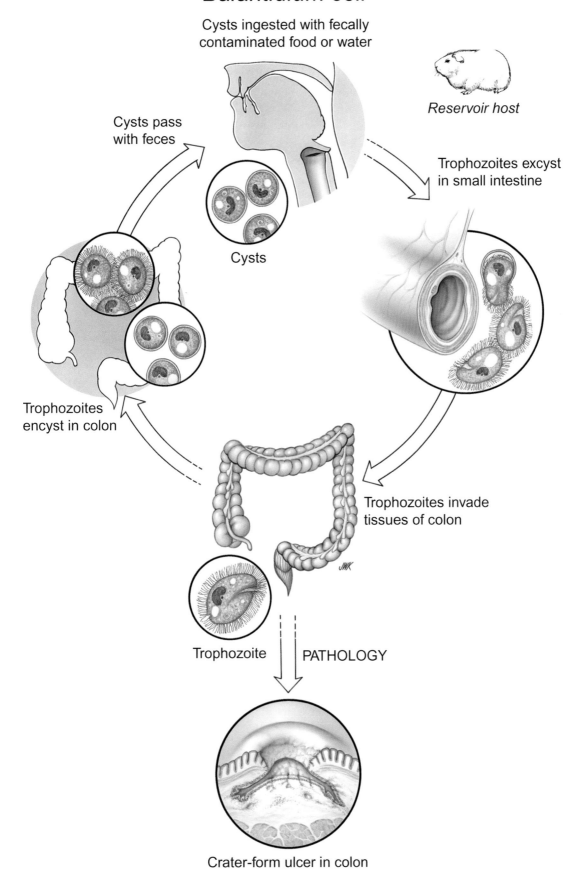

Cysts ingested with fecally contaminated food or water

Reservoir host

Cysts pass with feces

Cysts

Trophozoites excyst in small intestine

Trophozoites encyst in colon

Trophozoites invade tissues of colon

Trophozoite

PATHOLOGY

Crater-form ulcer in colon

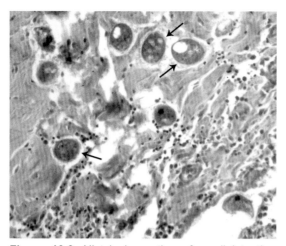

Figure 13.3. Histologic section of small intestine infected with *B. coli* (arrows).

Clinical Disease

Diarrhea, and occasionally dysentery, are the chief complaints of patients suffering from balantidiasis. Fever, nausea, vomiting, and asthenia have been described. However, most infected individuals are asymptomatic. Rarely, *B. coli* causes ulcerative and granulomatous disease in the colon and appendix leading to typhlitis and appendicitis.[13] AIDS patients suffer more severe disease and tend to have ectopic infections compared to immuncompetent infected individuals.[7]

Diagnosis

Definitive diagnosis is by identifying the organism (trophozoite or cyst; see Figs 13.1, 13.2) by microscopy in a sample of stool, or on a stained section of tissue from a biopsy of an ulcer identified by colonoscopy. There are no serologic tests. There is no need for culture, as the organisms are large and easily recognized.

Treatment

Tetracycline is the drug of choice, but metronidazole, paromomycin, chloroquine, and iodoquinol have been used to successfully treat balantidiasis. Surgery (bowel resection) is sometimes necessary in severe cases of dysentery.

Prevention and Control

Good sanitation and a clean source of drinking water are prerequisites for controlling the spread of *B. coli*. When pigs share the same space with humans, as is the case in many parts of the less-developed world (Fig. 13.5), hygiene is non-existent, and encourages infection with *B.coli*.

References

1.   Nakauchi K. The prevalence of *Balantidium coli* infection in fifty-six mammalian species. J Vet Med Sci. 61(1):63-5, 1999.

2.   Nuti M. De Comarmond C. De Dac C. An endemic focus of balantidiasis in the Seychelles Islands. In Abstracts of the 10th Internat Congr Trop Med Malaria. p 13, 1980.

3.   Chavalittamrong B. Jirapinyo P. Intestinal parasites in pediatric patients with diarrhoeal diseases in Bangkok. Southeast Asian J of Trop Med Pub Health 15(3):385-388, 1984.

4.   Currie AR. A human balantidiasis. A case report. S Afr J Surg 28:23-25, 1990.

5.   Clyti E. Aznar C. Couppie P. et al. A case of coinfection by *Balantidium coli* and HIV in French Guiana. Bull Soc Pathol Exotique 91(4):309-311, 1998.

6.   Hindsbo O, Nielsen CV, Andreassen J. et al. Age-dependent occurrence of the intestinal ciliate *Balantidium coli* in pigs at a Danish research farm. Acta Vet Scand 41:79–83. 2000.

7.   Vasilakopoulos A, Dimarongona K, et al. *Balantidium coli* pneumonia in an immunocompromised patient. Scand J Infect Dis 35:144–146. 2003.

8.   Malmsten PH. Infusorien als intestinal-Tiere beim Menschen. Arch Pathol Anat Physiol Klin Med (Virchow) 12:302-309, 1857.

9.   Wenger F. Abscesso hepatico producido por el *Balantidium coli*. Kasmera 2:433-435, 1967.

10. Arean VM. Koppisch E. Balantidiasis: a review and report of cases. Am J Pathol 32:1089-1117, 1956.

11. Zaman V. *Balantidium coli*. In: Topley and Wilson's Microbiology and Microbial Infections. (Collier, L. Balows, A. Sussman, M., eds.). Volume 5. Parasitology. (Cox, FEG. Kreier, Jp. Wakelin, D, volume eds.). Arnold Pubs. London. pp. 445-450, 1998.

12. Tempelis CH, Lysenko MG: The production of hyaluronidase by *B. coli*. Exp Parasitol 6:31-36, 1957.

13. Dodd LG: *Balantidium coli* infestation as a cause of acute appendicitis. J Infect Dis 163:1392, 1991.

14. Protozoans of Minor Medical Importance

Babesia spp.

Babesia spp. comprise a group of genetically related intracellular protozoa that infect red blood cells. They are closely allied to the malarias, and all are vector-borne infections transmitted by the bite of ticks. Babesiosis in humans can manifest as a mild fever or progress to a severe, life threatening illness. Each species has numerous reservoir hosts. *Babesia bigemina* occasionally infects humans, but primarily infects cattle, causing extensive economic loss wherever it is endemic. *B. microti* is the most common species infecting rodents and humans in the United States.[1] *B. gibsoni* infects dogs, and some human cases have been reported,[2] but may prove to be a related, as yet undescribed species.[3] The occurrence of babesiosis in humans is considered a rarity, yet 139 cases were reported from New York State between 1982 and 1993.[4] It is classified as an emerging infection by the Center for Disease Control and Prevention.

B. divergens is the most frequently occurring species in Europe[5] and is also considered an emerging infection in that region of the world. Many species overlap in their geographic distribution, but most have discrete ecological niches largely determined by the species of ticks found there.

Historical Information

Smith and Kilbourne, in 1893,[6] demonstrated that ticks were the vectors of *Babesia bigemina*, the cause of Texas Cattle Fever in the Southwestern United States, making this infectious agent the first one shown to be transmitted by the bite of an arthropod. Their finding inspired others to look for other vector-borne diseases. Shortly thereafter, the mosquito vectors for the yellow fever virus and *Plasmodium spp.* were described.

Life Cycle

The sexual aspects of the life cycle takes place in the tick, but almost nothing is known about the biology of Babesia once it is introduced into humans, its mammalian intermediate host. Infection begins by the introduction of sporozoites contained within the salivary secretions of the larval tick. *Ixodes scapularis* is the vector for *B. microti* in the United States (the same one that transmits Lyme Disease), and *Ixodes ricinus* transmitts *B. divergens* in Europe. Because it infects red cells, infections can also be acquired by blood transfusion.[7]

The sporozoites eventually infect erythrocytes, but little is known regarding potential involvement of any other site in the body. Babesia enters a red blood cell (Fig. 14.1) by inducing a deformation in the membrane, creating a parasitophorous vacuole.[8] There it grows and develops, eventually dividing into merozoites. Simultaneously, the parasitophorous vacuole breaks down, leaving the organism bathed in the naked red cell cyosol. It is inferred by its ecological niche that babesia ingests and utilizes hemoglobin as its sole nutritional source. In contrast with Plasmodium, Babesia does not discard haemazoin within the red blood cells. Reproduction is by schizogony. Occasionally, a merozoite differentiates into either a male or female gametocyte, as in the Plasmodia. High levels of parasitized red blood cells is the norm, sometimes without pathological consequences.[9, 10]

The sexual cycle takes place in a variety of tick organs. Two weeks after ingesting organisms, oocysts develop, containing infectious haploid sporozoites. This latter stage locates to the salivary glands. Larval ticks remain infected throughout the winter months. After developing to the nymph stage, they can transmit the infection to another host (mouse, bovine, dog, or human).[11]

Clinical Disease

Babesiosis induces high fever in adults, and has been frequently misdiagnosed in the United States on clinical grounds as tick-borne typhus (Rocky Mountain spotted fever). In the U.S., patients typically present in one of two ways. Immunocompetent individuals develop a self-limiting disease of mild duration, lasting two to four weeks.[12-14] It is typically accompanied by fever, malaise, headache, and occasionally bradycardia with lymphopenia.[15] Often, however, patients are coinfected with other tick-borne pathogens, such as *Borrelia burgdorferi* and *Ehrlichia spp.*, complicating the clinical picture.[16-21] Recovery following treatment is usual. In Europe, infection due to *B. divergens*[13, 14] is more severe. Intravascular haemolysis and haemaglobinuria is common, and may necessitate whole body transfusion as an emergency procedure.

In human infection with *B. microti*, the ratio of CD4+ to CD8+ T cells decreases during infection, while natural killer (NK) cells, interferon-γ, TNF, IL-2 and IL-6 increase, indicating that NK cells may be important in modulation of infection.[22] Patients suffering from AIDS may develop a long-term chronic infection following specific therapy for babesiosis.[23]

Patients without spleens are at greatest risk of dying from babesiosis.[24-27]

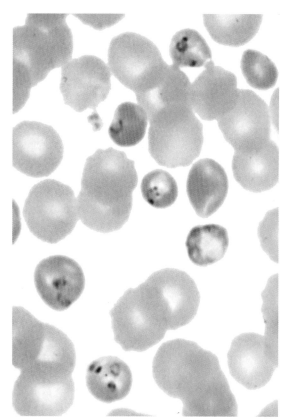

Figure 14.1. Red cells infected with various stages of *Babesia microti*.

Diagnosis

Reviews of the diagnosis and treatment of babesiosis are available.[28,29] Definitive diagnosis is by microscopy of a Giemsa-stained blood smear, or by PCR.[28] The PCR test is as sensitive as a blood smear for detecting organisms. An ELISA-based test has been developed and may prove to be useful in the diagnostic laboratory.[98]

Treatment

Azithromycin, clindamycin, and quinine[30] are effective in treating most cases of uncomplicated babesiosis. However, in some individuals, the infection may persist, even after receiving a combination of clindamycin and quinine, as determined by PCR.[31] As mentioned, whole body transfusion and quinine is necessary in many cases involving *B. divergens*.[14]

Prevention and control

Since *Babesia spp.* infect a number of reservoir host species, some domestic and some wild, avoiding environments in which infection occurs is not possible. Prevention on an individual level includes checking for nymphal stage ticks (note: this stage of Ixodes is quite difficult to see) at the end of each trip into a wooded area, and taking precautions to cover up the lower portion of pants with socks. This advice is particularly relevant for those living in the Northeastern regions of United States, where the prevalence of *Borrelia burgdorferi* in some populations of Ixodes ticks have been shown to be as high as 50%. DEET sprayed at the bottom of pants may also help. There are no vaccines against babesia for humans, but ones for use in cattle are under development.[32] Burning understory in wooded, tick-infested regions may prove useful in ecologically controlling infection in ticks.[33]

Isospora belli
(Wenyon, 1923)

Isospora belli [34] is an intracellular parasite of humans that lives within enterocytes of the small intestine. *I. belli* is a rare infection in immunocompetent individuals, but in recent years it has emerged as a serious diarrheal disease in patients suffering from HIV/AIDS.[35]

Life Cycle

Infection begins by ingesting the sporulated oocyst along with fecally contaminated food. The oocyst (Figs. 14.2, 14.3) measures approximately 25 μm by 15 μm. Four sporozoites reside within each of the two sporocysts contained by the oocyst. Digestion of the cyst wall causes the release of the sporozoites into the lumen of the small intestine, and there they enter columnar epithelial cells. Asexual reproduction follows, leading to increased numbers of meronts and zoites. *I. belli* infection in humans is similar to the sexual phase of *Toxoplasma gondii* in the cat (see page 75). Occasionally, gametocytes may develop, resulting in the pro-

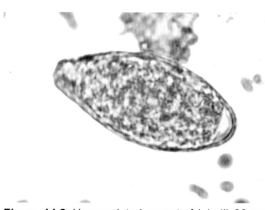

Figure 14.2. Unsporulated oocyst of *I. belli*. 20 μm.

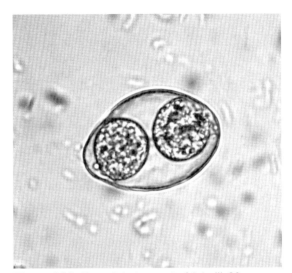

Figure 14.3. Sporulated oocyst of *I. belli*. 20 μm.

duction of an oocyst. The molecular events controlling oocyst formation have yet to be elucidated. Oocysts are passed in the fecal mass unsporulated and are therefore non-infectious. They rapidly sporulate upon reaching the external environment and are now infectious for another individual. In HIV/AIDS patients, *I. belli* can invade and reproduce in other organs, such as the gall bladder,[36] liver, spleen,[37] and lymph nodes.[38]

Pathogenesis

I. belli causes a protracted, secretory diarrhea in AIDS patients, resembling that induced by Cryptosporidium.[39] In most other patient populations, infection is either silent or the diarrhea is transitory. Malabsorption of fats in immunocompromised patients has been reported.[40]

Clinical Disease

Patients infected with *Isospora belli* may experience fever, cramping diarrhea, malaise, and weight loss. HIV/AIDS patients present with severe disease, including watery diarrhea, malabsorption syndrome, and may even die from wasting associated with protracted weight loss and electrolyte imbalance.[41]

Diagnosis

Identifying the unsporulated oocysts by microscopy is the definitive diagnostic test of choice. Biopsy of small intestinal tissue often reveals the intracellular parasites in heavy infections.

Treatment

Trimethaprim-sulfamethoxazole and pyrimethamine[42] are the drugs of choice for *I. belli* infection. Nitazoxanide may become the recommended drug of choice over the next few years.[43]

Prevention and control

Avoiding fecal contamination of food, and proper disposal of human feces is the best way to prevent infection. Regrettably, in many areas of the world, these recommendations are difficult or impossible to follow.

Cyclospora cayetanensis

Cyclospora cayetanensis causes watery diarrhea in humans and is acquired by the fecal-oral route,[44,45,46] mostly in contaminated food and perhaps in water, also. This infection was virtually unknown 15 years ago,[47] but has since emerged as an important health risk. In some populations, particularly in tropical regions of Peru, Brazil, and Haiti, it is considered endemic,[48] particularly among those suffering from HIV/AIDS.[49]

Epidemics are seasonal, but vary widely from region to region, occurring sometimes during periods of drought. Several outbreaks in the United States have been caused by ingestion of fecally contaminated imported raspberries.[50-52]

The life cycle can be completed in a single host species, but little is known about the details of the life cycle, or the role of reservoir hosts in maintaining infection in the environment.[53] A parasite similar in morphology to *C. cayetanensis* has been isolated from domestic dogs,[54] and one from non-human primates appears to be a different species based on its morphology.[55]

Life Cycle

Infection begins with the ingestion of a sporulated oocyst (Fig. 14.4). Presumably, sporozoites are released in the small intestine, attach to epithelial cells, and replicate in a manner similarly to those of *Cryptosporidium parvum*, a closely related pathogen.

Clinical Disease

Following infection, watery diarrhea ensues within a week or two, depending upon the initial number of oocysts ingested. Symptoms can last up to two weeks in immunocompetent individuals.[56] In those suffering from HIV/AIDS, diarrhea is protracted. Nausea, vomiting, anorexia, weight loss, and abdominal cramping are frequent symptoms during the acute phase of the infection.[54] One patient who recovered from infection with *C. cayetanensis* developed Guillian-Barre syndrome.[57]

Diagnosis

Diagnosis is by microscopic identification of oocysts in stool samples (Fig. 14.4). A PCR test useful in surveying food items[58] may soon prove useful in the laboratory diagnosis of this organism as well.

Treatment, Control, and Prevention

The drug of choice for treatment of infection with *C. cayetanensis* is trimethoprim- sulfamethoxazole.

The source of infection is typically fecally contaminated food, so prevention and control at the community level is possible by employing good public health practices, especially in agricultural settings.

Naegleria fowleri and *Acanthamoeba spp.*
(Culbertson, 1971)

Several groups of free-living amoebae cause serious disease in humans; *Naegleria fowleri*, various species of Acanthamoeba (*A. astronyxis, A. culbertsoni, A. castellani, A. polyphaga, A. rhysodes,* and *A. hatchetti*), and *Balamuthia mandrillaris*. A review of this group is available.[59] All of these species are worldwide in distribution and have been isolated from all types of fresh water habitats and soils. *N. fowleri* is thermophilic, thriving in standing fresh water environments such as hot springs, heated swimming pools, and hot tubs.

Naeglaria fowleri

Naegleria fowleri is a robust amoeba. The trophozoite (Fig. 14.5) measures 20-30 µm in diameter, while its cyst is smaller, measuring 8-10 µm in diameter. *N. fowleri* was found in abundance in the thermal spas built by a Roman legion in what is now Bath, England.[60] Its discovery there caused the spa to be temporarily closed, and the resulting archeological dig through the sediments that had built up over the centuries led to fascinating glimpses into the lives of this ancient army during its occupation of that region.

Clinical Disease

N. fowleri causes a serious, often fatal, fulminating infection in the central nervous system, referred to as Primary Amoebic Meningoencephalitis (PAM).[61,62]

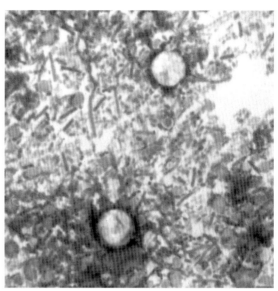

Figure 14.4. Oocyst of *C. cayetanensis*. 10 µm.

Cases of PAM have occurred in the United States, Europe, Australia, South and Central America, and Southeast Asia.

The infection is typically acquired by swimming or bathing in water above 37°C. It is presumed that this unusual environment results in the selection of an abundance of thermally tolerant organisms, including *N. fowleri*.[63] Diving or playful splashing activity can force heated water containing the trophozoites up into the nose and through the cribiform plate. Once inside the brain, amoebae lyse their way through tissue, probably aided by a pore-forming protein similar to that of *Entamoeba histolytica*,[64] causing extensive destruction. Symptoms include severe frontal headache, vomiting, confusion, fever and coma, followed by death.[65]

Diagnosis

Amoebae can be isolated from cerebrospinal fluid in many instances. In this case, the fluid should be concentrated, a smear made, stained with Giemsa or Wright's stain, and examined microscopically. Biopsy is another option that will reveal organisms. However, diagnosis is often delayed by the fact that PAM resembles symptoms of meningitis, a more commonly occurring clinical entity. Since death ensues within five days after the acquisition of PAM, rapid diagnosis is essential. *N. fowleri* should be suspected in any otherwise healthy young adult with a recent history of contact with heated water. No serological or PCR-based tests are available, although DNA probes specific for *N. fowleri* have been developed for its detection in water samples.[66]

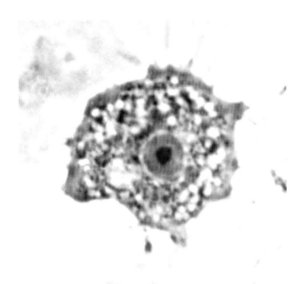

Figure 14.5. Trophozoite of *Naeglaria fowleri*. Phase contrast. 25 μm.

Treatment and Prevention

Since there is so little clinical experience with this usually fatal disease, there are no recommended drugs of choice. Amphotericin B is the only therapeutic agent with known efficacy,[67] but diagnosis is usually made too late in the disease for its use to be effective.

N. fowleri is ubiquitous in distribution, and therefore no specific recommendations on how to avoid contact with it can be given. One study conducted in Oklahoma showed that the number of pathogenic free-living amoeba species varied throughout the seasons, and were most prevalent in natural water sources (i.e., lakes and impoundments) in the spring and fall. This suggests that the organisms are normally found in benthic situations, and only gain access to the water column during periods of lake "turn over."[68]

Due to the rarity of this disease, most situations leading to infection must be classified as incidents of unlucky circumstance, especially when one considers the number of visits to hot tubs, spas and natural hot springs, and the number of user hours spent relaxing in them.

Acanthamoeba spp.

Clinical Disease

Acanthamoeba spp. infections most commonly occur in immunocompromised patients, especially those suffering from HIV/AIDS,[72] while those caused by *Balamuthia mandrillaris* can infect both immunocompromised and immunocompetent individuals. A review of the clinical aspects of infection with *Acanthamoeba spp.* is available.[73]

The route of infection of *Acanthamoeba spp.* and *B. mandrillaris* is most likely via the lungs or skin,[74] resulting in multiple foci of infection.[75] Like *Naegleria fowleri*, *Acanthamoeba spp.* can also invade the central nervous system.[76] In the brain, a slowly developing, ulcerative granulomatous disease develops, characterized by diplopia, frontal headache, seizures, and occasionally death. Patients with AIDS may experience overwhelming disseminated infection.[72, 77]

Ulcerative keratitis of the eye caused by *Acanthamoeba spp.* occurs primarily in those who use contact lenses that are routinely washed in unfiltered tap water.[78] This now considered a rare situation, primarily due to targeted public health education programs, and the availability of sterile lens cleaning solutions. Infection begins with the excystation of the trophozoite under the contact lens after it is applied to the eye. Amoebae invade the cornea and begin to erode the surface, creating the sensation of burning and a percieved "gritty" consistency under the lid when the eye is closed. A ring-enhancing lesion develops, impairing vision. Partial or total blindness may ensue if left untreated.

Diagnosis

Definitive diagnosis depends upon microscopically identifying the amoebae in biopsy tissue, CSF, or lachrymal secretions. A reliable staining method is available,[79] employing Field's staining reagent. This test is rapid, taking only 20 minutes to carry out, and is also a valuable adjunct for field surveys.

Treatment and Prevention

As with *Naeglaria fowleri*, so few cases have oc-

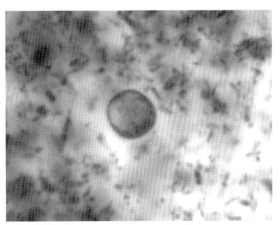

Figure 14.6. *Blastocystis hominis*. 6 μm.

curred that a reliable treatment cannot be recommended due to lack of clinical experience. Few patients with granulomatous disease of the CNS survive, regardless of treatment, particularly those suffering from HIV/AIDS. Keratitis is also difficult to treat, but some drugs show promise, particularly topical miconazole, propamidine and neosporin.[80] Prevention of keratitis is straightforward and simple: use only sterile contact lens cleaning solutions. These products are easily obtained at any drug store as over-the-counter preparations. In contrast, HIV/AIDS predisposes individuals to topical or inhalation entry routes, and since acanthamoebae are found in countless ecological settings, it is nearly impossible to advise a method of avoiding contact with this ubiquitous group of organisms.

Blastocystis hominis

Blastocystis hominis is an anaerobic protozoan of uncertain taxonomic status.[81] *B. hominis* has been recently described in detail at the electron microscope level,[82] and this study recognized only two stages: the vacuolar stage (Fig. 14.6) and the cyst. Division is by binary fission. No sexual aspect to its life cycle has been documented. Other morphologically distinct stages have been reported in the literature, but may have been produced as the result of less than optimal culture conditions. The fecal-oral route is presumed to be the way *B. hominis* infects, although a role for the cyst stage has yet to be defined. It can be grown axenically,[83, 84] permitting studies on its biochemical, genetic and biological properties.

Blastocystis hominis is a very common finding on routine stool examination worldwide, regardless of the health status of the individual being cared for. This organism is also frequently encountered with other more clinically defined pathogens, and this fact alone has made deciding on its status as pathogen, based upon its epidemiology, nearly impossible. Nonetheless, it is continually linked with GI symptoms, and several clear-cut cases have been described that could not have any interpretation other than illness caused by *B. hominis*, based upon an extensive negative laboratory finding regarding all other known pathogens of the GI tract. In one case, gastroenteritis accompanied by diarrhea and hypoalbuminemia in the complete absence of all other pathogens was reported.[85]

Many genetically distinct strains of *B. hominis* have been characterized,[86] so it is possible that some variants are pathogenic, while others are not.[87] This could explain the high degree of variability in its clinical presentation.[88,91] Most patients suffering from HIV/AIDS do not have an increased prevalence of *B. hominis* infection, nor do they appear to be any more affected by its presence than those harboring it in the general

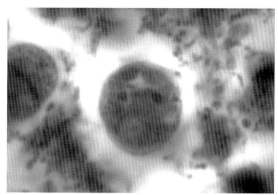

Figure 14.7. *Dientamoeba fragilis*. Note the two nuclei. 10 µm

immunocompetent population. Exceptions have been reported in which the patient was symptomatic with diarrhea and was treated successfully after diagnosis of *B. hominis* infection, only.[92] The very elderly may represent an exception, under certain as-yet-undefined conditions.[93]

Treatment of heavily infected individuals with metronidazole, a proven antimicrobial agent against most anaerobes, was not uniformly effective in eradicating *B. hominis*,[94] but nitazoxanide shows promise as an effective alternative therapeutic approach.[92]

Dientamoeba fragilis
(Jepps and Dobell, 1918)

Dientamoeba fragilis is taxonomically related to *Histomonas spp.*,[95] a flagellated protozoan, but it has the morphology of an amoeba. A review of general characteristics and clinical presentations is available.[96] Each trophozoite (Fig. 14.7) has two nuclei, and there is no cyst stage yet identified, although extensive research has been done in attempts to find one. It is responsible for causing a related series of gastroenteritis-like symptoms, including diarrhea and nausea. Transmission from one individual to another is assumed to be by the fecal-oral route, but since there is no evidence for a cyst stage, an alternate infection strategy suggests that it can hide inside pinworm eggs and gain entrance into the host by being swallowed along with them. This view has not been embraced by the majority of those in the infectious disease community, since the infection is widespread among adults who do not harbor pinworm. A counter-argument states that adults are less susceptible to pinworm than children, but could still ingest enough eggs to acquire *D. fragilis*, if this is actually the way in which the infection is acquired.

Diagnosis is either by direct examination of stool by microscopy, or by PCR.[97]

While numerous standard drugs have been shown to have some efficacy in treating infections, none are recommended, and treatment for this infection is still

References

1. Eskow ES. Krause PJ. Spielman A. et al. Southern extension of the range of human babesiosis in the eastern United States. J Clin Microbiol 37(6):2051-2, 1999.
2. Herwaldt BL. Kjemtrup AM. et al. Transfusion-transmitted babesiosis in Washington State: first reported case caused by a WA1-type parasite. J Infect Dis 175(5):1259-62, 1997.
3. Telford S R. Speilman A. Babesiosis of Humans In: Topley and Wilson's Microbiology and Microbial Infections. 9th ed. (Collier L. Balows A. Sussman M., eds.) Volume 5 Parasitology. (Cox FEG. Kreier J. Wakelin D., volume eds.) pp. 349-359. Arnold Pub., London. 1998.
4. White DJ. Talarico J. Chang HG. et al. Human babesiosis in New York State: Review of 139 hospitalized cases and analysis of prognostic factors. Arch Intern Med 158(19):2149-54, 1998.
5. Gray JS. Babesia spp.: emerging intracellular parasites in Europe. Pol J Microbiol 53 Suppl:55-60. 2004.
6. Smith T. Kilbourne FL Investigations into the nature, causation and prevention of Texas or south cattle fever. USDA Bureau Anim Indust Bull 1:1-301. 1893.
7. Leiby DA, Gill JE. Transfusion-transmitted tick-borne infections: a cornucopia of threats. Transfus Med Rev.18:293-306. 2004.
8. Rudzinska MA. Morphological aspects of host-cell-parasite relationships in babesiosis. In: Babesiosis (Ristic M. Kreier JP., eds.). Academic Press, Pubs pp. 87-141. 1981.
9. Christianson D. Pollack RJ. et al. Persistent parasitemia after acute babesiosis. N E J M 339:160-5, 1998.
10. Shih CM. Liu LP. et al. Human babesiosis in Taiwan: asymptomatic infection with a *Babesia microti*-like organism in a Taiwanese woman. J Clin Microbiol 35(2):450-4, 1997.
11. Piesman J. Mather TN. et al. Seasonal variation of transmission risk of Lyme Disease and human babesiosis. Am J Epidemiol 126:242-48, 1987.
12. Boustani MR. Gelfand JA. Babesiosis. Clinical Infect Dis 22:611-5, 1996.
13. Gorenflot A. Moubri K. Precigout E. et al. Human babesiosis. Annal Trop Med Parasit 92(4):489-501, 1998.
14. Uguen C. Girard L. Brasseur P. Leblay La. babesiose humainen 1992. Revue Med Interne 18(12):945-51, 1997.
15. Kim N. Rosenbaum GS. Cunha BA. Relative bradycardia and lymphopenia in patients with babesiosis. Clin Infect Dis 26(5): 1218-9, 1998.
16. Persing DH. The cold zone: a curious convergence of tick-transmitted diseases. Clin Infect Dis 25 Suppl 1:S35-42, 1997.
17. Hilton E. DeVoti J. Benach JL. et al. Seroprevalence and sero-conversion for tick-borne diseases in a high-risk population in the northeast United States. Am J Med 106(4):404-9, 1999.
18. Krause PJ. Telford SR 3rd. Spielman A. et al. Concurrent Lyme disease and babesiosis. Evidence for increased severity and duration of illness. JAMA 275(21):1657-60, 1996.
19. Mitchell PD. Reed KD. Hofkes JM. Immunoserologic evidence of coinfection with *Borrelia burgdorferi*, *Babesia microti*, and human granulocytic Ehrlichia species in residents of Wisconsin and Minnesota. J Clin Microbiol 34:724-7, 1996.
20. Magnarelli LA. Ijdo JW. et al. Human exposure to a granulocytic Ehrlichia and other tick-borne agents in Connecticut. J Clin Microbiol 36:2823-7, 1998.
21. dos Santos CC. Kain KC. Two tick-borne diseases in one: a case report of concurrent babesiosis and Lyme disease in Ontario. CMAJ 160:1851-3, 1999.
22. Shaio MF. Lin PR. A case study of cytokine profiles in acute human babesiosis. Am J Trop Med Hyg 58:335-7, 1998.
23. Falagas ME. Klempner MS. Babesiosis in patients with AIDS: a chronic infection presenting as fever of unknown origin. Clin Infect Dis 22:809-12, 1996.
24. Herwaldt B. Persing DH. Precigout EA. et al. A fatal case of babesiosis in Missouri: identification of another piroplasm that infects humans Annals Intern Med 124:643-50, 1996.
25. Slovut DP. Benedetti E. Matas AJ. Babesiosis and hemophagocytic syndrome in an asplenic renal transplant recipient. Transplant 62:537-9, 1996.
26. Bonoan JT. Johnson DH. Cunha BA. Life-threatening babesiosis in an asplenic patient treated with exchange transfusion, azithromycin, and atovaquone. Heart & Lung 27:424-8, 1998.
27. Hohenschild S. Babesiosis–a dangerous infection for splenectomized children and adults Klin Pad 211:137-40, 1999.
28. Krause PJ. Babesiosis diagnosis and treatment. Vector Borne Zoonotic Dis. 3:45-51. 2003.
29. Homer MJ, Aguilar-Delfin I. et al. Babesiosis. Clin Microbiol Rev.13:451-69. 2000.
30. Shaio MF. Yang KD. Response of babesiosis to a combined regimen of quinine and azithromycin. Trans Roy Soc Trop Med Hyg 91:214-5, 1997.
31. Krause PJ. Spielman A. Telford SR 3rd. et al. Persistent parasitemia after acute babesiosis. N E J M 339:160-5, 1998.
32. Beniwal RP. Nichani AK. et al. An immunisation trial with in vitro produced *Babesia bigemina* exoantigens. Trop Animal Health Product 29(4 Suppl):124S-126S, 1997.
33. Stafford KC 3rd. Ward JS. Magnarelli LA. Impact of controlled burns on the abundance of *Ixodes scapularis* (Acari: Ixodidae). J Med Entomol 35:510-3, 1998.
34. Wenyon CM. Coccidiosis of cats and dogs and the status of the Isospora of man. Ann Trop Med Parasitol 17:231-39, 1923.
35. Joshi M, Chowdhary AS, Dalal PJ, Maniar JK. Parasitic diarrhoea in patients with AIDS. Natl Med J India. 15:72-4. 2002.
36. Benator DA. French AL. et al. *Isospora belli* infection associated with acalculous cholecystitis in a patient with AIDS. Ann Intern Med 121:663-4, 1994.
37. Michiels JF. Hofman P. et al. Intestinal and extraintestinal *Isospora belli* infection in an AIDS patient. A second case report. Pathol Res Pract 190:1089-93, 1994.
38. Restrepo C. Macher AM. Radany EH. Disseminated extra-intestine isosporiasis in a patient with acquired immune deficiency syndrome. Am J Clin Pathol 87:536-42, 1987.
39. Heyworth MF. Parasitic diseases in immunocompromised hosts. Cryptosporidiosis, isosporiasis, and strongyloidiasis. Gastro Clin North Am 25:691-707, 1996.
40. Kitsukawa K. Kamihira S. Kinoshita K. et al. An autopsy case of T-cell lymphoma associated with disseminated varicella and malabsorption syndrome due to *Isospora belli* infection Jap J Clin Hematol 22:258-65,1981.
41. Pape JW. Johnson WD. *Isospora belli* infections. Prog Clin Parasitol 2:119, 1991.
42. St. Georgiev V. Opportunistic infections: treatment and developmental therapeutics of cryptosporidiosis and isosporiasis. Drug Develop Res 28:445-59, 1993.
43. Bialek R, Overkamp D, Rettig I, Knobloch Case report: Nitazoxanide treatment failure in chronic isosporiasis J Am J Trop Med Hyg. 65:94-5. 2001.
44. Ortega YR. Sterling CR. Gilman RH. *Cyclospora cayetanensis*. Adv Parasitol 40:399-418, 1998.
45. Rose JB. Slifko TR. Giardia, Cryptosporidium, and Cyclospora and their impact on foods: a review. J Food Prot 62:1059-70, 1999.
46. Mansfield LS, Gajadhar AA. *Cyclospora cayetanensis*, a food and waterborne coccidian parasite Vet Parasitol.126:73-90. 2004.
47. Sterling CR. Ortega YR. Cyclospora: an enigma worth unraveling. Emerg Infect Dis. 5:48-53, 1999.
48. Eberhard ML. Nace EK. Freeman AR. et al. *Cyclospora cayetanensis* infections in Haiti: a common occurrence in the absence of watery

diarrhea. Am J Trop Med Hyg 60:584-6, 1999.

49. Pape JW. Verdier RI. Boncy M. et al. Cyclospora infection in adults infected with HIV. Clinical manifestations, treatment, and prophylaxis. Ann Intern Med 121:654-7, 1994.
50. Caceres VM. Ball RT. et al. A foodborne outbreak of cyclosporiasis caused by imported raspberries. J Fam Pract 47:231-4, 1998.
51. Koumans EH. Katz DJ. et al. An outbreak of cyclosporiasis in Florida in 1995: a harbinger of multistate outbreaks in 1996 and 1997. Am J Trop Med Hyg 59:235-42, 1998.
52. Herwaldt BL. Beach MJ. The return of Cyclospora in 1997: another outbreak of cyclosporiasis in North America associated with imported raspberries. Ann Intern Med 130:210-20, 1999.
53. Shields JM, Olson BH. *Cyclospora cayetanensis*: a review of an emerging parasitic coccidian. Int J Parasitol. 33:371-91.2003.
54. Ortega YR. Nagle R. Gilman RH. et al. Pathologic and clinical findings in patients with cyclosporiasis and a description of intracellular parasite life-cycle stages. J Infect Dis 176:1584-9, 1997
55. Smith HV. Paton CA. Girdwood RW. Mtambo MM. Cyclospora in non-human primates in Gombe, Tanzania Vet Rec. 138:528, 1996.
56. Flynn PM. Isospora and Cyclospora Species. In: Principles and Practice of Pediatriic Infectious Diseases (Long S. Pickering LK. Prober CG., eds.). Churchill Livingstone, Pubs. pp.1392-1394. 1997.
57. Richardson RF Jr. Remler BF. Katirji B. Murad MH. Guillain-Barre syndrome after Cyclospora infection. Muscle Nerve 21: 669-71, 1998.
58. Jinneman KC. Wetherington JH. et al. An oligonucleotide-ligation assay for the differentiation between Cyclospora and Eimeria spp. polymerase chain reaction amplification products. J Food Prot 62:682-5
59. Schuster FL, Visvesvara GS. Amoebae and ciliated protozoa as causal agents of waterborne zoonotic disease. Vet Parasitol.126:91-120. 2004.
60. Kilvington S. Beeching J. Identification and epidemiological typing of *Naegleria fowleri* with DNA probes. Applied Environ Microbiol 61:2071-8, 1995.
61. Rodriguez R. Mendez O. Molina O. et al. Infection del sistema nervioso central por amoebas de vida libre: comunicacion de tres nuevos casos venezolanos. Rev Neurologia 26:1005-8, 1998.
62. Okuda DT, Hanna HJ, Coons SW, Bodensteiner JB. *Naegleria fowleri* hemorrhagic meningoencephalitis: report of two fatalities in children. J Child Neurol. 19:231-3. 2004
63. Visvesvara GS. Stehr-Green JK. Epidemiology of free-living amoeba infections. Journal of Protozoology 37:25S-33S, 1990.
64. Herbst R, Marciano-Cabral F, Leippe M. Antimicrobial and pore-forming peptides of free-living and potentially highly pathogenic *Naegleria fowleri* are released from the same precursor molecule. J Biol Chem. 279:25955-8. 2004.
65. Martinez AJ. Free-living Amoebic meningoencephalitides: comparative study. Neurologia-Neurocirugia-Psiquiatria 18(2-3 Suppl): 391-401, 1977.
66. Behets J, Seghi F. et al. Detection of Naegleria spp. and *Naegleria fowleri*: a comparison of flagellation tests, ELISA and PCR. Water Sci Technol. 47:117-22. 2003.
67. Schuster FL, Visvesvara GS. Opportunistic amoebae: challenges in prophylaxis and treatment. Drug Resist Updat. 7:41-51. 2004.
68. John DT. Howard MJ. Seasonal distribution of pathogenic free living amoebae in Oklahoma waters. Parasitol Res 81:193-201,1995.
69. Gao LY. Harb OS. Abu Kwaik Y. Utilization of similar mechanisms by *Legionella pneumophila* to parasitize two evolutionarily distant host cells, mammalian macrophages and protozoa. Infect Immun 65:4738-46, 1997.
70. Newsome AL. Scott TM. Benson RF. Fields BS. Isolation of an amoeba naturally harboring a distinctive Legionella species. Applied & Environmental Microbiology 64:1688-93, 1998.
71. Steinert M. Ockert G. Luck C. Hacker J. Regrowth of *Legionella pneumophila* in a heat-disinfected plumbing system. Zentral Bakteriol 288:331-42, 1998.
72. Paltiel M, Powell E, Lynch J, Baranowski B, Martins C. Disseminated cutaneous acanthAmoebiasis: a case report and review of the literature. Cutis. 73:241-8. 2004.
73. Marciano-Cabral F, Cabral G. *Acanthamoeba spp.* as agents of disease in humans. Clin Microbiol Rev.16:273-307. 2003.
74. Samuel LH. Petri WA. Acanthamoeba species. In: Principles and Practice of Pediatric Infectious Diseases (Long SS. Pickering LK. Prober CG., eds.). Churchill Livingstone, Pubs. pp. 1407-1409, 1997.
75. Martinez AJ. Infection of the central nervous system due to Acanthamoeba. Rev of Infect Dis 13 Suppl 5:S399-402, 1991.
76. Koide J. Okusawa E. et al. Granulomatous Amoebic encephalitis caused by Acanthamoeba in a patient with systemic lupus erythematosus. Clin Rheumatol 17:329-32, 1998.
77. Sison JP. Kemper CA. Loveless M et al. Disseminated Acanthamoeba infection in patients with AIDS: case reports and review. Clin Infect Dis 20:1207-16, 1995.
78. Auran JD. Starr MB. Jakobieo FA. Acanthamoeba keratitis. A review of the literature. Cornea 6:2-26, 1987.
79. Pirehma M. Suresh K. Sivanandam S. et al. Field's stain–a rapid staining method for *Acanthamoeba spp.* Parasitol Res 85:791-3, 1999.
80. Seal D. Treatment of Acanthamoeba keratitis. Expert Rev Anti Infect Ther. 1:205-8. 2003
81. Nasirudeen AM, Tan KS. Isolation and characterization of the mitochondrion-like organelle from *Blastocystis hominis*. J Microbiol Methods 58:101-9. 2004.
82. Windsor JJ, Stenzel DJ, Macfarlane L. Multiple reproductive processes in *Blastocystis hominis*. Trends Parasitol.19:289-90; author reply 291-2. 2003.
83. Zaman V. Zaki M. Manzoor M. et al. Postcystic development of Blastocystis. Int J Parasitol 27:941-5, 1997.
84. Carbajal JA. del Castillo L. et al. Karyotypic diversity among *Blastocystis hominis* isolates. Parasitol Res 85:437-40, 1999.
85. Nassir E, Awad J, et al. *Blastocystis hominis* as a cause of hypoalbuminemia and anasarca. Eur J Clin Microbiol Infect Dis. 23:399-402. 2004.
86. Clark CG. Extensive genetic diversity in *Blastocystis hominis*. Mol Biochem Parasitol 87:79-83, 1997.
87. Bohm-Gloning B. Knobloch J. Walderich B. Five subgroups of *Blastocystis hominis* from symptomatic and asymptomatic patients revealed by restriction site analysis of PCR-amplified 16S-like rDNA. Trop Med Internat Health 2:771-8, 1997.
88. Horiki N. Maruyama M. et al. Epidemiologic survey of *Blastocystis hominis* infection in Japan. Am J Trop Med Hyg 56(4):370-4, 1997.
89. Antonelli F. Cantelli L. De Maddi F. Lamba M. Infezione da *Blastocystis hominis*. Descrizione di un caso. Minerva Ped 48:571-573, 1996.
90. Giacometti A. Cirioni O. et al. Irritable bowel syndrome in patients with *Blastocystis hominis* infection. Eur J Clin Microbiol Infect Dis18:436-9, 1999.
91. Jelinek T. Peyerl G. et al. The role of *Blastocystis hominis* as a possible intestinal pathogen in travellers. J Infect 35:63-6,1997.
92. Cimerman S, Ladeira MC, Iuliano WA. Blastocystosis: nitazoxanide as a new therapeutic option. Rev Soc Bras Med Trop. 36:415-7. 2003.
93. Levy Y. George J. Shoenfeld Y. Severe *Blastocystis hominis* in an elderly man. J Infect 33:57-9, 1996.
94. Haresh K. Suresh K. Khairul Anus A. Saminathan S. Isolate resistance of *Blastocystis hominis* to metronidazole.Trop Med Internat Health 4:274-7, 1999.
95. Silberman JD. Clark CG. Sogin ML. *Dientamoeba fragilis* shares a recent common evolutionary history with the trichomonads. Mol Biochem Parasitol 76:311-4, 1996.
96. Johnson EH, Windsor JJ, Clark CG. Emerging from obscurity: biological, clinical, and diagnostic aspects of *Dientamoeba fragilis*. Clin Microbiol Rev. Jul;17:553-70. 2004.
97. Peek, R., F. R. Reedeker, and T. van Gool. Direct amplification and genotyping of *Dientamoeba fragilis* from human stool specimens. J. Clin. Microbiol. 42:631-635. 2004.
98. Loa CC. Adelson ME. et al. Serological diagnosis of human babesiosis by IgG enzyme-linked immunosorbent assay. Curr Microbiol. 49:385-9. 2004.

15. Non-Pathogenic Protozoa

Introduction

We are constantly being confronted with a plethora of microbes whose sole purpose is to colonize us and take advantage of our biochemical systems. The human body can be viewed as a series of ecological niches that select for numerous entities, including viruses, bacteria, fungi, protozoa, helminths, and arthropods. They enter through the GI, urogenital, and respiratory tracts, through abrasions, and other ports of entry. Fortunately, the vast majority of the world's microbes are incapable of remaining on or within these environments, and are repelled. This is mainly due to the inadequacy of their fundamental biological makeup, preventing them from thriving on or in us. The majority of those that have succeeded do us little or no harm. In fact, the great majority of cells on and in us are foreigners! We refer to them as commensals or symbionts. Commensals do us no harm. Symbionts actually help maintain our homeostatic mechanisms. The oral cavity alone harbors some 500 different species of bacteria, serving to exclude those that would lead to various states of ill health. Our intestinal tract is another good example of "peaceful" co-existence between us and our symbiotic microbes.

A few that have managed to run the gauntlet of our immune system and overcome the physiological barriers established by our complex metabolic regimes can and often do cause pathology leading to clinical conditions. These have been covered in the preceding chapters. This chapter is devoted to those organisms that we routinely harbor and which do us no harm. The clinician will undoubtedly receive a diagnostic slip from the laboratory with the name of one or more of them on it. How they should be approached in the context of the clinical setting is the subject of this chapter.

A number of commensal protozoan species have been selected for life within us. Under unusual conditions, a few have been known to be associated with disease, but have never been implicated as the primary reason for the illness. When a person is placed at risk from infection (e.g., surgery, immunosuppression, or infection with another pathogenic organism), some commensal organisms become opportunistic, growing and extending their range. At those times, the clinician has an extremely difficult time determining who did what to whom. The diagnostic microbiology laboratory now assumes a role of major importance, helping to catalogue microbes into the good, the bad, and the ugly. Resolving the primary cause of the disease often reverses the growth pattern of the opportunist. None

of the organisms listed in the tables, except for single cases of *Entamoeba dispar*[1, 2] and *E. gingivalis*[3] have ever been associated with patients suffering from HIV, and in these two exceptions, no serious disease due to the protozoan occurred.

The two tables are a summary of those protozoa whose presence indicates that the patient may have ingested fecally contaminated food or water. It is critical for the clinician to recognize the fact that even though the organism reported is not a pathogen, it is there because of the patient's exposure to a situation that led to the acquisition of another organism that may be. The search should focus on all other agents transmitted by the same route. A representative of each organism mentioned in the following summaries can be found in Appendix C.

Commensal flagellated protozoa

Trichomonas tenax, T. hominis, Enteromonas hominis, Retortamonas intestinalis, and *Chilomastix mesnili* all infect the human host, only, and are considered nonpathogenic by all standard criteria.[4] *T. tenax* lives in the oral cavity in plaque, and the rest of them are intestinal dwellers. Only *C. mesnili* has a cyst stage. All are considered amitochondriate, aerotolerant anaerobic protists.[5] Heavy growth of *T. tenax* was found concurrently with abscesses and tumors of the oral cavity.[6, 7] In addition, *T. tenax* has been isolated from cases of inhalation pneumonia,[8] and from pleural effusions from a patient in which ulceration of the esophagus resulted in communication with the pleural cavity. A PCR test for detecting *T. tenax* in dental plaque has been reported.[9] Due to the overwhelming number of people harboring this flagellate who do not experience any discomfort, *T. tenax* remains on the list of commensals.

A single case of *Enteromonas hominis* has been reported in which the patient experienced diarrhea and was treated successfully with metronidazole.[10] Neither *R. intestinalis* or *C. mesnili* have ever been linked to any abnormal health condition.

Commensal Amoebae

Entamoeba dispar, E. hartmanni, E. coli, Endolimax nana, and *Iodamoeba bütschlii* are organisms often identified in routine stool examination, and whose reporting often elicits confusion among clinicians seeking the causes for diarrheal disease in their patients. Some bear a resemblance to *Entamoeba histolytica*, especially to the inexperienced laboratory technician, and they sometimes err on the side of this pathogen, rather than the commensal. Hence, the patient receives treatment for an entity that is not causing the problem. After treatment, the illness often "recurs," and drug failure is blamed. Commensal amoebae do not respond to the standard drugs used to eradicate *Entamoeba histolytica*, the pathogen most often confused with *E. dispar* or *E. hartmanni*. The use of PCR allows for definitive diagnosis of the pathogenic amoebae.[11] Another approach uses monclonal antibodies to distinguish *E. histolytica* cysts from those *of E. dispar* and other commensal amoebae,[12] facilitating their use in an antigen capture mode for routine diagnosis.

Entamoeba polecki is an inhabitant of the gut tract of pigs that sometimes finds its way into humans, while *E. gingivalis* lives in the gingival flaps of a small subset of humans not yet defined, and is associated with, but does not cause pyorrhea. *E. gingivalis* was diagnosed by fine needle aspiration of an abscess of the neck, following radiation therapy.[13]

References

1. Allison-Jones E. Mindel A. et al. *Entamoeba histolytica* as a commensal intestinal parasite in homosexual men. N Engl J Med 315:353-6. 1986.
2. Haque R. Lyerly D. Wood S. Petri WA Jr. Detection of *Entamoeba histolytica* and *Entamoeba dispar* directly in stool. Am J Trop Med Hyg 50:595-6. 1999.
3. Lucht E. Evengard B. et al. *Entamoeba gingivalis* in human immunodeficiency virus type 1-infected patients with periodontal disease. Clin Infect Dis 27:471-3. 1998.
4. Aucott JN. Ravdin JI. Amoebiasis and "nonpathogenic" intestinal protozoa. Infect Dis Clin North Am 7:467-85. 1993.
5. Muller M. Enzymes and Compartmentalization of Core Energy Metabolism of Anaerobic Protists – a Special Case in Eukaryotic Evolution? In: Evolutionary Relationships Among Protozoa (Coombs GH. Vickerman K. Sleigh MA. Warren A., eds). Klewer, Dordrecht Pubs. pp. 110-132. 1998.
6. Duboucher C. Mogenet M. Perie G. Salivary trichomoniasis. A case report of infestation of a submaxillary gland by *Trichomonas tenax*. Arch Pathol Lab Med 119:277-9. 1995.
7. Shiota T. Arizono N. et al. *Trichomonas tenax* empyema in an immunocompromised patient with advanced cancer. Parasite 5:375-7. 1998.
8. El Kamel A. Rouetbi N. Chakroun M. Battikh M. Pulmonary eosinophilia due to *Trichomonas tenax* Thorax 51:554-5. 1996.
9. Kikuta N. Yamamoto A. Fukura K. Goto N. Specific and sensitive detection of *Trichomonas tenax* by the polymerase chain reaction. Lett Appl Microbiol 24(3):193-7. 1999.
10. Spriegel JR. Saag KG. Tsang TK. Infectious diarrhea secondary to *Enteromonas hominis*. Am J Gastroenterol 84:1313-4. 1989.
11. Acuna-Soto R. Samuelson J De Girolami P. et al. Application of the polymerase chain reaction to the epidemiology of pathogenic and non-pathogenic *Entamoeba histolytica*. Am J Trop Med Hyg 48:58-70. 1993.
12. Walderich B. Burchard GD. Knobloch J. Muller L. Development of monoclonal antibodies specifically recognizing the cyst stage of *Entamoeba histolytica*. Am J Trop Med Hyg 59:347-51. 1998.
13. Perez-Jaffe L. Katz R. Gupta PK. *Entamoeba gingivalis* identified in a left upper neck nodule by fine-needle aspiration: a case report. Diagn Cytopathol 18:458-61. 1998.

V. The Nematodes

Nematodes are non-segmented roundworms belonging to the phylum Nematoda, and are among the most abundant life forms on earth. The great majority of nematodes are free living, inhabiting most essential niches in soil and fresh and salt water, as well as other, more specialized ones. Only a small fraction of the total number of species are parasitic, and only some of these infect the human host. Most parasitic nematodes have developed a highly specific biologic dependence on a particular species of host, and are incapable of survival in any other. Only a few have succeeded in adapting to a variety of hosts. Best known by far among the free-living nematodes is *Caenorhabditis elegans*, whose entire genome has recently been sequenced (it has 19,080 genes). In contrast, the genome of *Trichinella spiralis*, a parasitic nematode, has more total DNA than *C. elegans*, and only 60% of it is homologous with its free-living relative. Thus, contrary to widely held speculation, some parasitic organisms may need more, not fewer, genes to survive inside the human host. Virulence factors, and other specialized compounds needed to resist digestion or immune attack are likely to be encoded by genes that permit the invader to live comfortably in the face of an exquisitely developed immune system.

Infections caused by nematodes are among the most prevalent, affecting nearly all of us at one time in our lives. The most common nematodes are three types of soil-transmitted helminths (STHs), the common roundworm *Ascaris lumbricoides*, the whipworm *Trichuris trichiura*, and the hookworms *Necator americanus* and *Ancylostoma duodenale*. Children are particularly susceptible to acquiring large numbers of these parasites, and consequently suffer greater morbidity. In many developing countries, children frequently harbor all three types of STHs (hence the moniker "the unholy trinity") and suffer from childhood malnutrition, physical growth retardation, and deficits in cognitive and intellectual development as a result. In 2001, The World Health Assembly called on its member states to treat at least 75 percent of school children for STH infections by 2010. If carried out, this would become the largest health program ever attempted.

The typical nematode, both larva and adult, is surrounded by a flexible, durable outer coating, the acellular cuticle, that is resistant to chemicals. It is a complex structure composed of a variety of layers, each of which has many components, including structural proteins, enzymes, and lipids. The cuticle of each species has a unique structure and composition; it not only protects the worm but may also be involved in active transport of small molecules, including water, electrolytes, and organic compounds. A further layer, the epicuticle, surrounds the cuticle of a few parasitic species, making them even more resistant to attack from enzymes, antibodies, and other host resistance factors.

All nematodes have a well-developed muscular system. The muscle cells form an outer ring of tissue lying just underneath the cuticle, and their origins and insertions are in cuticular processes. In addition, there is some muscle tissue surrounding the buccal cavity and esophageal and sub-esophageal regions of the gut tract. These muscles are particularly important elements of the feeding apparatus in both parasitic and free-living nematodes. Each muscle cell consists of filaments, mitochondria, and cytoplasmic processes that connect it with a single nerve fiber. The nervous system consists of a dorsal nerve ring or a series of ganglia that give rise to the peripheral nerves - two lateral, one dorsal, and one ventral branch. Commissures connect the branches and allow for integration of signaling, which results in fluid, serpiginous movements. Several classes of drugs interfere only with nematode nerve signaling, and are thus effective treatments for nematode infections in humans.

Nematodes have a complete, functional gut tract: the oral (i.e., buccal) cavity and esophagus, the midgut, and the hindgut with anus. The oral cavity and hindgut are usually lined by cuticle; the midgut consists of columnar cells, complete with microvilli. The function of the midgut is to absorb ingested nutrients, whereas the usually muscular esophagus serves to deliver food to the midgut.

In addition, a number of specialized exocrine glands open into the lumen of the digestive tract, usually in the region of the esophagus. These glands are thought to be largely concerned with digestion, but may be related to other functions as well. For example, in hookworms, the cephalic glands secrete an anticoagulant. In other instances, there is a single row of cells called stichocytes that empty their products directly into the esophagus via a cuticular-lined duct. These cells occupy a large portion of the body mass of Trichinella, Trichuris, and Capillaria, for example. The function of these cells is unknown, and may vary from species to species.

Nematodes excrete solid and fluid wastes. Excretion of solids takes place through the digestive tract. Fluids are eliminated by means of the excretory system, consisting of two or more collecting tubes connected at one end to the ventral gland (a primitive kidney-like organ) and at the other end to the excretory pore.

The adult female nematode has a large portion of her body devoted to reproduction. One or two ovaries lead to the vagina by way of a tubular oviduct and uterus. A seminal receptacle for storage of sperm is connected to the uterus. The male has a single testis connected to the vas deferens, seminal vesicle, ejaculatory duct, and cloaca. In addition, males of many species have specialized structures to aid in transfer of sperm to the female during mating. Their identification is often based on morphology of these structures. Most nematodes lay eggs, but some are viviparous. More about the biology of nematodes will be given within the text for each infectious agent as they are discussed, whenever it relates to the pathogenesis of the disease.

16. *Enterobius vermicularis*
(Linnaeus 1758)

Introduction

Enterobius vermicularis (pinworm), is the most prevalent nematode infection of humans in temperate climates. It affects nearly all children under the age of 12. Transmission of enterobiasis is especially frequent in elementary schools and daycare centers.[1] A new syndrome of eosinophilic colitis associated with *E. vermicularis* larvae has recently been described.[2] This nematode has no reservoir hosts.

Historical Information

Linnaeus named this organism *Enterobius vermicularis* in 1758. Later, in 1824, Johann Bremser[3] distinguished this roundworm from the other oxyurid and ascarid nematodes, and provided an accurate description of it that forms the basis for today's modern classification scheme. Pinworm ova have been recovered from human coprolites found in numerous archeological sites, some as old as 10,000 years,[4] and Enterobius DNA has been detected in ancient DNA from North and South American human coprolites.[5]

Life Cycle

Adult worms live freely in the lumen of the transverse and descending colon, and in the rectum. The female (Fig. 16.1) measures 8-13 mm in length and 0.3-0.6 mm in width. The male is typically smaller, measuring 2-5 mm by 0.2 mm. The tail of the male contains a single curved copulatory spicule. Adult pinworms feed on *E. coli* and other bacteria found in the formed stool.

The embryonated eggs (Fig. 16.2) are swallowed and hatch into the second-stage larvae once they reach the small intestine. Development to the third and fourth stages also occurs there. Finally, the adult worms take up residence in the large intestine (Figure 16.3.). The entire cycle is completed within 4-6 weeks after ingestion of the infectious egg. Alternatively, eggs can hatch on the skin at the site of deposition, and the second-stage larvae can crawl back through the anus into the rectum, and eventually the colon, where they develop into reproducing adults. This is referred to as retro-infection.

The adult worms mate, and within 6 weeks, each female contains approximately 10,000 fertilized, non-embryonated eggs. Males die shortly after copulation. The gravid female migrates out the anus onto the peri-

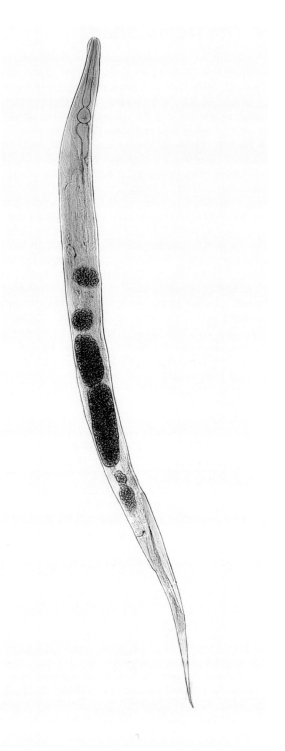

Figure 16.1. Adult female *Enterobius vermicularis*. 10mm.

anal skin at night, most likely stimulated to do so by the drop in body temperature of the host. There, she experiences a prolapse of the uterus, expels all her eggs, and dies. Expulsion can be so intense that the eggs become airborne. The eggs rapidly embryonate and

Enterobius vermicularis

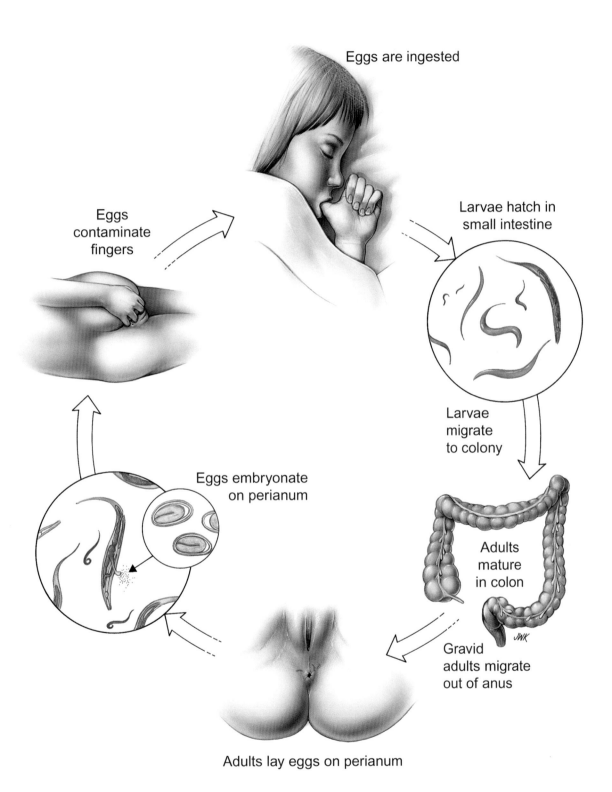

Eggs are ingested

Larvae hatch in small intestine

Eggs contaminate fingers

Larvae migrate to colony

Eggs embryonate on perianum

Adults mature in colon

Gravid adults migrate out of anus

Adults lay eggs on perianum

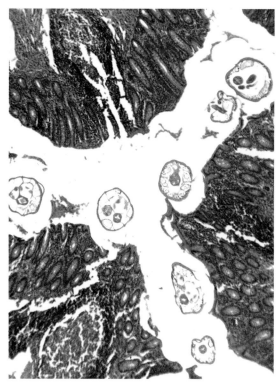

Figure 16.2. Cross sections of adult *E. vermicularis* in appendix.

become infective within 6 hours of being laid.

In female patients, the larvae that hatch on the skin near the anus occasionally crawl into the vagina instead of the rectum, establishing an aberrant infection. Less frequently, gravid parasites infect the fallopian tubes. Aberrant infections also include pelvic peritonitis,[6] ovarian infection,[7] granuloma of the liver,[8] the appendix.[9]

An association has been described between *E. vermicularis* and the amebo-flagellate *Dientamoeba fragilis*. This is based on the observation that human volunteer infections with *E. vermicularis* eggs has resulted in co-infection with *D. fragilis*.[10–12] It has been argued that this protozoan parasite "piggy-backs" onto the surface of *E. vermicularis* eggs [13] (see *Dientamoeba fragilis*, page 100).

Cellular and Molecular Pathogenesis

All stages of *E. vermicularis* develop in the gut tract, and thus the host does not experience any systemic reactions. The parasite elicits a mild, local inflammatory response that could be associated with a low-grade eosinophilia, but this has not been documented.

A few patients develop pruritis resulting from allergic responses to worm proteins. Whether pinworm infection causes secondary problems, such as appendicitis or pelvic inflammatory disease, is unclear. Pinworms

have been found in these organs at autopsy with no evidence of an inflammatory reaction. However, in other circumstances, pinworms have been implicated as an appendicolith that might have led to the chain of events leading to clinical appendicitis.

Although there are no comparable studies in humans, experimental evidence has shown that the immune status of the host affects the outcome of the infection. *Syphacia oblevata* is a pinworm species that infects mice only, and reaches much larger numbers in nude (athymic) mice than it does in the same mice into which a subcutaneous implant of thymic tissue from syngeneic donors was introduced.[14] In one unusual case, intense infiltration of the colon with eosinophils and neutrophils led to clinical eosinophilic enteritis in an 18 year old homosexual male who passed numerous *E. vermicularis* larvae. The larvae were definitively identified on the basis of characteristic 28S ribosomal RNA and 5S rRNA spacer genes by PCR.[2] Susceptibility to pinworm infection decreases with age in humans, but the reasons for this are not clear. It remains to be determined whether this difference in susceptibility has an immunological or physiological basis. The physiochemical basis by which *D. fragilis* associates with *E. vermicularis* eggs is not known.

Clinical Disease

The great majority of infected individuals are free of symptoms. Those few who are symptomatic experience intense itching of the perianal area, which in rare instances leads to cellulitis.[12] Aberrant vaginal infection leads to vaginal itching and sometimes serous discharge. Enuresis has been attributed to infection with pinworm, but no causal relation has been established.[13] Gnashing of teeth and sleep disturbances have not been definitely related to the pinworm either. Patients who experience abdominal pain during infection may do so because of co-infection with *D. fragilis*. Eosinophilic enteritis caused by *E. vermicularis* can be hemorrhagic and presents with abdominal pain and melena. Rarely, enterobiasis has been linked to clinical appendicitis.[9]

Diagnosis

The infection is best detected by microscopic examination of a sticky tape which has been applied to the perianal region as soon as the patient awakens (i.e., before a bath or bowel movement). It may be necessary to clear the tape with xylol or alcohol before examining it. The characteristic eggs (Fig. 16.2, Fig. C.37., Appendix C) can be readily detected in this

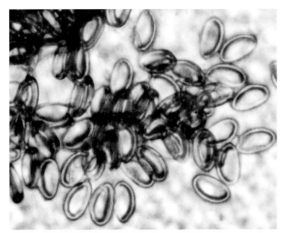

Figure 16.3. Embryonated eggs of *E. vermicularis*.

manner. They are not usually found in the feces, so examination of a stool specimen is futile. Serologic tests specific for *E. vermicularis* do not exist. Although low-grade eosinophilia has been reported in some cases, this relatively non-specific finding is not helpful for the diagnosis.

Adult pinworms can be readily identified when they are seen on histologic sections because of bilateral cuticular projections known as alae. In patients with abdominal pain or other gastrointestinal symptoms, a fecal examination may be necessary to rule out co-infection with *D. fragilis*. Colonoscopy of a patient with eosinophilic enteritis from *E. vermicularis* showed a purulent discharge from the rectum to the terminal ileum and ulcerations. The one patient described with this syndrome was noted to pass larvae instead of eggs or adult worms, which required PCR for identification.[2]

Treatment

Pyrantel pamoate in a single dose (11 mg/kg [max. 1 gram]), or either albendazole (400 mg) or mebendazole (100 mg)[15] in a single dose is the recommended therapy. Details regarding the safety of albendazole and mebendazole for young children are discussed in the section on trichuriasis. Neither drug kills the eggs or developing larvae, therefore, "blind" re-treatment is required 2 to 3 weeks after the original therapy. This destroys worms that have hatched from eggs ingested after the first treatment. Patients who are coinfected with dientamoebiasis can be treated with specific anti-protozoal agents including iodoquinol, paromomycin or tetracycline (in children older than 8 years of age).

Patients with *E. vermicularis*-associated eosinophilic colitis should be treated for three successive days with mebendazole (100 mg twice daily)

Prevention and Control

In the young child, infection and reinfection is frequent, because of the ready transmissibility of the pinworm. The groups showing highest prevalence of infection are schoolchildren and institutionalized individuals. Compounding the problem is the fact that the eggs can survive for several days under conditions of high humidity and intermediate to low temperatures. There are no predilections on the basis of sex, race, or socioeconomic class.

No effective means for prevention are currently available. Pinworm infection, per se, should not be considered evidence of poor hygiene. Any exaggerated attempts to eradicate the infection in the household should be discouraged by a rational discussion to allay anxiety. In rare cases, some children have been noted to be refractory to conventional anthelminthic therapy with mebendazole or albendazole. Although no evidence exists that the parasite in these patients has developed anthelminthic drug resistance, sometimes pyrantel pamoate has been noted to be of clinical benefit.

References

1. Crawford FG. Vermund SH. Parasitic infections in day care centers. Pediatr Infect Dis J 6: 744-749.1987.
2. Liu LX. Chil J. Upton MP. Ash LR. Eosinophilic colitis associated with larvae of the pinworm *Enterobious vermicularis*. Lancet 346: 410-412.1995.
3. Bremser JG. Oxyure vermiculaire. In: Traite zoologique et physilogique sur les vers intestinaux de l'homme. C.L.F. Panchouke, Paris. pp. 149-157, 1824.
4. Horne PD. First evidence of enterobiasis in ancient Egypt. J Parasitol 88: 1019-21. 2002.
5. Iniguez AM, Reinhard KJ, Araujo A, Ferreira LF, Vicente AC. Enterobius vermicularis: ancient DNA from North and South American human coprolites. Mem Inst Oswaldo Cruz 98 Suppl 1: 67-9, 2003.
6. Pearson RD. Irons Sr RP. Irons Jr RP. Chronic pelvic peritonitis due to the pinworm Enterobius vermicularis. JAMA 245:1340-1341, 1981.
7. Beckman EN. Holland JB. Ovarian enterobiasis-a proposed pathogenesis. Am J Trop Med Hyg 30:74-76, 1981.
8. Daly JJ. Baker GF. Pinworm granuloma of the liver. Am J Trop Med Hyg 33:62-64, 1984.
9. Arca MJ. Gates RL. et al. Clinical manifestations of appendiceal pinworms in children: an institutional experience and a review of the literature. Pediatr Surg Int. 20: 372-5. 2004.
10. Burrows RB. Swerdlow MA. *Enterobius vermicularis* as a probable vector of *Dientamoeba fragilis*. Am J Trop Med Hyg 5:258-265.1956.
11. Chang SL. Parasitization of the parasite. J Am Med Assoc 223:510, 1973.
12. Ockert G. Zur epidemiologie von *Dientamoeba fragilis*. II. Mitteilung: Versuche uber die ubertragung der art mit enterobius-eiern. J Hyg Epidemiol Immunol. 16:222-5. 1972.
13. Hotez PJ. The other intestinal protozoa: enteric infections caused by *Blastocystis hominis*, *Entamoeba coli*, and *Dientamoeba fragilis*. Sem. Pedi. Infect. Dis. 2000.
14. Jacobson RH. Reed ND. The thymus dependency of resistance to pinworm infection in mice. J Parasitol 60:976-979, 1974.
15. St. Georgiev V. Chemotherapy of enterobiasis (oxyuriasis). Expert Opin Pharmaother 2: 267-75, 2001.

17. *Trichuris trichiura*
(Linnaeus 1771)

Introduction

Trichuris trichiura, known as "whipworm" because of its characteristic shape, is one of the three major soil-transmitted helminths (STHs) that cause serious morbidity in school aged children in developing countries. Trichuris infection is frequently coincident with infections caused by the STHs, *Ascaris lumbricoides* and hookworm. The prevalence is estimated to be approximately 795 million infections, with the largest numbers of cases in Asia, Sub-Saharan Africa and the tropical regions of the Americas.[1]

T. trichiura has no reservoir hosts. Other species of Trichuris infect a wide range of mammals (e.g., *T. vulpis* in caenidae; *T. muris* in the mouse; *T. suis* in the pig). Trichuris infection is usually heavier in children than in adult patients, and is consequently more severe in that age group.[1] School aged children are particularly affected. Heavily infected children often go on to develop colitis and stunted growth.[1] New evidence indicates that chronically infected children also develop physical growth stunting and even intellectual and cognitive deficits.[2]

Historical Information

Linnaeus classified this parasite, then called "teretes," as a nematode in 1771. Morgagni accurately described the location of *T. trichiura* in the cecum and transverse colon in 1740.[3] This description was followed by a report by Roederer, in 1761,[4] depicting the external morphology of *T. trichiura*. Roederer's report was accompanied by scientific renderings that are still deemed highly accurate. Human infection with Trichuris has been identified by finding the petrified, characteristic eggs in coprolites of prehistoric humans.

Life Cycle

The adult female (Fig. 17.1) measures 30-50 mm, while the male (Fig. 17.2) is 30-45 mm in length. Infection begins when the embryonated egg (Fig. 17.3) is swallowed. The first-stage larva hatches in the small intestine, penetrates the columnar epithelium, and comes to lie just above the lamina propria. Four molts later, the immature adult emerges and is passively carried to the large intestine, where it re-embeds itself in the columnar cells and induces its essential niche. Adult *Trichuris trichiura* live in the transverse and descending colon (Fig 17.4). The anterior, narrow, elongate esophagus

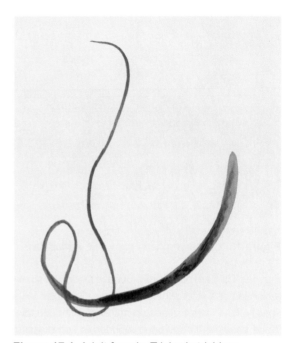

Figure 17.1. Adult female *Trichuris trichiura.*

is embedded within a syncytium of host cells created by the worm, probably as the result of exposure of the host to worm secretions emanating from its stichosome. The posterior abdomen protrudes into the lumen, allowing eggs to escape. Nothing is known about the nutritional requirements of this parasite, but experimental evidence on related species suggests that they do not ingest blood.[5] The parasites grow and mature in the large intestine, where mating also occurs.

Patency (i.e., the first time eggs are detectable in the feces) is about 90 days following the time of ingestion of embryonated eggs. Females can produce up to 3,000-5,000 eggs per day,[6] and are long-lived (1.5-2.0 years).[7] Fertilized eggs are deposited in soil with feces, and must embryonate there before becoming infec-

Figure 17.2. Adult male *Trichuris trichiura.*

Trichuris trichiura

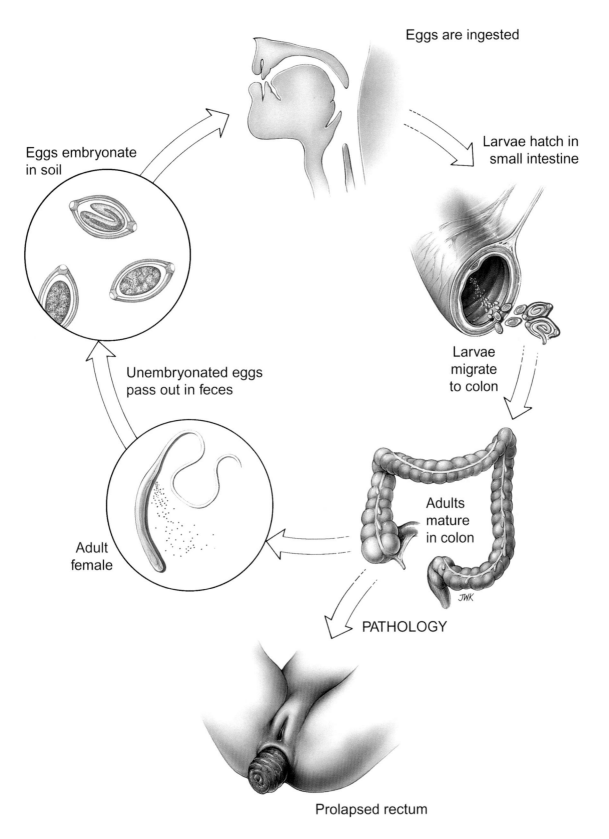

Eggs are ingested

Larvae hatch in
small intestine

Eggs embryonate
in soil

Larvae
migrate
to colon

Unembryonated eggs
pass out in feces

Adults
mature
in colon

Adult
female

JWK

PATHOLOGY

Prolapsed rectum

Figure 17.3. Fertilized, non-embryonated egg of *T. trichiura.* 50 μm x 20 μm.

tious. Environmental factors, including high humidity, sandy or loamy soil, and a warm temperature (20-30° C), favor rapid development of the embryo.[8] Under optimal conditions, embryonic development takes place over an 18-22 day period.[9]

Cellular and Molecular Pathogenesis

In Trichuris endemic areas, pediatric populations, especially children between the ages of 5 and 15 typically harbor the largest whipworm burdens. Why these heavy worm burdens diminish in older age groups is not known. However, new studies indicate that susceptibility to heavy Trichuris infections may depend on an inability to mount strong T helper cell type 2 responses.[10] There is also a genetic component to susceptibility.[11]

The presence of adult whipworms in the large intestine induces structural defects in the epithelium.[12] In order to invade the colonic mucosa, the adult Trichuris releases a novel pore-forming and channel-forming protein.[13] in vitro, these secreted proteins induce ion conducting pores in lipid bilayers. Pore formation in epithelial cell membranes may facilitate invasion and enable the parasite to maintain its syncytial environment in the caecal epithelium. Genes encoding these novel proteins are comprised of repeats.[14]

A low-grade inflammatory response to the presence of the adults occurs, but it cannot account for the observation that trichuriasis in children resembles inflammatory bowel disease (IBD) of ulcerative colitis or Crohn's disease.[15] The latter conditions are characterized by more extensive histopathologic damage to the gut. With heavy infections, the population of whipworms may extend from the cephalad to the terminal ileum and cause ileitis. Anemia results from capillary damage and erosion leading to blood loss, as well as the anemia of chronic inflammation.[15] Some anemia due to heavy infection with *Trichuris trichiura* is much

less severe than hookworm anemia.

Adult Trichuris worms exhibit immunomodulatory properties. Ironically these features of the whipworm have been exploited to develop a novel iatrogenic treatment of Crohn's disease. The porcine whipworm *T. suis* was shown to reduce the symptoms of Crohns in 21 of 29 patients.[16] The mechanism of why *T. suis* reduces host inflammation, and why *T. trichiura* actually causes IBD in non-Crohn's patients but not in Crohn's patients is unknown.

Clinical Disease

Clinical disease generally occurs only in children, because these are the most heavily-infected patients.[17] Children with very heavy Trichuris infections can present either acutely as dysentery or as a chronic colitis. Dysentery associated with heavy Trichuris infection is characterized by diarrhea containing blood and mucus. Trichuris dysentery in children results in weight loss, emaciation, and anemia. Because of the extensive mucosal swelling of the rectum, the urge to strain as if feces were present (tenesmus) is irresistible. Protracted tenesmus leads to rectal prolapse (Fig. 17.5).[12]

Chronic Trichuris colitis in pediatric patients resembles characteristics of better-known forms of inflammatory bowel disease, such as Crohn's disease and ulcerative colitis. Children suffering from heavy trichuriasis develop chronic malnutrition, short stature, anemia, and finger clubbing.[12] Following specific chemotherapy, many of these conditions abate, often resulting in rapid catch-up growth.

Increasing evidence suggests that in addition to the physical symptoms of trichuriasis, chronic infection can also produce long-term deficits in child cognitive and intellectual development.[2] The mechanism by which this occurs is as yet unknown.

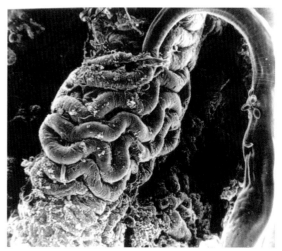

Figure 17.4. Scanning EM of adult Trichuris, *in situ.* Courtesy K. Wright.

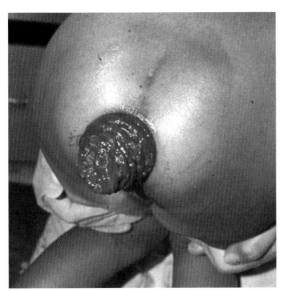

Figure 17.5. Prolapsed rectum with adult *T. trichiura*.

Diagnosis

Trichuris eggs are quite characteristic, and are easily identified in stool samples. Charcot-Leyden crystals in the stool should lead to further examination in the absence of identifying eggs on a first stool examination. In contrast with other forms of inflammatory bowel disease, the erythrocyte sedimentation rate is not usually elevated with Trichuris infection. In any case, a search for pathogenic protozoa such as *Entamoeba histolytica* or *Giardia lamblia* is indicated in view of the high frequency of multiple infections. It must be noted that identification of Trichuris eggs is relatively easy, whereas finding Giardia or Entamoeba is more difficult and requires an experienced observer. Adult Trichuris worms can also be identified by direct visualization on colonoscopy.[18] When doubt exists, it is reasonable to treat the patient for Trichuris infection and request expert advice only if the patient's symptoms do not abate. Failure to control diarrhea after Trichuris is eradicated mandates a more thorough evaluation of the cause(s) of the diarrhea. Stool cultures should be used to determine the possible presence of enteric prokaryotic or viral pathogens. In histologic preparations, Trichuris adults can be readily identified by the characteristic variability of its diameter in different sections.

Treatment

A benzimidazole — mebendazole or albendazole — is the treatment of choice for trichuriasis. The primary activity of these drugs is to inhibit microtubule polymerization by affinity binding to the unique beta-tubulin of invertebrates. Although most global anthelminthic de-worming programs rely on using a single dose of either drug, often several doses are required to effect cures for trichuriasis.[19] Alternatively, Trichuris de-worming can sometimes be improved by doubling or tripling the standard 400 mg dose of albendazole.[20] The drug oxantel can be used as an alternative agent; in many countries it is formulated with pyrantel pamoate.

To date, both albendazole and mebendazole have an excellent safety profile in children. In the doses used to treat STH infections, neither drug causes significant systemic toxicity in routine use, although transient abdominal pain, diarrhea, nausea and dizziness have been reported. Long-term use has been associated with bone marrow suppression, alopecia and hepatotoxicity. There is a single report that in children with asymptomatic trichuriasis, albendazole reportedly results in impaired growth,[17] although this observation has not been confirmed in other studies.

Mebendazole and albendazole are teratogenic and embryotoxic in pregnant laboratory rats at doses of 10 mg/kg (roughly equivalent to the human dose). In view of these findings, the use of mebendazole is currently not recommended in pregnant women, while albendazole is recommended only if the potential benefit justifies the potential risk to the fetus. Moreover, because mebendazole or albendazole have not been extensively studied in children under two years, their use in this age group needs to consider the relative benefits and risks. In anticipation of using mebendazole and albendazole among large pediatric populations in developing countries, the WHO convened an informal consultation on their use in children under the age of 2.[23] From this it was concluded that the incidence of side effects are likely to be the same in this population as in older children, and that both agents could be used to treatment children as young as 12 months using reduced dosages.

Prevention and Control

Trichuris trichiura infection is common in tropical areas, where prevalence as high as 80% has been documented. Most infections tend to be light and asymptomatic. Warm, moist soils in tropical and subtropical regions favor the maintenance of eggs, which can remain alive under these optimum conditions for months. As with Ascaris eggs, exposure of *T. trichiura* eggs to direct sunlight for 12 hours or exposure to temperatures in excess of 40° C for 1 hour kills the embryo inside the egg. Eggs are relatively resistant to chemical disinfectants, and can survive for protracted periods of time in raw or treated sewage. Proper disposal of feces is the primary means of prevention. In areas of the world where untreated human feces are used to fertilize crops, control of this infection is impossible.

Because school aged children typically harbor the heaviest Trichuris infections (as well as Ascaris infections), and specific anthelmintic chemotherapy with either albendazole or mebendazole can result in catch-up growth and improved cognition for heavily infected children,[24-26] these agents have been used in school-based programs throughout the developing world. In 2001, the World Health Assembly passed a resolution that recommended its member states to administer single dose albendazole and mebendazole on a frequent and periodic basis (1-3 times per year) in order to control soil-transmitted helminth (Ascaris, Trichuris, Hookworm) morbidity (www.who.int/wormcontrol). The resolution recommends treatment of 75 percent of all school aged children at risk for heavy in-

fection by 2010. Because school aged children contribute the largest to Trichuris and Ascaris transmission in the community, there is also some optimism that widespread treatment could theoretically interrupt these processes. However, high rates of post-treatment soil-transmitted helminth reinfection require that children must be treated at least on an annual basis. While there are clear health and educational benefits for school-based intervention, there are concerns that single doses of albendazole are often not sufficient to cure Trichuris infections, and frequent use of the drug could lead to emerging drug resistance. Therefore, if resources permit it, continuous monitoring for drug effectiveness and emerging drug resistance should be practiced along with de-worming.[26]

References

1. De Silva NR. Brooker S. et al. Soil-transmitted helminth infections: updating the global picture. Trends Parasitol 18: 547-51, 2003.
2. Cooper ES. Bundy DAP: Trichuris is not trivial. Parasitol Today 4:301-305.1988.
3. Nokes C. Grantham-McGregor SM, Sawyer AW, et al. Moderate to heavy infections of *Trichuris trichiura* affect cognitive function in Jamaican school children. Parasitology 104:539-547. 1992.
4. Morgagni GB. Epistolarum anatomicarum duodeviginti ad script pertinentium celeberrimi yin Antonii Marie Valsalvae pars Altera. Epistola Anatomica XIV. Apud Franciscum Pitheri, Venice. 1740.
5. Roederer JG. Nachrichten von der Trichuriden, der Societat der Wissenschaften in Gottingen. Gottingische Anzeigen von gelebrten Sachen: Unter der Aufsicht der Konigliche Gesellschaft der Wissenschaften. Part 25, pp. 243-245. 1761.
6. Pike EH. Bionomics, blood and 51Cr: investigations of *Trichuris muris* and studies with two related species. Doctoral dissertation, Columbia University pp. 1-207. 1963.
7. Brown HW. The Whipworm of Man [Seminar] (Vol 16). Merck Sharp & Dohme, West Point, PA, pp 19-22. 1954.
8. Belding D. Textbook of Parasitology. Meredith, New York. pp. 397-398. 1965.
9. Brown HW. Studies on the rate of development and viability of the eggs of *Ascaris lumbricoides* and *Trichuris trichiura* under field conditions. Parasitology 14:1-15. 1927.
10. Jackson JA. Turner JD. et al. T helper cell type 2 responsiveness predicts future susceptibility to grastrointestinal nematodes in humans. J Infect Dis 190: 1804-11. 2004.
11. Williams-Blangero S. McGarvey ST. et al. Genetic component to susceptibility to *Trichuris trichiura*: evidence from two Asian populations. Genet Epidemiol 22: 254-64. 2002.
12. MacDonald TT. Choy M-Y. et al. Histopathology of the caecum in children with the Trichuris dysentery syndrome. J Clin Pathol 44: 194-199. 1991.
13. Drake L. Korchev Y. Bashford L. et al. The major secreted product of the whipworm Trichuris, is a pore-forming protein. Proc. R Soc. Lond. B 257: 255-261. 1994.
14. Bennett AB. Barker GC. Bundy DA. A beta-tubulin gene from *Trichuris trichiura*. Mol Biochem Parasitol. 103:111-6. 1999.
15. Bundy DAP. Cooper ES. Trichuris and trichuriasis in humans. Adv Parasitol 28:107-173. 1989.
16. Summers RW, Elliott DE. et al. Trichuris suis therapy in Crohn's disease. Gut 54: 87-90. 2005.
17. Gilman RH. Chong YH. et al. The adverse consequences of heavy Trichuris infection. Trans R Soc Trop Med Hyg 77:432-438. 1983.
18. Joo JH. Ryu KH. et al. Colonoscopic diagnosis of whip-worm infection. Hepato-Gastroenterol 45(24):2105-9, 1998.
19. Sirivichayakul C, Pojjaroen-Anant C. et al. The effectiveness of 3, 5, or 7 days of albendazole for the treatment of *Trichuris trichiura* infection. Ann Trop Med Parasitol 97: 847-53. 2003.
20. Adams VJ, Lombard CJ. et al. Efficacy of albendazole against the whipworm *Trichuris trichiura*: a randomised, controlled trial. S Afr Med J 94: 972-6. 2004.
21. Maqbool S. Lawrence D. Katz M. Treatment of trichuriasis with a new drug, mebendazole. J Pediatr 86:463-465. 1975.
22. Forrester JE. Randomised trial of albendazole and pyrantel in symptomless trichuriasis in children. Lancet. 352:1103-8. 1998.
23. Montresor A. Awasthi S. Crompton DWT. Use of benzimidazoles in children younger than 24 months for the treatment of soil-transmitted helminthiases. Acta Tropica 86: 223-32. 2003.
24. deSilva NR. Impact of mass chemotherapy on the morbidity due to soil-transmitted nematodes. Acta Tropica 86: 197-214. 2003.
25. Nokes C, Grantham-McGregor SM, Sawyer AW, et al. Moderate to high infections of *Trichuris trichiura* and cognitive function in Jamaican school children. Proc R Soc 247: 77-81. 1991.
26. Albonico M. Engels D. Savioli L. Monitoring drug efficacy and early detection of drug resistance for human soil-transmitted nematodes: a pressing public health agenda for helminth control. Int J Parasitol 34:1205-10. 2004.

18. *Ascaris lumbricoides*
(Linnaeus, 1758)

Introduction

Ascaris lumbricoides is one of the largest nematodes to infect humans. The adult lives in the small intestine where it can grow to a length of more than 30 cm. This worm infection is found almost wherever poverty occurs in developing countries. Current estimates indicate that 1.22 billion people are infected, with more than 800 million cases in Asia alone.[1] The most severe consequences of Ascaris infection occur in children who are predisposed to suffer from heavier worm burdens than adults living under similar conditions. Ascaris eggs thrive in warm, moist soil, and are highly resistant to a variety of environmental conditions. The eggs can survive in the sub-arctic regions.[2] In some developing countries, Ascaris eggs are ubiquitous, and have been recovered on all sorts of environmental surfaces, even, in some cases, from the paper currency. The ability of Ascaris eggs to survive in these harsh environments accounts for the urban transmission of ascariasis in large cities.

There is a controversy as to whether pigs can serve as an animal reservoir of *A. lumbricoides*, or whether the related parasite, *Ascaris suum*, is also transmissible to humans.[3] The suggestion has been made that human infection arose in association with pig domestication, possibly first in China.[4] However, the available

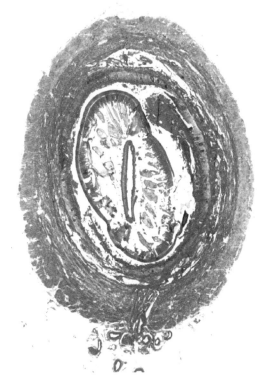

Figure 18.2. Adult Ascaris in appendix.

evidence suggests that Ascaris in humans and pigs comprise reproductively isolated populations, suggesting that zoonotic transmission is not common.[4]

Historical Information

Edward Tyson, in 1683 described the anatomy of *A. lumbricoides*, then known as *Lumbricus teres*.[5] Linnaeus gave it its current name on the basis of its remarkable similarity to the earth-worm, *Lumbricus terrestrias*, which he also named. The life cycle was accurately described by Brayton Ransom.[6] Shimesu Koino, in 1922, reported on a remarkable series of experiments, in which he infected both himself and his younger brother.[7] Luckily for Koino's brother, he chose to use *A. suum* eggs, instead of *A. lumbricoides* eggs. The pig ascarid usually fails to complete its life cycle in humans, thus sparing the younger Koino from an overwhelming infection. It is now known that in some cases, *A. suum* in man can result in the development of adult worms.[7] Unfortunately, the older Koino brother gave himself 500 *A. lumbricoides* eggs, enabling him to prove that a pneumonia-like syndrome developed during the early phase of the infection, caused by third-stage larvae migrating through the lungs on their way to the stomach. The older Koino became seriously ill, but fortunately did not suffer permanent disability.

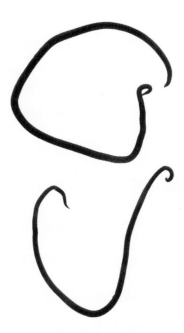

Figure 18.1. Adult female (upper) and male (lower) *Ascaris lumbricoides*. 13-18 cm in length.

Ascaris lumbricoides

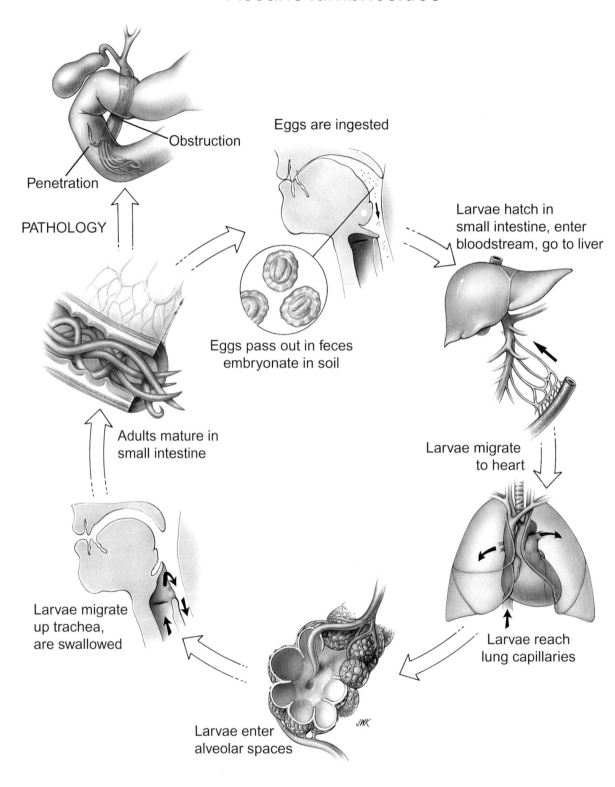

Obstruction

Penetration

PATHOLOGY

Eggs are ingested

Larvae hatch in
small intestine, enter
bloodstream, go to liver

Eggs pass out in feces
embryonate in soil

Adults mature in
small intestine

Larvae migrate
to heart

Larvae reach
lung capillaries

Larvae migrate
up trachea,
are swallowed

Larvae enter
alveolar spaces

"Parasitic Diseases" 5ᵗʰ Ed. © Apple Trees Productions, LLC., Pub. P.O. Box 280, New York, NY 10032

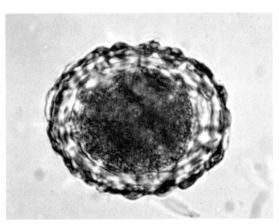

Figure 18.3. Fertilized, unembryonated egg of *A. lumbricoides*. 60 mm x 40 mm

Life Cycle

The adult worms (Fig. 18.1,18.2.) occupy the lumen of the upper small intestine, where they live on predigested food, or chyme, as well as host cellular debris. The worms maintain themselves in the lumen of the small intestine by assuming an S-shaped configuration, pressing their cuticular surfaces against the columnar epithelium of the intestine, and continually moving against the peristalsis. The worms are covered with a tough, thick cuticle composed of collagens and unusual lipids, thus enabling them to sucessfully resist being digested by hydrolases. In addition, the adult worms produce a battery of protease inhibitors, some of which may also interfere with host digestion.

The adult female worm is prolific producing, on average, 200,000 eggs per day. Her uterus may contain up to 27 million eggs at any one time. To synthesize the huge amounts of sterol necessary for massive egg production, Ascaris has evolved a means by which to carry out this oxygen-dependent reaction in the low-oxygen folds of the small intestine. It assembles the components of the reaction on a special oxygen-avid hemoglobin.[8] Since Ascaris is probably an obligate anaerobe, its hemaglobin might actually serve to detoxify its environment by removing oxygen through a unique chemical coupling with nitric oxide.[9, 10]

The eggs (Fig. 18.3.) pass out of the adult fertilized but non-embryonated. They become incorporated into the fecal mass and exit the host in feces. Embryonation takes place outside the host in soil, and is completed by week 2-4 after being deposited there. Eggs not reaching soil immediately can survive in moist environments for up to 2 months.[11] A unique lipoprotein, known as ascaroside, occupies a portion of the inner layer of the egg and may confer a number of the environmental resistance properties ordinarily attributed to Ascaris eggs.[12] A second mucopolysaccharide component on the surface provides adhesive properties for the eggs to associate with environmental surfaces.[13] Embryonated eggs must be swallowed for the life cycle to continue. The first stage larva develops into the second stage inside the egg, but retains the second stage cuitcle around its body.

In the host, the second stage larva is stimulated to hatch by a combination of alkaline conditions in the small intestine, and the solubilization of certain outer layers of the eggshell, facilitated by bile salts. These conditions induce the larva to produce a proteolytic enzyme, facilitating its exit from the egg. The egg protease is activated by alkaline conditions, thus insuring that it will hatch in the right place inside the host. The infectious process is accompanied by a dramatic shift in Ascaris metabolism from aerobic to anaerobic.[12]

The immature parasite, now in the intestinal lumen, penetrates the intestinal wall, enters the lamina propria, penetrates a capillary, and is carried by the portal circulation to the liver. In the liver, the worm feeds on parenchymal tissue and grows (Fig. 18.4.). It then migrates via the bloodstream to the heart, and into the pulmonary circulation. The larva molts twice and grows larger, both in length and in diameter. It becomes stuck in an alveolar capillary, since its diameter is now much greater than that of the vessel's. The worm receives a thigmotactic (touch) signal, initiating a behavior that results in its breaking out into the alveolar spaces (Fig. 18.5.). This is the phase of the infection that caused Koino to experience "verminous" pneumonia.

The larva migrates up the bronchi into the trachea and across the epiglottis; it is swallowed, finally reaching the lumen of the small intestine, again. There, after two additional molts, the worms grow prodigiously, maturing to adulthood in about 6 weeks. Adult worms then mate. Occasionally, egg production may precede mating. When it occurs, infertile eggs are released by

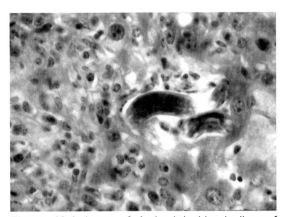

Figure 18.4. Larve of *A. lumbricoides* in liver of experimentally infected mouse.

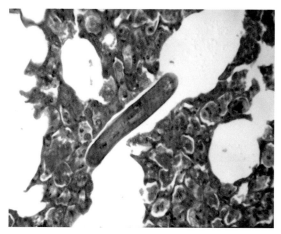

Figure 18.5. Larva of *A. lumbricoides* in lung of an experimentally infected mouse.

the worm. Rarely, a single female worm is acquired, resulting again in infertile egg production.

Cellular and Molecular Pathogenesis

The most intense host reactions occur during the migratory phase of infection. Ascaris antigens released during the molting process have allergenic properties that cause inflammation associated with eosinophilic infiltration of the tissues, peripheral eosinophilia, and an antibody response leading to an increase in serum immunoglobulin E (IgE) levels. At least one of these allergens is known as ABA-1. The suggestion has been made that host IgE antibody responses to ABA-1 and related antigens confer resistance to Ascaris infections.[13] Because of the links between IgE levels, eosinophilia and Ascaris infections, a number of hypotheses have been put forward to examine the impact of helminth infections such as ascariasis on the atopic state of the host. Among them is the notion that atopy evolved as an adaptive mechanism to promote resistance to helminths.[14] Indeed both processes may be linked to polymorphisms of the β-2-adrenoreceptor gene.[15] In addition, Ascaris adults secrete an anti-trypsin factor that enables it to ingest a portion of any meal before its absorbed.

School aged children are relatively predisposed to heavy infections with Ascaris, although the reason for this remains obscure. Many of the same children also harbor large numbers of *Trichuris trichiura*. Such children suffer from impairments in their physical growth and cognitive and intellectual developments.[16] One might suspect that Ascaris somehow interferes with host nutrition, possibly through competition of nutrients, but this hypothesis is as yet unproven. Some studies indicate, however, that Ascaris-infected children devel-

op malabsorption of fat, protein and vitamin A, lactose intolerance from damaged intestinal mucosa, impaired intestinal permeability, and anorexia.[17] It has been further hypothesized that chronic intestinal inflammation leads to anorexia and cachexia, although there is no strong evidence for this. The results of 10 longitudinal studies comparing the growth of Asian and African Ascaris-infected children with those given anthelminthics were reviewed recently.[18] Eight of 9 studies using weight in kg for hypothesis testing found a statistically significant improvement in weight after treatment. Treated children also had a greater increment in height than untreated children in 3 of 6 studies in which height was measured. The effects on growth are more pronounced in children with the heaviest infections. Additional studies also indicate that Ascaris can impair mental processing.[19]

Clinical Disease

Migratory Phase

The intensity of the systemic response to the larva of Ascaris is related directly to the number of worms migrating at any one time. If infection is light, and only a few parasites traverse the tissues, the host response is

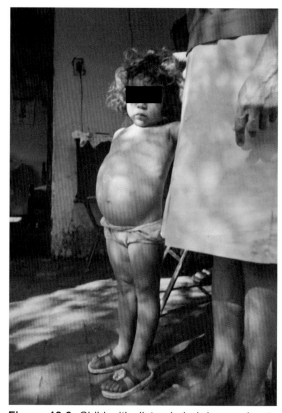

Figure 18.6. Child with distended abdomen due to large bolus of *A. lumbricoides* adult worms in small intestines.

Figure 18.7. Adult Ascaris recovered from child in Fig. 18.6. after treatment with mebendazole.

negligible and clinically inapparent. If infection is heavy, for example, after ingestion of hundreds to thousands of eggs, the patient experiences intense pneumonitis, enlargement of the liver, and generalized toxicity that may last up to 2 weeks. The pneumonitis is of the Löeffler's type, with eosinophilic infiltrates and elevated IgE. This can lead to a component of bronchospasm. Similar phenomena have also been described among uninfected laboratory workers who develop bronchospasm after previous sensitization to Ascaris allergens.[14]

Intestinal Phase

The adult worms in the intestine cause few symptoms, although when they are numerous their sheer bulk may cause fullness and even obstruction. Adult worms migrate when they are irritated (high fevers, drugs, etc.). They may perforate the intestine, penetrate the liver, obstruct the biliary tract, or cause peritonitis. Individuals with moderate infections are rarely symptomatic. Most commonly, such individuals become aware of the infection through casual examination of the stools for another reason, because of passage of an adult worm in the stool, or by regurgitation of it during an episode of vomiting. Heavy infections may lead to the formation of a large bolus of adults that obstructs the lumen (Fig. 18.6, 18.7). In developing countries, acute Ascaris obstruction is a leading cause of so-called "surgical abdomen" in children, accounting for up to 35% of all intestinal obstruction in these regions, and 10,000 deaths annually.[19]

Hepatobiliary Ascariasis (HPA)

The adult worms may also migrate into the biliary tree, causing hepatobiliary and pancreatic ascariasis. This problem occurs more commonly in small children who harbor large numbers of worms; it can lead to cholecystitis, cholangitis, hepatic abscess, pancreatitis, and death may ensue.[20, 21] Among adults screened

by ultrasonography from a general population in Kashmir, India, it was determined that 0.5% are affected by HPA.[21]

Neonatal Ascariasis

This may occur when Ascaris larvae enter the placenta.[22, 23] Although transplacental transmission is common among animal ascarids, the true extent of this phenomenon among humans is not known

Diagnosis

Ascaris lumbricoides infection cannot be specifically diagnosed on the basis of signs or symptoms during the migratory or intestinal phases of the infection. Hepatobiliary ascariasis is difficult to diagnose by conventional radiographic techniques, as the worms often move out of the bile or pancreatic duct after eliciting symptoms. In some endemic areas, ultrasonography and endoscopic retrograde cholangiopancreatography (ERCP) have been used diagnostically.[20, 21, 24] The clinical suspicion of infection with intestinal helminths is the usual reason to request a stool examination.

Ascaris eggs (Fig. 18.3; Fig. C.39., Appendix C) are easily recognized. If only a few eggs are present, they may be missed, but can be readily found if the stool specimen is concentrated by any of several standard techniques (see Appendix C). Usually, so many eggs are passed each day by individual female worms that the likelihood of finding them, even in those with light infections, is high. The presence of infertile Ascaris eggs is diagnostically significant, as the presence of even a single female worm may have serious clinical consequences if it were to migrate. Occasionally, defective eggs missing the outer mamillations are observed. There are no useful serological tests available.

Treatment

Albendazole and mebendazole are the treatments of choice for ascariasis.[25, 26] For school-based de-worming programs, usually a single dose of albendazole (400 mg) or mebendazole (500 mg) is effective. Details regarding the safety of these two agents is provided in the section on trichuriasis. The older drug pyrantel pamoate is also effective. Piperazine citrate can be used in cases of intestinal obstruction because it paralyzes the worm's myoneural junctions, allowing them to be expelled by peristalsis, although this drug is no longer widely available. The migratory (parenteral) phase of the infection is transitory, and thus seldom diagnosed. Hence, it is not typically treated. If infection is heavy, a pneumonia-like syndrome may alert the physician, and patients may be treated symptomatically with corticosteroids.[27]

Surgical intervention is sometimes necessary if the bolus induces intestinal stasis. This condition often presents as a medical emergency due to anaerobic necrosis of intestinal tissue. In some cases the adult worms can be removed endoscopically.

Prevention and Control

Ascaris lumbricoides is present in temperate and sub-tropical zones, but is at its highest prevalence in tropical, rural situations where sanitation is all but absent. In some regions of Africa, 95% of the population is infected, and in parts of Central and South America 45% are infected. In the United States, infection is most prevalent in southern, rural communities; in surveys conducted largely or predominantly among children, 20-67% infection rates have been recorded.[27] Sex or race are of no epidemiological consequence in the distribution of ascariasis. Although persons of all ages are susceptible, the infection predominates among school aged children. This population typically harbors the highest intensity infections. This observation, and the health and educational benefits of de-worming, has resulted in the use of single-dose treatments of children with albendazole or mebendazole as a cornerstone of a global de-worming programming recommended at the 2001 World Health Assembly (www.who.int/worm-control). The target goal is for the frequent and periodic (1-3 times annually) administration of a single dose of mebendazole and albendazole for 75 percent of all at risk school aged children by 2010. The health and educational benefits of this practice are discussed under Trichuriasis.

Ascaris eggs are destroyed by exposure to direct sunlight for 12 hours, and die when exposed to temperatures in excess of 40°C. Exposure to cold, however, does not affect the eggs. They have been known to survive the ordinary freezing temperatures of winter months in the temperate zones. The eggs are also resistant to many commonly used chemical disinfectants, and thrive in treated sewage for many months to years.

References

1. DeSilva NR, Brooker S. et al. Soil-transmitted helminth infections: updating the global picture. Trends Parasitol 19: 547-51. 2003.
2. Embil JA. Pereira CH. et al. Prevalence of *Ascaris lumbricoides* infection in a small Nova Scotian community. Am J Trop Med Hyg 33:595-598. 1984.
3. Mruyama H. Nawa Y. Noda S. Mimori T. An outbreak of ascariasis with marked eosinophilia in the southern part of Kyushu District, Japan, caused by infection with swine ascaris. SE Asian J Trop Med Public Health 28 Suppl 1: 194-6. 1997.
4. Peng W. Anderston TJ. Zhou X. Kennedy MW. Genetic variation in sympatric Ascaris populations from humans and pigs in China. Parasitology 355-61. 1998.
5. Tyson E. Lumbricus teres, or some anatomical observations on the roundworm bred on the human bodies. Philos Trans 13:153-161. 1683.
6. Ransom RH. Foster WD. Life history of *Ascaris lumbricoides* and related forms. J Agnc Res 11:395-398. 1917.
7. Koino S. Experimental infections on human body with ascarides. Jpn Med World 2:317-320. 1922.
8. Sherman DR. Guinn B. et al. Components of sterol biosynthesis assembled on the oxygen-avid hemoglobin of Ascaris. Science 258:1930-1932. 1992.
9. Minning DM. Gow AG. et al. Ascaris hemoglobin is a nitric oxide activated deoxygenase. Nature 401:497-502. 1999.
10. Goldberg DE. Oxygen avid hemoglobin of Ascaris. Chem Rev 99:3371-3378. 1999.
11. Bryan FD. Diseases transmitted by foods contaminated by waste water. J Food Protein 40: 45-56. 1977.
12. Harmych A. Arnette R. Komuniecki R. Role of dihyrolipoyl dehydrogenase (E3) and a novel E3-binding protein in the NADH sensitivity of the pyruvate dehydrogenase complex from anaerobic mitochondria of the parasitic nematode *Ascaris suum*. Mol Biochem Parasitol 125: 135-46. 2002.
13. McSharry C. Xia Y. Holland CV. Kennedy MW. Natural immunity to *Ascaris lumbricoides* associated with immunoglobulin E antibody to ABA-1 allergen and inflammation indicators in children. Infect Immun 67:484-9. 1999.
14. Lynch NR. Hagel IA. et al. Relationship between helminthic infection and IgE response in atopic and nonatopic children in a tropical environment. J Allergy Clin Immunol 101:217-21. 1998.
15. Ramsay CE. Hayden CM. et al. Association of polymorphisms in the beta-2-adrenoreceptor gene with higher levels of parasitic infection. Human Genetics 104:269-74. 1999.
16. Hadidjaja P. Bonang E. et al. The effect of intervention methods on nutritional status and cognitive function of primary school children infected with *Ascaris lumbricoides*. Am J Trop Med Hyg 59:791-5. 1998.
17. Crompton DWT. Nesheim MC. Nutritional impact of intestinal helminthiasis during the human life cycle. Ann Rev Nutr 22: 35-59. 2002.
18. O'Lorcain P. Holland CV. The public health importance of *Ascaris lumbricoides*. Parasitology 121: S51-71. 2000.
19. Crompton DW. Ascaris and ascariasis. Adv Parasitol 48: 285-375. 2001.
20. Khuroo MS. Zargar SA. Mahajan R. Hepatobiliary and pancreatic ascariasis in India. Lancet 335:1503-1506. 1990.
21. Khuroo MS. Hepatobiliary and pancreatic ascariasis. Indian J Gastroenterol 23 (Suppl 1): C28-32. 2001.
22. Costa-Macedo LMD. Rey L. *Ascaris lumbricoides* in neonate: evidence of congenital transmission of intestinal nematodes. Rev Inst Med Trop Sao Paulo 32:351-354. 1990.
23. Synovia CB. Vivakanandan S. Narayanan PR. Fetal response to maternal ascariasis as evidenced by anti-*Ascaris lumbricoides* IgM antibodies in the cord blood. Acta Paediatr Scand 80:1134-1138. 1991.
24. Schulman A. Ultrasound appearances of intra- and extrahepatic biliary ascariasis. Abdom Imaging 23:60-6. 1998.
25. Aubry ML. Cowell P. Davey MJ. et al. Aspects of the pharmacology of a new anthelmintic, pyrantel. Br J Pharmacol 38: 332-344. 1970.
26. Chevarria AP. Schwartzwelder JC. et al. Mebendazole, an effective broad spectrum anthelminthic. Am J Trop Med Hyg 22: 592-595. 1973.
27. Blumenthal DS. Schultz MG. Incidence of intestinal obstruction in children infected with *Ascaris lumbricoides*. Am J Trop Med Hyg 24:801-805. 1975.

19. The Hookworms:

Necator americanus
(Stiles 1902)
Ancylostoma duodenale
(Dubini 1843)

Introduction

Two major species of hookworm infect humans: *Necator americanus* and *Ancylostoma duodenale*. Adults of both species inhabit the small intestine and feed on host intestinal mucosa and blood. Blood loss resulting from adult hookworms in the intestine leads to protein and iron deficiency, as well as anemia. Hookworms infect approximately 740 million in the developing nations of the tropics,[1] making this one of the most prevalent human infections worldwide, and one of the most common causes of iron-deficiency anemia. In terms of disease burden, hookworm results in more deaths and disability adjusted life years (DALYs) lost than any other human helminth infections.[2, 3]

Children heavily infected with hookworms are likely to develop deficits in both physical and cognitive development and are more susceptible to other intercurrent infections.[2-4] Hookworm has been further identified as an important health threat for women of reproductive age, including an estimated 44 million pregnant women are infected with hookworms in endemic countries. The resulting iron deficiency and malnutrition during pregnancy adversely affects intrauterine growth, birth weight and even maternal survival.[5] Hookworm also increases the likelihood of premature birth, and may contribute to maternal mortality.[6]

The distribution of the two species was thought at

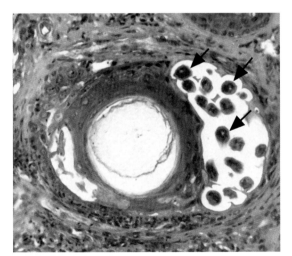

Figure 19.1. Hookworm larvae (arrows) in skin of experimentally infected dog.

Figure 19.2. Adult female *Ancylostoma duodenale*. 10 mm.

one time to be discrete and not overlapping; however, both species have been shown to occupy at least some of the same regions of Africa, South America, and Asia. *N. americanus* is the predominant hookworm worldwide, with the highest rates in Sub-Saharan Africa, tropical regions of the Americas, South China, and Southeast Asia. *A. duodenale* is more focally endemic in parts of China, India, North Africa, Sub-Saharan Africa, and a few regions of the Americas. A third species, *Ancylostoma ceylanicum*, is found mainly in cats but has occasionally been described in humans in Asia. The canine hookworm *A. caninum* has been implicated as the cause of eosinophilic enteritis syndrome in parts of northern Queensland, Australia.[7] *A. braziliense*, whose definitive hosts are dogs and cats, causes cutaneous larva migrans.

There are no known reservoir hosts for *A. duodenale* or *N. americanus*. The dog is the primary host for *A. caninum*, but it has not been well established whether this hookworm causes mature human infection, save for a few reported cases in Australia.

Historical Information

Hookworm disease is widespread in the tropics and subtropics. It has been common in the United States in the past (primarily in the rural South), as well as in Puerto Rico. Because hookworm disease was thought to be a major obstacle to the economic development of the affected areas, John D. Rockefeller, Sr. established the Rockefeller Sanitary Commission (which later became the Rockefeller Foundation) in 1909, for the sole purpose of eliminating hookworm from the

Necator americanus

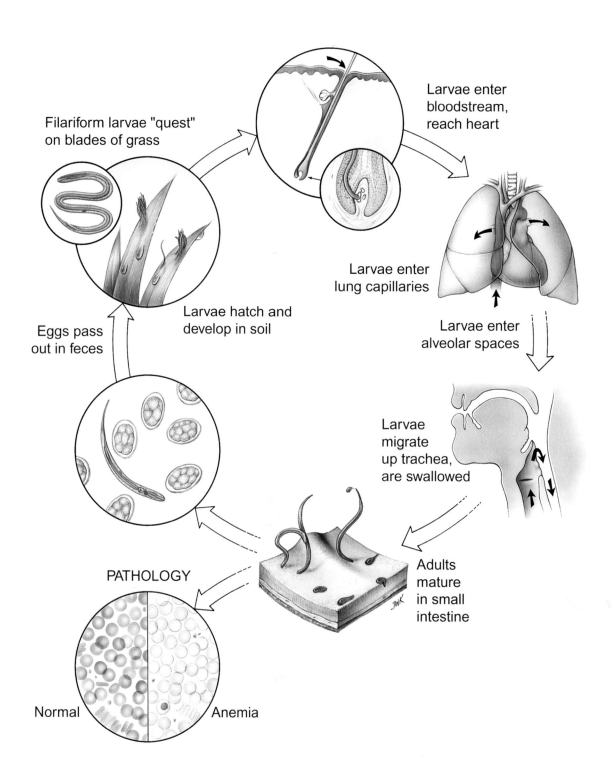

Filariform larvae "quest" on blades of grass

Larvae enter bloodstream, reach heart

Larvae enter lung capillaries

Larvae hatch and develop in soil

Eggs pass out in feces

Larvae enter alveolar spaces

Larvae migrate up trachea, are swallowed

Adults mature in small intestine

PATHOLOGY

Normal

Anemia

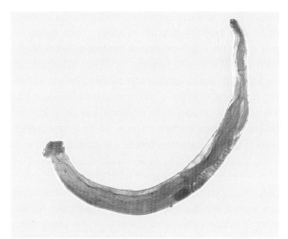

Figure 19.3. Adult male *A. duodenale*. Note hand-like bursa at tail end. 8 mm.

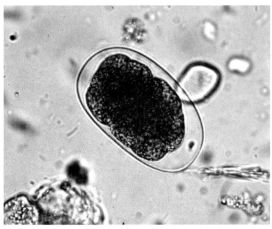

Figure 19.4. Fertilized, embryonated hookworm egg. 65 μm x 40 μm.

United States and Puerto Rico. Charles W. Stiles, in 1902,[8] first described *N. americanus*, and was largely responsible for convincing Frederick Gates, a Baptist minister and Rockefeller's key advisor, to establish the Commission. The prevalence of hookworm infection in the United States has been reduced almost to the point of eradication, but this resulted less from any planned intervention than from the general improvement in socioeconomic conditions. Economic development also accounts in a large part for the control of malaria and typhoid fever in the United States. However, much of our knowledge regarding the natural history and pathogenesis of hookworm infection was based on the work of investigators funded by the Rockefeller philanthropies, including William Cort, A.O Foster, A.C. Chandler, J. Allen Scott, and Norman Stoll. Stoll described hookworm as "the great infection of mankind."[9] Dubini first reported human infection with *A. duodenale* in 1843;[10] but it was Looss, working in Egypt, who demonstrated percutaneous transmission of hookworm infection and clarified its life cycle. The life cycle was further defined by Schad, who demonstrated the ability of *A. duodenale* larvae to remain in a dormant arrested state in human tissues.[11]

Life Cycle

Infection begins when the filariform larvae actively penetrate the cutaneous tissues, usually through a hair follicle (Fig. 19.1) or an abraded area. Skin invasion may be facilitated by the release of larval hydrolytic enzymes. Once in the subcutaneous tissues, the larvae enter capillaries and are carried passively through the bloodstream to the capillaries of the lungs. The third-stage larvae break out of the alveolar capillaries and complete the migratory phase of the life cycle by

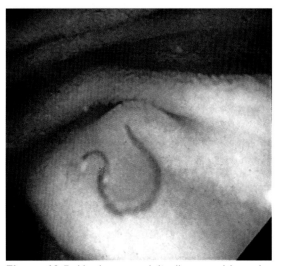

Figure 19.5. Hookworm adult, diagnosed by colonoscopy.

crawling up the bronchi and trachea, over the epiglottis, and into the pharynx. They are then swallowed, and proceed into the stomach. This portion of the life cycle (i.e., parenteral phase) closely parallels those of *Ascaris lumbricoides* and *Strongyloides stercoralis*. Two molts take place in the small intestine, resulting in the development of an adult worm (Fig. 19.2, 19.3).

Ancylostoma duodenale larvae are also infective orally. In some regions, oral ingestion may be the predominant mode of transmission. Larvae that infect orally may undergo two molts to adulthood without leaving the gastrointestinal tract.

Forty days, following maturation and copulation, the female worms begin laying eggs (Fig. 19. 4), completing the life cycle. Adult worms live an average of one year in the case of *A. duodenale* and 3-5 years in the case of *N. americanus*.[12] The maximum recorded survival time is 15 years.[13]

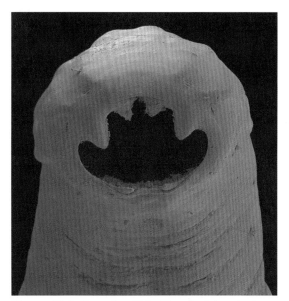

Figure 19.6. Scanning EM of head of *Ancylostoma duodenale*. Note teeth. Photo D. Scharf.

In endemic areas, where reinfections are continual, the development of some filariform larvae of *A. duodenale* (but not *N. americanus*) is interrupted. After entering the host, these larvae penetrate into bundles of skeletal muscles and become dormant. They can later resume their development and complete the life cycle.[10] Larval arrested development in human tissues occurs during times of the year when the external environmental conditions are unfavorable to parasite development in the soil. Larval arrest also occurs during pregnancy, and development resumes at the onset of parturition. When these larvae appear in breast milk, vertical transmission of *A. duodenale* infection in neonates may result.

The adult worms feed on intestinal mucosa and blood in the small intestine (Fig. 19.5). Morphologically, each species can be differentiated on the basis of the mouth parts of the adults. *A. duodenale* possesses cutting teeth (Fig. 19.6), whereas *N. americanus* has rounded cutting plates (Fig. 19.7). Moreover, their body sizes differ. The adult male hookworms are differentiated from the females by the presence of a copulatory bursa.

Ancylostoma duodenale and *N. americanus* exhibit major differences in their life cycles and pathogenicity. *A. duodenale* is generally considered the more virulent of the two species because it is larger, causes more blood loss, produces more eggs, and has several modes of transmission other than penetrating skin. The female passes eggs into the lumen of the small intestine. *A. duodenale* produces about 28,000 eggs per day, and *N. americanus* about 10,000. The eggs

embryonate to the four- and eight-cell stages immediately after they are passed. In warm, moist, sandy, or loamy soil the eggs develop to the first-stage, rhabditiform larvae, within 48 hours of deposition in the soil. After hatching, the larvae feed on debris in the immediate surroundings, and grow and molt twice to develop into the infective, third-stage, filariform larvae. Filariform larvae do not consume food, and are generally considered to be in a developmentally arrested state.[14] However, these larvae do not lie motionless; rather, they actively seek out the highest point in the environment (e.g., the tops of grass blades, small rocks), where they are more likely to come into direct contact with human skin. In endemic areas, it is common for many third-stage larvae to aggregate on dewy grass, increasing the chances for multiple infections of the same host. Sandy soils, such as those found in coastal areas, are particularly favorable for hookworm larval migrations and hookworm transmission.

Cellular and Molecular Pathogenesis

Third-stage hookworm larvae penetrate skin with the aid of secreted macromolecules that include a metalloprotease and a family of cysteine-rich secretory proteins, known as the Ancylostoma secreted proteins.[15–17] Repeated infection results in an immediate hypersensitivity and other inflammatory responses comprising hookworm dermatitis. Subsequent larval migration through the lungs may result in pulmonary inflammation, resulting in a pneumonitis.

Most of the pathology of hookworm infection results

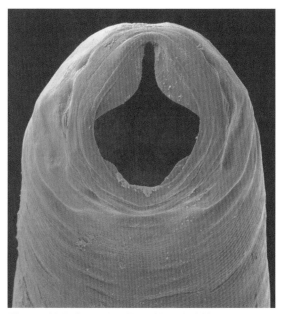

Figure 19.7. Scanning EM of head of *Necator americanus*. Note cutting plates. Photo by D. Scharf.

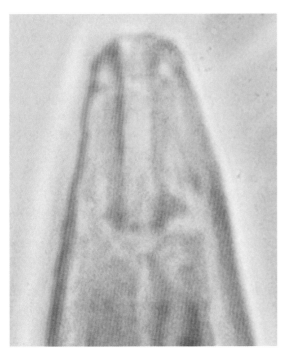

Figure 19.8. Buccal cavity of hookworm rhabditiform larva. It is longer than that of the same stage of *Strongyloides stercoralis* (see Fig. 20.7).

from the presence of adult hookworms in the small intestine. The adult worms derive their nourishment from eating villous tissue. They also suck blood directly from their site of attachment to the intestinal mucosa and submucosa. Adult worms possess a well-developed esophageal bulb, enabling them to pump blood from the capillary bed of the mucosa. Adult parasites secrete an anticoagulant that blocks the action of host factor Xa and VIIa/ tissue factors.[18, 19] Hence, blood loss continues after the worms move to a new location. Each *A. duodenale* adult sucks 0.1-0.2 ml of blood per day, while each *N. americanus* adult worm sucks 0.01-0.02 ml of blood per day.[19]

Following blood ingestion, the adult hookworms rupture the red blood cells with the aid of hemolysins,[20] and then break down host hemoglobin in an ordered manner through the activities of specific hemoglobin-specific proteases.[20, 21]

Repeated exposure to hookworm infection may result in immunity, but the data supporting this conjecture are controversial. Although a humoral antibody response to numerous hookworm antigens can be demonstrated in naturally-infected individuals, the presence of specific antibodies often does not correlate with resistance to infection.[22] Some immunoglobulins may even serve as a marker for hookworm infection.[23] The absence of effector immunity may explain why the intensity of hookworm infection often increases with age in endemic regions, in contrast to the other major

soil-transmitted helminth infections (e.g., Ascaris and Trichuris) for which the intensity peaks in childhood.[3] This could also explain why reinfection with hookworms can occur within just a few months of anthelmintic treatment.[24] It may also account for the difficulties associated with the control of hookworm. The absence of resistance to hookworms may reflect the parasite's ability to escape host immunity.[25]

Clinical Disease

Penetration of the skin by filariform larvae may not result in symptoms in previously uninfected individuals. However, those experiencing repeated infections develop a pruritic papular vesicular dermatitis at the site of larval entry, known as ground itch, or dew itch.

In heavily infected individuals, there may be symptoms of pneumonia during the migratory phase of the developmental cycle of these worms. The tissue migrating larval stages induce an intense circulating eosinophilia comprised predominantly of hypodense activated eosinophils.[27]

The intestinal phase can be asymptomatic, although it frequently results in epigastric pain and abdominal discomfort. A syndrome known as Wakana disease occurs when large numbers of larvae are ingested, and is associated with nausea, vomiting, dyspnea, and eosinophilia.[22]

Generally speaking, severe illness resulting from hookworm infection results only when large numbers of hookworms are present in the small intestine. In most endemic areas, hookworm infections are said to be "aggregated."[28, 29] This means that anywhere from two-thirds to three-fourths of the infections in a given area are sufficiently light in terms of intensity (numbers of worms) that they are clinically silent. The clinical features of hookworm disease usually occur only in a minority of individuals who harbor large numbers of worms. In some regions, certain individuals might be predisposed to acquiring heavy infections.[29]

The major clinical feature of hookworm disease is iron-deficiency anemia, which occurs as the result of blood loss in the intestinal tract.[30, 31] Intestinal blood loss is proportional to the number of hookworms present in the intestine, although whether or not true iron-deficiency anemia subsequently develops depends upon the predominant species of hookworm in the intestine (*A. duodenale* is associated with larger blood loss than *N. americanus*), the iron reserves of the host, and the daily intake of iron.[31-34] Severe anemia is associated with lassitude, palpitations, and exertional dyspnea, which may lead to angina pectoris and congestive heart failure. The physical signs of hookworm anemia include the signs of iron deficiency, such as pale sclera and fingernail concavities (koilonychia). In addition, children may manifest a yellow-green discoloration of the skin known as chlorosis.[35] Children with severe hookworm infection also show signs of protein malnutrition that result from hookworm-associated plasma protein loss, and they may develop abdominal distension, facial edema, and hair loss.

A syndrome of infantile ancylostomiasis has been described that is associated with severe anemia, melena, abdominal distension and failure to thrive.[36, 37] There is circumstantial evidence suggesting that these neonates ingested *A. duodenale* through breast milk.

Chronic hookworm anemia during childhood causes physical growth retardation, as well as deficits in child cognition and intellectual development.[1-3] As with other soil-transmitted helminth infections, growth retardation is often reversible by administration of anthelminthic chemotherapy,[38] but intellectual and cognitive skills cannot always be reversed by therapy. Chronic hookworm anemia during pregnancy can result in prematurity or low birthweight.[5] Many of these chronic sequelae account for the tremendous impact of hookworms on maternal child health. In its World Development Report, the World Bank cited hookworm as a leading cause of morbidity among school aged children.[39]

Diagnosis

Diagnosis is established by the microscopic identification of characteristic eggs in the stool (Fig. 19.4, C.42., Appendix C). Quantitative methods for determining the number of eggs per gram of feces are also available; under some circumstances, these provide some estimate of the overall worm burden. No distinction can be made among eggs of any of the hookworm species. Differentiation depends upon the examination of either third-stage larvae (Fig. 19.8), or by recovering the adult worms.

Treatment

Adult hookworms are usually susceptible to the two major benzimidazole anthelmintic drugs, albendazole and mebendazole, although albendazole is more effective in a single dose compared with single dose mebendazole.[40] In some cases outright failures of a single dose mebendazole to remove hookworms from the gastrointestinal tract have been reported.[41] To ensure a therapeutic effect for the treatment of hookworm, mebendazole must usually be given over three consecutive days, usually as 100 mg.

Details on the safety of benzimidazole anthelminthics for very young children and pregnant women are discussed in the section on trichuriasis. These two hu-

man populations are also considered especially vulnerable to the effects of hookworm anemia. In Africa, hookworm was found to make a substantial contribution to anemia in preschool children,[42] while in Nepal hookworm was a significant cause of anemia in pregnancy.[43] Regarding the latter, pregnant women who received antenatal albendazole were shown to exhibit significant improvements in maternal anemia, birthweight, and infant mortality.[44] Therefore, the concerns about the toxicities of the benzimidazoles need to be weighed against their potentially important benefits in pregnancy.

The benzimidazoles work by binding to the microtubules of the parasite. Anthelminthic resistance to the benzimidazoles has been well-described among nematodes of veterinary importance, and occurs via mutations in the parasite tubulin alleles. Recent reports on the outright failure of mebendazole to treat human hookworm infections in Mali,[44] and the reduced efficacy of mebendazole with frequent and periodic use,[44] have raised possible concerns that benzimidazole drug resistance may be emerging among hookworms. However, there is as yet no direct experimental evidence that drug resistance has occurred, but it is recommended that efficacy of these drugs should be monitored.[44] Pyrantel pamoate and levamisole have been used as second-line agents for the treatment of hookworm.

Most children and adults with hookworm infection can be treated with benzimidazole anthelminthics alone and do not require iron supplementation. However, pregnant women with severe hookworm anemia and their unborn children have been shown to benefit from simultaneous oral supplementation with iron such as ferrous sulfate along with anthelminthic drugs.[44]

Prevention and Control

The traditional methods of hookworm control in endemic areas have included (1) sanitary disposal of feces through the implementation of latrines; (2) health education; and (3) encouraging use of shoes or other footwear. However, despite decades of widespread attempts to control hookworm through these traditional methods, the global prevalence and intensity of hookworm has remained the same. Among the reasons why traditional methods have failed are the ability of *A. duodenale* hookworm larvae to infect humans through ingestion, the ability of *N. americanus* larvae to penetrate all aspects of the body including the hands and abdomen, the high rate of occupational exposure to hookworm that occurs during agricultural pursuits, and the continued reliance on human feces for fertilizing crops.[45]

At the World Health Assembly in 2001, member

states were urged to control the global morbidity of hookworm and other soil-transmitted helminth (STH) infections through the frequent and periodic use of anthelminthic drugs (www.who.int/wormcontrol). There are concerns, however, that this approach might have less of an impact on hookworm than the other STH infections such as Trichuris and Ascaris. As noted above, the highest hookworm intensities in a community are often not in children, so that targeting children is not expected to reduce hookworm transmission.[46] More importantly, high rates of post-treatment hookworm reinfection occurs in many communities,[24] especially those with high levels of transmission, which sometimes requires thrice-yearly anthelminthic treatment. As noted above, the diminishing efficacy of mebendazole with

frequent and periodic use has raised concerns about emerging drug resistance.

As a complementary control strategy, the Human Hookworm Vaccine Initiative has developed a first-generation recombinant vaccine that targets the infective larval stages.[4, 48] The vaccine is comprised of a recombinant ASP formulated with Alhydrogel.[16, 49] Host anti-ASP antibody responses inhibit larval invasion and reduces hookworm burdens in laboratory animals when used as a vaccine.[48, 49] Clinical testing of the vaccine is in progress. Because it only targets the larval stages, it has been proposed that the vaccine would be used immediately following a dose of albendazole or mebendazole, which would remove existing adult hookworms from the human gastrointestinal tract.

References

1. DeSilva NR, Brooker S. et al. Soil-transmitted helminth infections: updating the global picture. Trends Parasitol 19:547-51. 2003.
2. Hotez PJ, Brooker S. et al. Hookworm infection. N Engl J Med 351:799-807. 2004.
3. Hotez PJ. Bethony J. et al. Hookworm: "The great infection of mankind." Adv Parasitol 58:197-288. 2005.
4. Brooker S. Bethony J. Hotez PJ. Human hookworm infection in the 21st century. Adv Parasitol 58: 198-288. 2004.
5. Sakti H. Nokes C. et al. Evidence for an association between hookworm infection and cognitive function in Indonesian school children. Trop Med Int Health 4:322-334. 1999.
6. Bundy DAP. Chan MS. Savioli L. Hookworm infection in pregnancy. Trans R Soc Trop Med Hyg 89:521-2. 1995.
7. Prociv P. Croese J. Human eosinophilic enteritis caused by dog hookworm, *Ancylostoma caninum*. Lancet 335:1299-1302. 1990.
8. Stiles CW. A new species of hookworm (*Uncinaria americana*) parasitic in man. Am Med 3:777-778. 1902.
9. Stoll NR. On endemic hookworm, where do we stand today? Exp Parasitol 12: 241-51. 1962.
10. Dubini A. Nuovo verme intestinale umano *Ancylostoma duodenale*, constitutente un sesto genere dei nematoidei proprii dell'uomo. Ann Univ Med Milano 106:5-13. 1843.
11. Schad GA. Chowdhury AB. et al. Arrested development in human hookworm infections: an adaptation to a seasonally unfavorable external environment. Science 180:502-4. 1973.
12. Hoagland KE. Schad GA. *Necator americanus* and *Ancylostoma duodenale*: Life history parameters and epidemiological implications of two sympatric hookworms on humans. Exp Parasitol 44:36-49. 1978.
13. Plamer ED. Course of egg output over a 15-year period in a case of experimentally induced necatoriasis americanus. Am J Trop Med Hyg 4:756-757. 1955.
14. Hawdon JM. Hotez PJ. Hookworm: Developmental biology of the infectious process. Curr Op Genetics Develop 6: 618-23. 1996.
15. Zhan B. Hotez PJ. Wang Y. Hawdon JM. A developmentally regulated metalloprotease secreted by host-stimulated *Ancylostoma caninum* third-stage infective larvae is a member of the astacin family of proteases. Molec Biochem Parasit 120:291-6. 2002.
16. Asojo OA, Goud G. et al. X-ray structure Na-ASP-2, a pathogenesis-related-1 protein from the nematode parasite, *Necator americanus*, and a vaccine antigen for human hookworm infection. J Molec Biol 346: 801-14. 2005.
17. Cappello M. Vlasuk GP. et al. *Ancylostoma caninum* anticoagulant peptide (AcAP): a novel hookworm derived inhibitor of human coagulation factor Xa. Proc Natl Acad Sci USA 92: 6152-6156. 1995.
18. Stanssens P. Bergum PW. et al. Anticoagulant repertoire of the hookworm *Ancylostoma caninum*. Proc Natl Acad Sci USA 93:2149-2154. 1996.
19. Roche M. Layrisse M. The nature and causes of "hookworm anemia". Am J Trop Med Hyg 15:1031-1102. 1996.
20. Don TA. Jones MK. et al. A pore-forming haemolysin from the hookworm, *Ancylostoma caninum*. Int J Parasitol 34: 1029-35. 2004.
21. Williamson AL. Lecchi P. et al. A multi-enzyme cascade of hemoglobin proteolysis in the intestine of blood-feeding hookworms. J Biol Chem 279: 35950-7. 2004.
22. Pritchard DI. Quinnell RJ. et al. Epidemiology and immunology of *Necator americanus* infection in a community in Papua New Guinea: humoral responses to excretory-secretory and cuticular collagen antigens. Parasitol 100:317-26. 1990.
23. Palmer DR. Bradley M. Bundy DA. IgG4 responses to antigens of adult *Necator americanus*: potential for use in large-scale epidemiological studies. Bull WHO 74: 381-386. 1996.
24. Albonico M. Smith PG. et al. Rate of reinfection with intestinal nematodes after treatment of children with mebendazole or albendazole in a highly endemic area. Trans R Soc Trop Med Hyg 89: 538-541. 1995.
25. Kumar S. Pritchard DI. Skin penetration by ensheathed third-stage infective larvae of *Necator americanus*, and the host's immune response to larval antigens. Int J Parasitol 22:573-579. 1992.
26. White CJ. Maxwell CJ. Gallin JI. Changes in the structural and functional properties of human eosinophils during experimental hookworm infection. J Infect Dis 159:778-783. 1986.
27. Yoshida Y. Nakanishi Y. Mitani W. Experimental studies on the infection mode of *Ancylostoma duodenale* and *Necator americanus* to the definitive host. Japanese J Parasitol 7:102-112. 1958.

28. Bundy DAP. Is the hookworm just another geohelminth? In: Hookworm Disease, Current Status and New Directions (Schad GA, Warren KS, eds). Taylor & Francis, Pubs. London: pp 147-164. 1990.

29. Schad GA. Anderson RM. Predisposition to hookworm infection. Science 228:1537-40. 1985.

30. Albonico M. Stoltzfus RJ. et al. Epidemiological evidence for a differential effect of hookworm species, *Ancylostoma duodenale* or *Necator americanus*, on iron status of children. Int J Epidemiol 27: 530-7. 1998.

31. Stoltzfus RJ. Albonico M. et al. Hemoquant determination of hookworm-related blood loss and its role in iron deficiency in African Children. Am J Trop Med Hyg 55:399-404. 1996.

32. Stoltzfus RJ. Chwaya HM. et al. Epidemiology of iron deficiency in Zanzibari school children: the importance of hookworms. Am J Clin Nutr; 65:153-159. 1997.

33. Stoltzfus RJ, Dreyfuss M. et al. Hookworm control as a strategy to prevent iron deficiency. Nutrition Rev 55: 223-32. 1997.

34. Brooker S. Peshu N. et al. The epidemiology of hookworm infection and its contribution to anaemia among preschool children on the Kenyan coast. Trans R Soc Trop Med Hyg 93:240-246. 1999.

35. Crosby WH. What became of chlorosis. JAMA 257:2799-2800. 1987.

36. Hotez PJ. Hookworm disease in children. Pediatr Infect Dis J 8:516-520. 1989.

37. Yu SH. Jiang ZX. Xu LQ. Infantile hookworm disease in China. A review. Acta Tropica 59:265-270. 1995.

38. Stephenson LS. Latham MC. et al. Treatment with a single dose of albendazole improves growth of Kenyan school children with hookworm, *Trichuris trichiura*, and *Ascaris lumbricoides* infections. Am J Trop Med Hyg 41:78-87. 1989.

39. World Development Report 1993. Investing in health. Oxford University Press

40. Albonico M. Crompton DWT. Savioli L. Control strategies for human intestinal nematode infections. Adv Parasitol 42: 277-341. 1999.

41. DeClercq D. Sacko M. et al. Failure of mebendazole in treatment of human hookworm infections in the southern region of Mali. Am J Trop Med Hyg 57: 25-30. 1997.

42. Brooker S. Peshu N. et al. The epidemiology of hookworm infection and its contribution to anaemia among preschool children on the Kenyan coast. Trans R Soc Trop Med Hyg 93:240-246. 1999.

43. Christian P. Khatry SK. West KP Jr. Antenatal anthelminthic treatment, birthweight, and infant survival in rural Nepal. Lancet 364:981-3. 2004.

44. Albonico M. Engels D. Savioli L. Monitoring drug efficacy and early detection of drug resistance for human soil-transmitted nematodes: a pressing public health agenda for helminth control. Int J Parasitol 34:1205-10. 2004.

45. Humphries DL. Stephenson LS. et al. The use of human faeces for fertilizer is associated with increased intensity of human hookworm infection in Vietnamese women. Trans R Soc Trop Med Hyg 91:518-520. 1997.

46. Chan MS. Bradley M. Bundy DAP. Transmission patterns and the epidemiology of hookworm. Int J Epidemiol 26: 1392-400. 1997.

47. Brooker S, Bethony JM. et al. Epidemiologic, immunologic and practical considerations in developing and evaluating a human hookworm vaccine. Expert Rev Vaccines 4:35-50. 2005.

48. Goud GN. Zhan B. et al. Cloning, yeast expression, isolation and vaccine testing of recombinant Ancylostoma secreted protein 1 (ASP-1) and ASP-2 from Ancylostoma ceylanicum. J Infect Dis 189:919-29. 2004.

49. Mendez S. Zhan B. et al. Effect of combining the larval antigens Ancylostoma secreted protein 2 (ASP-2) and metalloprotease 1 (MTP-1) in protecting hamsters against hookworm infection and disease caused by Ancylostoma ceylanicum. Vaccine 2005. in press

20. *Strongyloides stercoralis*
(Bavay 1876)

Introduction

Strongyloides stercoralis is a parasitic nematode with a worldwide distribution, and is particularly prevalent throughout tropical and subtropical regions. In North America, it occurs frequently among Southeast Asian immigrants, and is endemic in parts of Appalachia.[1] It still occurs in Europe, as well, but in low numbers. Because of the difficulty in establishing a definitive diagnosis, and because the parasite may cause long-lasting asymptomatic infections,[1] the true global prevalence of human strongyloidiasis is unknown. Some estimates indicate that there may be as many as 100 million cases.[2]

Reservoir hosts play an important part in this nematode's biology. For example, dogs and non-human primates can harbor Strongyloides. Because of this, there have been numerous outbreaks of strongyloidiasis among animal handlers.[3] In addition, *S. stercoralis* can undergo a facultative, free-living phase in soil, allowing for many potential sources of human infection.

A second form of human strongyloidiasis, caused by *S. fuelleborni*, has been described in infants living in Papua, New Guinea,[4, 5] and in sub-Saharan Africa. Children there develop a special clinical syndrome called swollen belly syndrome (SBS). This condition is associated with a high rate of mortality. In some rural villages, the prevalence of *S. fuelleborni* may reach nearly 100% during the early years of life, then it declines in older children and adults.

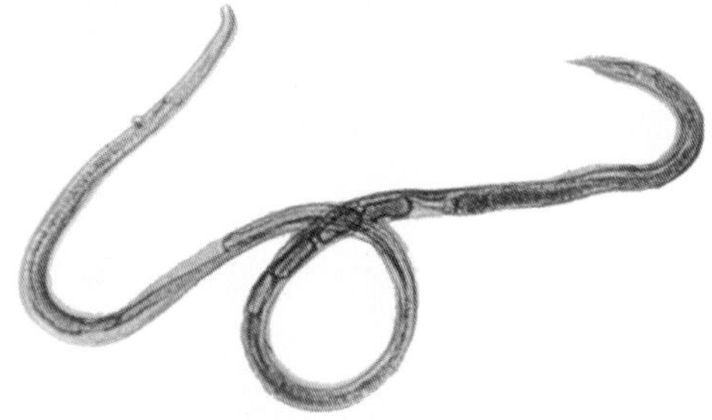

Figure 20.2a. Parasitic female of *S. stercoralis*. 2.5 mm x 35 μm. Courtesy L. Ash and T. Orihel.

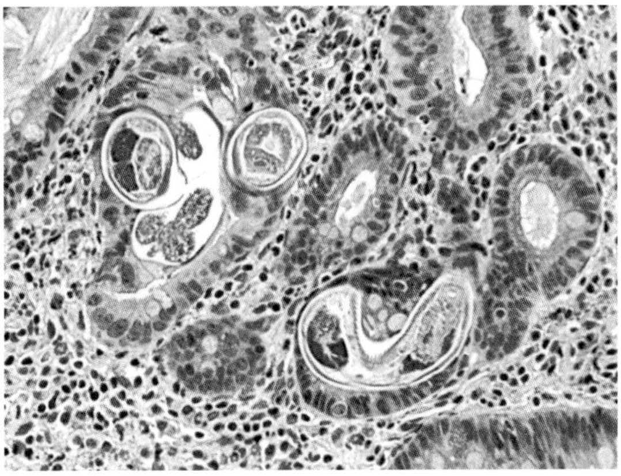

Figure 20.2b. Small intestine with numerous sections of a parasitic female *S. stercoralis*.

Figure 20.1. Free-living adult of *Strongyloides stercoralis.* This stage occurs in soil only. 600 μm.

Historical Information

The clinical aspects of infection with *Strongyloides stercoralis* was first described by Bavay[6] and Normand[7] in 1876, while they were working together in Toulon, France. Their patients were French army personnel, newly arrived from Cochin, Indochina; thus the term for strongyloidal enteritis, "Cochin China diarrhea." Bavay recovered numerous larvae of a nematode that had not been previously described from the stool of these patients, and named it *Anguillula stercoralis*.

Askanazy[8] described the pathology of strongyloidiasis, and the life cycle was reported by Fuelleborn.[9] He conducted experiments in dogs and learned that infective larvae penetrate unbroken skin. Nishigoii, in 1928,[10] described auto-infection with *S. stercoralis*, and also showed that infected dogs made constipated with morphine and bismuth subnitrate passed infective third-stage larvae, rather than non-infective second-stage larvae. In addition, he noted that the number of larvae passed by these animals increased,

Strongyloides stercoralis

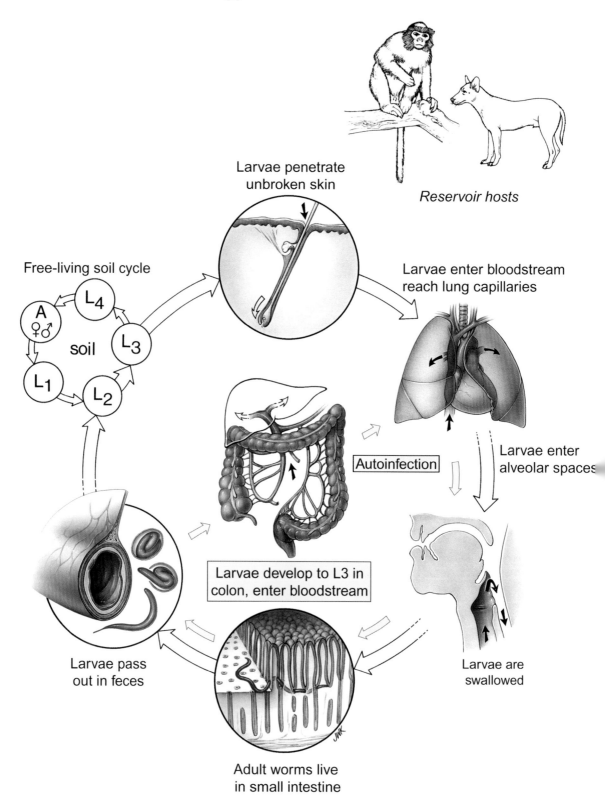

Reservoir hosts

Larvae penetrate
unbroken skin

Free-living soil cycle

Larvae enter bloodstream
reach lung capillaries

soil

Autoinfection

Larvae enter
alveolar spaces

Larvae develop to L3 in
colon, enter bloodstream

Larvae pass
out in feces

Larvae are
swallowed

Adult worms live
in small intestine

so long as constipation was maintained. These studies preceded the clinical description of autoinfection now known to also occur in humans.

Life Cycle

Strongyloides stercoralis exists both as a free-living (Fig. 20.1) and as a parasitic animal (Fig. 20.2a). The parasitic adult female is about 2 mm long and 35 μm wide. The nematode lives embedded within a row of columnar epithelial cells in the small intestine (Fig. 20.2b), usually in the lamina propria of the duodenum and proximal jejunum. Reproduction is by parthenogenesis. There is apparently no parasitic male.

The embryonated eggs hatch rapidly into first-stage larvae, which emerge into the lumen of the small intestine and proceed into the colon. There, they molt once, becoming second-stage rhabditiform (stumpy) larvae. Ordinarily, the rhabditiform larvae are deposited in soil with feces. Alternatively, they may molt into third-stage filariform (long, slender) larvae while still within the lumen of the colon, burrow into the mucosa, and enter the circulation directly. This aspect of the parasitic phase of the life cycle is known as autoinfection. Free-Living Phase (Heterogonic Life Cycle) Rhabditiform larvae require warm, moist, sandy, or loamy soil for the next developmental phase of the cycle to take place. In the proper soil, and under optimal environmental conditions, they develop to free-living adult worms. This occurs by four successive molts. Adult worms of both sexes are found during the free-living phase. They mate, and the female produces embryonated eggs that hatch and molt twice to third-stage filariform larvae (Fig. 20.3). Usually, this happens when conditions become unfavorable for the continuation of the free-living phase (e.g. lack of nutrition, low moisture). The third-stage filariform larvae can remain in soil for several days. When the infective larvae encounter a suitable host,

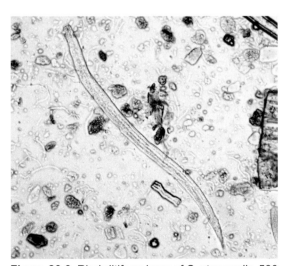

Figure 20.3. Rhabditiform larva of *S. stercoralis*. 580 μm x 15 μm.

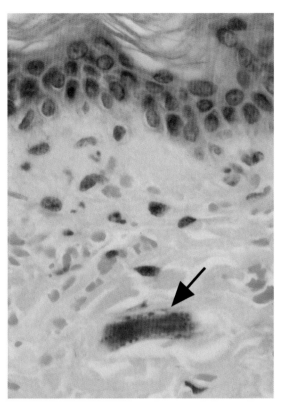

Figure 20.4. Filariform larva (arrow) of *S. stercoralis* in cutaneous layer of skin.

they penetrate the skin (Fig. 20.4.) and begin the parasitic phase of the infection. Filariform larvae can also "swim" in aquatic environments, giving them a greater range in which to find a host as compared to hookworm filariform larvae, which cannot do so. If filariform larvae fail to locate a host within 3 days, they expend all their stored glycogen and die.

Parasitic Phase (Homogonic Life Cycle)

Third stage filariform larvae enter the host through the skin, a process facilitated by the release of a protease by the parasite.[11] Upon entry into the host, the larvae probably enter venules and/or lymphatics before they are carried through the afferent circulation to the right heart, pulmonary artery, and pulmonary capillaries. The larvae rupture into the alveolar space, actively crawl up the respiratory tree, pass through the trachea into the pharynx, cross the epiglottis, and are swallowed. *S. stercoralis* may not always migrate through the lungs to reach the intestinal tract.[12] The larvae undergo a final molt in the small intestine and become parasitic females. They begin egg production within 25-30 days after the initial infection.

Autoinfection, Hyperinfection, and Disseminated Infection

In some groups of patients,[13] rhabditiform larvae develop within the colon to the infective filariform stage. The infective larvae may reenter the circulation before they migrate through the lungs and are swallowed. This process is referred to as autoinfection. By this means, the parasite can cycle through the human body for many years. Some investigators have suggested that low levels of autoinfection are common and may occur commonly during a first experience with the parasite.[14] In debilitated, malnourished or immunocompromised patients, autoinfection can amplify, leading to hyperinfection with a large increase in worm populations. *S. stercoralis* is one of the few parasitic nematodes infecting humans that can increase its numbers within the same individual (the other being *Capillaria philippinensis* (see Fig. 26.1). Hyperinfection can also lead to disseminated infection, characterized by the presence of *S. stercoralis* adults and larvae at ectopic sites, including the central nervous system.

Vertical Transmission

The mode of transmission of *S. fuelleborni* infection leading to SBS is unknown, although the high incidence of this parasite in infants has led to the speculation that it is transmitted through mothers' milk. In support of this notion, the larvae of *S. fuelleborni* have been demonstrated in mammary secretions.[15]

Cellular and Molecular Pathogenesis

Parasitic females induce essentially no damage to the mucosa of the small intestine, but do elicit local inflammation. In some experimental studies, T-cell function appears to be necessary for the development of resistance to Strongyloides infection.[16] Impairment of T-cell function has been proposed as the basis by which a subset of infected individuals fail to regulate the number of worms in their small intestines, thus developing Strongyloides hyperinfection and disseminated infection. However, when patients with HIV/AIDS failed to show a higher-than-expected incidence of hyperinfection and disseminated infection,[17, 18] some investigators began to question the role of T-cell mediated immunity in the control of these phenomena. Recently, the sug-

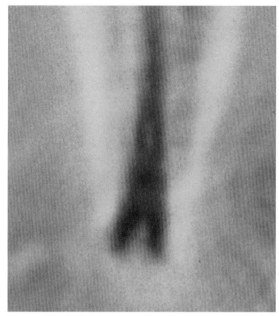

Figure 20.6. Notched tail of filariform larva of *S. stercoralis,* Hookworm filariform larva has a pointed tail.

gestion has been made that hyperinfection occurs in response to elevated steroid levels in patients at risk for these conditions.[18] In some cases, such as in patients with autoimmune disorders or following orthologous transplantation or cancer chemotherapy, hyperinfection may occur as a result of exogenous steroids.

There is an association between human T-cell lymphotropic virus 1 (HTLV-1) infection and strongyloidiasis.[19] This has been observed on the islands of Okinawa and Jamaica.[20, 21] The basis for this association is unknown, although the suggestion has been made that patients with HTLV-1 may have selective deficits in parasite-specific antibodies, including IgE.[22] Severe strongyloidiasis has also been described in an IgA-deficient patient.[22]

In cases of hyperinfection or disseminated infection, penetrating larvae often carry enteric microorganisms, which may lead to local infection or bacteremia, followed by general sepsis. Larvae can be found throughout the body at this time. Hence, in individuals with Strongyloides hyperinfection and disseminated infection, bacterial infections including bacterial meningitis are common causes of death.

Clinical Disease

Clinical disease in immunocompetent individuals presents as a watery, mucosal diarrhea, the degree of which varies with the intensity of the infection. States of alternating diarrhea and constipation are also common. These episodes typically last a total of about six weeks before immunity develops, causing the adult worms to egress from the small intestine. Children with *S. stercoralis* develop a syndrome characterized by anorexia,

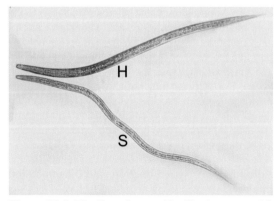

Figure 20.5. Filariform larvae. H = Hookworm and S = Strongyloides. Courtesy L. Ash and T. Orihel.

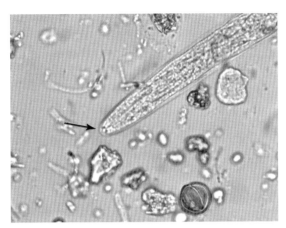

Figure 20.7. Buccal cavity of the rhabditiform larva of *S. stercoralis*. Compare with Figure 19. 8.

cachexia, chronic diarrhea, fat and protein malabsorption, and abdominal distension. They have impaired growth, which is reversible after specific anthelminthic chemotherapy.[23] Infants with SBS from *S. fuelleborni* may present acutely, but usually without fever and diarrhea.[4, 5] Instead, these children develop abdominal ascites as a result of protein loss, which can accumulate to the point of causing respiratory embarrassment.

During the migratory phase of the infection, symptoms may resemble those described for ascariasis and hookworm disease (e.g., pneumonitis), although in the absence of disseminated infection, pulmonary symptoms are not usually prominent. More commonly, pulmonary strongyloidiasis is characterized by asymptomatic circulating eosinophilia.[24] Migration of larvae through the skin gives rise to a serpiginous, creeping urticarial eruption, a condition known as *larva currens*.[25]

Hyperinfection and Disseminated Infection

The above symptoms are exaggerated if hyper-infection is superimposed on an already chronic infection. Massive invasion by Strongyloides larvae due to hyperinfection has an impressive presentation as acute enteritis, with severe diarrhea and ulcerating disease of the small and large intestine. These patients often have secondary bacterial enterocolitis that can result in a paralytic ileus, and bacterial invasion that results in metastatic abscesses and bacterial meningitis. During disseminated infection, the larvae themselves may enter the central nervous system with secondary abscesses. Pulmonary invasion is also exaggerated during disseminated infection and can lead to a clinical picture of pneumonia or intrapulmonary hemorrhage.

Diagnosis

Strongyloides infection should be considered in a

patient with unexplained gastrointestinal symptoms and eosinophilia. Identification of the larvae in stool samples is the definitive method of diagnosis. It can be a difficult task, however, if only a single specimen is sent to the diagnostic laboratory. This is because the number of organisms per gram of stool is usually small. As few as 50 progeny per day are released by each adult Strongyloides. Compare this figure with that of Ascaris, which produces more than 200,000 eggs per day. Moreover, larvae are released in a sporadic manner, causing considerable sample error.[16] It has been estimated that the sensitivity of a single fecal examination may be as low as 30%.[1] Therefore, a large quantity of stool (e.g., a 24-hour sample) must be made available, and all of it should be processed by a sedimentation method to concentrate the larvae, thus improving the chances for seeing them on microscopic examination (Figs. 20.3, 20.7). Even when sedimentation techniques are used, low-grade infections are usually missed, and so a rigorous search with multiple stool examinations must be carried out before a patient can be declared free of the infection. *S. stercoralis* larvae can be differentiated from those of hookworm (Fig. 20.5) by two characteristics. The rhabditiform larva has a short buccal cavity (Fig. 20.7), while the filariform larva has a notched tail (Fig. 20.6). Laboratories that are comfortable with handling the organism can enhance the sensitivity of their stool examinations by plating out a fecal pat on an agar plate and detecting the tracks of bacteria dragged along by migrating larvae. Alternatively, some laboratories can amplify the number of Strongyloides larvae by mixing the stool with bone charcoal and incubating the preparation under conditions that permit the heterogonic life cycle to take place.[16]

In patients with hyperinfection or disseminated infection, the yield of Strongyloides larvae may be increased by recovering them from duodenal fluid. Typically this is done through flexible endoscopy; intestinal biopsy is also a useful adjunct. During disseminated infections, it is common to identify the parasite from sputum and bronchoalveolar lavage fluid. Patients with disseminated disease do not always manifest eosinophilia, but often have leukocytosis with a left shift because of secondary bacterial infections.

Serological tests include the ELISA method. It is both specific and sensitive,[26] but it is not commonly done because of the limited availability of parasite antigen. No kit using recombinant Strongyloides antigens is commercially available. Individuals who test positive should be treated.

Individuals who harbor *S. fuelleborni* shed eggs in their stool rather than larvae. More than 100,000 eggs per gram of feces have been recovered from infants with SBS.

Treatment

For uncomplicated strongyloidiasis, either thiabendazole or ivermectin are the drugs of choice. Thiabendazole is highly effective, and cure rates of nearly 100% have been achieved after one or two courses. However, side effects from this drug are frequent and include nausea, vomiting, a foul taste in the mouth, and foul-smelling urine. Because this drug is detoxified in the liver, undesirably high blood levels can be achieved in patients with liver disease. There are no guidelines for drug dose in these patients. Ivermectin has fewer side effects and may replace thiabendazole as the drug of choice.[27-30]

For patients with hyperinfection, thiabendazole therapy is extended to between 5 days and several weeks. Ivermectin use is less proven, but may also be effective for treating hyperinfective strongyloidiasis.[27,28] Intensive supportive therapy, including antimicrobial agents, is often required in patients with hyperinfection

from *S. stercoralis*, as well as parenteral nutrition for extensive protein and lipid losses. *S. fuelleborni* infection is also treated successfully with thiabendazole.

Prevention and Control

Reservoir hosts include dogs and primates, most notably chimpanzees. As mentioned, a small outbreak of human strongyloidiasis that originated in dogs has been described.[3] However, the role of primates as a foci of human infection in rural tropical areas is doubtful.

Custodial institutions are foci of infection, manifesting most intensely among mentally retarded patients. Efforts to diagnose and screen individuals who harbor *S. stercoralis* are sometimes carried out among patients who are candidates for immunosuppressive therapy.[31] Transmammary transmission of *S. fuelleborni* may be prevented by treating pregnant women, although many of the available anthelminthics are relatively contraindicated during pregnancy.

References

1. Genta RM. Weesner R. et al. Strongyloidiasis in US veterans of the Vietnam and other wars. JAMA 258:49-52. 1987.
2. Genta RM. Global prevalence of strongyloidiasis: Critical review with epidemiologic insights into the prevention of disseminated disease. Rev Infect Dis 11:755-67. 1989.
3. Georgi JR. Sprinkle CL. A case of human strongyloidosis apparently contracted from asymptomatic colony dogs. Am J Trop Med Hyg 23: 899-901. 1974.
4. Ashford RW. Vince JD. Gratten MJ. Miles WE. Strongyloides infection associated with acute infantile disease in Papua, New Guinea. Trans R Soc Trop Med Hyg 72:554. 1978.
5. Barnish G. Ashford RW. *Strongyloides cf. fuelleborni* and hookworm in Papua, New Guinea: Patterns of infection within the community. Trans R Soc Trop Med Hyg 83:684-688, 1989.
6. Bavay A. Sur l'*anguillule stercorale*. C R Academ Sci (Paris) 83: 694-696. 1876.
7. Normand LA. Sur la maladie dite diarrhie de Cochinchine. C R Hebd Sean Acad Sci 83:316-318. 1876.
8. Askanazy M. Uber Art und Zweck der Invasion der *Anguillula intestinalis* in die Darmwand. Zbl Bakt 27:569 578. 1900.
9. Fuelleborn F. Untersuchungen uber den Infektionsweg bei Strongyloides und Ankylostomum und die Biologie diesen Parasiten. Arch Schiffs Trop 18:26-80. 1914.
10. Nishigoii M. On various factors influencing the development of *Strongyloides stercoralis* and autoinfection. Taiwan Sgakkai Zassi 27:1-56. 1928.
11. Mckerrow JH. Brindley P. et al. *Strongyloides stercoralis*: identification of a protease whose inhibition prevents larval skin invasion. Exp Parasitol 70:134-143. 1990.
12. Schad GA. Aikens LM. Smith G. *Strongyloides stercoralis*: is there a canonical migratory route through the host? J Parasitol 75:740-749. 1989.
13. Shekamer JH. Neva FA. Finn DR. Persistent strongyloidiasis in an immunodeficent patient. Am J Trop Med Hyg 31:746-751. 1982.
14. Schad GA. Smith G. et al. *Strongyloides stercoralis*: An initial auto-infective burst amplifies primary infection. Am J Trop Med Hyg 48: 716-725. 1993.
15. Brown RC. Girardeau MHF. Trans-mammary passage of *Strongyloides spp.* larvae in the human host. Am J Trop Med Hyg 26:215-219. 1977.
16. Genta RM. Walzer PD. Strongyloidiasis. In: Parasitic infections in the Compromised Host (Walzer PD. Genta RM., eds.). Marcel Dekker, New York, 1989.
17. Lucas SB. Missing infections in AIDS. Trans R Soc Trop Med Hyg 84 (suppl 1): 34-38. 1990.
18. Robinson RD. Parasitic infections associated with HIV/AIDS in the Caribbean. Bull PAHO 29:129-137. 1995.
19. Genta RM. Dysregulation of strongyloidiasis: a new hypothesis. Clin Microbiol Rev 5:345-355. 1992.
20. Dixon AC. Yanaghihara ET. Kwock DW. Nakamura JM. Strongyloidiasis associated with human T-cell lymphotropic virus type 1 infection in a non-endemic area. West J Med 151:410-413. 1989.
21. Arakaki T. Kohakura M. et al. Epidemiological aspects of Strongyloides stercoralis infection in Okinawa, Japan. J Trop Med Hyg 95: 210-213. 1992.
22. Neva FA. Murphy EL. Gam A. et al. Antibodies to Strongyloides stercoralis in healthy Jamaican carriers of HTLV-1. N Engl J Med 320: 252-3. 1989.
23. Leung VK. Liew CT. Sung JJ. Strongyloidiasis in a patient with IgA deficiency. Trop Gastroeneterol 16: 27-30. 1995.
24. Burke JA. Strongyloidiasis in childhood. Am J Dis Child 132: 1130-1136. 1978.
25. Berk SL. Verghese A. et al. Clinical and epidemiologic features of strongyloidiasis, a prospective study in rural Tennessee. Arch Intern Med. 147:1257-1261. 1987.
26. Von Kuster LC. Genta RM. Cutaneous manifestations of strongyloidiasis. Arch Dermatol 124: 1826-1830, 1988.
27. Neva FA. Biology and immunology of human strongyloidiasis. J Infect Dis 153:397-406, 1986.
28. Naquira C. Jimenez G. et. al. Ivermectin for human strongyloidiasis and other intestinal helminths. Am J Trop Med Hyg 40: 304-309. 1989.
29. Lyagoubi M. Datry A. Mayorga R. et al. Chronic persistent strongyloidiasis cured by ivermectin. Trans R Soc Trop Med Hyg 86: 541. 1992.
30. Wijesundera MD. Sanmuganathan PS. Ivermectin therapy in chronic strongyloidiasis. Trans R Soc Trop Med Hyg 86:291. 1994.
31. Genta RM. Global prevalence of strongyloidiasis: critical review with epidemiologic insights into the prevention of disseminated disease. Rev Infect Dis 11:755-767. 1989.

21. *Trichinella spiralis*
(Railliet 1896)

Introduction

The genus Trichinella has undergone revision, due to the advent of reliable DNA probes that can be used to distinguish the various species that have been recently described.[1, 2] There are 8 recognized genotypes (two are provisional).[3] Members of the genus Trichinella are able to infect a broad spectrum of mammalian hosts, making them one of the world's most widely-distributed group of nematode infections. *Trichinella spp.* are genetically related to *Trichuris trichiura* and *Capillaria spp;* all belong to the family Trichurata. These roundworms constitute an unusual group of organisms in the phylum Nematoda, in that they all live a part of their lives as intracellular parasites.

The diseases that *Trichinella spp.* cause are collectively referred to as trichinellosis. Currently, prevalence of trichinellosis is low within the United States, occurring mostly as scattered outbreaks,[4] and the majority of human cases are due to *Trichinella spiralis* and *T. murrelli.* The domestic pig is the main reservoir host for *T. spiralis.* This species is significantly higher in prevalence in people living in certain parts of Europe, Asia, and Southeast Asia than in the United States. It is now considered endemic in Japan and China. A large outbreak of trichinellosis occurred in Lebanon in 1997, infecting over 200 people.[5] *Trichinella spiralis* infection in humans has been reported from Korea for the first time.[6] In contrast, trichinella infections in wildlife within the United States are now thought to be largely due to the T5 strain, tentatively designated *T. murrelli.*[7]

An outbreak of *T. pseudospiralis* in Thailand has been reported.[8] This species can also infect birds of prey. Foci have also been described in Sweden,[9] The

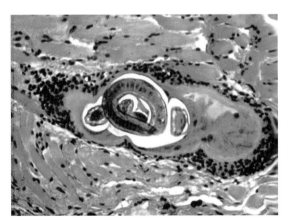

Figure 21.1. Infective first stage larva of *Trichinella spiralis* in its Nurse cell in muscle tissue. The worm measures 1mm x 36 μm.

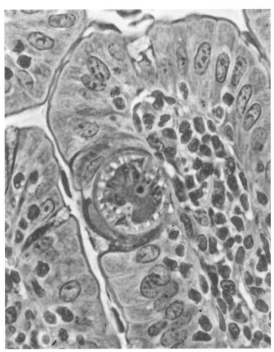

Figure 21.2. Adult *T. spiralis in situ.* Small intestine of experimentally infected mouse. The worm is embedded within the cytoplasm of the columnar cells.

Slovak Republic,[10] and Tasmania (Australia).[11] *Trichinella paupae* (provisional), apparently similar in biology to *T. pseudospiralis,* has been described in wild and domestic pigs in Papua New Guinea.[12]

Humans can also be infected with *T. nativa* and *T. britovi.*[13, 14] Reservoir hosts for *T. nativa* include sled dogs, walruses, and polar bears. *T. britovi* is the sylvatic form of trichinellosis throughout most of Asia and Europe. There are numerous reports in the literature of infections with this parasite in fox, raccoon, dog, opossum, domestic and wild dogs, and cats.

T. nelsoni is restricted to mammals in Equatorial Africa, such as hyenas and the large predatory cats.[15] Occasionally people acquire infection with *T. nelsoni.* Most animals in the wild, regardless of their geographic location, acquire trichinella by scavenging. The recently discovered *T. zimbabwensis* infects crocodiles and mammals in Africa, and is a non-encapsulate species.[16] No human cases have been reported, so far. Puerto Rico and mainland Australia remain trichinella-free. *T. pseudospiralis* has been isolated from the Tasmanian Devil, but not from humans living in that part of Australia.[11] For an accounting of the history of the discovery of *Trichinella spiralis,* see www.trichinella.org/history_1.htm and www.trichinella.org/index_ppt.htm.

Life Cycle

Infection is initiated by ingesting raw or undercooked meats harboring the Nurse cell-larva complex (Fig. 21.1). Larvae are released from muscle tissue by digestive enzymes in the stomach, and then locate to the upper two-thirds of the small intestine. The outermost cuticular layer (epicuticle) becomes partially digested.[17,18] This enables the parasite to receive environmental cues[19] and to then select an infection site within the small intestine. The immature parasites penetrate the columnar epithelium at the base of the villus. They live within a row of these cells, and are considered intra-multi-cellular organisms (Figs. 21.2, 21.7).[20]

Larvae molt four times in rapid succession over a 30-hour period, developing into adults. The female measures 3 mm in length by 36 μm in diameter (Fig. 21.3), while the male measures 1.5 mm in length by 36 μm in diameter (Fig. 21.4).

Patency occurs within five days after mating. Adult females produce live offspring — newborn larvae (Fig. 21.5) — which measure 0.08 mm long by 7 μm in diameter. The female produces offspring as long as host immunity does not develop. Eventually, acquired, protective responses interfere with the overall process of embryogenesis and creates physiological conditions in the local area of infection which forces the adult parasites to egress and relocate further down the intestinal tract. Expulsion of worms from the host is the final ex-

Figure 21. 4. Adult male *T. spiralis*. Note claspers on tail (lower end). 1.5mm x 36 μm.

pression of immunity, and may take several weeks.

The newborn larva is the only stage of the parasite that possesses a sword-like stylet, located in its oral cavity. It uses it to create an entry hole in potential host cells. Larvae enter the lamina propria in this fashion, and penetrate into either the mesenteric lymphatics or into the bloodstream. Most newborn larvae enter the general circulation, and become distributed throughout the body.

Migrating newborns leave capillaries and enter cells (Fig. 21.6). There appears to be no tropism for any particular cell type. Once inside, they can either remain or leave, depending upon environmental cues (yet to be determined) received by the parasite. Most cell types die as the result of invasion. Skeletal muscle cells are the only exception. Not only do the parasites remain inside them after invasion, they induce a remarkable series of changes, causing the fully differentiated muscle cell to transform into one that supports the growth and development of the larva (Figs 21.8, 21.9). This process is termed Nurse cell formation.[21] Parasite and host cell develop in a coordinated fashion. *T. spiralis* is infective by the 14th day of infection, but the worm continues to grow in size through day 20.[22] The significance of this precocious behavior has yet to be appreciated.

Parasites inside cells other than striated muscle

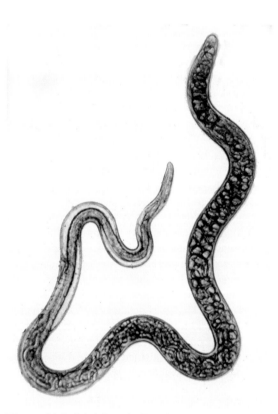

Figure 21.3. Adult female *T. spiralis*. 3 mm x 36 μm. Note fully formed larvae in uterus.

Trichinella spiralis

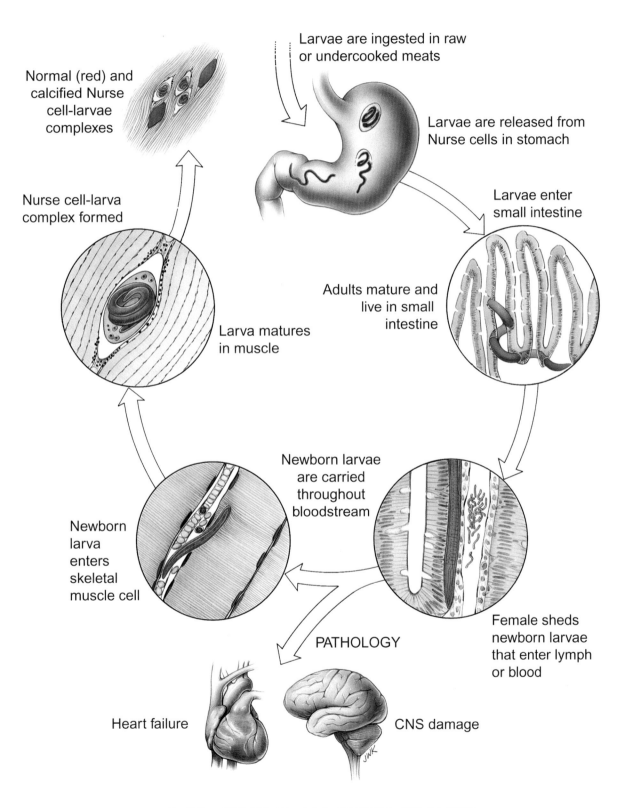

Larvae are ingested in raw or undercooked meats

Larvae are released from Nurse cells in stomach

Larvae enter small intestine

Normal (red) and calcified Nurse cell-larvae complexes

Nurse cell-larva complex formed

Adults mature and live in small intestine

Larva matures in muscle

Newborn larvae are carried throughout bloodstream

Newborn larva enters skeletal muscle cell

Female sheds newborn larvae that enter lymph or blood

PATHOLOGY

Heart failure

CNS damage

JWK

cells fail to induce Nurse cells, and either reenter the general circulation or die. Nurse cell formation results in an intimate and permanent association between the worm and its intracellular niche. At the cellular level, myofilaments and other related muscle cell components become replaced over a 14-16 day period by whorls of smooth membranes and clusters of dysfunctional mitochondria. The net result is that the host cell switches from an aerobic to an anaerobic metabolism.[23] Host cell nuclei enlarge and divide,[24] amplifying the host's genome within the Nurse cell cytoplasm.[25] The Nurse cell-parasite complex can live for as long as the host remains alive. Most do not, and are calcified within several months after forming. In order for the life cycle to continue, an infected host must die and be eaten by another mammal. Scavenging is a common behavior among most wild mammals, and this helps to ensure the maintenance of *T. spiralis* and its relatives in their respective host species.

Cellular and molecular pathogenesis

The enteral (intestinal) phase includes larval stages 1 through 4, and the immature and reproductive adult stages. In humans, this phase can last up to 3 weeks or more. Developing worms damage columnar epithelium, depositing shed cuticula there. Later in the infection, at the onset of production of newborns, local inflammation, consisting of infiltration by eosinophils, neutro-

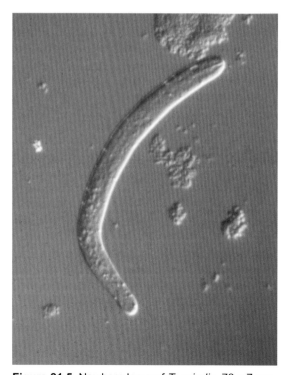

Figure 21.5. Newborn larva of *T. spiralis*. 70 x 7 μm.

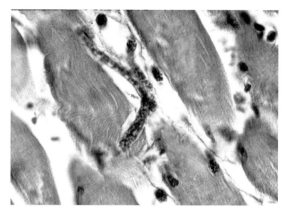

Figure 21.6. Newborn larva of *T. spiralis* entering muscle cell.

phils, and lymphocytes, intensifies in the local area. Villi flatten and become somewhat less absorbent, but not enough to result in malabsorption syndrome.

When larvae penetrate into the lymphatic circulation or bloodstream, a bacteremia due to enteric flora may result, and cases of death due to sepsis have been reported. Loss of wheat germ agglutinin receptors along the entire small intestine occurs.[26] The myenteric electric potential is interrupted during the enteral phase, and as the result, gut motility slows down.[26]

The parenteral phase of infection induces most of the pathological consequences. It is dose dependent and is attributable directly to the migrating newborn larvae as they randomly penetrate cells (e.g., brain, liver, kidney, heart) in their search for striated skeletal muscle cells (Fig. 21.6). Cell death is the usual result of these events. The more penetration events there are, the more severe the resulting pathology. The result during heavy infection is a generalized edema. Proteinuria may ensue. Cardiomyopathies and central nervous system abnormalities are also common in those experiencing moderate to heavy infection.[1]

Experimental infections in immunologically-defined strains of rodents have shown that the total number of muscle larvae produced was dependent upon numerous factors related to the immune capabilities of a given strain. Induction of interleukins 4, and 13,[27] as well as production of eosinophils and IgE antibodies,[28] appear to be essential for limiting production of newborn larvae and for the expulsion of adult worms. TNF-induced nitric oxide (NO) production is, however, not one of the effector mechanisms, since knockout mice unable to produce NO expelled their parasites in a normal fashion in the absence of local gut damage.[29] In NO+ mice, expulsion of adults was accompanied by cellular pathology surrounding the worms. Local production of nitric oxide during the development of inflammation may be a contributing factor to the development of intestinal pathology during infection with trichinella. Whether or not these same mechanisms are invoked during infection in the human host is not known.

For an in depth look at the biology of *Trichinella spiralis*, see www.trichinella.org.

Clinical Disease

The clinical features of mild, moderate, and severe trichinellosis have been reviewed (Fig. 21.10).[1, 30] The presentation of the disease varies over time, and, as a result, resembles a wide variety of clinical conditions. Trichinellosis is often misdiagnosed for that reason. The severity of disease is dose-dependent, making the diagnosis based solely on symptoms difficult, at best. In severe cases, death may ensue. There are signs and symptoms that should alert the physician to include trichinellosis into the differential diagnosis.

The first few days of the infection are characterized by gastroenteritis associated with diarrhea, abdominal pain, and vomiting. Enteritis ensues, and is secretory in nature. This phase is transitory, and abates within 10 days after ingestion of infected tissue. A history of eating raw or undercooked meats helps to rule in this parasitic infection. Others who also ate the same meats and are suffering similarly reinforces the suspi-

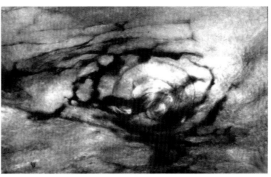

Figure 21.8. Nurse cell-parasite complex of *T. spiralis, in situ*. Infected mouse was injected with India ink to visualize circulatory rete.

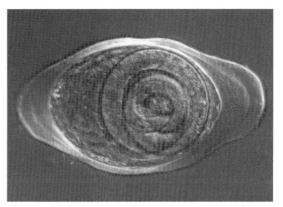

Figure 21.9. Nurse cell-parasite complex. Phase interference. Photo by E. Gravé.

cion of trichinellosis. Unfortunately, most clinicians opt for a food poisoning scenario at this juncture.

The parenteral phase begins approximately one week after infection and may last several weeks. Typically, the patient has fever and myalgia, bilateral periorbital edema, and petechial hemorrhages, which are seen most clearly in the subungual skin, but are also observable in the conjunctivae and mucous membranes. Muscle tenderness can be readily detected. Laboratory studies reveal a moderately elevated white blood cell count (12,000-15,000 cells/mm^3), and a circulating eosinophilia ranging from 5% to as high as 50%.

Larvae penetrating tissues other than muscle gives rise to more serious sequelae. In many cases of moderate to severe infection, cardiovascular involvement may lead to myocarditis, but this aspect of the infection has been overrated as a clinical feature typical of most infections with this parasite, since most instances encountered by the clinician are of the mild variety.[31] Electrocardiographic (ECG) changes can occur during this phase, even in the absence of symptoms. Parasite invasion of the diaphragm and the accessory muscles of respiration result in dyspnea. Neuro-trichinellosis oc-

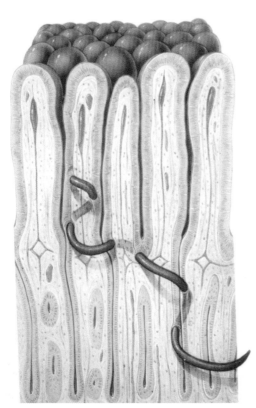

Figure 21. 7. An adult female *T. spiralis, depicted in situ*. Drawing by J. Karapelou.

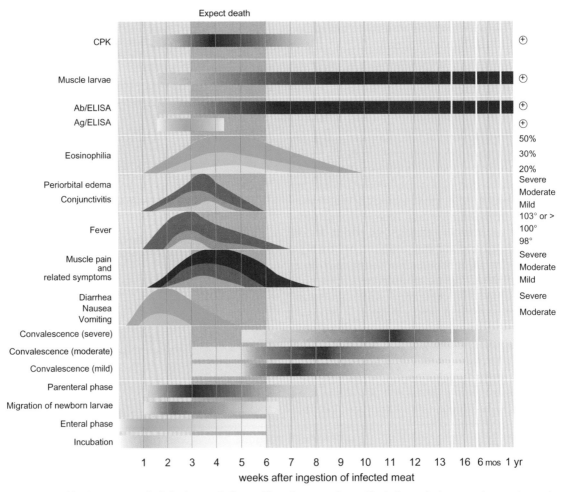

Figure 21.10. Summary of clinical correlations. The degree of manifestation of signs and symptoms is dependent upon the dose of larvae ingested. The stages of the parasite and the signs and symptoms associated with them are shown in the same colors.

curs in association with invasion of the central nervous system. Convalescent phase follows the acute phase, during which time many, but not all, Nurse cell-parasite complexes are destroyed.

Two clinical presentations have been described for *T. nativa* infections resulting from the ingestion of infected polar bear or walrus meat: a classic myopathic form, and a second form that presents as a persistent diarrheal illness. The second form is thought to represent a secondary infection in previously sensitized individuals.[32]

Diagnosis

Definitive diagnosis depends upon finding the Nurse cell-parasite complex in muscle biopsy by microscopic examination (Fig 21.1), or detection of Trichinella–specific DNA by PCR.[33] PCR is very sensitive and specific for detecting small numbers of larvae in muscle tissue, but due to the infrequency of request

and the costs associated with maintaining such a capability, PCR is usually prohibitive for most hospital laboratories. This will undoubtedly change in the near future, as more and more parasitic infections become diagnosed routinely by PCR-based methods.

Muscle biopsy can be negative, even in the heaviest of infections, due to sampling errors. In addition, the larvae may be at an early stage of their development, making them inconspicuous, even to experienced pathologists. A rising, plateauing and falling level of circulating eosinophils throughout the infection period is not direct proof of infection, but armed with this information, the clinician could treat the patient as if the diagnosis of trichinella had been made. Bilateral periorbital edema, petechiae under the fingernails, and high fever, coupled with a history of eating raw or undercooked meats, is further indirect evidence for this infection. It is helpful to remember that wild mammals can also be sources of infection. Outbreaks of trichinellosis have been traced to hunters and the recipients of their kills.[34, 35, 36]

Muscle enzymes, such as creatine phosphokinase (CPK) and lactic dehydrogenase (LDH), are released into the circulation causing an increase in their serum levels. Serological tests begin to show positive results within two weeks. ELISA can detect antibodies in some patients as early as 12 days after infection.[37]

Treatment

There is no specific anthelminthic therapy, even after a definitive diagnosis is made. Mebendazole given early during the infection may help reduce the number of larvae that might lead to further clinical complications, but the likelihood of making the diagnosis in time to do so is remote. Anti-inflammatory corticosteroids, particularly prednisolone, are recommended if the diagnosis is secure.[1, 29] Rapidly destroying larvae with anthelminthics without use of steroids may actually exacerbate host inflammatory responses and worsen disease (e.g., Jarisch-Herxheimer reaction). The myopathic phase is treated in conjunction with antipyretics and analgesics (aspirin, acetaminophen), and should be continued until the fever and allergic signs recede. Because of their immunosuppressive potential, steroids should be administered with caution.

Prevention and control

Within the last 10 years, outbreaks of trichinellosis in the United States have been rare and sporadic in nature.[38] Most have been associated with the ingestion of raw or undercooked meats from game animals and not from commercial sources. This represents a shift in the epidemiology of outbreaks compared to 20-30 years ago, when commercial pork sources of infection were much more common than today. Pigs raised on individual farms, as compared to commercial farm operations, are more likely to be fed uncooked garbage,

and thus acquire the infection. This is because feeding unprocessed garbage containing meat scraps is against federally mandated regulations. In the past 10 years, small farms have, in the main, been bought up and replaced with larger so-called "factory" farms, in which upwards of 10,000 pigs can be managed with a minimum of labor. Enforcement of laws governing the running of large production facilities is a full time activity and has been key in reducing the spread of diseases infecting livestock and humans alike.[38]

As already mentioned, top carnivores such as bear, fox, cougar, and the like often become infected. Hunters sharing their kill with others are best warned to cook all meat thoroughly. Herbivores can harbor the infection as well, since most plant eaters occasionally ingest meat when the opportunity arises. Epidemics due to eating raw horsemeat have been reported from France, Italy, and Poland.[39]

Meat inspection is nonexistent in the United States with respect to trichinella. In Europe, the countries participating in the common market employ several strategies for examining meat for muscle larvae. Most serve to identify pools of meat samples from given regions. If they are consistently negative, then a trichinella-free designation is applied to that supply of meat. Nonetheless, rare outbreaks occur, despite this rigorous system of inspection.

Trichinellosis due to *Trichinella spiralis* can be prevented by either cooking meat thoroughly at 58.5° C for 10 minutes or by freezing it at -20° C for three days. However, with other species of trichinella, the story is quite different, since they are mostly found in wild animals. For example, bears and raccoons have special proteins in their muscle cells that prevent ice crystals from forming during periods of hibernation, inadvertently permitting survival of the larvae at temperatures below freezing.[40] Hence, the only way to render those meats edible is to cook them thoroughly.

References

1. Bruschi F. Murrell KD. New aspects of human trichinellosis: the impact of new Trichinella species. Postgrad Med J. 78:15-22. 2002.
2. Rombout YB. Bosch S. Van Der Giessen JW. Detection and identification of eight Trichinella genotypes by reverse line blot hybridization. J Clin Microbiol. 39:642-6. 2001.
3. Murrell KD. Lichtenfels RJ. Zarlenga DS. Pozio E. The systematics of the genus Trichinella with a key to species. Vet Parasitol. 93:293-307. 2000.
4. Moorehead A. Grunewald PE. Deitz VJ. Schantz PM. Trichinellosis in the United States, 1991-1996: declining but not gone. Am J Trop Med Hyg 60:66-69. 1999.
5. Haim M. Efrat M. et al. An outbreak of Trichinella spiralis infection in southern Lebanon. Epidemiology & Infection 119:357-62. 1997.
6. Sohn WM. Kim HM. Chung DI. Yee ST. The first human case of Trichinella spiralis infection in Korea. Korean J Parasitol 38:111-5. 2000.
7. Pozio E. La Rosa G. Trichinella murrelli n. sp: etiological agent of sylvatic trichinellosis in temperate areas of North America. J Parasitol. 86:134-9. 2000.
8. Jongwutiwes S. Chantachum N. et al. First outbreak of human trichinellosis caused by Trichinella pseudospiralis. Clin Infect Dis 26:111-115. 1998.
9. Pozio E. Christensson D. et al. Trichinella pseudospiralis foci in Sweden. Vet Parasitol. 125:335-42. 2004.
10. Hurnikova Z. Snabel V. et al. First record of Trichinella pseudospiralis in the Slovak Republic found in domestic focus. Vet Parasitol.

128:91-8. 2005.

11. Obendorf DL. Handlinger JH. et al. *Trichinella pseudospiralis* infection in Tasmanian wildlife. Aust Vet J. 67:108-10. 1990.

12. Pozio E. Owen IL. et al. *Trichinella paupae* n. sp. (Nematoda), a new non-encapsulated species from domestic and sylvatic swine. Int J Parasitol 29:1825-1839. 1999.

13. Pozio E. Kapel CM. *Trichinella nativa* in sylvatic wild boars. J Helminthol. 73:87-9. 1999.

14. Pozio E. Miller I. et al. Distribution of sylvatic species of Trichinella in Estonia according to climate zones. J Parasitol. 84:193-5. 1998.

15. La Rosa G. Pozio E. Molecular investigation of African isolates of Trichinella reveals genetic polymorphism in *Trichinella nelsoni*. Int J Parasitol. 30:663-7. 2000.

16. Pozio E. Foggin CM. et al. *Trichinella zimbabwensis* n.sp. (Nematoda), a new non-encapsulated species from crocodiles (*Crocodylus niloticus*) in Zimbabwe also infecting mammals. Int J Parasitol. 32:1787-99. 2002.

17. Stewart GL. Despommier DD. Burnham J. Reins K. *Trichinella spiralis*: Behavioral, structural, and biochemical studies on larvae following exposure to components of the host enteric environment. Exp Parasitol 63:195-204. 1987.

18. Modha J. Roberts MC. et al. The surface coat of infective larvae of *Trichinella spiralis*. Parasitol.118:509-22. 1999.

19. Despommier, D. Behavioral cues in migration and location of parasitic nematodes, with special emphasis on *Trichinella spiralis*. In: Cues that influence behavior of internal parasites (W.S. Bailey, ed.)., Agricuturual Research Service Workshop. Auburn, Alabama. May, 1982. pp. 110-126.

20. Wright K. *Trichinella spiralis*: an intracellular parasite in the intestinal phase. J Parasitol 65:441-445. 1979.

21. Despommier DD. How does trichinella make itself a home? Parasitol Today, August 14:318-323. 1998.

22. Despommier DD. Aron L. Turgeon L. *Trichinella spiralis*: growth of the intracellular (muscle) larva. Exp Parasitol 37:108-116. 1975.

23. Despommier DD. Biology. In: Trichinella and trichinellosis (Campbell WC, ed.). Plenum Press, Pub. New York. pp 75-152. 1983.

24. Despommier DD. Symmans WF. Dell R. Changes in Nurse cell nuclei during synchronous infection with *Trichinella spiralis*. J Parasitol 77:290-225. 1991.

25. Jasmer DP. *Trichinella spiralis* infected skeletal muscle cells arrest in G2/M and cease muscle gene expression. J Cell Biol. 121:785-93. 1993.

26. Castro GA. Bullock GR. Pathophysiology of the gastrointestinal phase. In: Trichinella and trichinellosis. (Campbell WC, ed.). Plenum Press, Pub,. New York. pp. 209-241. 1983.

27. Finkelman FD. Shea-Donohue T. et al. Interleukin-4- and interleukin-13-mediated host protection against intestinal nematode parasites. Immunol Rev. 201:139-55. 2004.

28. Bell RG. The generation and expression of immunity to *Trichinella spiralis* in laboratory rodents. Ad Parasit 41:149-149. 1998.

29. Lawrence CE. Paterson JC. et al. Nitric oxide mediates intestinal pathology but not immune expulsion during *Trichinella spiralis* infection in mice.J Immunol.164:4229-34. 2000.

30. Pozio E. Gomez Morales MA. Dupouy-Camet J. Clinical aspects, diagnosis and treatment of trichinellosis. Expert Rev Anti Infect Ther 1:471-82. 2003.

31. Lazarevic AM, Neskovic AN. et al. Low incidence of cardiac abnormalities in treated trichinosis: a prospective study of 62 patients from a single-source outbreak. Am J Med.107:18-23. 1999.

32. MacClean JD. Poirier L. et al. Epidemiologic and serologic definition of primary and secondary trichinosis in the arctic. J Infect Dis 165:908-912. 1992.

33. Wu Z. Nagano I. Pozio E. Takahashi Y. Polymerase chain reaction-restriction fragment length polymorphism (PCR-RLFP) for the identification of Trichinella isolates. Parasitol 118:211-218. 1999.

34. Centers for Disease Control and Prevention (CDC). Trichinellosis associated with bear meat – New York and Tennessee, 2003. MMWR Morb Mortal Wkly Rep. 53:606-10. 2004.

35. Garcia E. Mora L. et al. First record of human trichinosis in Chile associated with consumption of wild boar (*Sus scrofa*). Mem Inst Oswaldo Cruz. 100:17-8. 2005.

36. Rah H, Chomel BB, Serosurvey of selected zoonotic agents in polar bears (Ursus maritimus). Vet Rec. 156:7-13. 2005.

37. Despommier DD Trichinellosis: In: Immumodiagnosis of Parasitic Diseases. Vol. 1. Helminth Diseases (Schantz PM. Walls KW. eds.). Academic Press, Orlando, Fla. pp. 43-60. 1987

38. Roy SL. Lopez AS. Schantz PM. Trichinellosis surveillance – United States, 1997-2001. MMWR Surveill Summ. 52:1-8. 2003.

39. Murrell KD. Djordjevic M. et al. Epidemiology of Trichinella infection in the horse: the risk from animal product feeding practices. Vet Parasitol. 123:223-33. 2004.

40. Kapel CM. Pozio E. Sacchi L. Prestrud P. Freeze tolerance, morphology, and RAPD-PCR identification of *Trichinella nativa* in naturally infected arctic foxes. J Parasitol. 85:144-7. 1999.

22. Lymphatic Filariae

Wuchereria bancrofti
(Cobbold 1877)

Brugia malayi
(Brug 1927)

Introduction

Wuchereria bancrofti and *Brugia malayi* are thread-like nematodes, and the adults live within the lumen of lymphatic vessels.[1] Approximately 120 million people in 83 countries are infected with some form of filariasis, of which the vast majority of cases occur as a result of *W. bancrofti* infection. Of these, approximately 40 million suffer from clinical disease. Only about 10 to 20 million people are infected with *B. malayi*. *B. timori* is a minor filarial parasite restricted to southeastern Indonesia. Elephantiasis, a disfiguring disease caused by blockage of the lymphatic vessels, affects large numbers of individuals living in endemic areas. The worms are ovoviviparous, and their larvae are called microfilariae. Lymphatic filariasis (LF) is transmitted by mosquitoes that take up microfilariae in a blood meal.

For *W. bancrofti*, humans are the exclusive host. The infection is widely distributed in the tropics, especially in South Asia, Africa (including Egypt) and tropical regions of the Americas. The major vectors are culicine mosquitoes in most urban and semi-urban areas, anophelines in rural areas of Africa and elsewhere, and Aedes species in the Pacific islands. With the exception of strains in the South Pacific, most of the *W. ban-*

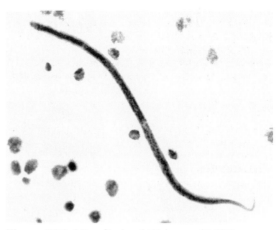

Figure 22.2. Microfilaria of *W. bancrofti.* 250 μm

crofti strains are nocturnal, referring to the periodicity with which the microfilariae appear in the peripheral circulation.

B. malayi infection, on the other hand, is a zoonosis, with both feline and monkey reservoir*s. Mansonia spp.* serve as the major vector, although anopheline mosquitoes are also sometimes involved in transmission. *B. malayi* infection is found in India, Malaysia, and other parts of Southeast Asia. There are other minor members of the genus Brugia that cause disease in humans,[2] including *B. timori* on the Indonesian islands of Timor and Flores, and accidental zoonotic Brugia infections (e.g., *B. beaveri* and *B. lepori*) that occur sporadically in the United States.[3]

A major global effort is underway to eliminate LF over the next 10-20 years.[4, 5] The term 'elimination' refers to the reduction of disease incidence to zero or close to zero, with a requirement for ongoing control efforts.[6] The strategy for LF elimination relies on interrupting mosquito transmission by mass administration of combination therapy in endemic regions in order to reduce the number of microfilariae circulating in the bloodstream of infected individuals.

Historical Information

Demarquay, in 1863,[7] described microfilariae of Wuchereria, while Cobbold, in 1877,[8] wrote a description of the adult worm. Lewis[9] did the same in India that same year. In 1878, Manson[10] completed the description of the cycle while working in Amoy (now called Xiamen) along the Chinese coast in Fujian Province. Today, lymphatic filariasis has been largely eradicated from China. Manson first demonstrated that mosquitoes were intermediate hosts for the parasite. For two decades, Manson maintained that infection was acquired when individuals drank water contaminated with larvae released from dead or dying mosquitoes. Eventually, he came to accept the concept that larvae were

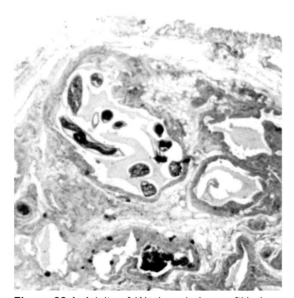

Figure 22.1. Adults of *Wuchereria bancrofti* in lymphatic vessels.

Wuchereria bancrofti

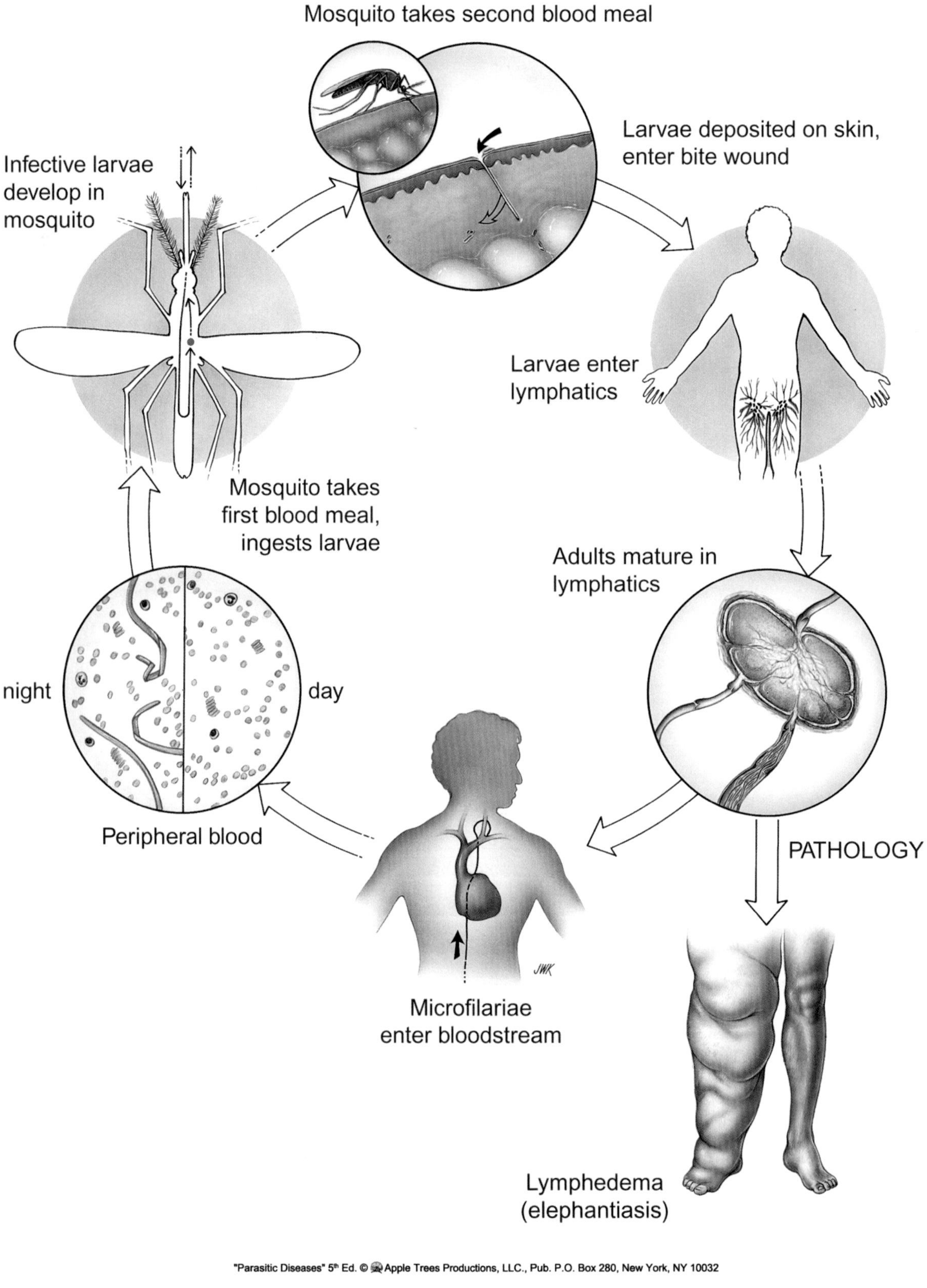

Mosquito takes second blood meal

Larvae deposited on skin, enter bite wound

Infective larvae develop in mosquito

Larvae enter lymphatics

Mosquito takes first blood meal, ingests larvae

Adults mature in lymphatics

night   day

PATHOLOGY

Peripheral blood

Microfilariae enter bloodstream

Lymphedema (elephantiasis)

transmitted by the bite of mosquitoes. Filariasis may, in fact, be a water-borne disease under some circumstances, since experimental infections can be induced by the oral route.[11]

One of the most important developments in the history of LF control was the discovery by Chinese parasitologists during the 1970s and 1980s that it is possible to dramatically reduce the prevalence through simultaneous administration of the drug diethylcarbamazine (DEC) to infected populations. This was achieved primarily through medication of regional salt supplies with DEC. Ironically, the LF life cycle was discovered in China and LF was first eliminated in China. The accomplishments of the Chinese provided proof-of-principle that it might be possible to eliminate LF worldwide through similar measures.

Life Cycle

Adult worms occupy the lumen of lymphatic vessels (Fig. 22.1), and have been found at all sites within the lymphatic circulation. It is presumed that they also occupy the adjacent subcutaneous tissues. Most commonly, they live in the lymphatics of the lower and upper extremities and male genitalia. Both species are about the same size. The female typically measures 4 to 10 cm in length, and the male 2 to 4 cm. After mating, the female worm can release 10,000 or more offspring per day. Instead of releasing eggs, the worms release first-stage larvae, which are known as microfilariae. Each microfilaria (Fig. 22.2, 22.3) measures approximately 270 μm by 10 μm and contains nuclei that characteristically do not extend to the tip of the tail. Another distinguishing feature is that the microfilaria is encased in a sheath comprised of chitin. The sheath is possibly a remnant of its eggshell.

Microfilariae migrate from the lymphatic circulation into the bloodstream. However they are typically present in large numbers in the peripheral blood only at night (between 10 PM and 6 AM) in most endemic

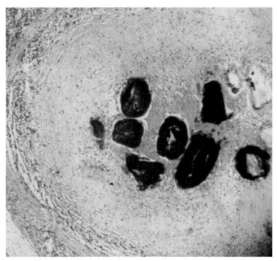

Figure 22.4. Calcified adults of *W. bancrofti* in blocked lymphatic vessel.

areas of the world. During the day, the microfilariae aggregate in the capillaries of the lungs when activity of the host is increased (i.e., during strenuous exercise). Nocturnal periodicity can be a result of the microfilaria's penchant for low oxygen tension, at which time they are found in the peripheral blood stream,[12] or it may reflect subtle pH changes in the pulmonary venous circulation during sleep. Experiments in which sleep habits of infected volunteers were reversed also reversed the periodicity of microfilariae. The diurnal periodicity pattern characteristic of the South Pacific strain has not been satisfactorily explained. A less-frequently occurring sub-periodic filariasis caused by *W. bancrofti* occurs in certain regions of the world. Microfilariae live for about 1.5 years, and must be ingested by a mosquito to continue their life cycle.

W. bancrofti is transmitted by a wide variety of mosquito genera and species, the most important being *Culex pipiens quinquefasciatus, Culex pipiens pipiens, Anopheles gambiae,* and *A. polynesiensis. Aedes aegypti*, the yellow fever mosquito, can also transmit the infection in some of the Pacific Islands. Ingested microfilariae penetrate the stomach wall of the female mosquito and locate to the thoracic flight muscles. There, they undergo three molts, developing into third-stage larvae and become infective after 10-20 days of growth and development in the insect muscle tissue.

Infective larvae locate to the biting mouthparts, and are deposited onto the skin adjacent to the bite wound during consumption of a subsequent blood meal. When the mosquito withdraws her mouthparts, larvae crawl into the open wound. Immature worms migrate through the subcutaneous tissues to the lymphatic vessels. The worms slowly develop into mature adults in about 1 year, and soon after copulation, begin shedding microfilariae. The longevity of adults, measured

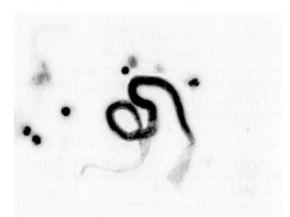

Figure 22.3. Microfilaria of *Brugia malayi*. 220 μm

by the continuous production of microfilariae, is estimated at 5-8 years. Infections lasting 40 years have been reported.[13]

The adult and larval stages of *B. malayi* resemble those of *W. bancrofti*. The life cycles of the two species of filariae are similar, although animal reservoirs occur for some members of the genus Brugia. The sub-periodic strain of *B. malayi* is a zoonosis acquired from forest monkeys and other wild animals, and transmitted through the bite of *Mansonia spp.* mosquitoes.[2]

Cellular and Molecular Pathogenesis

Pathogenesis of lymphangitis leading to elephantiasis has not been fully explained. It may result from a sequence of host-mediated immunopathologic events that occur in response to dead and dying adults within the lymphatics (Fig. 22.4). In contrast, living adult worms or the microfilariae are believed to suppress these responses. Hence, the processes associated with lymphangitis and elephantiasis can take years to develop and therefore are not commonly seen in children. Exactly how living worms and microfilariae suppress the host inflammatory response is unknown, except for the observations that microfilariae produce prostaglandin E2, a modulatory agent for leukocytes,[14]

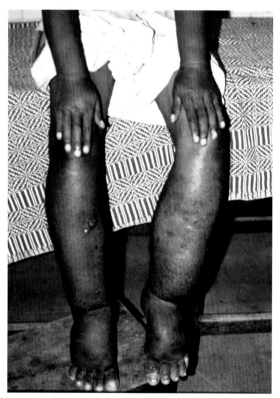

Figure 22.5. Patient suffering from long-term infection with *W. bancrofti*. Most adult worms have died and calcified, blocking all lymphatic drainage from the groin. The result is elephantiasis of both legs.

and adult worms secrete anti-mitotic and immunosuppressive substances.

When dead and dying adult worms relinquish control of the host's defense mechanisms, the result is a series of inflammatory reactions causing alterations of the walls of the lymphatics. After an intense lymphocytic infiltration, the lumen of the vessel eventually closes, and the remnants of the adult worms calcify. The blockage of lymphatic circulation continues in heavily infected individuals until most major lymph channels are occluded, causing lymphedema in the affected region of the body. In addition, hypertrophy of smooth muscle tissue occurs in the area immediately surrounding the site of involvement.

As already implied, the process of lymphatic blockage is a protracted one and results from repeated infections. Consequently, individuals visiting endemic areas for short periods usually do not develop lymphedema, even though they often have microfilaremia.

Not all patients with chronic exposure of infective larvae of *W. bancrofti* develop overt clinical disease. There is an intense clinical investigative effort underway at several laboratories to understand why, despite relatively equal levels of exposure, some infected residents remain largely asymptomatic but with evidence of microfilaremia, whereas other individuals progress to advanced clinical disease comprised of lymphangitis and elephantiasis. Frequently, patients with advanced clinical disease do not have evidence of circulating microfilariae. Differences in host cytokine patterns have been noted among these different groups of patients, and it has been suggested that different populations are prone to either Th2 or Th1 biases in their cellular inflammatory responses.[15-17]

Two major observations within the last several years have challenged the conventional thinking about how the pathologic sequence of events leading to lymphangitis, lymphedema and elephantiasis occurs.

First, there is evidence from ultrasound studies conducted in LF-endemic areas that the living adult filarial worms induce important pathologic changes, including lymphatic dilatation, which may lead to subsequent chronic lymphatic changes. This observation has challenged the notion that only dead and dying worms initiate the pathologic sequence. Adding to the complexity is an ultrasound observation that one part of the adult worm can die and calcify while another can remain alive and moving.

Second, there is evidence that secondary bacterial and fungal infections contribute significantly to the chronic pathology of elephantiasis. It has been further established that adult *W. bancrofti* worms harbor bacterial symbionts of the genus Wolbachia. Adult *W. bancrofti* depend on these symbionts for their survival, and antibiotics that target them exhibit an anthelminthic effect. Further, Wolbachia contain endotoxin-like molecules and it is believe that these molecules may contribute to the inflammatory responses seen to dead and dying worms. Therefore, there is an emerging picture that Wolbachia contributes a major role to the pathogenesis of filarial disease.[18]

Clinical Disease

There is a spectrum of clinical manifestations resulting from *W. bancrofti* or *B. malayi* infections, ranging from asymptomatic infection to advanced elephantiasis.

Asymptomatic Infection (Lymphatic Dilatation)
The majority of residents living in an endemic area do not manifest strong inflammatory responses to their filarial parasite load. They are noted to be asymptomatic even though they harbor circulating microfilariae. Recently some of these so-called asymptomatic patients have been observed to exhibit subtle pathology when examined more closely by ultrasound or radionuclide studies.[19] It is currently thought that the central event in the pathogenesis of more advanced disease may begin at this stage when dilatation of the lymphatic vessels begins to occur. This dilatation initiates a subsequent series of events that results in the chronic clinical manifestations of LF, including lymphedema and hydrocele.[20] In some cases, the dilated vessels rupture to produce chyluria and chylocele.

Acute Lymphadenitis and Filarial Fevers
Death of the adult worm causes the next step in the progression of disease by producing an acute inflammatory response that is manifested as acute lymphadenitis. In endemic areas, this occurs frequently during the adolescent years and is manifested with fevers and painful swellings over the lymph nodes.[21] This typically occurs in the inguinal area. Episodes of painful swellings can last up to a week and commonly recur. Secondary bacterial infections may also result. Acute filarial lymphadenitis is exacerbated by secondary bacterial infections.

Some short-term travelers to endemic areas can also develop acute lymphadenitis, but the pathogenesis of this process occurs by a poorly understood process. This phenomenon was described in the 1940s among American troops returning from war in the Pacific theatre.

Elephantiasis
A subset of patients with acute lymphangitis and filarial fevers will go on to develop lymphedema of the arms, legs, breasts and genitalia leading to elephantiasis (Figure 22.5.). During these inflammatory processes, the skin becomes doughy and exhibits some degree of pitting, though it is rather firm. As the inflammatory reaction continues, the area becomes firmer still, and pitting disappears. There is substantial encroachment on the subcutaneous tissue and consequent loss of elasticity of the overlying skin. Characteristically, and in contrast to cellulitis caused by some bacteria, filarial cellulitis shows no demarcation line between the affected and the healthy skin. In Bancroftian filariasis, the legs are more likely to be involved than are the upper extremities, and the lower portions of the legs are more involved than the upper ones. The scrotum is frequently affected in the form of hydroceles and may become gigantic, weighing up to 10 kg; much larger scrotums have been described in rare cases.

Tropical Pulmonary Eosinophilia (TPE)
TPE develops in some individuals with filarial infections. This syndrome, which occurs frequently in southern India, particularly in young adult men, is characterized by high levels of serum immunoglobulin E (IgE), nocturnal asthma with interstitial infiltrates on chest radiographs, fatigue, weight loss, and eosinophilia.[22] Left untreated, TPE can progress to chronic restrictive lung disease. Diethylcarbamazine is highly effective in these patients. The pathogenesis of this syndrome is related to local immune responses to microfilariae in the pulmonary vasculature, and results in eosinophil accumulation in the lung with the release of cytotoxic eosinophil products (e.g., major basic protein and eosinophil cationic protein).[22]

Diagnosis

Lymphatic filariasis should be suspected in an individual who resides in an endemic region, is beyond the first decade of life, and has lymphedema in the extremities or genitalia. Definitive diagnosis has traditionally depended upon microscopically observing the characteristic microfilariae in the blood (Figs. 22.2, 22.3; Figs. C.46. – C.53., in Appendix C). Occasionally, infection is so heavy that microfilariae can be observed on a thin blood smear stained with Giemsa. In lighter infections, methods include filtering blood onto a 0.45µm pore sized nucleopore filter, then staining it with Giemsa solution. In the case of very light infection, 1 ml of blood is preserved in 9 ml of 1% formalin and then concentrated by centrifugation (Knott test; see Appendix B). The pellet contains red blood cell ghosts and microfilariae. Stained smears of the pellet are then examined microscopically. Because of the nocturnal periodicity of some strains, it is best to draw blood during the customary hours of sleep (usually between 22:00 and 02:00 hours). It is possible, however, to provoke migration of microfilariae at other times by administering 1 mg of diethylcarbamazine to an adult patient and collecting blood 45-60 minutes later.

Two monoclonal-based ELISAs that detect circulating *W. bancrofti* antigens have been developed. One of these is available as a rapid format card test. The assay, which recognizes a 200 kDa antigen of adult worm origin, has a sensitivity of 96-100 percent and a specificity of 100 percent.[23] The other assay is marketed as Trop-Ag *W. bancrofti*, which is manufactured by JCU Tropical Biotechnology Pty. Ltd (Townsville, Queensland, Australia). This assay also has a sensitivity of 100 percent in microfilaremic patients. For both assays, the circulating filarial antigen remains diurnally constant, so that blood for diagnosis can be collected during the day. PCR-based tests are also being developed.

Increasingly, ultrasound has provided an important noninvasive modality for monitoring the efficacy of antifilarial drugs.[18] Ultrasound examination of the lymphatic vessels of the spermatic cord of infected men results in a distinctive sign, known as the "filarial dance sign" reflective of nests of live worms in the lymphatics. Adult worm death following treatment with DEC can be subsequently followed.

Treatment

It is recommended that all patients be treated, because even patients with so-called asymptomatic infection may have abnormal lymphatics, and there is increasing evidence that early treatment may prevent subsequent lymphatic damage. Diethylcarbamazine (DEC) has both macrofilaricidal (adult worm) and microfilaricidal properties, and is the treatment of choice for such patients. In many regions it is given in a dose of 6 mg/kg/day for 12 consecutive days for a total of 72 mg/kg body weight.[18, 24] For *W. bancrofti* infections, this results in at least a 90% decrease in microfilaremia within one month. DEC decreases the incidence of filarial lymphangitis, although it is not clear whether this reverses existing lymphatic damage. In men, the efficacy of treatment can be monitored by serial ultrasound examinations (see above), and by serial blood sampling.[18] Since DEC is only partially effective against the adult worm, repeat treatments are often required. This is often done every 6-12 months.[18] Recent data has suggested that single dose treatment with 6 mg/kg of DEC has comparable macrofilaricidal and long-term microfilaricidal therapy. Some clinicians have suggested that single-dose treatment can be repeated every 6-12 months.[18] DEC is associated with fever (probably resulting from disintegration of a few of the adult worms), occasional nausea and vomiting, and fleeting skin rashes. Ivermectin, a drug effective for therapy of onchocerciasis, also kills microfilariae of *W. bancrofti*, but it appears to have no macrofilaricidal properties.

Aside from the use of anthelminthic drugs, there are several treatment modalities that help to improve the chronic sequelae of LF, including lymphedema and elephantiasis. Both conditions, when they occur in the leg, are reversible with a hygienic regimen that includes prevention of secondary bacterial infections by prompt antibiotic treatment of acute bacterial attacks, aggressive treatment of skin lesions including those caused by Candida and other fungi, and physiotherapy.[18] Treatment of secondary bacterial infections has been identified as a critical treatment modality for worsening lymphedema and elephantiasis. Possibly this includes the treatment of Wolbachia symbionts. Hydrocele drainage, while it does provide relief, is often associated with reaccumulation of fluid.[19] For certain affected areas, (e.g., the scrotum) surgical excision and exteriorization of the testes to restore fertility may be required. However, even after surgery the affected area invariably becomes edematous once again. Microsurgery, in which shunting of lymphatic vessels around the area of blockage with stents has been employed, is quite effective in some cases, and surgical teams in India have perfected the procedure. Overall, however, for most clinicians the surgical management of lymphedema is being replaced by the medical management practices outlined above.

As noted in the section on cellular and molecular pathogenesis, a promising new modality of treatment is the use of doxycycline, rifampicin and other antibiotics in order to target the Wolbachia symbionts of *W. bancrofti*.[25] Studies are in progress to determine whether this approach might complement existing DEC treatment strategies.

Prevention and Control

Patent microfilaremia is first detected in children 5 to 10 years old who live in endemic regions.[2] Transplacental immunity and breast-feeding may limit the intensity of infection in younger individuals. The prevalence of microscopically confirmed infection gradually increases up to the age of 30-40 years.

The frequency of exposure to third-stage larvae by vectors is the most important determinant in the community prevalence of filariasis.[26] Prevention depends upon control of mosquito vectors, which, unfortunately, has had limited success because mosquitoes develop resistance to insecticides. Urbanization of vast areas of tropical Asia has resulted in a concomitant rise in the prevalence of both *W. bancrofti* and *B. malayi* varieties of filariasis, carried by mosquitoes that breed in nonsylvatic habitats.

In 1997, the World Health Assembly passed a resolution calling on its member states to undertake a global elimination program for LF. The major strategy for LF elimination is based on two principles: 1) to interrupt transmission of infection and 2) to alleviate and prevent the suffering and disability caused by LF (www.filariasis.org). To interrupt transmission, it is essential to reduce the levels of microfilariae in the blood for a sustainable period. This is achieved by administering a yearly, single-dose, 2-drug regimen.[27] For most countries, the recommended drugs are DEC (6 mg/kg) and albendazole (400 mg). However, in many parts of Sub-Saharan Africa (and Yemen as well) where there is epidemiological overlap with loiasis and onchocerciasis, the toxicities caused by DEC in people with these conditions necessitate substituting ivermectin (200 mcg/kg). Such populations would receive ivermectin and albendazole. A period of 5 years of annual treatments is currently recommended. To date, the number of serious adverse events from LF control mass chemotherapy has been remarkably low. In some areas, a treatment regimen comprised of daily DEC-fortified salt is used.

To alleviate suffering and decrease the disability caused by LF, the major streategy has been to decrease secondary bacterial and fungal infections of the affected limbs and genitals. This includes meticulous local hygiene, judicious use of antibiotics, physiotherapy and health education.

Finally, there has been great interest in evaluating whether LF control practices that employ albendazole and ivermectin could have an impact on other co-endemic helminth infections including onchocerciasis and soil-transmitted helminth infections. Such integrated pro-poor strategies are attractive because of their economy of scales and cost-effectiveness.[28]

References

1. Nelson GS. Filariasis. N Engl J Med 300:1136-1139.1979.
2. Nanduri J. Kazura JW. Clinical and laboratory aspects of filariasis. Clin Microbiol Rev 2:39-50. 1989.
3. Baird JK. Alpert LI. Friedman R. North American brugia filariasis: report of nine infections of humans. Am J Trop Med Hyg 35:1205-1209. 1986.
4. Molyneux DH. Bradley M. et al. Mass drug treatment for lymphatic filariasis and onchocerciasis. Trends Parasitol 19: 516-22. 2003.
5. Molyneux DH, Zagaria N. Lymphatic filariasis elimination: progress in global programme development. Ann Trop Med Parasitol 96 (Suppl. 2): S15-40. 2003.
6. Hotez PJ, Remme JHF. et al. Combating tropical infectious diseases: report of the disease control priorites in developing countries project. Clin Infect Dis 38: 871-8. 2004.
7. Demarquay M. Note sur une tumeur des bourses contenant un liquide laiteux (galactocele de Vidal) et refermant des petits etres vermiformes que l'on peut considerer comme des helminths hematoides a l'etat d'embryon. Gaz Med Pans 18:665-667. 1863.
8. Cobbold TS. Discovery of the adult representative of microscopic filariae. Lancet 2:70-71. 1877.
9. Lewis T. *Filaria sanguinis hominis* (mature form), found in a bloodclot in naevoid elephantiasis of the scrotum. Lancet 2:453-455. 1877.
10. Manson P. Further Observations on *Filaria sanguinis hominis*. Medical Reports, China Imperial Maritime Customs, Shanghai, no. 14. pp. 1-26, 1878.
11. Gwadz RW. Chernin E. Oral transmission of *Brugia pahangi* to jirds (*Meriones unguiculatus*). Nature 238:524-525. 1972.
12. Hawking F. Pattanayak S. Sharma HL. The periodicity of microfilariac. XI. The effect of body temperature and other stimuli upon the cycles of *Wuchereria bancrofti*, *Brugia malayi*, *B. ceylonensis* and *Dirofilaria repens*. Trans R Soc Trop Med Hyg 60:497-513, 1966.
13. Carme B. Laigret J. Longevity of *Wuchereria bancrofti* var. *pacifica* and mosquito infection acquired from a patient with low parasitemia. Am J Trop Med Hyg 28:53-55. 1979.
14. Liu Lx. Buhlmann JE. Weller PF. Release of prostaglandin E2 by microfilariae of *Wuchereria bancrofti* and *Brugia malayi*. Am J Trop Med Hyg 46:520-523, 1992.
15. Almeida AB. de Silva MCM. et al. The presence or absence of active infection, not clinical status, is most closely associated with cytokine responses in lymphatic filariasis. J Infect Dis 173:1453. 1996.
16. Piessens WF. Mcgreevy PB. et al. Immune responses in human infections with *Brugia malayi*: specific cellular unresponsiveness to filarial antigens. J Clin Invest 65:172-179. 1980.
17. Ottesen EA. Infection and disease in lymphatic filariasis – an immunological perspective. Parasitology 104:571. 1992.
18. Taylor MJ. A new insight into the pathogenesis of filarial disease. Curr Mol Med 2: 299-302. 2002.
19. Freedman DO. Filho PJ. Besh S. et al. Lymphoscintigraphic analysis of lymphatic abnormalities in symptomatic and asymptomatic human filariasis. J Infect Dis 170:927. 1994.
20. Addiss DG, Dreyer G. Treatment of lymphatic filariasis. In: Nutman, TB, ed. Lymphatic Filariasis (Tropical Medicine: Science and Practice). London: Imperial College Press; 2000: 151-199.
21. Pani SP. Uvaraj J. et al. Episodic adenolymphangitis and lymphedema in patients with bancroftian filariasis. Trans R Soc Trop Med Hyg 89:72. 1995.
22. Ottesen EA. Nutman TB. Tropical pulmonary eosinophilia. Annu Rev Med 43:417-424, 1992.
23. Well GJ. Jam DC. Santhanam S. et al. A monoclonal antibody-based enzyme immunoassay for detecting parasite antigenemia in Bancroftian filariasis. J Infect Dis 156:350-355, 1987.
24. Kazura JW. Filariasis. In: Tropical Infectious Diseases, Principles, Pathogens, & Practice, Volume 2 (Guerrant RL. Walker DH. Weller PF. eds). Churchill Livingstone, pp. 852-60, 1999.
25. Taylor MJ, Hoerauf A. A new approach to the treatment of filariasis. Curr Op Infect Dis 14: 727-31. 2001.
26. Piessens WF. Partono F. Host-vector-parasite relationships in human filariasis. Semin Infect Dis 3:131-152. 1980.
27. Kazura JW. Greenberg J. et al. Comparison of single dose diethylcarbamazine and ivermectin for treatment of bancroftian filariasis in Papua New Guinea. Am J Trop Med Hyg 49:804. 1993.
28. Fenwick A, Molyneux D, Nantulya V. Achieving the Millennium Development Goals. Lancet 365: 1029-30. 2005.

23. *Onchocerca volvulus*
(Leuckart 1893)

Introduction

Onchocerca volvulus is a vector-borne, filarial nematode parasite. The adult worm lives in the subcutaneous tissues. Its offspring, microfilariae migrate and induce injury to a variety of anatomical sites contiguous with that tissue. There are no reservoir hosts for this parasite. The blackfly, *Simulium spp.*, is the vector of *O. volvulus*. This filarial parasite occurs mostly in West Africa, northern South America, and throughout Latin America. Onchocerciasis used to be the major cause of blindness[1] throughout sub-Saharan Africa, often affecting more than 50% of the inhabitants of towns and villages in endemic areas. The disease also causes a disfiguring dermatitis that at one time was second only to polio as a cause of long term disability in endemic areas. It was once so prevalent that people could not live in many places along riverbanks.

Vector control, together with a program of donation and administration of the Merck drug ivermectin (Mectizan) have resulted in dramatic reductions in the incidence and prevalence of this disease. For instance, between 1974 and 2002, the Onchocerciasis Control Program halted transmission in 11 west African countries (Benin, Burkina Faso, Cote d'Ivoire, Ghana, Guinea, Guinea-Bissau, Mali, Niger, Senegal, Sierra, Leone and Togo), and prevented an estimated 600,000 cases of blindness. It has been further estimated that 18 million children born in the OCP area are now free from the risk of river blindness, and approximately 25 million hectares of land have now been rendered free of the disease.[2]

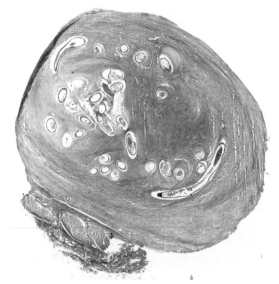

Figure 23.1. Cross section of nodule (onchocercoma) induced by *Onchocerca volvulus*. Numerous sections of adult worms are seen. 2.5 cm in diam.

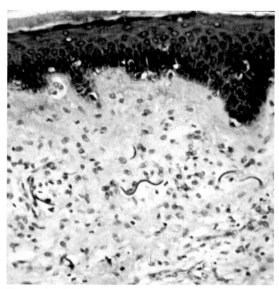

Figure 23.2. Section of skin with numerous microfilariae of *O. volvulus*.

Current estimates indicate that approximately 18 million people remain infected worldwide, with 99 percent or more living in Sub-Saharan Africa, Yemen, and small foci in Latin America (Mexico, Ecuador, Guatemala, Colombia, Venezuela and Brazil). Through a new African initiative, the African Programme for Onchocerciasis Control (APOC), a partnership under the leadership of the World Bank, WHO, UNDP, and FAO, which builds on the previous successes of the OCP, there is optimism that onchocerciasis might be completely eradicated in the coming decades. APOC aims to treat 75 million people with ivermectin per year by 2010, extending its reach to the remaining 19 endemic countries in Central and East Africa (Angola, Burundi, Cameroon, Central African Republic, Chad, Democratic Republic of Congo, Equatorial Guinea, Ethiopia, Gabon, Kenya, Liberia, Malawi, Mozambique, Nigeria, Rwanda, Sudan, Tanzania and Uganda).[2] Similarly the Onchocerciasis Elimination Program for the Americas (OEPA) is working to eliminate river blindness in the seven Latin American countries by 2007.

Historical Information

Onchocerca volvulus was first described in Africa by Leuckart. He recounted his discovery of the parasite to Patrick Manson, who, in turn, published the full description in 1893, giving Leuckart full credit.[3] Earlier, O'Neill[4] observed the microfilariae of this filarial nematode in the skin of a patient from West Africa. Onchocerciasis in Latin America was not reported until 1917, when Robles[5] found ocular disease associated with the presence of nodules on the forehead of a small boy. He dissected the nodule and found that it contained

Onchocerca volvulus

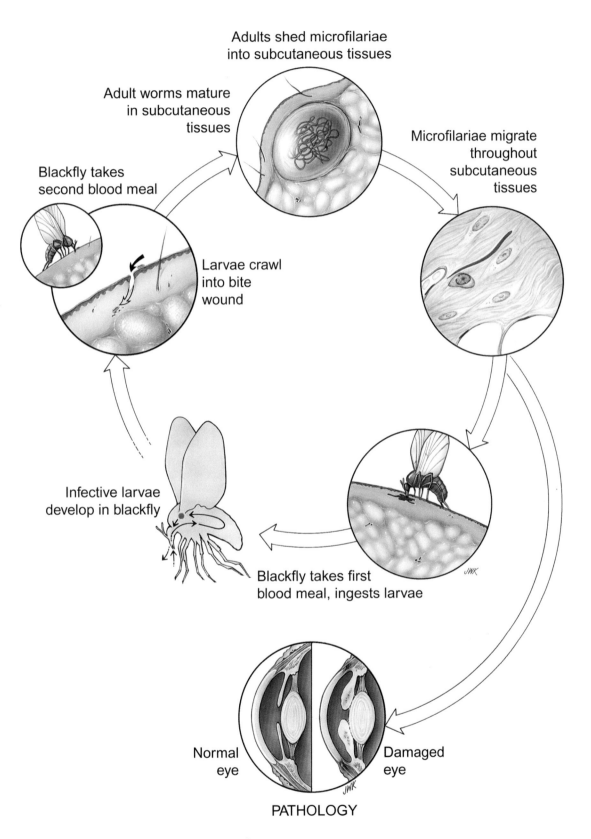

Adults shed microfilariae
into subcutaneous tissues

Adult worms mature
in subcutaneous
tissues

Microfilariae migrate
throughout
subcutaneous
tissues

Blackfly takes
second blood meal

Larvae crawl
into bite
wound

Infective larvae
develop in blackfly

Blackfly takes first
blood meal, ingests larvae

Normal
eye

Damaged
eye

PATHOLOGY

the adult worms. Later Robles described the anatomy of the worm, the pathology of the disease, and epidemiology of the infection. Moreover, he suspected that the blackfly was the vector, which was later proved by Blacklock[6] in 1927.

Life Cycle

Adult females measure about 40 cm in length and 0.3 cm in width, while the male measures about 3 to 5 cm in length. Both sexes lie entwined about each other, locating to subcutaneous fibrous nodules, onchocercomas (Fig. 23.1), which vary in size depending on the number of adult worms in them. Some nodules are so small that they cannot be palpated.[7] Microfilariae are produced within the nodules, and leave these sites to migrate throughout the subcutaneous tissues (Figs. 23.2, 23.3). The blackfly (Fig. 38.5) acquires the larvae while taking a blood meal. The immature worms penetrate the insect's hemocele and the muscle fibers of the flight wing bundles in the thorax. After 6-8 days of development, during which the larvae molt twice, the now infective larvae leave the muscles, enter the cavity of the proboscis, and are deposited on the skin when the fly bites. Larvae enter the bite wound after the fly withdraws its biting mouthparts. The immature parasites invade the subcutaneous tissues with the aid of a protease[8] and take up residence there. After completing their development, they mate. Adults produce hundreds to thousands of microfilariae during their life span (about 700 microfilariae per day) of 8-10 years. Growth and molting of worms in the subcutaneous tissues induces formation of the fibrous nodules and also elicits an angiogenic response,[9, 10] resulting in the production of a network of vessels, the function of which is presumably to supply nutrients to the parasites and carry away metabolic wastes. A similar angiogenic response is induced by the Nurse cell-parasite complex of *Trichinella spiralis*.[11]

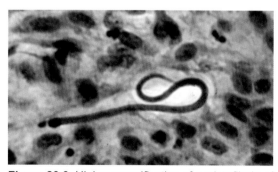

Figure 23.3. Higher magnification of a microfilaria of *O. volvulus* in skin. 310 μm x 7 μm.

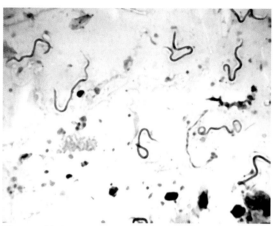

Figure 23.4. Impression smear of a skin snip from a patient heavily infected with *O. volvulus*. Microfilariae were visualized with Giemsa stain.

Cellular and Molecular Pathogenesis

Onchocerca larvae migrate through the tissues with the aid of macromolecules that promote tissue degradation, angiogenesis, and plasmin-mediated proteolysis.[8-10, 12] *O. volvulus* has impressive immunomodulatory properties, with the capacity to bias host responses to a Th2-type pattern. By this mechanism, host-cell-mediated Th1-type immunity is suppressed leading to impaired responses to PPD skin testing for tuberculosis,[13] tetanus, and other vaccinations,[14] and even increased susceptibility to intercurrent infections with lepromatous leprosy.[15]

The degree of pathogenesis varies directly with the intensity of infection and the degree of host responsiveness to dying adult worms and microfilariae and their secretions. Dead microfilariae induce inflammatory reactions that become more severe as the infection persists; this point is important when considering therapy. The lesions, primarily involving the skin and the eyes, occur as a consequence of cell-mediated immunity to parasite antigens. Individuals with the most vigorous cell-mediated immune responses develop the most severe manifestations.[1, 12, 17] The magnitude of the host immunopathologic response significantly influences the severity of clinical onchodermatitis.[17] Host mast cells play an important role in this phenomenon.[18]

The major ocular lesions occur in the cornea to produce a keratitis.[16] In this case, the keratitis results from an accumulation of punctate opacities in the cornea that arise from a unique immunopathologic damage to microfilariae in the eye. This is a Th2-dependent process with a heavy reliance on host interleukin 4.[16] In the skin, similar immune responses lead to pruritus and angioedema.

Subcutaneous nodules, the other hallmark of clinical onchocerciasis, vary in size from barely discernable to approximately 5 cm in diameter. Nodules develop over an 18-month period depending on the number of adult worms in each. The number of nodules also varies, from an occasional one to several hundred, occupying large areas of subcutaneous tissue. In the latter instance, blackflies biting such individuals may actually expire due to the overwhelming nature of the infection in their flight wing muscles. Those areas in which peripheral lymphatics converge (e.g., occiput, suboccipital areas, intercostal spaces, axilla, and iliac crests) have the highest predilection for nodules. The body regions most affected differ according to geographic locales. In Africa, for example, the nodules predominate in the lower part of the body, whereas in Central America they tend to be found more often in the upper portions of the body. This difference is related to the biting habits of the vector insects, and the styles of clothing worn by the inhabitants of each endemic area.

O. volvulus, like *Wuchereria bancrofti*, contain bacterial symbionts of the genus Wolbachia. These are rickettsia-like organisms that are found in the body wall, in oocytes, and in all embryonic stages, including microfilariae.[19] The Wolbachia symbionts are believed to be essential for nematode fertility and are transmitted transovarially to the next worm generation, in a manner similar to mitochondria.[20] Wolbachia also contains endoxin-like products that are proinflammatory. This has led to the hypothesis that the bacterial symbionts contribute significantly to the skin and eye pathology of *O. volvulus*-infected patients.[19, 20]

Clinical Disease

Clinical onchocerciasis includes dermatitis, eye lesions, and onchocercomas.

Onchodermatitis

Mild infection (less than five nodules per infected individual) is usually asymtomatic. In contrast, moderate to severe infection (ten or more nodules, with many in the head and neck region) produce correspondingly more serious and more numerous symptoms. Involvement of skin is characterized by intense itching, which is associated with a rash consisting of numerous small, circular, elevated papules 1-3 mm in diameter. On white skin, the papules are reddish, but on black skin, they tend to be dark brown. The pruritus of onchodermatitis is intense and disabling. Occasional suicides result from the extreme discomfort associated with it.[1] The affected areas of skin become edematous and thickened, and lose their elasticity. The skin can take on an orange-peel quality. Over time, the skin will atrophy, especially over the buttocks, with appearance of wrinkles. Depigmentation can also occur, especially over the shins. Sometimes this is known as "leopard skin". These sequelae are more common in Africa than in Central America, but Central American children who are infected may have facial lesions, reddish in color, described as *erysipelas de la costa*.

Lymphadenopathy

Lymph node involvement in Africa is usually found in the inguinal and femoral nodes, whereas in the American tropics it is in the head and neck. Advanced lymph node involvement can lead to adenocele formation.[1]

Ocular Lesions

All parts of the eye are affected in chronic, long-term infections. Initially, there may be conjunctivitis, with irritation, lacrimation, and photophobia, a reaction analogous to the dermatitis in response to dead microfilariae. The cornea at this time reveals the punctate lesions of keratitis. Slit-lamp examination reveals motile or dead microfilariae in the conjunctiva. A long-standing infection produces sclerosis and vascularization. Sclerosing keratitis is the leading cause of blindness due to onchocerciasis, and develops over a 20- to 30-year period. Onchocercal blindness peaks in those between 30 and 40 years of age; individuals most responsible for taking care of their families.[1] The anterior chamber is also invaded, and microfilariae can be seen there with a slit lamp. Finally, there may be iritis, iridocyclitis, and secondary glaucoma. Invasion of the posterior segment of the eye causes optic neuritis and papillitis; the choroid and the retina are also involved.

Diagnosis

Because of its highly focal distribution, a travel history is critical in order to entertain a clinical suspicion of onchocerciasis. A definitive diagnosis is usually made by examining a piece of skin (2-5 mm^2) dissected from the affected part of the body. In Africa, the specimen should be obtained from the lower part of the body, and in Central America from the upper part. The skin should be alcohol-cleansed, elevated with a needle, and cut with a scalpel blade. Next, a preferably bloodless piece should be placed in warm physiological saline and examined microscopically for motile microfilariae within 10 minutes. A representative sample of skin can be weighed and the number of microfilariae per milligram of tissue calculated as an index of the intensity of infection. In addition, the piece of skin can be pressed against a dry microscope slide, and the impression stained with Giemsa solution and examined microscopically for microfilariae (Fig. 23.4). Histologic sections of a subcutaneous nodule (Fig. 23.2, 23.3) may also reveal microfilariae. The sensitivity of skin snips has recently been improved by PCR amplification.[21, 22] The Mazzotti Test is a provocative challenge test using a 50 mg dose of diethylcarbamazine (DEC). Within 3 hours after treatment, patients with *O. volvulus* infection will develop pruritus. In heavily infected patients, the Mazzotti reaction can be severe and may exacerbate the ocular pathology in a patient. As an alternative, some physicians perform a type of patch test by applying DEC to a small region in order to elicit a local Mazzotti-like reaction.[23]

Serologic tests that measure IgG antibodies to O. volvulus are sensitive, but their specificity is poor, and not yet useful to the clinician. Efforts are underway to develop recombinant immunodiagnostic reagents.

Treatment

Ivermectin is the drug of choice for onchocerciasis. Ivermectin inhibits the release of microfilariae from the female.[24] Usually, a single oral dose of 150 mcg/kg administered every 6 months will slow or reverse the progression of both ocular and cutaneous diseases.[25] The drug is available through the Mectizan® Donation Program established in 1988 by Merck & Co. Ivermectin does not kill the adult worms encased in a nodule. Therefore, repeat dosing is necessary to suppress the release of microfilariae. In some patients more frequent interval dosing is required in order to suppress pruritus. Community-wide chemotherapy interrupts transmission of onchocerciasis.[26, 27] The major toxicity of ivermectin is generally not from the drug itself but rather from its ability to increase the antigen load from dead and dying parasites, leading to fever, angioedema and pruritus. These symptoms usually occur within 24 hours of treatment. In those patients with concurrent *Loa loa* infection, ivermectin can elicit severe reactions, including encephalopathy.[28] This point is especially critical in areas such as West and Central Africa, where there is epidemiologic overlap between the two helminth infections. In Latin America, the surgical removal of palpable subcutaneous nodules has led to successful resolution of the infection in some instances.

The possible role of Wolbachia endosymbionts in the inflammatory processes that lead to eye and skin changes in *O. volvulus* infection, as well as their role in embryogenesis and parasite fertility, has led to the suggestion that antibiotics could have a therapeutic activity for patients with onchocerciasis.[29] Prolonged administration of doxycycline (200 mg/day for 4-6 weeks) was shown to interrupt *O. volvulus* embryogenesis.[19] Further investigations on the role of antibiotics for the treatment of onchocerciasis are in progress.

Prevention and Control

Onchocerca volvulus distribution follows that of the dipteran vectors. Blackflies breed in fast-running water of mountainous streams in regions of Africa and South and Central America, and they have a fairly long flight range. Thus, onchocerciasis can be found several miles from the nearest endemic breeding site. Because much of the coffee of the world is grown on mountain-

ous hillsides, the prevalence of onchocerciasis among workers on coffee plantations is high. The OCP was launched in 1974, with a primary emphasis on reducing simulium larval vector populations with DDT and other insecticides.[30] With the increasing availability of ivermectin In the later years of the program, the OCP increasingly focused on control using this drug as an agent of mass chemotherapy.[31]

In Africa, efforts to control onchocerciasis are currently being conducted by APOC.[2] Critical to the success of APOC is the Merck Mectizan Donation Program (MMDP), one of the first and largest public private partnerships devoted to a neglected disease. The MMDP was launched in 1987 when Roy Vagelos, then CEO of Merck made a historic announcement that his company would donate Mectizan® to anyone who needed it, for as long as it was needed.[2, 31] The MMDP works closely with the Task Force for Child Survival and Development, an affiliate of Emory University for this purpose. To date, the MMDP has donated an estimated 300 million treatments worth approximately $450 million.[2]

APOC works with the organizations previously involved with the OCP, as well as Merck, the governments of 19 developing countries, 27 donor countries, at least 30 NGOs, and more than 80,000 rural Africa communities.[2] This is done by coordinating with the ministries and NGOs to deliver Mectizan along with existing national health systems of the participating African countries. To accomplish its mission, APOC has implemented a novel system of community-directed treatment programs. By 2010 it is anticipated that the sight of nearly 500,000 people will be saved. In addition, the community-based health systems created by APOC are expected to provide a framework for additional pro-poor health interventions including those that target other neglected diseases such as soil-transmitted helminth infections, schistosomiasis, and trachoma.

In the seven onchocerciasis-endemic Latin American countries, OEPA has also made great strides through extensive use of Mectizan® treatments. Headquartered in Guatemala City, OEPA together with the Carter Center has reduced the number of people at risk for onchocerciasis from 4.7 million in 1995 to an estimated 500,000 persons in 2003 (www.cartercenter. org). In 2001, the Careter Center's International Task Force for Disease Eradication targeted onchocerciasis for eradication in the Americas.

As a complementary approach to onchocerciasis control, there have been some efforts to develop recombinant vaccines.[31, 32] This includes the Onchocerca homologue of a hookworm ASP and an aldolase, which have shown promise in laboratory animals.[33, 34]

References

1. Greene BM. Modern medicine versus an ancient scourge: progress toward control of onchocerciasis. J Infect Dis 166:15-21. 1992.
2. Levine R and the What Works Working Group. Millions Saved, Proven Successes in Global Health, Case 6, Controlling Onchocerciasis in Sub-Saharan Africa, Washington DC: Center for Global Development 2004; pp. 57-64
3. Manson P. *Filaria volvuloxus*. In: Hygiene and Diseases of Warm Climates (Davidson AH., ed). Y.J. Pentland, London. p. 1016. 1893.
4. O'Neill J. On the presence of a filaria in "crawcraw." Lancet 1:265-266. 1875.
5. Robles R. Enfermidad nueva en Guatemala. Juventud Med 17: 97-115. 1917.
6. Blacklock DB. The insect transmission of *Onchocerca volvulus* (Leuckart 1893). The cause of worm nodules in man in Africa. BMJ 1:129-133, 1927.
7. Duke BO. The population dynamics of *Onchocerca volvulus* in the human host. Trop Med Parasitol 44:61-8. 1993.
8. Lackey A. James ER. Et al. Extra-cellular proteases of *Onchocerca volvulus*. Exp Parasitol 68:176-185. 1993.
9. Tawe W. Pearlman E. Unnasch TR. Lustigman S. Angiogenic activity of *Onchocerca volvulus* recombinant proteins similar to vespid venom antigen 5. Mol Biochem Parasitol 109: 91-9. 2000.
10. Higazi TB. Pearlman E. et al. Angiogenic activity of an *Onchocerca volvulus* Ancylostoma secreted protein homologue. Mol Biochem Parasitol 129: 61-8. 2003.
11. Capo V. Despommier DD. Polvere RI. *Trichinella spiralis*: vascular endothelial growth factor is up-regulated within the Nurse cell during early phase of its formation. J Parasit 84:209-214. 1998.
12. Jolodar A. Fischer P. et al. Molecular cloning of an alpha-enolase from the human filarial parasite *Onchocerca volvulus* that binds human plasminogen. Biochim Biophys Acta 19: 1627: 111-20. 2003.
13. Rougemont A. Boisson Pontal ME. et al. Tuberculin skin tests and BCG vaccination in hyperendemic area of onchocerciasis (letter). Lancet 1:309. 1977.
14. Cooper PJ. Espinel I. et al. Human onchocerciasis and tetanus vaccination: impact on the postvaccination antitetanus antibody response. Infect Immun 67: 5951-7. 1999.
15. Prost A. Nebout M. Rougemont A. Lepromatous leprosy and onchocerciasis. BMJ 1:589-90. 1979.
16. Pearlman E. Lass JH. et al. Interleukin 4 and T helper type 2 cells are required for development of experimental onchocercal keratitis (river blindness). J Exp Med 182:931-40. 1995.
17. Ali MM. Baraka OZ. et al. Immune responses directed against microfilariae correlate with severity of clinical onchodermatitis and treatment history. J Infect Dis 187: 714-7. 2003.
18. Cooper PJ. Schwartz LB. et al. Association of transient dermal mastocytosis and elevated plasma tryptase levels with development of adverse reactions after treatment of onchocerciasis with ivermectin. J Infect Dis 186: 1307-13. 2002.
19. Hoerauf A. Buttner D. Adjei O. Pearlman E. Onchocerciasis. BMJ 326: 207-210. 2003.
20. Keiser PB. Reynolds SM. et al. Bacterial endosymbionts of *Onchocerca volvulus* in the pathogenesis of post-treatment reactions. J Infect Dis 185: 805-11. 2002.
21. Boatin BA. Toe L. et al. Detection of *Onchocerca volvulus* infection in low prevalence areas: a comparison of three diagnostic methods. Parasitology. 125:545-52. 2002.
22. Bradley JE. Unnasch TR. Molecular approaches to the diagnosis of onchocerciasis. Adv. Parasitol 37:57-106. 1996.
23. Kilian HD. The use of a topical Mazzotti test in the diagnosis of onchocerciasis. Trop Med Parasitol 39:235-238, 1988.
24. Greene BM. Taylor HR. et al. Comparison of ivermectin and diethylcarbamazine in the treatment of onchocerciasis. N Engl J Med 313:133-138. 1985.
25. Burnham G. Ivermectin treatment of onchocercal skin lesions: Observations from a placebo-controlled, double-blind trial in Malawi. Am J Trop Med Hyg 52:270-6. 1995.
26. Taylor HR. Pacque M. Munoz B. Greene BM. Impact of mass treatment of onchocerciasis with ivermectin on the transmission of infection. Science 250:116-118. 1990.
27. Cupp EW. Ochoa JO. et al. The effects of repetitive community-wide ivermectin treatment on transmission of *Onchocerca volvulus* in Guatemala. Am J Trop Med Hyg 47:170-180. 1992.
28. Chippaux J-P. Ernould J-C. et al. Ivermectin treatment of loiasis. Trans R Soc Trop Med Hyg 86:289. 1992.
29. Hoerauf A. Mand S. et al. Doxycycline in the treatment of human onchocerciasis: Kinetics of Wolbachia endobacteria reduction and of inhibition of embryogenesis in female Onchocerca worms. Microbes Infect 5:261-73. 2003.
30. Omura S. Crump A. The life and times of ivermectin – a success story. Nature Rev Microbiol 2: 984-9. 2004.
31. Peters DH. Phillips T. Mectizan donation program: evaluation of a public-private partnership. Trop med Int Health 9: A4-15. 2004.
32. Lustigman S. James ER. Tawe W. Abraham D. Towards a recombinant antigen vaccine against *Onchocerca volvulus*. Trends Parasitol 18: 135-41. 2002.
33. Nutman TB. Future directions for vaccine-related onchocerciasis research. Trends Parasitol 18: 237-9. 2002.
34. MacDonald AJ. Tawe W. et al. Ov-ASP-2, the *Onchocerca volvulus* homologue of the activation associated secreted protein family is immunostimulatory and can induce protective anti-larval immunity. Parasite Immunol 26: 53-62. 2004.
35. McCarthy JS. Wieseman M. et al. *Onchocerca volvulus* glycolytic enzme fructose-1,6-bisphosphate aldolase as a target for a protective immune response in humans. Infect Immun 70: 851-8. 2002.

24. *Loa loa*
(Cobbold 1864)

Introduction

Loa loa is a filarial nematode infection acquired in Central and West Africa, where it infects up to 13 million individuals. In some hyperendemic regions, prevalence may be as high as 40%.[1] Loiasis is an emerging infection in areas where the establishment of rubber plantations has altered the rain forest ecology.[2] Increasingly, *L. loa* infection is seen in returning travelers who spend long periods of time in rural Africa; this includes a diverse array of people with unique occupational exposures, such as anthropologists and individuals involved in ecotourism. The adult worm lives in subcutaneous tissues. Its main vectors are dipteran flies of the genus Chrysops. *Loa loa* has no reservoir hosts.

Historical Information

Argyll-Robertson, in 1895,[3] gave the first complete description of the worm and the clinical presentation of the infection. The woman from whom he removed two adult worms (one of each sex) had lived in Old Calabar (a portion of which is now Nigeria). Swellings in her arms accompanied her infections, and were described in detail. These inflammatory lesions are still referred to as Calabar swellings. Leiper, in 1913,[4] described two species of dipterans, *Chrysops dimidiata and C. silacae,* as the vectors of *L. loa.*

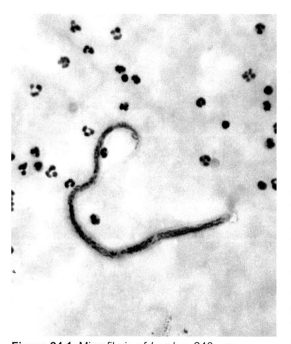

Figure 24.1. Microfilaria of *Loa loa*. 240 μm

Life Cycle

Female adults measure 0.5 mm wide and 60 mm long; the males are 0.4 mm by 32 mm. Adult worms deposit microfilariae (Fig. 24.1), while they wander throughout the subcutaneous tissues. Microfilariae (80 μm long by 7 μm in diameter) penetrate capillaries and enter the bloodstream, where they circulate until they become ingested in a blood meal by a mango fly (*Chrysops spp.*). *L. loa* microfilariae exhibit diurnal periodicity that coincides with the feeding habits of Chrysops.[5] Larvae penetrate the stomach of the fly, and locate to the fat body. Eight to ten days later, the infective third-stage larvae migrate to the cavity of the biting mouthparts, and are released into the bite wound when the fly takes another blood meal. The larvae, now in the subcutaneous tissues of the host, develop slowly into adults within 1-4 years. The adult worms can live in the tissues for up to 17-years.[6] Mature worms mate, and the females begin depositing microfilariae. The nutritional requirements of *L. loa* are unknown.

Cellular and Molecular Pathogenesis

Neither the adult worms in the subcutaneous tissues of the host nor the microfilariae in the bloodstream cause any direct pathologic changes. However, in some individuals the parasite can elicit a number of immune-mediated responses that have an allergic basis. There appear to be at least three major groups of individuals who experience different immunopathological responses to the parasite. One of these groups is comprised of asymptomatic individuals who have diminished anti-Loa allergic responses. These groups typically have high levels of circulating microfilariae. The second group is typified by individuals who develop pronounced immunopathology with characteristic recurrent angioedema and Calabar swellings.[7] These individuals develop swellings as a local inflammatory reaction that may precede the migrating adult worms. It is presumed to result from a robust host IgE response and interleukin-5 production in response to secretions from the adults, or from those of the microfilariae that are released inside the female adult parasite during their development there. Upregulation of IL-5 results in circulating eosinophilia.[8, 9] The Calabar swellings are typically more severe in visitors to endemic areas than in residents who live for many years in these same regions.[10, 11] There is a third group of infected individuals who neither have circulating microfilariae nor Calabar swellings. These are individuals living in hyperendemic

Loa loa

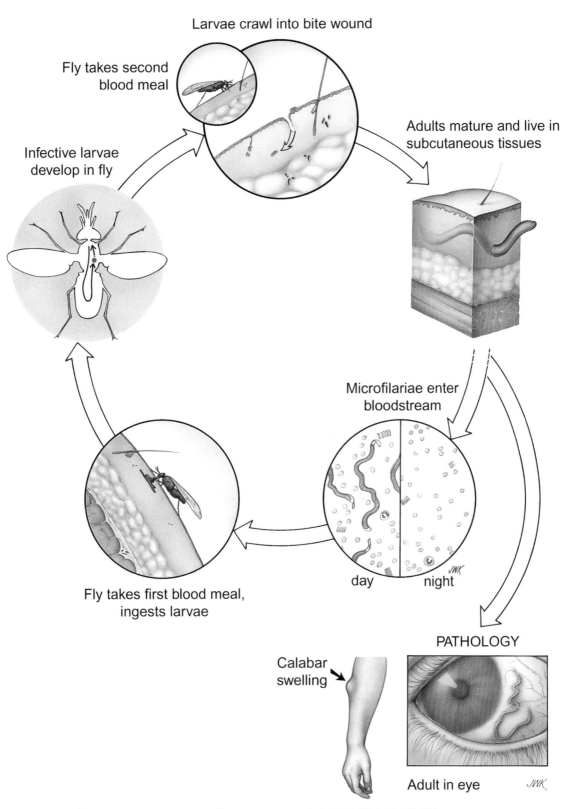

Larvae crawl into bite wound

Fly takes second blood meal

Infective larvae develop in fly

Adults mature and live in subcutaneous tissues

Microfilariae enter bloodstream

day   night

Fly takes first blood meal, ingests larvae

PATHOLOGY

Calabar swelling

Adult in eye

areas, yet are believed to have developed protective immunity.[12, 13] Unlike *W. bancrofti*, there is currently no evidence that *L. loa* contains Wolbachia symbionts.[14]

Clinical Disease

Calabar swellings are 10-20 cm non-erythematous, angioedematous swellings that last for a few days. They occur most typically on the extremities and the face, particularly in the periorbital region. The angioedema is often preceded by pain and itching. Recurrences are common. The occasional passage of an adult worm across the subconjunctival space of the eye is perhaps the most disturbing aspect of *L. loa* to most infected individuals. Patients with more serious complications, including cardiomyopathy, nephropathy, and pleural effusions, have been reported.[11] Some complications occur only after administration of diethylcarbamazine. These sequelae may result from immune complex deposition. Encephalitis has also been described in patients with very high levels of microfilariae, including microfilariae in the cerebrospinal fluid.[12] Most of these individuals have received diethylcarbamazine, and the syndrome probably occurs as part of the host immune response in the central nervous system. A rare cardiac condition known as endomyocardial fibrosis may result from eosinophilic infiltration of the myocardium in response to *L. loa*.[15]

Significant differences in the clinical presentation of loiasis occur among long-term visitors to endemic areas, in contrast to people native to these areas.[8] People living in endemic regions are asymptomatic, despite high levels of microfilaremia, whereas visitors and expatriates suffer from a variety of allergic responses, such as frequent episodes of angioedema, Calabar swellings, hypereosinophilia, and hyper-gammaglobulinemia. This disorder is sometimes referred to as the "hyper-responsive syndrome" of loiasis, reflecting elevated humoral and cell-mediated immune responses to the parasite.[11]

Diagnosis

Patients returning from West or Central Africa with localized angioedema or a worm beneath the conjunctiva should be suspected of having loaiasis. The Calabar swellings should be clinically differentiated from other causes of angioedema, including C1 inhibitor deficiency.[16] Definitive diagnosis is by identifying the microfilariae microscopically in a thin blood smear stained with either Giemsa or Wright's solution. Among the distinguishing features of *L. loa* microfilariae (Fig. C.50 and C.51, Appendix C) are their diurnal periodicity, the presence of a sheath, and three or more terminal nuclei.[13] Adult worm can be recovered from the subconjunctival space and various subcutaneous tissues. There are serologic tests available but largely on a research basis. Anti-Loa antibodies of the IgG4 immunoglobulin subclass are a reliable marker of active infection.[16] This includes IgG4 antibody against the Loa recombinant antigen L1-SXP-1.[17] However, testing is limited to a few laboratories that have access to *L. loa* antigen prepared from the worms. There is also a PCR-based assay that has been developed to detect microfilarial genomes in blood.[18]

Treatment

Diethylcarbamazine (DEC) at a dose of 8-10 mg/kg/day for 21 days is the drug of choice for loiasis. The drug destroys both adult worms and microfilariae. The full dose of the drug is not typically started on the first day of treatment. Instead, it is given in a graded manner, beginning with a test dose on day 1 of 1 mg/kg p.c. (50 mg p.c. adult dose), followed by 1 mg/kg tid (50 mg tid adult dose) on day 2,1-2 mg/kg tid (100 mg tid adult dose) on day 3, and 9 mg/kg/d in three doses on days 4-21. This is done to reduce the likelihood of treatment-associated complications, including encephalopathy, that occur as a consequence of mass destruction of Loa microfilariae.[19] It has been suggested that concerns about iatrogenic complications of loiasis increase when the microfilarial concentration in blood exceeds 2500 mf/ml.[13] In very heavy infections, apheresis has been reported to effectively lower microfilarial counts prior to definitive treatment.[20] Albendazole and ivermectin have also been used to reduce microfilaremia in this manner.[13, 21] Antihistamines or corticosteroids may be required to decrease allergic reactions during treatment. In up to 50% of patients, DEC treatment may need to be repeated several times in order to effect a cure.[22] Adult worms in the eye must be removed surgically. Weekly chemoprophylaxis with DEC given in a dose of 300 mg is effective in preventing loiasis among long-term visitors.[22]

Prevention and Control

In hyperendemic regions of central Africa, 95% of the population have antibodies to *L. loa* antigen by the age of two years.[20] In the Chailu Mountains in Democratic Republic of Congo, 19% of the native populations are microfilaremic, and more than 50% of the adults have reported sub-conjunctival migrations of an adult worm. Mass or targeted chemotherapy with diethylcarbamazine may reduce transmission in these areas.[23, 24] Spraying mango groves with insecticides, particularly DDT, remains an effective method for controlling populations of the vector, since resistance to this insecticide in Chrysops has not yet developed.

Widespread use of periodic chemotherapy in Sub-Saharan Africa for purposes of controlling lymphatic filariasis and onchocerciasis have raised concerns about *L. loa* co-infections. The potential complications of unmonitored DEC treatment of loiasis and the risk of encephalopathy are a major reason why this agent is not used routinely. However, even the alternative combination of ivermectin and albendazole poses some risk. For instance, Loa encephalopathy is associated with ivermectin treatment of individuals with Loa microfilaremia > 30,000 MF/ml blood, with most of the cases of ivermectin-induced encephalopathy occurring in Cameroon.[24] In order to reduce the risks associated with ivermectin in this region, albendazole has been evaluated as a possible first-line measure to gradually lower microfilariae burdens.[25, 26] So far, however, the results have been inconclusive.

References

1. Noireau F. Carme B. et al. *Loa loa* and *Mansonella perstans* filariasis in the Chaillu mountains, Congo: Parsitological prevalence. Trans R Soc Trop Med Hyg 83: 529. 1989.
2. Rodhain F. Hypothesis on the dynamic ecology of Loa infections. Bull Soc Pathol Exot 73:182. 1980.
3. Argyll-Robertson DMCL. Case of Filaria loa in which the parasite was removed from under the conjunctiva. Trans Ophthalmol Soc UK 15:137-167. 1895.
4. Leiper RT. Report of the Helminthologist for the Half Year Ending 30 April, 1913. Report of the Advisory Commission on Tropical Diseases Research Fund. 1913-1914.
5. Duke BOL. Studies of the biting habits of Chrysops. J Ann Trop Med Parasitol 49: 193. 1955.
6. Eveland LK. Yerkakov V. Kenney M. *Loa loa* infection without microfilaremia. Trans R Soc Trop Med Hyg 69:354. 1975.
7. Olness K. Franciosi RA. Johnson MM. Freedman DO. Loiasis in an expatriate American child: diagnosis and treatment difficulties. Pediatrics 80:943-946. 1987.
8. Kilon AD. Massougbodji A. et al. Loiasis in endemic and non-endemic populations: immunologically mediated differences in clinical presentation. J Infect Dis 163:1318-1325. 1991.
9. Limaye AP. Abrams JS. et al. Regulation of parasite-induced eosinophilia: selectively increased interleukin 5 production in helminth-infected patients. J Exp Med 172:399-402. 1990.
10. Nutman TB. Miller KD. et al. *Loa loa* infection in temporary residents of endemic regions: Recognition of a hyper-responsive syndrome with characteristic clinical manifestations. J Infect Dis 154:10. 1986.
11. Nutman TB. Reese W. Poindexter RW. Ottesen EA. Immunologic correlates of the hyper-responsive syndrome of loiasis. J Infect Dis 157:544-550. 1988.
12. Kilon AD. Einstein EM. et al. Pulmonary involvement in loiasis. Am Rev Respir Dis 145:961-963. 1992.
13. Kilon AD. Nutman TB. Loiasis and Mansonella infections In: Tropical Infectious Diseases, Principles, Pathogens, and Practice. Vol. 2 (Guerrant RL. Walker DH. Weller PF., eds.). Churchill Livingstone, Pubs. New York. pp. 861-872. 1999.
14. Grobusch MP, Kombila. M. et al. No evidence of Wolbachia endosymbiosis with *Loa loa* and *Mansonella perstans*. Parasitol Res 90: 405-8. 2003.
15. Andy JJ. Bishara FF. et al. Loiasis as a possible trigger of African endoyocardial fibrosis: a case report form Nigeria. Acta Trop 38:179. 1981.
16. Akue JP. Egwang TG. Devaney E. High levels of parasite-specific IgG4 in the absence of microfilaremia in *Loa loa* infection. Trop Med Parasitol 45:246. 1994.
17. Klion AD. Vijaykumar A. et al. Serum immunoglobulin G4 antibodies to the recombinant antigen, L1-SXP-1, are highly specific for *Loa loa* infection. J Infect Dis 187: 128-33. 2003.
18. Nutman TB. Zimmerman PA. et al. ELISA-based detection of PCR products: A universally applicable approach to the diagnosis of filarial and other infections Parasitol Today 10:239. 1994.
19. Carme B. Boulesteix I. Boutes H. Francke M. Five cases of encephalitis during treatment of loiasis with diethylcarbamazine. Am J Trop Med Hyg 44:684-690. 1991.
20. Ottesen EA. Filarial infections. Infect Dis Clin North Am. 7(3): 619-33. 1993.
21. Kilon AD. Massougbodji A. et al. Albendazole in human loiasis: Results of a double-blind, placebo-controlled trial. J Infect Dis 168:202. 1993.
22. Kilon AD. Ottesen EA. Nutman TB. Effectiveness of diethylcarbamazine in treating loiasis acquired by expatriate visitors to endemic regions: long-term follow-up. J Infect Dis. 169:602. 1994.
23. Nutman TB. Miller KD. et al. Diethylcarbamazine prophylaxis for human loiasis. Results of a double-blind study. N Engl J Med 319:752. 1988.
24. Molyneux DH. Bradley M. et. al. Mass drug treatment for lymphatic filariasis and onchocerciasis. Trends Parasitol 19: 516-22. 2003.
25. Tabi TE, Befidi-Mengue R. et. al. Human loiasis in a Cameroonian village: a double-blind, placebo-controlled, crossover clinical trial of a three-day albendazole regimen. Am J Trop Med Hyg 71: 211-5. 2004.
26. Tsague-Dongmo L, Kamgno J. et. al. Effects of a 3-day regimen of albendazole (800 mg daily) on *Loa loa* microfilaremia. Ann Trop Med Parasitol 96: 707-15. 2002.

25. *Dracunculus medinensis*
(Linnaeus 1758)

Introduction

Dracunculus medinensis (the 'guinea worm'), sometimes referred to as "the fiery serpent", used to occur throughout Central Africa, Yemen, India, Pakistan, and, to a lesser extent, Latin America. In 1986, the World Health Assembly adopted a resolution calling for the eradication of drancunculiasis. At that time, there were an estimated 3.5 million cases in 20 countries. However, through an extraordinary global eradication campaign spearheaded by a coalition that included the Centers for Disease Control and The Carter Center in Atlanta, Georgia, as well as other agencies, the prevalence of guinea worm infection has fallen greater than 99 percent. In 8 countries, the disease has been eradicated, while in the 12 of the remaining countries, five report fewer than 100 cases. Of the remaining cases, 90 percent are reported from Sudan (approximately 20,000 cases), Ghana (approximately 8,000 cases), and Nigeria (approximately 1,500 cases).[1]

Most of the remaining cases occur in the southern region of the Sudan where civil conflict and war has limited the access of public health interventions. Even in the Sudan, however, former President Jimmy Carter was able to negotiate a several month long cease-fire to allow eradication efforts to continue.[2, 3] Therefore, there is some optimism that the last case of guinea worm infection could be eradicated by the coming decade, some thirty years after the world was declared free from smallpox.

Infection with *D. medinensis* disfigures the skin and subcutaneous tissues with unsightly scars, and often results in serious infection because of secondary bacterial infections. *D. medinensis* still ranks as an important infection, because of the disability it causes and the resulting economic impact. Like other so-called

Figure 25.1. *Dracunculus medinensis*. The large circular blister, from which the worm is emerging, will heal leaving a disfiguring scar.

neglected diseases, guinea worm promotes poverty in developing countries. Cats, dogs, monkeys, horses, cattle, raccoons, and foxes have been implicated in the transmission of *D. medinensis*, but there are several other species that may be confused with it, so the epidemiologic importance of these hosts as potential reservoirs is unknown.

Historical Information

Dracunculus medinensis infection has been recognized for thousands of years due to its overt clinical presentation and "therapy." The latter, which involves a slow extraction procedure by gently pulling out the anterior end of the worm and winding it on a stick until it is removed, is still used in many locales throughout the world. Bastian[4] provided the first formal description of the anatomy of *D. medinensis* in 1863. Seven years later, Fedchenko[5] reported a partial outline of its life cycle, in which he recognized a crustacean, Cyclops, as the intermediate host. Turkhud[6] in India in 1914 pieced together all the crucial steps in the life cycle, and fulfilled the requirements of Koch's postulates for this infection in human volunteers.

Life Cycle

The female adult parasite is long and thin, measuring more than 100 cm by 1.5 mm. The smaller male typically measures 40 mm by 0.4 mm. Some members of the species are red in color, but the reason for this is not known. Adult worms live in the subcutaneous tissues, usually in the lower extremities. Members of both sexes have acutely curved tails which serve to anchor them in the tissues. The female induces a vesicular, ulcerated lesion in the skin of the host surrounding her vulva. When the ulcer comes in contact with fresh water, the worm undergoes a uterine prolapse, releasing motile larvae into the vulvar cavity, and then into the water. Larvae are ingested by copepods of many genera, including Cyclops, Mesocyclops, and Thermocyclops. The larvae rapidly penetrate the hemocele of the crustacean intermediate host, and develop within 2-3 weeks into the infective third-stage larvae. Infected copepods become swallowed by humans, usually in drinking water, and are digested in the small intestine, releasing the infective larvae. Larvae penetrate the wall of the small intestine, and migrate within the connective tissues up to a year, during which time they molt twice more and mature to adults. Gravid females migrate through the subcutaneous tissues into the extremities of the trunk, where they cause indurated papules that vesiculate, eventually becoming ulcerated. The life cycle is completed when the ulcer comes in contact with water.

Dracunculus medinensis

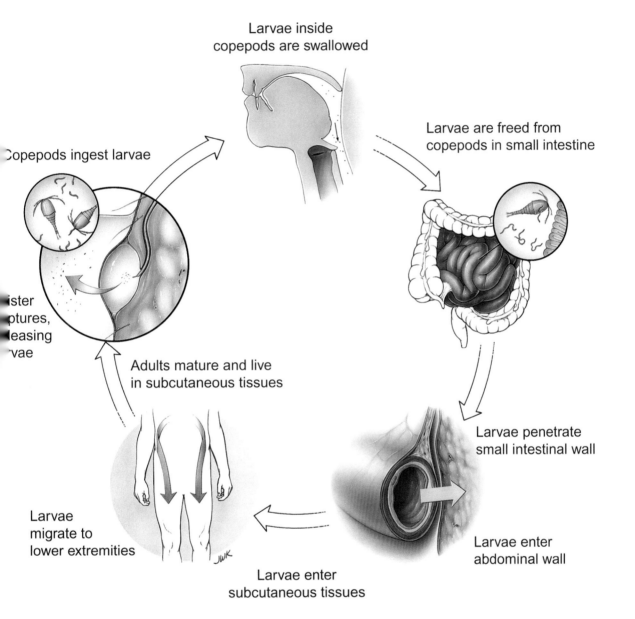

Larvae inside
copepods are swallowed

Larvae are freed from
copepods in small intestine

Copepods ingest larvae

Blister
ruptures,
releasing
larvae

Larvae penetrate
small intestinal wall

Adults mature and live
in subcutaneous tissues

Larvae enter
abdominal wall

Larvae
migrate to
lower extremities

Larvae enter
subcutaneous tissues

Cellular and Molecular Pathogenesis

During a primary infection, there are no apparent host responses to the presence of the worm during its maturation process. If worms do not complete their migration and die, they may either disintegrate or become calcified, which causes problems if the calcification event happens to occur near a joint. At the conclusion of a successful migration, the worm secretes a toxin, as yet uncharacterized, that causes local inflammation, leading to ulcer formation. Ulcers occur most frequently on the lower part of the body (legs and feet), but can also locate on the upper extremities and the trunk.Patients can become sensitized to secretions of the worm, with the consequent allergic reactions of urticaria and pruritus. Anaphylactic reactions have also been reported. If left untreated, ulcers often become secondarily infected, leading to tetanus, gangrene, and even death. About 1% of the cases worldwide are fatal.

Clinical Disease

Multiple cutaneous blisters and ulcers are characteristic manifestations of infection with *Dracunculus medinensis*. Allergic reactions usually occur in advance of the rupture of the blister, or with attempts to remove the worm. Dracunculiasis is not usually a fatal disease, but it causes substantial disability (3-10 weeks) in nearly half of the affected individuals. In Nigeria, dracunculiasis was responsible for 25% of the absenteeism in infected school children.[7] As mentioned, secondary bacterial infections are common, with cellulitis spreading along the track of the worm. In about 20% of cases, ankylosing of joints, arthritis, or contractures often develops, and leads to permanent disability.[7] At one time in Nigeria it was estimated that guinea worm infection in adults resulted in an average of 100 days of work lost per year.[8]

Diagnosis

Definitive diagnosis is by locating the head of the adult worm in the skin lesion and/or identifying the lar-vae that are released into fresh water. Radiographs may reveal calcifications corresponding to the adult worms in the subcutaneous tissues. There is a reliable ELISA test for *D. medinensis*,[9] but its availability is limited.

Treatment

The time-honored therapy involves winding the worm on a thin stick until it is totally extracted (Fig. 24.1). This must be done slowly to insure that the worm does not break. Surgical removal of the worms has been effective, but may exaggerate allergic reactions. Mebendazole treatment of dracunculiasis is controversial.[10] Some clinicians advocate metronidazole or niridazole for the treatment of this infection, and anti-inflammatory drugs are effective for alleviating symptoms related to the death of the worm.

Prevention and Control

Successful eradication of dracunculiasis has been possible because (1) there is no human carrier state (beyond a 1-year incubation period); (2) there are few animal reservoirs; (3) transmission is seasonal; (4) cases are easily detected by observing individuals with protruding worms; and (5) the methods for controlling transmission are relatively simple.[11, 12]

The major approaches to guinea worm prevention and eradication include (1) filtering drinking water through finely-woven cloth in order to mechanically remove copepods, (2) treating contaminated water with a larvicide known as temephos (ABATE®), (3) health education to prevent infected individuals from entering drinking water sources when guinea worms are emerging, and (4) providing clean water from wells.[1]

The successes of this approach have resulted in international acclaim, and in large measure reflect extraordinary advocacy efforts personally championed by former President Jimmy Carter, his associate Dr. Donald Hopkins, and the staff of the Carter Center. Guinea worm eradication is considered one of the most impressive accomplishments ever achieved by a former U.S. President.

References

1. Centers for Disease Control and Prevention (CDC). Progress toward eradication of drancunculiasis, 2002-2003. MMWR Morb Mortal Wkly Rep 53(37): 871-2. 2004.
2. Implementation of health initiatives during a cease fire – Sudan, 1995. MMWR 44: 433-436. 1995.
3. Imported dracunculiasis – United States, 1995 and 1997. MMWR 47: 209. 1998.
4. Bastian HC. On the sturcture and the nature of Dracunculus, or Guinea worm. Trans Linn Soc 24: 101-134 1863.
5. Fedehenko AP. Concerning the structure and reproduction of the guinea worm (Filaria medinensis, L). Izv Imper Obscuh Liubit Estes Anthrop Ethnog 8: 71-81. 1870.
6. Turkhud DA. Repoert of the Bombay Bacteriological Laboratory for the Year 1913. Report presented by Major W. Glen Liston. Government Central Press, Bombay. pp. 14-16. 1914.
7. Llegbodu VA. Oladele KO, Wise RA, et al. Impact of guinea worm disease on children in Nigeria. Am J Trop Med Hyg 35: 962-964. 1986.
8. Kale OO. The clinico-epidemiological profile of Guinea worm in the Ibadan District of Nigeria. Am J Trop Med Hyg 26: 208- 214. 1977.
9. Klicks MM. Rao CK. Development of a rapid ELISA for early sero-diagnosis of dracunculosis. J Commun Dis 16: 287-294. 1984.
10. Chippaux J-P. Mebendazole treatment of dracunculiasis. Trans R Soc Trop Med Hyg 85: 280. 1991.
11. Hopkins DR. Ruiz-Tiben E. Strategies for dracunculiasis eradication. Bull WHO 69: 533-540. 1991.
12. Hopkins DR. Foege WH. Guinea worm disease (letter to the editor). Science 212-495. 1981.

26. Nematode Infections of Minor Medical Importance

Several nematode infections of low to moderate prevalence present with serious clinical consequences wherever they occur, and hence deserve mention. Table 26.1 lists their geographic distribution, major pathologic effects, mode of infection, method of diagnosis, and therapy. A brief description of those preceded by an asterisk is given in the text below.

Mansonella ozzardi
(Manson 1897)

Mansonella ozzardi is a filarial infection found throughout South and Central America and the Caribbean islands, especially Haiti. In some highly endemic regions, up to 70% of the population may harbor circulating microfilariae.[1] Vectors include biting midges and black flies of the genus Simulium.[2] Adult worms locate to the visceral adipose tissue, the peritoneal or thoracic cavities, or even the lymphatics. Microfilariae are non-periodic and possess a characteristic sharp tail. They can be found circulating in the blood stream. This infection may produce allergic-type symptoms such as urticaria and lymphadenopathy, although it usually results in asymptomatic eosinophilia. The infection has been implicated as a possible cause of chronic arthritis. Diagnosis depends upon finding the microfilariae on a stained blood smear, or by the Knott technique. Based on a single case report, ivermectin may be the treatment of choice for *M. ozzardi* infection. This agent was shown to reduce the number of circulating microfilariae and reduced symptoms in a patient.[3] Neither diethylcarbamazine or benzimidazole anthelminthics are effective against *M. ozzardi*.

Mansonella perstans
(Manson 1891)

Mansonella perstans is a filarial parasite found in Africa, and in northeastern South America and parts of the Caribbean. It is transmitted from person to person by biting midges. In Africa, gorillas and chimpanzees may be significant animal reservoirs. The adults live free in serous cavities such as the pleural, pericardial, or peritoneal cavities, where they produce microfilariae that circulate in the blood stream. *M. perstans* infection is usually asymptomatic, but it is known to cause painless nodules in the conjunctiva with swelling of the eyelids in Africa, where it is known as the Ugandan eye worm or Kampala eye worm.[4] The organism may also result in symptoms that are similar to *Loa*

loa infection, such as angioedemia and Calabar swellings. Microfilariae of *M. perstans* are often observed in peripheral blood, and can be demonstrated by examination of a stained blood smear or by the Knott test. There is no clear cut drug of choice for *M. ozzardi* infection. There is no consensus on the efficacy of benzimidazole anthelminthics. A 30 day course of mebendazole has been reported to be efficacious in a case report,[5] whereas treatment failures have been reported for albendazole,[6] although the Medical Letter also recommends a 10 day course of albendazole (400 mg b.i.d.) Similarly, Ivermectin at a dose of 200 micrograms/kg may be effective,[6] but was reported to fail in some patients.[7] Diethylcarbamazine is probably not effective. Co-infections with M. perstans do not appear to significantly alter post-treatment reaction profiles to single-dose ivermectin/albendazole for patients with lymphatic filariasis.[8]

Mansonella streptocerca
(Macfie and Corson 1922)

Mansonella streptocerca is filarial parasite with a distribution restricted to tropical rainforests in Central Africa. Adult worms locate to the subcutaneous tissues, as do microfilariae. The infection is transmitted by midges. The major clinical manifestation of this infection is a pruritic dermatitis with hypopigmented macules that may resemble onchocerciasis. There is often an associated axillary or inguinal lymphadenopathy. Diagnosis is made by microscopically identifying microfilariae in specimens of skin or impression smears made from them. Microfilariae must be differentiated from those of *Onchocerca volvulus*, usually by attempting to identify the characteristic hook-shaped tail, which is sometimes referred to as a "shepherd's crook."[9] Diethylcarbamazine is the drug of choice, but it may exacerbate pruritus; in which case, anti-inflammatory agents and antihistamines may be necessary. Ivermectin may also be effective,[10] especially against microfilariae, but not against adult worms.

Dirofilaria immitis (Leidy 1856) and other *Dirofilaria* spp.

Dirofilaria immitis, the dog heart worm, is an accidental parasite in the lungs of humans, where it produces solitary nodules. The pulmonary lesion probably results from a dead worm being washed into the pulmonary artery from the right ventricle, followed by embolization to the lung.[11] These nodules are frequently diagnosed on chest radiographs as a "coin lesion" that mimics lung carcinoma. Therefore, the diagnosis of pulmonary dirofilariasis is usually made after recovering adult worms from the resected "tumor." A number of cases have been identified in the United States, particularly in Texas, Florida, and Louisiana.[11] Human cases of dirofilariasis usually present with a single, spherical, sub-pleural pulmonary infarct.[11] The seroprevalence in humans[12] can be estimated by immunodiagnostic tests using either excretory-secretory products[13] or somatic antigen[12] from the adult worm. Treatment is usually surgical. *Dirofilaria tenuis*, a parasite of raccoons and related *Dirofilaria spp.*, cause zoonotic subcutaneous infections in humans that result in discrete nodules.[14] The diagnosis is typically established when upon sectioning the parasite is noted to be present. Some patients have eosinophilia.

Capillaria hepatica (Bancroft 1893)

Capillaria hepatica is a parasite of rodents, particularly the rat. Adult worms live and lay eggs in the liver parenchyma within a syncytium. Eggs embryonate and are then infective for another host. Infective eggs are ingested, and hatch in the small intestine. The exact route of infection after the egg hatches is still unknown. Eventually, larvae mature to adults and reach the liver. After mating, they begin to lay eggs, thus completing the life cycle. The liver serves as the source of nourishment for adults. If enough parasites are present, the host may suffer liver failure and die. Humans rarely become infected by ingesting the eggs. Too few clinical cases of this infection have been recorded to determine what constitutes a lethal dose. There is a clinical resemblance between *C. hepatica* infection and visceral larva migrans caused by *Toxocara canis* (see Aberrant Nematode Infections). However, patients with the former frequently present with marked liver enlargement. Diagnosis requires liver biopsy. Often the disease is unsuspected and discovered only at autopsy. Occasionally, patients may be asymptomatic and pass *C. hepatica* eggs in their stools (Fig. C.55, Appendix C) because they ingested the liver of infected animals. No treatment has been developed.[19]

Capillaria philippinensis
(Chitwood, Valesquez, and Salazar 1968)

The genus Capillaria has four members capable of infecting humans: *C. philippinensis, C. hepatica, C. plica,* and *C. aerophila*.[15] Only *C. philippinensis* is a significant regional public health problem. Infection with *C. philippinensis* occurs mainly in parts of Thailand and the Philippines, where infection can lead to death.[16] Most deaths were associated with an outbreak of chronic gastroenteritis in central Luzon. Four cases have also been reported in Japan, Taiwan, and Korea and the infection has emerged recently in Egypt.[17, 18]

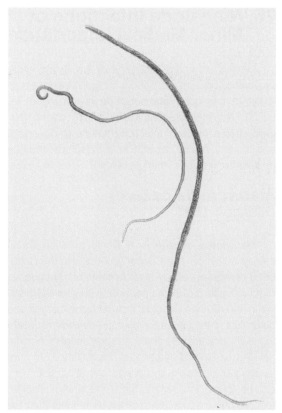

Figure 26.1 Adults of *Capillaria philippinensis*. The female is 3 mm x 45 µm, and the male is 2.5 mm x 30 µm.

Adult worms resemble those of *Trichinella spiralis* in both size (Fig. 26.1) and general biology. Like Trichinella and Trichuris, the adults have an attenuated anterior end with an esophagus surrounded by a row of secretory cells called stichocytes.[15] The worms locate to the intracellular compartment of the columnar epithelium of the small intestine, and deposit living larvae there. Larvae are infectious within the host, and in this respect its biology mimics the auto-infectious cycle of *Strongyloides stercoralis*. In contrast, there is no evidence that patients harboring *C. philippinensis* are immunosuppressed. As infection progresses, the patient first begins passing embryonated, then unembryonated eggs in the stools.

Capillaria philippinensis is most likely a parasite of waterfowl that feed on fish and crustaceans, which are the intermediate hosts for this nematode. Humans become infected by eating raw or undercooked infected fish or shrimp. In the Philippines, ingestion of "jumping salad," which consists of vegetables and a variety of live aquatic animals including shrimp, is thought to be a common source of this infection. The clinical disease consists of a rampant diarrhea[18] associated with malaise, anorexia, and vomiting. Patients frequently develop a protein-losing enteropathy and malabsorption of

Table 26.1. Nematode infections of minor importance

Parasite	Geographic distribution	Major pathologic consequences	Mode of infection	Diagnosis
Capillaria hepatica	Worldwide	Necrotic lesions in liver	Oral route	Biopsy
Capillaria philippinensis[a]	Philippines	Malabsorption syndrome, diarrhea	Oral route	Stool examination for larvae and eggs
Dioctophyma renale	North and South America, China	Complete destruction of kidneys	Oral route	Urine examination for eggs
Mansonella perstans[a]	Central and South America, Africa	None	Bite of infected midge	Blood smear or Knott test for microfilariae
Mansonella streptocerca[a]	Africa	Pruritic dermatitis	Bite of infected midge	Impression smear of skin snip for microfilariae
Mansonella ozzardi[a]	Central and South America, Caribbean	Chronic arthritis	Bite of infected midge	Blood smear or Knott test for microfilariae
Oesophagostomum bifurcum	West Africa	Intestinal nodules	Oral route	Stool examination for eggs
Syngamus laryngeus	South America, Caribbean, Philippines	Asthma, hemoptysis	Unknown	Sputum or stool examination for eggs
Ternidens diminutus	Africa	Iron-deficiency anemia	Unknown	Stool examination for eggs
Trichostrongylus spp.	Worldwide	Anemia	Oral route	Stool examination for eggs

[a] Discussed in the text.

fats and carbohydrates, which, in turn, leads to a wasting syndrome. Patients who are ill for more than several months without treatment develop profound electrolyte imbalance.[15] Death results from cachexia, heart failure, and secondary bacterial infections. The mortality rate approaches 10% in some endemic areas. Numerous *C. philippinensis* worms can be identified at all stages in the lumen, and in the intestinal mucosa at autopsy. As many as 200,000 worms have been recovered in 1 liter of bowel fluid,[15] a consequence of auto-infection.

Diagnosis depends upon finding eggs or larvae in feces. They are usually present in patients presenting with abdominal pain, diarrhea, and weight loss.[15] Eggs bear some resemblance to those of *Trichuris trichiura* (Fig. C.58, Appendix C).

Mebendazole or albendazole are the treatments of choice for intestinal Capillariasis.[15] Albendazole is preferable, as the drug appears to act on larvae as well as adult worms, and relapses have not yet been reported.[16, 17] Because of the risk of auto-infection, all infected patients should be treated.

During the epidemic in central Luzon, the lagoons were contaminated with bed sheets soiled with feces from infected patients.[15] This situation helped to propagate the life cycle in fish and other intermediate hosts. Avoidance of raw or undercooked fish and crustaceans is recommended to prevent infection. Cultural eating habits are, however, extremely difficult to change.

Oesophagostomum bifurcum (Creplin 1849)

Oesophagostomum bifurcum is a nematode infecting non-human primates in Africa and Asia. In northern Togo and northeastern Ghana,[20] *O. bifurcum* affects up to 30% of these human population, with an estimated 250,000 cases.[21, 22] Sporadic cases have been described in other parts of Africa, Asia and South America.[22] In these regions, adults aged 30-40 years have the highest prevalence. These nematodes are often called nodular worms because they cause nodule formation on the wall of the intestine. Adult worms produce about 5,000 eggs per day, which pass with feces and mature to infective larvae in soil.[23] Eggs morphologically resemble those of hookworms. Humans are infected when they ingest infective larvae, which then develop to adults while encased in intestinal nodules approximately 4-5 mm in diameter. Some patients develop multinodular disease, while, in others, a single nodular mass develops.[21] The nodules in male patients are larger than the ones in females.[21] The nodular disease of Oesophagostomum infection often presents as an abdominal mass, which can be painful and mimic a surgical abdomen. Often the mass is asymptomatic. As a result, the infection is frequently diagnosed at biopsy, although ultrasound is also of great value.[24] However, fecal examination is the diagnostic method of choice. Pyrantel pamoate is the recommended drug for treating infections due to *O. bifurcum*,[18] but albendazole is also effective.[25] Surgical resection of the nodule is sometimes necessary.

Ternidens diminutus

Ternidens diminutus is a minor nematode infection of humans that resembles *O. bifurcum*. Ternidens eggs resemble hookworm eggs, so that *T. diminutus*

is sometimes referred to as "the false hookworm."[26] It is primarily a parasite of non-human primates but has been demonstrated to cause zoonosis in Zambia and Zimbabwe. In humans, *T. diminutus* can result in colonic ulcerations and nodular lesions, but there are usually few symptoms. Both pyrantel pamoate and thiabendazole have been used to treat patients, although other benzimidazoles may also be effective.[26, 27]

References

1. Marinkelelle CJ. German E. Mansonelliasis in the Comiasria del Vaupes of Colombia. Trop Geogr Med 22:101. 1970.
2. Nathan MB. Tikasingh ES. Munroe P. *Filariasis* in Amerindians of western Guyana with observations on transmission of *Mansonella ozzardi* by Simulium species of the amazonia group. Trop Med Parasitol. 33(4):219-22. 1982.
3. Nutman TB. Nash TE. Ottesen EA. Ivermectin in the successful treatment of a patient with *Mansonella ozzardi* infection. J Infect Dis 156:662. 1997.
4. Baird JK. Neafie RC. Connor DH. Nodules in the conjunctiva, bung-eye, and bulge-eye in Africa caused by *Mansonella perstans*. Am J Trop med Hyg 38:553-557. 1988.
5. Wahlgren M. Frolov I. Treatment of *Dipetalonema perstans* infections with mebendazole. Trans Roy Soc Trop Med Hyg 77:422-423. 1983.
6. Gardon J. Kamgno J. et al. Efficacy of repeated doses of ivermectin against *Mansonella perstans*. Trans R Soc Trop Med Hyg 96: 325-6. 2002.
7. Van den Enden E. Van Gompel A. et al. Mansonella pertsans filariasis: failure of albendazole treatment. Ann Soc Belg Med Triop 72:2115. 1992.
8. Keiser PB. Coulibaly YI. et al. Clinical characteristics of post-treatment reactions to ivermectin/albendazole for *Wuchereria bancrofti* in a region co-endemic for *Mansonella perstans*. Am J Trop Med Hyg 69: 331-5. 2003.
9. Orihel TC. The tail of the *Mansonella streptocerca* microfilaria. Am J Trop Med Hyg 33: 1278. 1978.
10. Fischer P. Tukesiga E. Buttner DW. Long-term suppression of *Mansonella streptocerca* microfilariae after treatment with ivermectin. J Infect Dis 180: 1403-5. 1999.
11. Asimacopoulos PJ. Katras A. Christie B. Pulmonary diofilariasis: the largest single hospital experience. Chest 102:851-855. 1992.
12. Muro Alvarez A. Cordero Sanchez M. et al. Seroepidimiological studies on human pulmonary dirofilariasis in Spain. Ann Trop med Parasitol 84:209-213. 1990.
13. Akao N. Kondo K. Fujita K. Immunoblot analysis of *Dirofilaria immitis* recognized by infected humans. Ann Trop Med Parasitol 85:455-460. 1991.
14. Orihel TC. Helentjaris D. Alger J. Subcutaneous dirofilariasis: Single inoculum, multiple worms. Am J Trop Med Hyfg. 56:45. 1997.
15. Cross J. Intestinal capillariasis. Clin Microbiol Rev. 5:120-129. 1992.
16. el-Karaksy H, el-Shabrawi M. et al. *Capillaria philippinensis*: a cause of fatal diarrhea in one of two infected Egyptian sisters. J Trop Pediatr 50: 57-60. 2004.
17. Bair MJ. Hwang KP. et. al. Clinical features of human intestinal capillariasis in Taiwan. World J Gastroenterol 10: 2391-3. 2004.
18. Watten Rh. Beckner WM. et al. Clinical studies of *Capillaria philippinensis*. Trans Roy Soc Trop Med Hyg 66:828-832, 1970.
19. McQuown AL. Capillaria hepatica: repoted genuine and spurious cases. Am J Trop Med Hyg 30:761-767, 1950.
20. Polderman AM. Kepel HP. et al. Oesophagostomiasis, a common infection of man in northern Togo and Ghana. Am J Trop Med Hyg 44:336-344. 1991.
21. Storey PA. Seenhard NR. et al. Natural progression of *Oesophagostomum bifurcum* pathology and infection in a rural community of northern Ghana. Trans R Soc Trop Med Hyg 95: 295-9. 2001.
22. Bogers JJ. Storey PA. et al. Human oesophagostomiasis: a histomorphometric study of 13 new cases in northern Ghana. Virchows Arch 439: 21-6. 2001.
23. Kepel HP. Polderman AM. Egg production of *Oesophagostomum bifurcum*, a locally common parasite of humans in Togo. Am J Trop Med Hyg 46:469-472. 1992.
24. Storey PA, Spannbrucker A. et al. Intraobserver and interobserver variation of ultrasound diagnosis of *Oesophagostomum bifurcum* colon lesions. Am J Trop Med Hyg 67: 680-3. 2002.
25. Ziem JB, Kettenis IM. et al. The short-term impact of albendazole treatment on *Oesophagostomum bifurcum* and hookworm infections in northern Ghana. Ann Trop Med Parasitol 98: 385-90. 2004.
26. Bradley M. Rate of expulsion of *Necator americanus* and the false hookworm *Ternidens diminutus* Ralliet and Henry 1909 (Nematoda) from humans following albendazole treatment. Trans R Soc Trop Med Hyg 84: 720. 1990.
27. Goldsmid JM. Saunders CR. preliminary trial using pyrantel pamoate for the treatment of human infections with *Ternidens diminutus*. Trans Roy Soc trop Med Hyg 66:375. 1972.

27. Aberrant Nematode Infections

Many nematodes are zoonotic and only occasionally infect humans. These nematodes are incapable of maturing to adult parasites in the human body. Cutaneous larva migrans (CLM) and visceral larva migrans (VLM) are two diseases caused by this type of parasite. The parasites causing CLM and VLM and the clinical manifestations of these diseases are listed in Tables 27.1 and 27.2. Although the number of nematode species resulting in aberrant infections is large, this chapter emphasizes only the most important ones, as defined by the seriousness of the diseases they induce.

Cutaneous Larva Migrans (CLM)

CLM (Table 27.1) has a worldwide distribution. It is caused by larvae of the dog and cat hookworms *Ancylostoma braziliense*, and *Uncinaria stenocephala* completing their life cycle in animal hosts, similar to the way human hookworms behave. Zoonotic transmission from the dog hookworm *Ancylostoma caninum* also occurs in humans, but disease from this parasite usually causes eosinophilic enteritis rather than CLM (see The Hookworms). Other less common nematodes may also be responsible for CLM, including a raccoon-transmitted *Strongyloides procyonis* that results in "duck hunter's itch." The filariform larvae (Fig. 27.1) of *A. braziliense* survive in sandy, moist soils for several days. These larvae are especially common on beaches in Southeast Asia, the Caribbean, and Puerto Rico, where dogs and cats are permitted to defecate. In the U.S., CLM occurs along the Gulf Coast and the Atlantic coasts of Florida and the Carolinas. In the human host, infection begins when the filariform larvae penetrate unbroken skin but fail to receive the proper environmental cues. Instead of going further in the life cycle, they then migrate laterally in the deeper layers of the epidermis (Fig. 27.2).[1] The larvae can survive there for about 10 days before dying.

An intense inflammatory reaction, associated with itching in the affected areas, develops within days after the larvae enter the dermis, and is provoked by the secretions of the larvae, which consist of hydrolytic enzymes. The serpiginous lesions known as "creeping eruption" are evident after an incubation period of one week. Secondary bacterial infections caused by scratching are common. In a review of 44 CLM patients seen at a travelers' clinic, 39 percent of the lesions appeared on the feet, 18 percent on the buttocks, 16 percent on the abdomen, and the remainder on the lower legs, arms, and face.[2] Some patients with CLM manifest esinophilia or elevated IgE, but laboratory findings generally play little or no role in establishing a diagnosis of CLM. The treatment of choice for CLM is oral albendazole (400 mg daily x 3d) or ivermectin (200 µg/kg x 1-2d). Thiabendazole applied topically to the affected areas can also kill the larvae.[3]

Visceral Larva Migrans (VLM)

Toxocara canis (Johnston 1916)
Toxocara cati (Brumpt 1927)

Visceral larva migrans (VLM) and ocular larva migrans (OLM) are typically caused by *Toxocara canis* and *T. cati*. Aberrant migration of larvae through the viscera (Table 27.2) results in a far more serious condition than cutaneous larva migrans. Human infection with *Toxocara spp.* was first described by Wilder in 1950,[4] who discovered a larva within a retinal granuloma of a child. In 1952, Beaver and colleagues[5] reported on a series of children who had a high circulating eosinophilia, and suffered severe multisystem disease cause by *T. canis* and *T. cati* larvae. Both *T. canis* and *T. cati* have a life cycle in their respective hosts resembling that of Ascaris in humans. Toxocara adults (Fig. 27.3) are smaller than those of Ascaris, but are similar to them regarding nutritional requirements and physiologic behavior. The clinical and epidemiological aspects of VLM and OLM have been reviewed.[6] In humans, infection begins when they ingest the embryonated eggs of Toxocara (Fig. 27.4). This commonly occurs where children are playing on sandboxes and in playgrounds contaminated with Toxocara eggs. Pathology results when larvae hatch and migrate through the body, invading all organs. There is controversy as to whether these are second- or third-stage larvae. The degree of host damage varies with the tissues invaded; the liver, lungs, and central nervous system (CNS - Fig. 27.5), including the eyes, are the organ systems most seriously affected. Ultimately, the larvae die, followed by marked delayed-type and immediate-type hypersensitivity responses. These inflammatory responses manifest as eosinophilic granulomas. The immediate hypersensitivity responses to dead and dying larvae in the viscera, including the lungs, liver, and brain, result in VLM. In the eye, the larvae causing OLM can affect the retina, where the larval tracks and granulomas are sometimes mistaken for retinoblastoma (Fig. 27.6.). As a result of this similarity, unnecessary enucleation has been carried out in some cases. In many cases, the granuloma itself was responsible for the loss of sight.

Epidemiologic evidence suggests that ocular disease tends to occur in the absence of systemic involvement and vice versa, which has led to the proposal that the two manifestations of this infection be reclassified as ocular larva migrans and visceral larva migrans.[7] Thus, there may be strains of *T. canis* with specific tropisms. Alternatively, VLM may reflect the consequences of a host inflammatory response to repeated waves of migrating larvae through the viscera, whereas ocular larva migrans occurs in individuals who have not been previously sensitized.[6]

Visceral larva migrans (VLM) is mainly a disease of young children (<5 years of age).[8, 9] It presents with fever, enlargement of the liver and spleen, lower respiratory symptoms (particular bronchospasm, resembling asthma), eosinophilia sometimes approaching 70%, and hypergammaglobulinemia of immunoglobulin M (IgM) and IgG classes. Myocarditis, nephritis, and involvement of the CNS have been described. CNS involvement can lead to seizures, neuropsychiatric symptoms, or an encephalopathy. *T. canis* can also be associated with a eosinophilic meningoencephalitis.[10] There has been an increasing appreciation that more subtle clinical manifestations might also arise as a result of larval migrations. So-called "covert toxocariasis" ranges in spectrum from asymptomatic infection to larvae migrating in specific target organs.[11-13] In the lungs, larval migrations may result in asthma;[14,15] indeed, *T. canis* has been suggested as an environmental risk factor for asthma among some inner-city populations.[16] Similarly, in the brain, *T. canis* has been implicated as one of the causes of so-called "idiopathic" seizure disorders,[17] has been found to be significantly higher in children with mental retardation, including non-institutionalized children.[18] Toxocariasis has also been linked to functional intestinal disorders, arthritis and skin rashes.[13, 14, 20] It is apparent that the full clinical spectrum of disease of covert toxocariasis has yet to be explored.

Ocular larva migrans (OLM) usually occurs in older children (5-10 years old), and typically presents as unilateral vision impairment that is sometimes accompa-

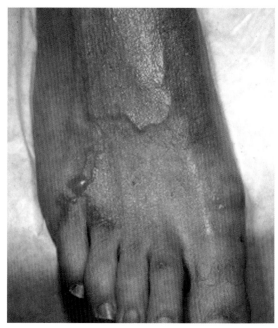

Figure 27.2. "Creeping eruption" on the foot of a patient who stepped on an infective larva of *A. braziense*. Courtesy G. Zalar.

nied by strabismus.[19] In temperate climates, such as in the UK, it is estimated that the prevalence of OLM may be as high as 9.7 cases per 100,000 persons.[21] The most serious consequence of the infection is invasion of the retina, leading to granuloma formation, which occurs typically peripherally or in the posterior pole. These granulomas drag the retina and create a distortion, heteropia, or detachment of the macula.[22] The degree of visual acuity impairment depends upon the specific area involved, and blindness is common. Ocular larva migrans can also cause diffuse endophthalmitis or papillitis; secondary glaucoma can follow.

Any pediatric aged patient with an unexplained febrile illness and eosinophilia should be suspected of having VLM. Hepatosplenomegaly and evidence of multisystem disease and history of pica make the diagnosis of VLM more likely. Similarly, OLM should be suspected in any child with unilateral vision loss and strabismus. Diagnostic tests for VLM are primarily immunological.[23] The precipitin test is subject to cross-reactions with common antigens of the larvae and blood group substance A. The enzyme-linked immunosorbent assay (ELISA) test, which employs antigens secreted by the second-stage larva, has sufficient specificity to be the best indirect test for diagnosing this infection. The ELISA has a high degree of sensitivity (approximately 78%) and specificity (approximately 92%) at a titer greater than 1:32. One of the major *T. canis* antigens, TES-120, has been cloned and

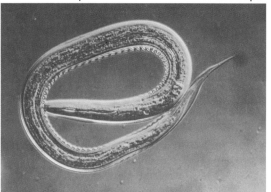

Figure 27.1. Third stage larva of *Ancylostoma braziliense*. Photo E. Gravé

Table 27.1. Cutaneous larva migrans: clinical manifestations

Organism	Predominant location in body	Major pathologic consequences	Diagnosis
Ancylostoma braziliense	Skin	Urticaria, serpiginous lesion	Biopsy
Uncinaria stenocephala	Skin	Urticaria, serpiginous lesion	Biopsy
Strongyloides procyonis	"Duck-hunter's itch"	Urticaria	Biopsy
Dirofilaria conjunctivae	Palpebral conjunctivae,	Abscess formation subcutaneous tissues	Biopsy
Dirofilaria repens	Subcutaneous tissues	Fibrotic, painless nodule formation	Biopsy
Anatrichosoma cutaneum	Subcutaneous tissues	Serpiginous lesions	Biopsy
Rhabditis niellyi	Skin	Papule, urticaria	Biopsy
Lagochilascaris minor	Subcutaneous tissues around head and neck	Abscess formation	
Gnathostoma spinigerum	Subcutaneous tissues	Abscess formation	Biopsy, ELISA
Thelazia callipaeda	Conjunctival sac, corneal conjunctiva	Paralysis of lower eyelid muscles, ectropion, fibrotic scarring	Ophthalmoscopic examination of conjunctiva

ELISA: enzyme-linked immunosorbent assay.

Table 27.2. Visceral larva migrans: clinical manifestations

Organism	Predominant location in body	Major pathologic consequences	Diagnosis
Toxocara cati	Viscera, eye	Blindness	ELISA or RIA
Toxocara canis	Viscera, eye	Blindness	ELISA or RIA
Baylisascaris procyonis	Meninges	Meningoencephalitis	CSF examination
Angiostrongylus cantonensis	Meninges	Meningoencephalitis	CSF examination
Angiostrongylus costaricensis	Mesenteric arterioles	Peritonitis	Biopsy
Anisakis spp.	Stomach wall	Granuloma	Biopsy
Phocanema spp.	Stomach wall	Granuloma	Biopsy
Terranova spp.	Stomach wall	Granuloma	Biopsy
Oesophagostonum stephanostomum var. thomasi	Small and large intestinal wall	Granuloma	Biopsy
Gnathostoma spinigerum	Striated muscles, subcutaneous tissues, brain, small intestinal wall	Abscess, meningoencephalitis	Biopsy, ELISA
Dirofilaria immitis	Lung, heart	Granuloma in lung	Biopsy

ELISA: enzyme-linked immunosorbent assay; RIA: radioimmunoassay; CSF: cerebrospinal fluid

expressed in yeast,[24] and shows promise for use in a standardized serodiagnostic assay.

Other indicators include hypergammaglobulinemia and an elevated isohemoagglutin titer. Thus, a constellation of clinical disease described above, a history of pica, eosinophilia, and positive serology strongly point to the diagnosis. Liver biopsy may reveal a granuloma surrounding a larva, but a successful diagnosis using this approach is fortuitous at best and thus not recommended. Ocular larva migrans is diagnosed primarily on the basis of clinical criteria during an ophthalmologic examination. The immunodiagnostic tests used for VLM are not as reliable for OLM. In one study, only 45% of patients with clinically diagnosed OLM had titers higher than 1:32.[25]

Albendazole is the treatment of choice for toxocariasis. Patients receiving a 5-day treatment course of albendazole (10 mg/kg/day in two divided doses) improved relative to patients who received treatment with the older anthelminthic drug thiabendazole.[26] The Medical Letter has also suggested a dose of 400 mg of albendazole b.i.d. for 5 days.[20] Because the other commonly used benzimidazole, mebendazole, is poorly absorbed outside the gastrointestinal tract, this agent is a second line treatment, although some success has been reported in patients who ingest 1 g or more of this agent for a 21 day course.[27] Symptomatic treatment, including administration of corticosteroids, has

Toxocara canis and Toxocara cati

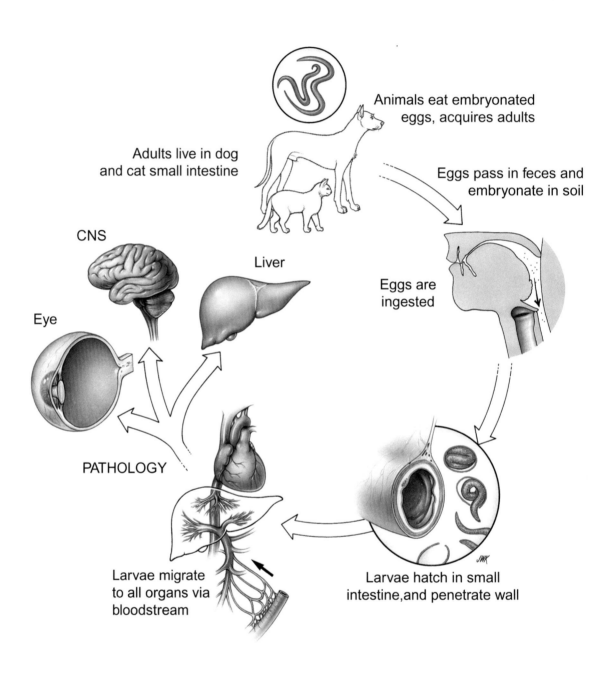

Animals eat embryonated eggs, acquires adults

Adults live in dog and cat small intestine

Eggs pass in feces and embryonate in soil

CNS

Liver

Eye

Eggs are ingested

PATHOLOGY

Larvae migrate to all organs via bloodstream

Larvae hatch in small intestine, and penetrate wall

been helpful for suppressing intense manifestations of the infection. OLM is treated either by surgery (vitrectomy), anthelminthic chemotherapy, and/or corticosteroids.[28, 29]

The Toxocara group of parasites is common in young pets. For example, young puppies often harbor these worms since the infection can be transplacentally acquired. Having a litter of puppies in the home has been identified as a significant risk factor.[28] Children with pica are at risk of ingesting embryonated eggs from soil. Adult patients who have been institutionalized for mental retardation are also at risk.[29] Treatment of dogs and control of their feces are major control measures for this disease. Toxocariasis is an understudied and underreported disease. Through scattered serological surveys, there is increasing evidence that it is one of the most common helminthic diseases in temperate climates of North America and Europe, including some large inner-city urban areas, as well as in Brazil and elsewhere.[30, 31, 32]

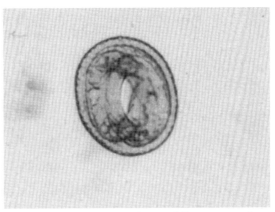

Figure 27.4. Embryonated egg of *Toxocara canis*.

Baylisascaris procyonis
(Sprent, 1968)

Baylisascaris procyonis, the raccoon ascarid, causes visceral larva migrans and neural larva migrans in humans when they accidentally ingest embryonated eggs that are shed in sylvatic environs, as well as suburban dwellings accessible to racoons such as attics and gutters of houses.[23,–25] Although it is rare, the pathological consequences of infection with the larva of *B. procyonis* is generally more severe than that caused by *T. canis*. Neural larva migrans can result in neurodevastation, even with anthelminthic chemotherapy and steroids.[33] The large, developing larvae (up to 2 mm.) cause considerable mechanical damage.[33] Larvae migrating brain tissues result in eosinophilic meningitis associated with high mortality (Fig. 27.7). Neural larva migrans is associated with ocular disease characterized by retinitis and multiple choroidal infiltrates.[36] Since antibodies to *B. procyonis* antigens do not cross-react with *T. canis*, the excretory and secretory products of *B. procyonis* have been examined as a possible species-specific immunodiagnostic reagent.[37] Most human cases have been diagnosed at autopsy, and there are but a few cases diagnosed to date, so there is little overall experience with anthelminthic therapy for baylisascariasis, although it appears that neural larva migrans can progress to neurodevastation even with appropriate anthelminthic treatment.[34]

Angiostrongylus cantonensis
(Chen 1935)

Angiostrongylus costaricensis
(Morera and Céspedes 1971)[26]

Angiostrongylus cantonensis infection occurs in Southeast Asia, the Philippine Islands, Taiwan, and both North and South Pacific islands. Human infec-

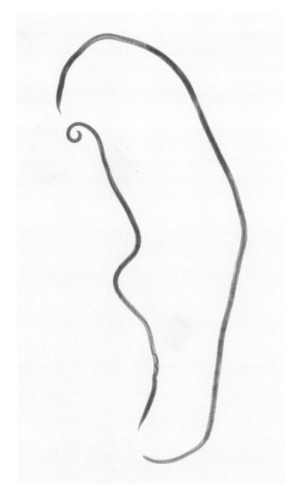

Figure 27.3. Adults of *Toxocara canis*. The female is 9 cm, the male is 6 cm.

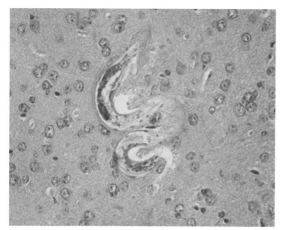

Figure 27.5. Larvae in brain of mouse experimentally infected with *T. canis*.

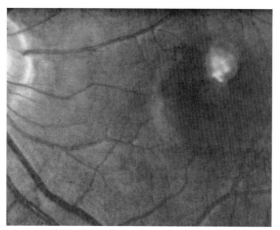

Figure 27.6. Granuloma in retina of patient with OLM. The lesion consists largely of eosinophils.

tion was first described in Taiwan when larvae of the parasite were isolated from the CSF of a child. Infected rodents, but not human cases, have also been reported from East Africa. A survey of wharf rats in New Orleans revealed a high rate of infection, although none had been detected several years prior to that study.[32]

Acquisition of human infection depends upon the locale and the nutritional habits of specific population. A case in Hawaii resulted from ingestion of a raw slug given for a traditional medicinal purpose. In Tahiti, epidemics have resulted from consumption of raw fresh water prawns (i.e., shrimp-like crustaceans), and elsewhere, other invertebrates (e.g., planarians) either consumed directly or in vegetation. Widespread education about the proper cooking of food and vegetable washing, as well as the control of mollusks and planarians in vegetable gardens, can reduce the incidence of infections.[31]

Gnathostoma spinigerum
(Owen 1838)

Gnathostoma spinigerum is parasitic in various mammals, including cats, dogs, and the mongoose; the intermediate hosts include (1) copepods in the genus Cyclops, and (2) snakes, frogs, fish, and birds. Gnathostomiasis in humans is prevalent throughout Thailand, Asia,[33] and Mexico, where infections are commonly acquired in and around Acapulco.[34]

Female adults are 25-54 mm in length, while males measure 11-25 mm. Adults live coiled in the wall of the small intestine in their definitive hosts. Eggs pass in feces and hatch in water, releasing larvae that are ingested by macroinvertebrate crustaceans. Fish, snakes, and birds eat infected crustaceans and the infective stage for humans then develops within them. Humans eat these infected vertebrates and the larvae invade and migrate into the deep tissues. Subcutaneous swellings may result. Alternatively, ocular larva migrans, or even eosinophilic meningitis, may develop. The disease is typically self-limited. Surgical removal or a 21-day course of albendazole (400 mg po qD) is an effective regimen for treatment of gnathostomiasis.[33]

Anisakiasis and Related Illnesses

Anisakiasis in humans is caused by a number of species of nematodes belonging to the genera *Anisakis*, *Phocanema*, *Terranova*, and *Contracoecum*. They infect sea mammals, particularly dolphins, whales, sea lions, and seals.[35] In these hosts, adults

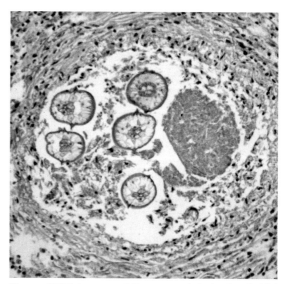

Figure 27.7. Larvae of *B. procyonis* in brain of child who died of VLM.

live in the lumen of the intestinal tract. Anasakid first-stage larvae infect a number of crustacean species. Second, third, or fourth-stage larvae infect a wide variety of bottom-feeding fish species.

Raw or undercooked saltwater fish, often in the form of sushi or sashimi, has become a popular style of cuisine throughout the world.[36, 37] When an infected piece of raw fish is eaten, the parasites in the muscle tissue are released by the enzymes in the stomach, or more rarely, into the small intestine. Tissue invasion is facilitated by release of parasite hydrolytic enzymes.[38] All species of anasakid worms die within a few days in humans. Dead parasites provoke an eosinophilic granulomatous infiltration. Initially, infection may be asymptomatic, but soon thereafter vague upper abdominal pain may develop. Symptoms may mimic gastric ulcer.[39] Radiographic evidence of infection resembles that of a tumor, which may lead to misdiagnosis as carcinoma of the stomach. Definitive diagnosis and treatment is made by endoscopic removal of the parasite. Serological tests using an Anisakis-specific monoclonal antibody is available in some countries.[40] Thorough cooking or freezing of seafood items prior to ingestion can prevent infection by anisakid nematodes. Most sushi restaurants in the United States and elsewhere now carefully inspect pieces of raw fish prior to serving them. The incidence of anasakid VLM in Europe and North America due to the consumption of raw fish has been reduced to a few sporadic cases annually in recent years.

References

1. Sulica VI. Berberian B. Kao GF. Histopathologic findings of cutaneous larva migrans. J Cutan Pathol 15:346, 1988.
2. Blackwell V. Vega-Lopez F. Cutaneous larva migrans: clinical features and management of 44 cases presenting in the returning traveler. Br J Dermatol 145: 434-7. 2001.
3. Albanese G. Venturi C. Albendazole: a new drug for human parasitoses. Dermatol Clin 21: 283-90. 2003.
4. Wilder HC. Nematode endophthalmitis. Trans Am Acad Ophthalmol Otolaryngol 55:99-104. 1950.
5. Beaver PC. Snyde CH. et al. Chronic eosinophilia due to visceral larva migrans. Pediatrics 9:7-19. 1952.
6. Despommier D. Toxocariasis: clinical aspects, epidemiology, medical ecology, and molecular aspects. Clin Microbiol Rev 16: 265-72. 2003.
7. Glickman LI. Schantz PM. Epidemiology and pathogenesis of zoonotic toxocariasis. Epidemiol Rev 10:143-148, 1982.
8. Kazacos KR. Visceral and ocular larva migrans. Semin Vet Med Surg (Small Anim) 6:227-235, 1991.
9. Worley G. Green IA. Frothingham TE. et al. *Toxocara canis* infection: clinical and epidemiological associations with seropositivity in kindergarten children. J Infect Dis 149:591-597, 1984.
10. Xinou E. Lefkopoulos A. et al. CT and MR imaging findings in cerebral toxocaral disease. AJNR Am J Neruroradiol 24: 714-8. 2003.
11. Taylor MR. Keane CT. O'Connor P. et al. The expanded spectrum of toxocaral disease. Lancet 1:692-694 1988.
12. Nathwani D. Laing RB. Currie PF. Covert toxocariasis – a cause of recurrent abdominal pain in childhood. Br J Clin Pract 46:271, 1992.
13. Sharghi N. Schantz P. Hotez PJ. Toxocariasis: An occult cause of childhood asthma, seizures, and neuropsychological deficit? Sem Pediatr Infect Dis 11:257-60. 2000.
14. Buijs J. Borsboom G. et al. Toxocara seroprevalence in 5-year old elementary schoolchildren: relation with allergic asthma. Am J Epidemiol 140:839-847. 1994.
15. Tariq SM. Matthews S. et al. Epidemiology of allergic disorders in early childhood. Ped Pulmonol - Suppl. 16:69. 1997.
16. Sharghi N. Schantz PM. et al. Environmental exposure to Toxocara as a possible risk factor for asthma: a clinic based case-control study. Clin Infect Dis 32: E111-6. 2001.
17. Critchley EM. Vakil SD. et al. Toxoplasma, Toxocara, and epilepsy. Epilepsia 23: 315-323. 1982.
18. Kaplan M, Kalkan A. et al. The frequency of Toxocara infection in mental retarded children. Mem Inst Oswaldo Cruz 99: 121-5. 2004.
19. Konate A. Duhamel O. et al. Toxocariasis and functional intestinal disorders. Presentation of 4 cases. Gastroenterol Clin Biol 20:909-911. 1996.
20. Dinning WJ. Gillespie SH. Cooling RI. Maizels RM. Toxocariasis: a practical approach to management of ocular disease. Eye 2:580-582, 1988.
21. Good B, Olland CV. et al. Ocular toxocariasis in schoolchildren. Clin Infect Dis 39: 173-8. 2004.
22. Small KW. McCuen BW. De Juan E. Machemer R. Surgical managment of retinal retraction caused by toxocariasis. Am I Ophthalmol 108:10-14.1989.
23. Schantz PM. Toxocara larva migrans now. Am J Trop Med Hyg 41(Suppl):21-34. 1989.
24. Fong MY. Lau YL. Recombinant expression of the larval excretory-secretory antigen TES-120 of *Toxocara canis* in the methylotrophic yeast Pichia pastoris. Parasitol Res 92: 173-6. 2003.
25. Schantz PM. Meyer D. Glickman LT. Clinical, serologic, and epidemiologic characteristics of ocular toxocariasis. Am J Trop Med Hyg 28: 24-28. 1979.
26. Sturchler D. Schubarth P. et al. Thiabendazole v. albendazole in treatment of toxocariasis: a clinical trial. Ann Trop Med Parasitol 83:473-478. 1989.
27. Hotez PJ. *Toxocara canis*. In: Gellis & Kagan's Current Pediat-ric Therapy, 15th ed. (Burg FD, Wald ER, Ingelfinger JR, Polin PA, eds.). WB Saunders, Pubs. Philadelphia. 1995.
28. Marmor M. Glickman L. et al. *Toxocara canis* infection of children: epidemiologic and neuropsychologic findings. Am I Public Health

77:554-559. 1987.

29. Hummer D. Symon K. et al. Seroepidemiologic study of toxocariasis and strongyloidiasis in institutionalized mentally retarded adults. Am J Trop Med Hyg 46: 278-281. 1992.

30. Gauthier JL. Gupta A. Hotez P. Stealth parasites: the under appreciated burden of parasitic zoonoses in North America. In: North American Parasitic Zoonoses (eds. Richardson DJ, Krause PJ), Kluwer Academic Publishers, Boston/Dordrecht/London, pp. 1-21. 2001.

31. Hotez PJ. Reducing the global burden of human parasitic diseases. Comp Parasitol 69: 140-45. 2002.

32. Anaruma Filho F. Chieffi PP. et al. Human toxocariasis: incidence among residents in the outskirts of Campinas, State of Sao Paulo, Brazil. Rev Inst Med Trop Sao Paulo 45: 293-4. 2003.

33. Kazacos KR. Boyce WM. Baylisascaris larva migrans. J Am VeMed Assoc 195: 894-903, 1990.

34. Gavin PJ. Kazacos KR. et al. Neural larva migrans caused by the raccoon roundworm *Baylisascaris procyonis*. Pediatr Infect Dis J 21: 971-5. 2002.

35. Sorvillo F. Ash LR. Berlin OG. Morse SA. *Baylisascaris procyonis*: an emerging helminthic zoonosis. Emerg Infect Dis 8: 355-9. 2002.

36. Mets MB, Noble AG. et al. Eye findings of diffuse unilateral subacute neurotetinitis and multiple choroidal infilatrates associated with neural larva migrans due to *Baylisascaris procyonis*. Am J Ophthalmol 135: 888-90. 2003.

37. Boyce WM. Asai DI. Wilder JK. Kazacos KR. Physiochemical characterization and monoclonal and polyclonal antibody recognition of *Baylisascaris procyonis* larval excretory-secretory antigens. J Parasitol 75:540-548. 1989.

38. Lo Re V 3rd. Gluckman SJ. Eosinophilic meningitis. Am J Med 114: 217-23. 2003.

39. Morera P. Life history and redescription of *Angiostrongylus costaricensis* (Morera and Cespedes, 1971). Am J Trop Med Hyg 22: 613-621.1973.

40. Kim DY. Stewart TB. Bauer RW. Mitchell M. Parastrongylus (=Angiostrongylus) cantonensis now endemic in Louisiana wildlife. J Parasitol 88: 1024-6. 2002.

41. Cross IH (ed). Studies on angiostrongyliasis in eastern Asia and Australia. Namru-2-Sp 44:1-164. 1979.

42. Hulbert TV. Larsen RA. Chandrasoma PT. Abdominal angiostrongyliasis mimicking acute appendicitis and Meckel's diverticulum: report of a case in the United States and review. Clin Infect Dis 14: 836-840. 1992.

43. Tsai HC. Liu YC. et al. Eosinophilic meningitis caused by *Angiostrongylus cantonensis*: report of 17 cases. Am J Med 111: 109-14. 2001.

44. Slom TJ, Cortese MM. et al. An outbreak of eosinophilic meningitis caused by *Angiostrongylus cantonensis* in travelers returning from the Caribbbean. N Engl J Med 346: 668-75. 2002.

45. Jin E, Ma D. et al. MRI findings of eosinophilic myelomeningoencephalitis due to *Angiostrongylus cantonensis*. Clin Radiol 60: 242-50. 2005.

46. Tsai HC, Liu YC. et al. Eosinophilic meningitis caused by *Angiostrongylus cantonensis* associated with eating raw snails: correlation of brain magnetic resonance imaging scans with clinical findings. Am J Trop Med Hyg 68: 281-5. 2003.

47. Shih S-L. Hsu C-H. et al. *Angiostrongylus cantonensis* infection in infants and young children. Pediatr Infect Dis J 11:1064-1066. 1992.

48. Koo I. Pien F. Kliks MM. Angiostrongylus (Parastrongylus) eosinophilic meningitis. Rev Infect Dis 10:1155-1162. 1988.

49. Fan CK. Su KE. Cross-reactions with *Ascaris suum* antigens of sera from mice infected with A. suum, *Toxocara canis*, and *Angiostrongylus cantonensis*. Parasitol Int. 53:263-71. 2004.

50. Alto W. Human infections with *Angiostrongylus cantonensis*. Pac Health Dialog. 8:176-82. 2001.

51. Campbel BG. Little MD. The finding of *Angiostrongylus cantonensis* in rats in New Orleans. Am J Trop Med Hyg 38: 568-573. 1988.

52. Kraivichian P. Kulkumthorn M. et al. Albendazole for the treatment of human gnathostomiasis. Trans R Soc Trop Med Hyg 86: 418-421. 1992.

53. Diaz Camacho SP Zazueta Ramos M. et al. Clinical manifestations and immunodiagnosis of gnathostomiasis in Culiacan, Mexico. Am J Trop Med Hyg. 59:908-15. 1998.

54. Menard A, Dos Santos G. et al. Imported cutaneous gnathostomiasis: report of five cases. Trans R Soc Trop Med Hyg 97: 200-2. 2003.

55. Jackson GJ. The "new disease" status of human anisakiasis and North American cases: a review. J Milk Food Technol 38: 769-773. 1975.

56. Schantz PM. The dangers of eating raw fish. N Engl J Med 320: 1143-1145. 1989.

57. Mckerrow IH. Sakanani IA. Deardorif TL. Revenge of the "sushi parasite." N Engl J Med 319: 1228-1229. 1988.

58. Sakanari IA. Mckerrow IH. Identification of the secreted neutral proteases from *Anisakis simplex*. J Parasitol 76:625-630. 1990.

59. Wittner M. Turner IW. Jacquette G. Eustrongylidiasis-a parasitic infection acquired by eating sushi. N Engl J Med 320:1124-1126. 1989.

60. Alonso-Gomez A, Moreno-Ancillo A. et al. *Anisakis simplex* only provokes allergic symptoms when the worm parasitizes the gastrointestinal tract. Parasitol Res 93: 378-8. 2004.

61. Lopez-Saez MP, Zubeldia JM. et al. Is *Anisakis simplex* responsible for chronic urticaria? Alllergy Asthma Proc 24: 339-45. 2003.

62. Arlian LG, Morgan MS. et al. Characterization of allergens of *Anisakis simplex*. Allergy 58: 1299-303. 2003.

63. Yagihashi A. Sato N. et al. A serodiagnostic assay by microenzyme-linked immunosorbent assay for human anisakiasis using a monoclonal antibody specific for Anisakis larvae antigen. J Infect Dis 161: 995-998. 1990.

VI. The Cestodes

The phylum Platyhelminthes includes the class Cestoidea (tapeworms), all of which are parasitic in the gut tracts of various vertebrate hosts. Tapeworms are flat, segmented worms, composed of a head (scolex), and a series of segments, known as proglottids. Together, all proglottids are referred to as the strobila. The scolex is the point of attachment between the host and the parasite. It may be equipped with suckers, hooks, or grooves, which aid in the attachment process. The scolex contains nerves terminating in ganglia, while the segments contain only nerves. The neck region of the scolex is metabolically active, and is the site in most tapeworms from which new proglottids form.

The tapeworm does not have a functional gut tract. Rather, the segments are enclosed in a specialized tegument, whose structure and function are directly related to nutrient acquisition. Evenly-spaced microvilli cover the entire surface of the tegument, underneath which lie mitochondria, vesicles (perhaps involved in tegument replacement), and related structures. The tapeworm obtains some of its nutrients by actively transporting them across the tegument. Each proglottid is able to absorb a wide variety of low-molecular-weight substrates, but its precise metabolic requirements have yet to be fully defined.

High levels of ATPase in the tegument are related to active transport, but may also help the worm resist digestion by the mammalian host. Inhibitors of tapeworm ATPase, such as niclosamide, cause disintegration of adult tapeworms by digestion in the presence of pancreatic secretions.

Each proglottid has two layers of muscle – longitudinal and transverse – enabling the segment to move. The worm is innervated by two lateral branches of nerves, with perpendicular commissures branching out into the parenchyma of each segment. Segments are anatomically independent, but they are all connected by a common nervous system emanating from cerebral ganglia located in the scolex. Osmoregulation and excretion of wastes is via a lateral pair of excretory tubules.

Mature proglottids possess both male and female sex organs, but self-mating within a segment is unusual. Typically, sperm are transferred between mature proglottids which lie next to each other. Gravid proglottids develop after mating, and contain hundreds to thousands of embryonated eggs. They then detach from the parent organism and exit via the host's feces. In some species, proglottids exit intact, while in others, segments disintegrate before leaving the host. Eggs are usually passed embryonated, and contain a hexacanth larva referred to as an oncosphere. Eggs may remain viable in the external environment for weeks to months after being deposited in soil. Hatching occurs typically within the small intestine of the intermediate host. The oncosphere then penetrates the gut tract and lodges within the tissues, developing into the metacestode. This stage is ingested by the definitive host and transforms to the adult in the lumen of the small intestine.

Generally speaking, adult tapeworms do not cause much pathology in the human intestine. Unlike adult nematodes or trematodes, the adult cestodes are not significant causes of childhood physical growth and intellectual retardation. However, when humans serve as intermediate hosts, the cestodes become significant causes of global morbidity. For instance, neurocysticercosis caused by the larval stages of the pork tapeworm, *Taenia solium*, is a leading cause of neurologic disease; in many countries it is the leading cause of pediatric epilepsy. In 2003, the World Health Assembly highlighted the public health importance of neurocysticercosis infection and recommended it as a target for control (www.who.int).[1,2]

References

1. Ito A. Nakao M. Wandra T. Human taeniasis and cysticercosis in Asia. Lancet 362: 1918-20, 2003.
2. Flisser A, Viniegra AE. et al. Portrait of human tapeworms. J Parasitol 90: 914-6. 2004.

28. *Taenia saginata* (Goeze 1782)

Introduction

Taenia saginata belongs to the order Cyclophyllidea, and is one of the largest parasites infecting humans, often achieving lengths approaching 8-10 m. Like all other adult tapeworms, it lives in the lumen of the upper half of the small intestine. There are no reservoir hosts for *T. saginata*. This tapeworm occurs wherever cattle husbandry is prevalent, and where human excreta are not disposed of properly. It is commonly referred to as the beef tapeworm, although the adult parasite lives exclusively in humans. Endemic foci include vast regions of sub-Saharan grasslands in Africa, particularly in Ethiopia, large portions of Northern Mexico, Argentina, and to a lesser extent, middle Europe. It is infrequently acquired in the United States, where most clinical cases are imported.

A sub-species, *Taenia saginata-asiatica*, infects people in Taiwan, Korea, China, Vietnam, and Indonesia.[1–3] Many investigators feel that this organism should be considered a separate species (*T. asiati-*

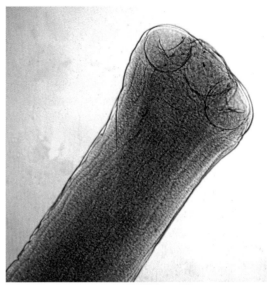

Figure 28.2. Scolex of *T. saginata*. Note four suckers.

ca) from *T. saginata*, particularly since the intermediate host is porcine not bovine.[3, 4] The full clinical spectrum of disease caused by *T. asiatica* is still not fully appreciated.

Historical Information

Tyson, in 1683,[5] described several species of tapeworms, which he recovered from dogs. Plater, a Swiss physician, in 1656, wrote about the distinctions between *Taenia spp.* and *Diphyllobothrium latum* (then called *Lumbricus latus*).[6] Andry, in 1700[7], is credited with the first report of *T. saginata*, but he didn't recognize that each proglottid was a separate unit, and did not distinguish this worm from other, similar tapeworms. Goeze was the first to describe the worm correctly. He outlined in 1782, in a larger treatise on helminthology, the first recognizable classification of *T. saginata* and *Taenia solium* adult worms.[8] Von Siebold, in 1850, speculated that "bladder worms" (i.e., cysticerci) could develop into adult tapeworms.[9] Unfortunately, he also offered the alternate hypothesis that these cysticerci were nothing more than degenerated adults.

Leuckart, in 1863,[10] reported on experiments showing that the proglottids of *T. saginata*, when fed to young calves, developed into cysticerci (metacestodes) in the animals' muscles. Oliver, in 1870,[11] demonstrated that after ingestion of the "bladder worms," humans develop adult *T. saginata* infections. He further suggested, correctly, that thorough cooking of infected meat would prevent infection with adult tapeworm.

Figure 28.1. A rare beef tenderloin.

Taenia saginata

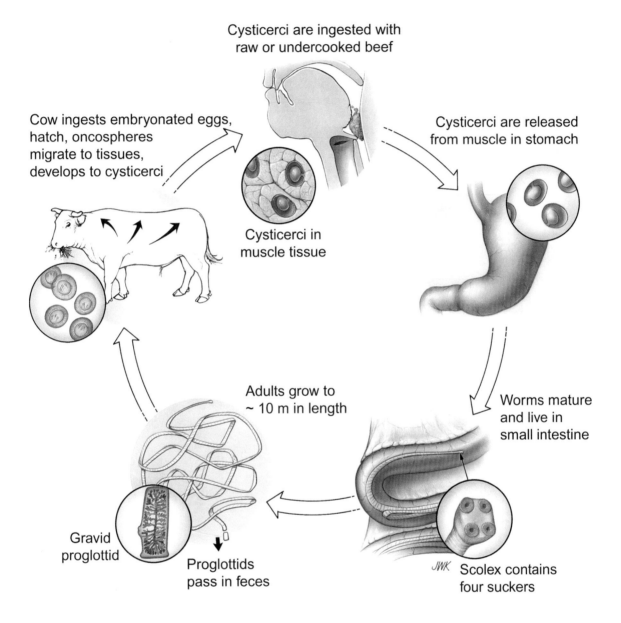

Cysticerci are ingested with raw or undercooked beef

Cow ingests embryonated eggs, hatch, oncospheres migrate to tissues, develops to cysticerci

Cysticerci in muscle tissue

Cysticerci are released from muscle in stomach

Worms mature and live in small intestine

Adults grow to ~ 10 m in length

Gravid proglottid

Proglottids pass in feces

Scolex contains four suckers

JWK

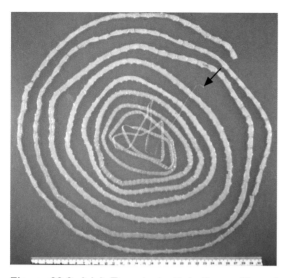

Figure 28.3. Adult *T. saginata*. Note the position of the scolex (arrow). Courtesy of U. Martin.

Life Cycle

Infection begins when the cysticercus is ingested along with raw or undercooked beef (Fig. 28.1). The cyst enters the small intestine and the wall of the cyst is digested away, freeing the worm inside. The parasite then everts its scolex and attaches to the intestinal wall with the aid of four sucker disks (Fig. 28.2). A mature adult tapeworm (Fig. 28.3) takes about three months to grow to full length. The developing proglottids (segments) extend down the small intestine, sometimes reaching the ileum. All adult tapeworms feed by actively transporting nutrients (e.g., sugars, amino acids, nucleic acids) across their tegumental surface, since they have no digestive tract. Segments mature as they progress towards the terminal end of the worm. Terminal proglottids, gravid with hundreds of embryonated, infectious eggs, may detach from the colony, and may even actively migrate out the anus, where they are deposited on the ground. Sometimes, whole ribbons of worms (20-30 segments) "escape" from an infected person.

A cow must then ingest the gravid segment, usually along with grass or hay, in order for the life cycle to continue. Eggs lying inside the lumen of the uterine branches of the proglottid are freed from the tapeworm tissue by the cow's digestive enzymes, stimulating the eggs to hatch in the small intestine (Fig. 28.5). The oncosphere (hexacanth or six-hooked larva) penetrates the intestinal wall, most likely aided by its hooks and peptidases that it secretes.[12] The larva enters the blood stream and is passively carried throughout the body. Oncospheres can lodge in any one of a variety of tissues, depending upon where the circulation takes them. Mostly, they infect striated skeletal muscle tissue. There they encyst, and develop to the cysticercus (metacestode). Cysticerci live for several years before calcifying.

Cattle can experience disease due to the space-filling lesions created by cysticerci,[13] especially if the cysts develop in sensitive areas (i.e., neurological tissues). Usually, however, they do not show signs of infection, since cattle are routinely slaughtered within several years of being born, and live cysticerci tend not to cause problems, even in neurological tissues (see cysticercosis, Chapter 32).

It is important to note that cattle cannot become infected with adult parasites if they accidentally ingest cysticerci. Similarly, humans cannot harbor the metacestode, since *Taenia saginata* eggs will only hatch in the stomachs of cows.

Most infected individuals harbor a single adult parasite, but there have been cases where numerous worms were recovered from a single infected individual. In these instances, the worms tend to be shorter due to crowding.

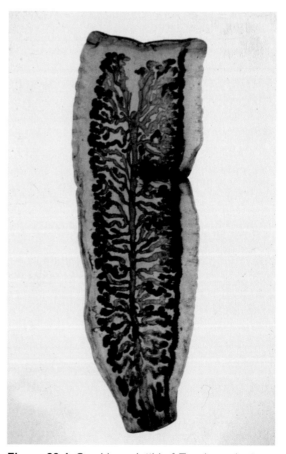

Figure 28.4. Gravid proglottid of *Taenia saginata*.

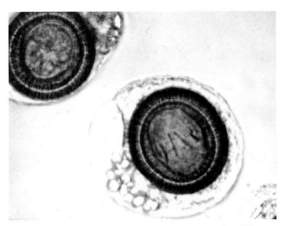

Figure 28.5. *Taenia spp.* eggs. They cannot be differentiated from eggs of other members of the taeniid family.

Cellular and Molecular Pathogenesis

Taenia saginata occupies a large part of the lumen of the small intestine, but it is flexible and relatively fragile. Therefore, bowel obstruction does not occur. Adult worms are immunogenic, and specific serum antibodies are produced throughout the infection period,[14] but local gut inflammatory responses are minimal.

In cattle, immunity to reinfection develops locally in the small intestine, and is directed at newly arrived onchospheres. Challenge infection was prevented by vaccination of cows with recombinant egg antigens.[15] IgA antibodies are thought to play a major role in this protective response, because colostrum from immune mothers protects sheep from invasion by oncospheres in experimental infections with closely related tapeworms.[16]

Clinical Disease

Most infections induce no symptoms, but some people may experience epigastric fullness. Rarely, postprandial nausea and vomiting occurs, and individual cases of jejunal performation and Meckel's diverticulitis have been reported.[17, 18] Infection is usually first detected by noting proglottids in stool. Frequently, proglottids migrate out of the infected person overnight, and can be discovered in bedding or clothing the following morning.

Diagnosis

Definitive diagnosis is by inspection of proglottids. Gravid proglottids should be fixed in 10% formaldehyde solution, and the uterus injected with India ink, with the aid of a 26 gauge needle (Fig. 28.4). *T.*

saginata proglottids typically have 15 or more side branches on either side of the uterus. Eggs of *T. saginata* are occasionally found in stool, since most progottids usually pass out of the host intact. However, if an egg is seen on stool examination, the species cannot be determined based on morphology, since all members of the family Taeniidae produce identically-shaped ova. Several investigators have reported success in differentiating *T. saginata* eggs from T. solium eggs by PCR,[19-22] as well as *T. saginata* from *T. saginata asiatica*.[23] Regrettably, this test is not available in most diagnostic laboratories.

A sticky tape test (see diagnosis for *Enterobius vermicularis*) is often positive for eggs of *Taenia spp.*, as they readily adhere to the perianal skin. An enzyme-linked immunosorbent assay has been developed that detects soluble *T. saginata* antigens in stool samples (coproantigens) of infected humans.[24]

Treatment

Praziquantel (5-10 mg/kg) is effective for the treatment of *T. saginata* infection,[25] and often allows recovery of the intact scolex thereby confirming cure of the patient. Niclosamide[26] is also effective in a single dose.[27] Niclosamide inhibits the parasite's ATPase, thus preventing it from interfering with host digestive enzymes. The consequence of treatment is dissolution of the adult worm. Hence, a search for the scolex is futile. Quinacrine has also been reported to be effective for patients with niclosamide-resistance *T. saginata* infection, but it is not considered standard therapy.[28]

Prevention and Control

Preventing tapeworm infection in the community is through proper disposal of human feces, but has proven difficult in some parts of the world, since untreated human feces is widely used as fertilizer. Infection is fully prevented by cooking beef thoroughly, or by thoroughly freezing it prior to cooking. Meat inspection programs are effective in identifying contaminated meat, but inspection is not carried out at all in many endemic areas. A vaccine against the oncosphere of *T. saginata* for use in cattle has been developed[29, 30] and may prove useful in some endemic situations where vaccines are affordable, but will most likely not have much of an effect in Africa, where incidence of cysticercosis in cattle is highest. The development of an ELISA test that detects antibodies in cattle, specific for the cysticercus stage, will allow for efficient evaluation of control programs,

References

1. Fan PC. Annual economic loss caused by *Taenia saginata asiatica* taeniasis in three endemic areas of east Asia. Southeast Asian J Trop Med Public Health. 28 Suppl 1:217-21. 1997.
2. McManus DP. Molecular genetic variation in Echinococcus and Taenia: an update. Southeast Asian J Trop Med Public Health. 28 Suppl 1:110-6. 1997.
3. Ito A. Nakao M. Wandra T. Human taeniasis and cysticercosis in Asia. Lancet 362: 1918-20. 2003.
4. Flisser A. Viniegra AE. et al. Portrait of human tapeworms. J Parasitol 90: 914-6. 2004.
5. Tyson E. Lumbricus latus, or a discourse read before the Royal Society, of the joynted worm, wherein great many mistakes of former writers concerning it, are remarked; its natural history from more exact information is attempted; and the whole urged, as a difficulty against doctrine of univocal generation. Philos Trans 13:113-144. 1683.
6. Plater F. Praxeos Medicae Opus. Basel. 1656.
7. Andry N. De la Generation des Vers dans le Corps de l'Homme Paris. 1700.
8. Goeze JAE. Versuch ciner Naturgeschichte der Eingeweiderwumer Thierischer Korper. Blankenburg, P. A. Pape. 1782.
9. Von Siebold CTE. Uber den Generationswechsel der Cestoden nebst einer Revision der Gattung Tetrarhynchus. Z Wissensch Zool 2:198-253. 1850.
10. Leuckart R. Die menschlichen Parasiten und die von ihnen her ruhenden Krankheiten. Em Handund Lehrbuch fur Naturforscher und Arzte. C. E. Wintersche Verlagshandlung, Leipzig. 1863.
11. Oliver JH. The importance of feeding the cattle and the thorough cooking of the meat, as the best preservatives against tapeworms. Seventh Annual Report of the Sanitary Commissioner (1870) with the Government of India, Calcutta, 1871. pp 82-83.
12. White AC Jr. Baig S. Robinson P. *Taenia saginata* oncosphere excretory/secretory peptidases. J Parasitol. 82:7-10. 1997.
13. Oryan A. Gaur SN. Moghaddar N. Delavar H. Clinico-patholoical studies in cattle experimentally infected with *Taenia saginata* eggs. J S Afr Vet Assoc. 69(4):156-62. 1998.
14. Lightowlers MW. Mitchell GF. Rickard MD: Cestodes. In Warren KS, Agabian N (eds) Immunology and Molecular Biology of Parasitic Infections (3rd ed). Blackwell, London. 1991.
15. Lightowlers MW. Rolfe R. Gauci CG. *Taenia saginata*: vaccination against cysticercosis in cattle with recombinant oncosphere antigens. Exp Parasitol. 84(3):330-8. 1996.
16. Gemmell MA. Blundell-Hasell SK. Macnamara FN. Immunologcal responses of the mammalian host against tapeworm infections. IX. The transfer via colostrum of immunity to Taenia hydatigena. Exp Parasitol. 26(1):52-7. 1969.
17. Jongwutiwes S. Putaporntip C. Chantachum N. Sampatanukul P. Jejunal perforation caused by morphologically abnormal *Taenia saginata* saginata infection. J Infect 49: 324-8. 2004.
18. Chirdan LB. Yusufu LM. Ameh EA. Shehu SM. Meckel's diverticulitis due to *Taenia saginata*: case report. East Afr Med J 78: 107-8. 2001.
19. Gonzalez LM, Montero E. et al. Differential diagnosis of *Taenia saginata* and *Taenia solium* infection by PCR. J Clin Microbiol 38: 737-44. 2000.
20. Gonzalez LM, Montero E. et al. Differential diagnosis of *Taenia saginata* and *Taenia solium* infections: from DNA probes to polymerase chain reaction. Trans R Soc Trop Med Hyg 96 Suppl 1: S243-50. 2002.
21. Rodriguez-Hidalgo R, Geysen D. et al. Comparison of conventional techniques to differentiate between *Taenia solium* and *Taenia saginata* and an improved polymerase chain reaction-restriction fragment length polymorphism assay using a mitochondrial 12S rDNA fragment. J Parasitol 88: 1007-11. 2002.
22. Nunes CM, Lima LG. et al. *Taenia saginata*: polymerase chain reaction for taeniasis diagnosis in human fecal samples. Exp Parasitol 104: 67-9. 2003.
23. Gonzalez LM, Montero E. et al. Differential diagnosis of *Taenia saginata* and *Taenia saginata asiatica* taeniasis through PCR. Diagn Microbiol Infect Dis 49: 183-8. 2004.
24. Deplazes P. Eckert J. et al: An enzyme-linked immunosorbent assay for diagnostic detection of *Taenia saginata* copro-antigens in humans. Trans R Soc Trop Med Hyg 85:391-396.1991.
25. Pawlowski ZS. Efficacy of low doses of praziquantel in taeniasis. Acta Trop (Basel) 48:83-88. 1991.
26. Keeling JED: The chemotherapy of cestode infections. Adv Chemother 3:109-152. 1978.
27. Vermund SH. MacLeod S. Goldstein RG. Taeniasis unresponsive to a single dose of niclosamide: case report of persistent infection with *Taenia saginata* and a review of therapy. Rev Infect Dis 8:423-426. 1986.
28. Koul PA, Wahid A. et al. Mepacrine therapy in niclosamide resistant taeniasis. J Assoc Physicians India 48: 402-3. 2000.
29. Lightowlers MW. Rolfe R. Gauci CG. *Taenia saginata*: vaccination against cysticercosis in cattle with recombinant oncosphere antigens. Exp Parasitol 84(3):330-8, 1996.
30. Lightowlers MW, Colebrook AL. et al. Vaccinationa against the cestode parasites: anti-helminth vaccines that work and why. Vet Parasitol 115: 83-123. 2003.
31. Onyango-Abuje JA. et al. Diagnosis of *Taenia saginata* cysticercosis in Kenyan cattle by antibody and antigen ELISA. Vet Parasitol. 61:221-30. 1996.

29. *Taenia solium* (Linnaeus 1758)

Introduction

Taenia solium belongs to the order Cyclophyllidea, and its occurrence is coincident with the raising of pigs. It is commonly known as the pork tapeworm, although the adult only occurs in humans. In order to transmit this parasite, human feces, contaminated with the mature segments of the worm, must be a regular contaminant of the pigs' environment, and eating raw or undercooked pork products must prevail as the cultural norm. Unfortunately, these conditions exist in many undeveloped parts of the world.

T. solium is a large tapeworm, often achieving lengths of more than 6 m. It lives in the lumen, attached to the wall of the small intestine. There are no reservoir hosts for this parasite. However, infection with the metacestode form, referred to as cysticercosis, can be a serious, even fatal disease (see Chapter 32). Neurocysticercosis is now the leading cause of acquired epilepsy, worldwide.[1]

T. solium is endemic in most of South America (particularly in the Andean region and Brazil), Central America and Mexico, China, the Indian subcontinent and Southeast Asia, sub-Saharan Africa (especially West Africa, Democratic Republic of Congo, and South Africa), and Eastern Europe.[2] In some of

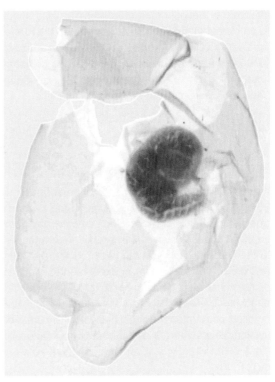

Figure 29.2. Isolated whole cysticercus of *Taenia solium*, measuring 2-5 mm in diameter.

these endemic regions up to 6 percent of the population may harbor *T. solium* tapeworms.[1] The highest prevalence of *T. solium* infection in the United States occurs among Hispanic populations in Southern California, New Mexico, and Texas, as the result of large number of immigrants from some of those endemic areas mentioned above.[1, 2, 3] Among adult migrant workers in California, for instance, the sero-prevalence of *T. solium* is approximately 1-2 percent.[4, 5] In endemic regions, *T. solium* occurs more commonly in children and adolescents.[1]

In 2003, the Fifty-Sixth World Health Assembly highlighted the public health threat caused by *T. solium* and urged its member states to increase measures to control this infection.[2]

Historical Information

Goeze[6], in 1782, described the adult parasite, but it was Aristole who wrote about the cysticercus stage of the worm in the muscles of pigs. There is no evidence that Goeze comprehended the relation between the larval infection in the pig and the adult infection in humans. Cysticercosis in pigs was described by Hartmann in l688.[7] Kuchenmeister,[8] in 1855, in a remarkable experiment, transmitted the

Figure 29.1. A section of infected pig muscle. Note numerous cysticerci.

infection to a condemned murderer who was about to be executed; he secretly contaminated the man's food with cysticerci (some last meal!). At autopsy, 120 hours after the prisoner had dined on contaminated meat, Kuchenmeister recovered immature adults of *T. solium* in the man's small intestine.

Life Cycle

Infection in the human host begins by eating raw or undercooked pork that harbors the encapsulated cysticercus (i.e., juvenile) stage of the worm (Figs. 29.1, 29.2). The capsule is digested in the stomach freeing the juvenile parasite. Upon entering the small intestine, the worm everts its scolex, then attaches to the intestinal wall with the aid of its four suckers and crown of hooklets. In an experimental infection of hamsters with onchospheres of *T. solium*, the attachment site in the gut tract was studied.[9] The hooklets penetrated the intestinal wall, while the four suckers all attached to cells of the surrounding villi. Host cell damage was observed in and around each sucker disk.

The life cycle of *T. solium* is very similar to that of *T. saginata*. The juvenile parasite develops to the adult (Fig. 29.3) in the small intestine over a three-

Figure 29.4. Scolex of *Taenia solium*. Note four suckers and hooks. Photo E. Gravé

month period, after which gravid (egg-laden) proglottids begin passing from the host. Adult *Taenia solium* closely resemble the adult worm of *T. saginata*, except that *T. solium* scolex possesses two rows of hooklets, in addition to four sucker disks (Fig. 29.4). Usually, adult *T. solium* do not live in the human gastrointestinal tract for more than 5 years.[1]

The adult of *T. solium* will not develop in the pig if it accidentally ingests cysticerci from contaminated pork scraps. However, unlike infection with *Taenia saginata*, humans can become infected with the cysticercus of *T. solium* by ingestion of embryonated eggs (Fig. 29.5). In some cases, it is believed that humans auto-infect with the contaminated eggs of their own tapeworm. The frequency of *T. solium* auto-infection is not known, although it has been observed that up to 15 percent of patients with cysticercosis also harbor an adult *T. solium* tapeworm.[1]

Cellular and Molecular Pathogenesis

The adult parasite does not usually cause a significant host inflammatory response, but it does elicit the formation of humoral antibodies.[10] Infected pigs

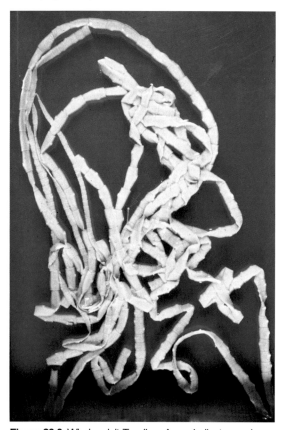

Figure 29.3. Whole adult *T. solium*. Arrow indicates scolex.

Taenia solium

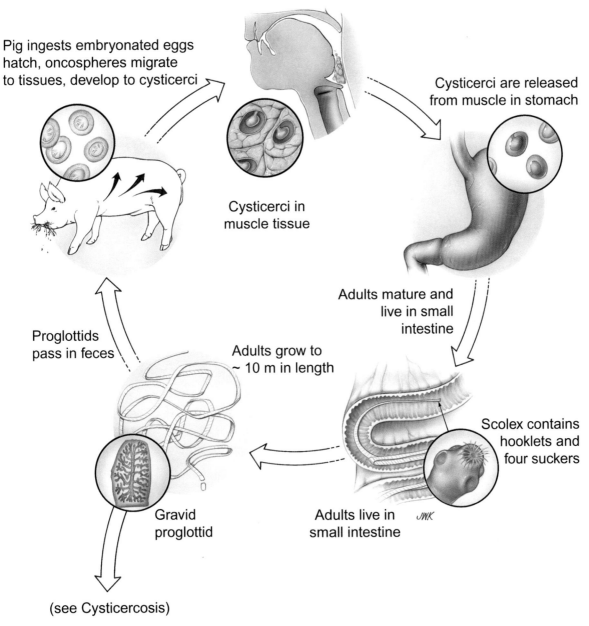

Cysticerci are ingested
with raw or undercooked pork

Pig ingests embryonated eggs
hatch, oncospheres migrate
to tissues, develop to cysticerci

Cysticerci are released
from muscle in stomach

Cysticerci in
muscle tissue

Adults mature and
live in small
intestine

Proglottids
pass in feces

Adults grow to
~ 10 m in length

Scolex contains
hooklets and
four suckers

Gravid
proglottid

Adults live in
small intestine

JWK

(see Cysticercosis)

"Parasitic Diseases" 5ᵗʰ Ed. © Apple Trees Productions, LLC., Pub. P.O. Box 280, New York, NY 10032

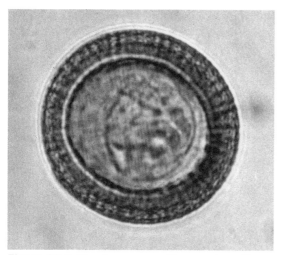

Figure 29.5. *Taenia spp.* egg. The species of tapeworm cannot be determined based on its morphology. Eggs measure 30-40 mm in diameter.

Figure 29.6. Commercial feedlot. This environment is frequently contaminated with human feces in many regions of the world where pigs are raised. Courtesy P. M. Schantz.

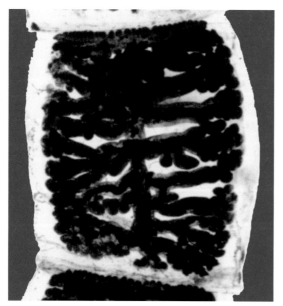

Figure 29.7. Gravid proglottid of *Taenia solium.* Uterus contains less than 12 lateral branches on each side.

do not become re-infected when they ingest more eggs, most likely because they are protected by immune responses directed against the oncosphere. A similar situation exists between *T. saginata* and cattle. The cDNAs encoding two *Taenia solium* glucose transporter molecules have been expressed in bacteria, and their fusion proteins identified and characterized.[11] One is on the tegumental surface of the adult worm (TGTP1) and the other is on the surface of the larva (TGTP2). Both molecules have the potential for being used as targets of vaccines aimed at preventing each stage from accessing host glucose.

Clinical Disease

T. solium does not cause symptoms of epigastric fullness. Patients are asymptomatic, and do not become aware of their infection until they discover the proglottids in stool, on the perianal skin, or in clothing, bed sheets, etc. Some patients report abdominal pain, distension, diarrhea, and nausea, but there are no controlled studies to demonstrate their link with the presence of *T. solium* in the gut.[1] Two patients with *T. solium* infection were reported to develop ascites, chronic diarrhea, and malabsorption, which resolved following anthelminthic therapy,[12] but this should be considered a rare situation.

Diagnosis

Traditionally, diagnosis is by identifying the Taenia eggs by microscopy, by analysis of the gravid proglottids, or by recovery and identification of the scolex.

Overall, the sensitivity of stool microscopy is poor, and even then, *T. solium* eggs are morphologically indistinguishable from *T. saginata* eggs. A DNA dot blot test can differentiate *T. solium* from *T. saginata*.[13] Perianal scraping with adhesive tape to trap eggs has been used to improve the sensitivity of microscopy, but this technique is not as effective for *T. solium* infection as it is for *T. saginata*.

Gravid proglottid segments should be fixed in 10% formaldehyde solution, and injected with India ink to fill the uterus. Proglottids of *T. solium* have less than 14 uterine branches per side (Fig. 29.7), compared to those of *T. saginata*, which have 15 or more (Fig. 28.4). Extreme caution must be exercised when handling unfixed proglottids of *T. solium*, since the embryonated eggs are infectious. Both species' egg can be distinguished from the other by PCR.[14]

Because of the distinct morphological features of the *T. solium* scolex compared with that of *T. saginata*, the gold standard of taeniasis diagnosis has traditionally been the recovery and visualization of this parasite organ. Polyethylene glycol salt purges to improve bowel cleaning significantly improves the likelihood of scolex recovery.[15]

The highest diagnostic sensitivity (95 percent) and specificity (99 percent) of *T. solium* infection is achieved by performing an ELISA that detects fecal antigen (coproantigen).[16] Patients with adult tapeworms also produce antibodies that can be detected by immunoblot assay.[17] This assay is particularly useful for epidemiological studies.

Treatment

Niclosamide is the drug of choice (2 g orally in a single dose), because it is not absorbed from the intestinal lumen.[1, 18] In contrast, praziquantel (5-10 mg/kg orally in a single dose) is also effective against adult *T. solium*, but its use must be tempered by the possibility that this treatment will also destroy occult cysticerci in the brain, and trigger central nervous system manifestations.[1] Praziquantel is usually available in developing countries, particularly because of its use for global schistosomiasis control, and its proven success in Mexico in reducing the prevalence where taeniasis is endemic.[2] Generally speaking, no purgatives should be used,[19] because this increases the risk of regurgitating eggs into the stomach, and thus initiating infection leading to cysticercosis.[20]

Prevention and Control

Taenia solium is a significant public health problem, even outside the endemic areas, due to the association of cysticercosis with the adult infections.[21] For example, an outbreak of cysticercosis was reported among an orthodox Jewish community in New York City resulting from the ingestion of *T. solium* eggs passed from domestic employees who were recent emigrants from Latin America.[22] It has been suggested that recent emigrants from countries in which *T. solium* infection is endemic should be screened for tapeworm infection before they are employed as housekeepers or food handlers.[22]

In many impoverished regions in developing countries, pigs are more affordable than cows, since pigs behave like omnivores. That is why owners allow them to roam free and eat garbage and human feces.[1] The infection in pigs is preventable by protecting their feed from contamination by human feces (Fig. 29.7). Individual infection is prevented by thoroughly cooking pork, or by freezing it at -10 °C for a minimum of 5 days. Cysticerci can survive in meat refrigerated at 4°C for up to 30 days.[23]

In 2003, the World Health Assembly identified several measures to control *T. solium* infection, including identification and treatment of individuals who carry the adult tapeworm, universal or selected treatment with praziquantel to reduce the prevalence in areas where *T. solium* infection is endemic, veterinary sanitary measures, such as enforced meat inspection and control, improvement of pig husbandry, and treatment of infected animals with single-dose therapy using oxfendazole and other drugs, and case management, reporting and surveillance of people with cysticercosis. Finally, it was recommended that anthelminthic chemotherapy programs need to be integrated with other health programs using a wider intersectoral approach.[2]

Inoculation of pigs with recombinant antigens cloned from parasite oncosphere mRNA appears to be an effective vaccine,[24-26] and could be used to reduce the incidence of adult tapeworm in a few countries, such as Mexico, where public health programs can be integrated with prevention on the farm.[27] In one experimental study, treating all pigs with oxfendazole eliminated 100% of viable cysticerci.[28] Serological testing in the abattoir is now also possible.[29] Any of these three approaches, or in combination, could significantly reduce transmission of *T. solium* to humans, if applied rigorously to commercial pig farms in endemic areas.

Some black bears in California have acquired cysticercosis, most likely as the result of feeding at garbage dumps near camp grounds.[30] Hunting bears is a popular sport in The United States, and distributing meat from kills to neighbors is common practice among hunters. Hunter organizations should issue warnings, advising hunters that any meat obtained from carnivores or omnivores should be cooked well before eating. This practice will also limit outbreaks due to sylvatic species of trichinella.

References

1. Garcia HH. Gonzalez AE. Eveans CAW. Gilman RH. for the Cysticercosis Working Group in Peru. Lancet 361: 547-56. 2003.
2. World Health Organization, Control of neurocysticercosis, Report by the Secretariat, Fifty-Six Worth Health Assembly. 2003 (www.who.int).
3. Despommier DD. Tapeworm infection-the long and the short of it. N Engl J Med 327:727-728. 1992.
4. Richards FO. Schantz PM. et al: Cysticercosis in Los Angeles county. JAMA 254:3444-3448.1985.
5. DeGiorgio C. Pietsch-Escueta S. et al. Sero-prevalence of *Taenia solium* cysticercosis and *Taenia solium* taeniasis in California, USA. Acta Neurol Scand 111: 84-8. 2005.
6. Goeze JAE. Versuch einer Naturgeschichte der Eingewiderwurmer Thierischer Korper. P. A. Pape, Blankenburg. 1782.
7. Hartmann PJ. Miscellanea curiosa sive ephemeridium medicophysicarum Germanicarum Academiae Imperialis Leopoldineae naturae curiosorum decuriae II. Observatio 34. Literis Joonnis Ernesti Adelbuneri, Nurnberg, pp 58-59. 1688.
8. Kuchenmeister F. Experimenteller nachweis, dass Cysticercus cellulosae innerhalb des menschlichen darmkanales sichlil in *Taenia solium* umwandelt. Wiener Medizinische Wochenschrift. 5:1-4. 1855.
9. Merchant MT. Aguilar L. et al. *Taenia solium*: description of the intestinal implantation sites in experimental hamster infections. J Parasitol. 84:681-5. 1998.
10. Camacho SD. Ruiz AC. et al: Serology as an indicator of *Taenia solium* tapeworm infections in a rural community in Mexico. Trans R Soc Trop Med Hyg 84:563-566. 1990.
11. Rodriguez-Contreras D. Skelly PJ. et al. Molecular and functional characterization and tissue localization of 2 glucose transporter homologues (TGTP1 and TGTP2) from the tapeworm *Taenia solium*. Parasitology. 117:579-88. 1998.
12. Song E. Kim IH. Lee SO. Unusual manifestations of *Taenia solium* infestation. J Gastroenterol 39: 288-91. 2004.
13. Chapman A. Vallejo V. et al. Isolation and characterization of species-specific DNA probes from *Taenia solium* and *Taenia saginata* and their use in an egg detection assay. J Clin Microbiol. 33:1283-8. 1995.
14. Yamasaki H, Allan JC. et al. DNA differential diagnosis of taeniasis and cysticercosis by multiplex PCR. J Clin Microbiol 42: 548-53. 2004.
15. Jeri C, Gilman RH. et al. Species identification after treatment for human taeniasis. Lancet 363: 949-50. 2004.
16. Allan JC, Avila G. et al. Immunodiagnosis of taeniasis by coproantigen detection. Parasitology 101: 473-7. 1990.
17. Wilkins PP. Allan JC. et al. Development of a serologic assay to detect *Taenia solium* taeniasis. Am J Trop Med Hyg. 60:199-204. 1999.
18. Keeling IED. The chemotherapy of cestode infections. Adv Chemother 3:109-152. 1968.
19. The Medical Letter. 2000.
20. Richards FR. Schantz PM. Treatment of *Taenia solium* infections. Lancet 1:1264-1265. 1985.
21. Lara-Aguilera R. Mendoza-Cruz IF. Martinez-Toledo JL. *Taenia solium* taeniasis and neurocysticercosis in a Mexican rural family. Am J Trop Med Hyg 46:85-88. 1992.
22. Schantz PM. Moore AC. Munoz JL. Neurocysticercosis in an orthodox Jewish community in New York City. N Engl J Med 327: 692-695. 1992.
23. Fan PC. Ma YX. Kuo CH. Chung WC. Survival of *Taenia solium* cysticerci in carcasses of pigs kept at 4°C. J Parasitol. 84:174-5. 1998.
24. Manoutcharian K. Rosas G. et al. Cysticercosis: identification and cloning of protective recombinant antigens. J Parasitol. 82:250-4, 1996.
25. Lightowlers MW. Eradication of *Taenia solium* cysticercosis: a role for vaccination of pigs. Int J Parasitol. 29:811-7. 1999
26. Lightowlers MW. Gauci CG. Vaccines against cysticercosis and hydatidosis. Vet Parasitol 101: 337-52. 2001.
27. Molinari JL. Rodriguez D. et al. Field trial for reducing porcine *Taenia solium* cysticercosis in Mexico by systematic vaccination of pigs. Vet Parasitol. 69:55-63. 1997.
28. Gonzales AE. Garcia HH. et al. Effective, single-dose treatment for porcine cysticercosis with oxfendazole. Am J Trop Med Hyg. 54:391-4, 1996.
29. D'Souza PE. Hafeez M. Detection of *Taenia solium* cysticercosis in pigs by ELISA with an excretory-secretory antigen. Vet Res Commun. 23:293-8. 1999
30. Theis JH. Cleary M. et al. DNA-confirmed *Taenia solium* cysticercosis in black bears (*Ursus americanus*) from California. Am J Trop Med Hyg. 55:456-8, 1996.

30. *Diphyllobothrium latum*
(Linnaeus 1758)

Introduction

Diphyllobothrium latum belongs to the order Pseudophyllidea and achieves a length of more than 10 m in length, making it the longest parasite to infect humans. It is acquired by eating raw or under-cooked fish, and its common name is the fish tapeworm. As with all other adult tapeworms, it lives in the lumen of the small intestine and does little harm to its host. It has a unique affinity for vitamin B12, and sometimes this has pathological consequences for the infected individual.

All parasites in this group of tapeworms have complex life cycles, and in most cases they use invertebrates (e.g., copepods) and fresh water fish as intermediate hosts. Most carnivores are susceptible to infection with *D. latum*, including dog, bear, cat, fox, martin, mink, and other wild mammals. Some are important reservoir hosts.

D. latum infection is common throughout Scandinavia,[1] though prevalence in that region has decreased in recent years, due, in large part, to vastly improved sanitation. The infection was probably introduced to North America (especially in the Great Lakes region and in

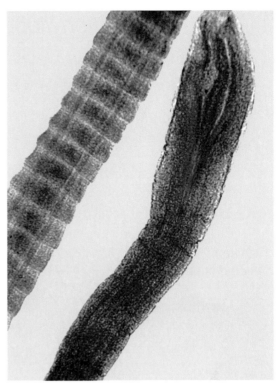

Figure 30.2. The scolex and mature proglottids of *D. latum*. Courtesy H. Zaiman.

Lake Winnipeg, Manitoba) by northern European immigrants.[2] Today, new infections are reported commonly in Russia, Brazil, and Japan,[2] although infections have also been reported in Asia, Europe and the Americas. Overall, it is believed that the number of new cases of *D. latum* infection are declining in North America, but possibly increasing in South America.[3] A related subspecies, *D. latum* var. *parvum* infects humans in Korea and China.[4] In circumpolar regions, infection due to *D. dendriticum* (a more benign variant) is common in both people and animals.[5]

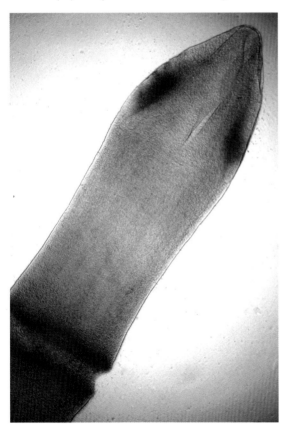

Figure 30.1. The plerocercoid stage of *D. latum*. This is the infective stage for the definitve host.

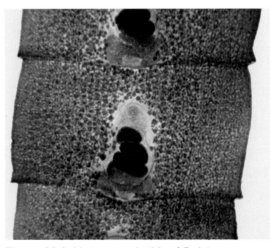

Figure 30.3. Mature proglottids of *D. latum*.

Diphyllobothrium latum

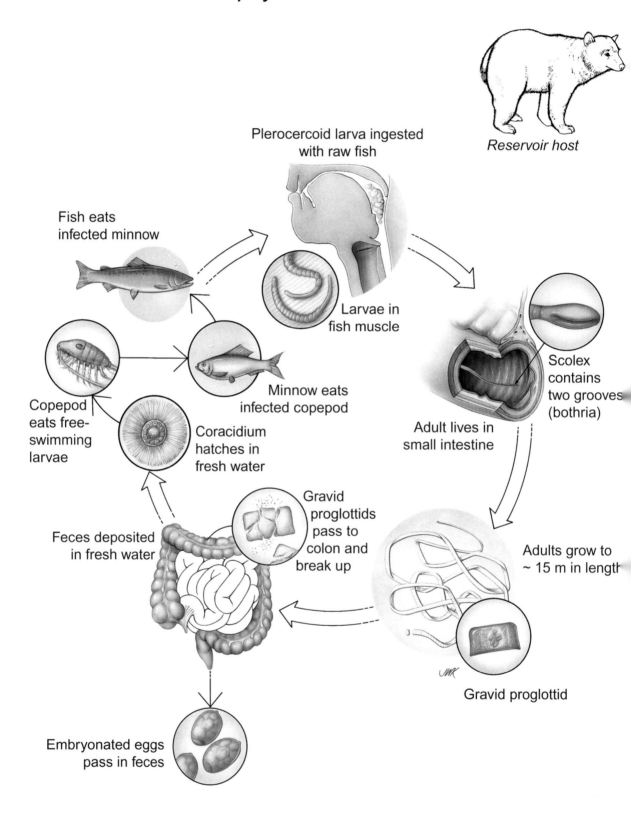

Reservoir host

Plerocercoid larva ingested
with raw fish

Fish eats
infected minnow

Larvae in
fish muscle

Scolex
contains
two grooves
(bothria)

Adult lives in
small intestine

Minnow eats
infected copepod

Copepod
eats free-
swimming
larvae

Coracidium
hatches in
fresh water

Adults grow to
~ 15 m in length

Gravid
proglottids
pass to
colon and
break up

Feces deposited
in fresh water

Gravid proglottid

Embryonated eggs
pass in feces

"Parasitic Diseases" 5ᵗʰ Ed. © Apple Trees Productions, LLC., Pub. P.O. Box 280, New York, NY 10032

Figure 30.4. Gravid proglottids of *D. latum*.

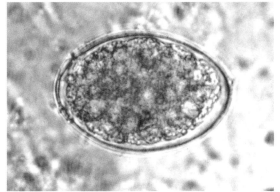

Figure 30.5. Unembryonated egg of *D. latum*. 65 x 45 μm

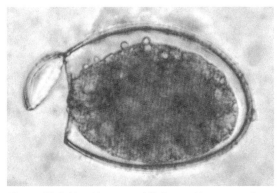

Figure 30.6. Hatching egg of *D. latum*. Note operculum.

Historical Information

Plater, in 1609,[6] observed and reported that *Diphyllobothrium latum* infected humans, while Linnaeus, in 1751,[7] classified it. In 1917, Janicki,[8] in a series of elegant epidemiological observations and experiments, described and illustrated its complex life cycle.

Life Cycle

Infection begins when undercooked or raw fish, infected with the plerocercoid metacestode of the parasite, is eaten (Fig. 30.1). In the north, pike and percids

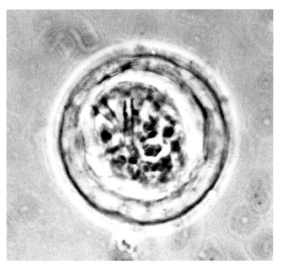

Figure 30.7. Ciliated coracidium. 60 μm in diameter.

are the most common source of infection.[2] The parasite is released from the fish's flesh in the stomach, passes to the small intestine, and attaches to the intestinal wall by applying two bothria (grooves) to the epithelial surface. There, it grows and develops into the adult worm (Fig. 30.2), becoming a fully formed strobila within three months.

Usually, only one tapeworm of *D. latum* infects a given individual. The adult worm, which has a life span of up to 4.5 years,[2] obtains nutrition through its tegumental surface, absorbing small molecular weight compounds from the partially digested meal of the host. This tapeworm has a particular avidity for vitamin B12.

Proglottids (segments) are greater in width than length (Figs. 30.3, 30.4), and contain both sets of sex organs. Proglottids fertilize eggs in nearby segments. As fertilized proglottids become gravid, eggs (Fig. 30.5) exit from the centrally located uterine pore, entering into the lumen of the small intestine. Gravid segments can also break off from the strobila and disintegrate in the small intestine. The fertilized, unembryonated eggs pass out of the host with the feces, and must be deposited in fresh water if the life cycle is to continue.

The eggs measure 70 mm, and embryonate over a 9-12 day period before hatching (Fig. 30.6). The motile coracidium (Fig. 30.7) (ciliated oncosphere) emerges from the egg, and immediately begins to swim. Free-living coracidia can live for 3-4 days before exhausting their food reserves. Motile coracidia attract the attention of zooplankton crustacean predators; e.g., *Cyclops spp.* and *Diaptomus spp.* (Fig. 30.8), and become ingested. The coracidium burrows into the crustacean's body cavity and develops into an immature metacestode referred to as a procercoid (Fig. 30.9)

When infected crustacea are consumed by small

fresh water fish, particularly various species of minnows, the procercoid is freed from the crustacean, and penetrates the wall of the small intestine of the fish, eventually lodging in the muscles. It then differentiates and grows into a plerocercoid metacestode, the infective stage for humans.

Infected minnows eaten by large predator fish species, such as members of the perch, pike, and salmonid families, transfer plerocercoids to the larger fish. The plerocercoid penetrates the body wall and takes up residence in muscle tissue just under the skin.

Cellular and Molecular Pathogenesis

Vitamin B12 deficiency accompanying *D. latum* infection is prevalent among individuals living in Finland. This is not true for those living throughout the rest of Scandinavia, suggesting that there are genetic differences among the peoples of this northern region regarding their susceptibility to this clinical condition (Roberts, Personal Communication).

Pseudophyllidean tapeworms absorb large quantities of vitamin B12 and their analogues. They employ a tegumental cyanocobalamin receptor that has a high affinity for several analogues of this compound, including cobalamin.[9] Cobalamin is converted to adenosyl-cobalamin, a coenzyme for methyl-malonyl-CoA mutase. Anaerobic energy metabolism relies on the production of propionate, and these two enzymes are integral to that metabolic pathway.[10]

Clinical Disease

Exhaustion of vitamin B12 is a slow process, taking many months to years.[11] The full picture of megaloblastic anemia is indistinguishable from that due to other causes. Less than 2% of infected individuals develop megaloblastic anemia.[12] The reason for the relative infrequency of megaloblastic anemia among most of

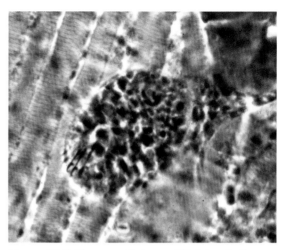

Figure 30.9. Procercoid stage of *D. latum* in tissues of *Diaptomus spp.* Note hooklets. (Phase-contrast)

those infected with of *D. latum* is not well understood. There may be host genetic factors that predispose certain infected individuals to suffer the effects of this deficiency. One study indicated that patients with megaloblastic anemia due to infection with *D. latum* had less intrinsic factor than those who were free of anemia but who also harbored the worm. This observation has not been confirmed by other studies.[12] Diarrhea is a rare complaint.

Diagnosis

Segments of worm in stool (Fig. 30.3, 30.4) sometimes alert patients to the fact that they harbor a tapeworm, but, as already mentioned, most proglottids break up in the intestinal tract before exiting the host. Diagnosis is therefore typically made by microscopic identification of non-embryonated eggs (Fig. 30.5; Fig. C.58., Appendix C) in stool. There are no specific serologic tests for *D. latum*.

Treatment

The drug of choice is praziquantel (5-10 mg/kg once). Niclosamide is also effective.

Prevention and Control

In sylvatic settings, numerous reservoir hosts are potentially important for maintaining the life cycle. Thus, interference with this phase of its ecology is not possible. On an individual basis, the best way to avoid infection with *D. latum* is to eat only well-cooked or once-frozen fresh water fish. Sushi is predominantly made from saltwater fish species which do not acquire *D. latum* or related tapeworm species. A few cases

Figure 30.8. *Diaptomus spp.* infected with *D. latum.*

have been reported from eating sushi prepared from Pacific coast salmon, which spend a portion of their life in fresh water.[13] The culinary habit among many Jewish mothers or grandmothers of teaching their daughters to prepare gefilte fish by tasting the raw mixture led many a female to acquire this infection in the United States, and was popularized in a medical anthropological description by Desowitz.[14] Today, proper disposal of human feces in the Great Lakes region of the United States has greatly reduced prevalence of *D. latum* in that ethnic group. In Scandinavian countries, gravlax, and a wide variety of other marinated raw fish dishes, remain common sources of infection for this tapeworm. A recent outbreak of fish tapeworm in Ribeirao, Brazil involved 18 patients and one traveler from Holland (see www.promed.org). The source of the epidemic and the species of fish were not known at the time of this printing.

References

1. Kyronseppa H. The occurrence of human intestinal parasites in Finland. Scand J Infect Dis. 25:671-3. 1993.
2. Dick TA. Nelson PA. Choudhury A. Diphyllobothriasis: update on human cases, foci patterns and sources of human infections and future considerations. Southeast Asian J Trop Med Public Health 32 (Suppl 2): 59-76. 2001.
3. Torres P. Franjola R. et al. Registro de nuevos casos de difilobotriasis humana en Chile (1981-1992), incluido un caso de infeccion multiple por *Diphyllobothrium latum*. Bol Chil Parasitol. 48:39-43. 1993.
4. Lee SH. Chai JY. et al. Two rare cases of *Diphyllobothrium latum parvum* type infection in Korea. Kisaengchunghak Chapchi. 32:117-20. 1994.
5. Curtis MA. Bylund G. Diphyllobothriasis: fish tapeworm disease in the circumpolar north. Arctic Med Res. 50:18-24. 1991.
6. Plater F. Praxeos seu de cognoscendis, praedicendis praecudensis curandiso affectibus homini incommodantibus tractatus tertius et ultimus. De vitiis, libris duobus agens; quorum primum corpis; secundus, Exretorum vitia continet. Typis Conradi Waldkirchii, Basel. 1609.
7. Linnaeus C. Taenia osculis lateralibus solitaris. Amoenitates Academicae. Holmiae: Laurentium Salvium 2: 80-81. 1751.
8. Janicki C. Le cycle evolutif du Dibothriocephalus latus L. Soc Neuchateloise Sci Natur Bull 42:19-53.1916-1917.
9. Friedman PA. Weinstein PP. Mueller JF. Allen RH. Characterization of cobalamin receptor sites in brush-border plasma membranes of the tapeworm Spirometra mansonoides. J Biol Chem 258:4261-4265. 1983.
10. Smyth JD. McManus DP. The Physiology and Biochemistry of Tapeworms. Cambridge University Press. 1989.
11. Goodman KI. Salt WB 2d. Vitamin B12 deficiency. Important new concepts in recognition. Postgrad Med. 88:147-50, 153-8. 1990.
12. Saarni M. Nyberg W. et al: Symptoms in carriers of *Diphyllobothrium latum* and in uninfected controls. Acta Med Scand 173:147-154.1963.
13. Hutchinson JW. Bass JW. Demers DM. Myers GB Diphyllobothriasis after eating raw salmon. Hawaii Medical Journal. 56:176-7. 1997.
14. Desowitz RS. New Guinea Tapeworms and Jewish Grandmothers: A Tale of Parasites and People. W. W. Norton, Co., Pubs. 1981.

31. Tapeworms of Minor Medical Importance

Hymenolepis nana (Siebold 1852)

Introduction

Hymenolepis nana, in the order Cyclophyllidea, has a worldwide distribution, and infects mostly children.[1] In Asia and elsewhere, *H. nana* infection is a common infection among children living in poor neighborhoods and in institutional settings.[2, 3] As its species name implies, this is a small tapeworm, measuring 34-45 mm in length. The adult consists of 150-200 proglottids, and lives in the lumen of the small intestine, loosely attached to the epithelial cells of the villi. Its scolex has four suckers and a single row of hooks. Rodents are significant reservoir hosts for this tapeworm.

A second related species, *Hymenolepis microstoma*, has been described in *H. nana*-infected patients from remote communities in Western Australia.[4]

Historical Information

Bilharz, in 1852,[5] identified *Hymenolepis nana* as a pathogen when he discovered it on autopsy of a six-year-old boy who died of meningitis, and whose small intestine harbored numerous adult parasites. *H. nana* infections, however heavy, are not life threatening.

Life Cycle

Infection can begin in one of two ways; by ingesting the cysticercoid metacestode (Fig. 31.1) along with an infected insect, or by ingesting embronated eggs. Infective stages of *H. nana* are sometimes present in tenebrio larvae (i.e., meal worms often found contaminating cereals and grains) or in rat feces. If eggs are ingested (Fig 31.2), the oncospheres hatch in the small intestine and penetrate the lamina propria of a villus. There, each larva differentiates into the cysticercoid (juvenile stage).

The cysticercoid reenters the intestinal lumen, and attaches to the surface of the villous tissue (Fig. 31.3), where it rapidly differentiates into an immature adult parasite with four suckers and a single row of hooklets (Fig. 31.4). *H. nana* grows to full maturity within a three to four-week period. If the cysticercoid is ingested, then it attaches to the wall of the small intestine and differentiates and matures to the adult worm, usually within a two week period.

Mating between nearby proglottids (Fig. 31.5) produces hundreds of fertilized eggs. Gravid segments break off from the strobila and disintegrate in the small intestine, releasing the fertilized, embryonated eggs. Auto-infection, with released eggs hatching directly within the intestine, is a possibility, but rarely occurs,[6] as immunity to reinfection develops in most instances. Eggs deposited in the feces may be ingested by the larvae of beetles, rodents, or humans. In the invertebrate host, the oncospheres hatch and penetrate the gut to enter the hemocoel where they differentiate into cysticercoid metacestodes. In the rat or human, infection is as described at the beginning of this section.

Cellular and Molecular Pathogenesis

Infection is usually self-limited in adult patients, but not in very young children, probably reflecting the age-specificity of development of protective immunity. A low but detectable humoral immune response occurs.[1] In experimental infections of mice, the cysticercoid attracts eosinophils by secreting factors into the local

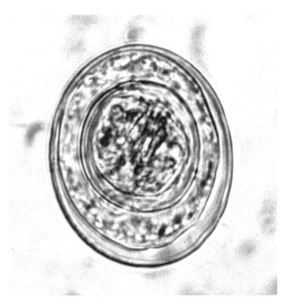

Figure 31.2. Egg of *Hymenolepis nana*. 35 μm x 40 μm.

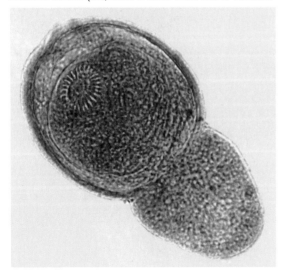

Figure 31.1. The cysticercoid of *Hymenolepis nana*. 350 μm x 200 μm.

Treatment

Praziquantel is the drug of choice because it affects both the cysticercoid in the villus tissue and the adult. A higher dose (25 mg/kg once) than that required for other tapeworms is usually required. In contrast, niclosamide kills the adult, but it is not effective against the metacestode. If niclosamide is the only drug available, re-examining the patient's stool after therapy is important, because an additional course of therapy is usually necessary. The drug nitazoxanide has been investigated as a broad-spectrum antiparasitic for children with multiple intestinal protozoa and helminths, including *H. nana*.[12]

Prevention and Control

Preventing contamination of food and water supplies with human feces is the best approach to controlling *H. nana* infection. In treating individuals, especially small children, it is sometimes difficult to effect a cure, due to auto-infection. Rodent reservoir hosts contaminate the environment and, in many situations, controlling their populations has reduced the incidence of infection, but more often than not, rodent populations cannot be reduced. Hence, reinfection in endemic areas is the norm.

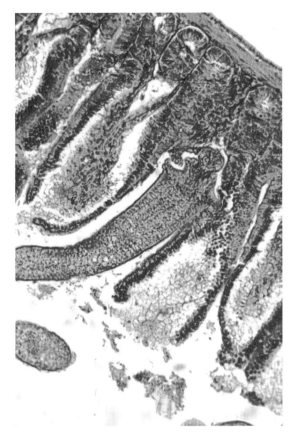

Figure 31.3. Histological section of *H. nana, in situ.*

area of infection, especially during reinfection,[8] and these host cells may play a role in preventing establishment of new infections with *Hymenolepis nana*.[9] In addition, regardless of the immunological background of the mouse strain, INF-γ is always a dominant feature of their response to infection,[10] and expulsion of worms may be due directly to the up regulation of this peptide. Antibodies of the IgE class may also play a role in protection.[11]

Clinical Disease

Diarrhea is the dominant symptom in heavy infections.[3] Light infections are unnoticed. There is no evidence of a causal relation between headaches and convulsions and infection with *Hymenolepis nana*.

Diagnosis

Microscopic identification of embryonated eggs (see Fig. 32.2) in the stool is the definitive diagnosis. When whole pieces of strobila are passed, they can be identified directly, or the eggs can be expressed from gravid proglottids and then identified.

Figure 31.4. Scolex of *Hymenolepis nana.* It has four suckers as well as hooks.

Figure 31.5. Mature proglottids of *Hymenolepis nana.* 400 μm wide.

Hymenolepis diminuta (Rudolphi 1819)

Introduction

Hymenolepis dimunuta is found throughout the world and has many reservoir hosts, including dogs, cats, and many species of rodents. As with *H. nana*, it is primarily an infection of children.

Historical Information

Rudolphi, in 1819,[13] described the morphology of *Hymenolepis diminuta*, and Weinland, in 1858,[14] described the infection in humans.

Life Cycle

Infection begins when the cysticercoid is ingested with the infected insect. The immature worm attaches to the intestinal wall with the aid of four suckers on its scolex. The adult worm matures within 18 days, and grows to a length of 50 cm in length. The strobila contains about 1,000 proglottids at any one time.

Gravid proglottids detach from the strobila and disintegrate in the small intestine. Eggs (Fig. 32.6) pass with the feces, and must be ingested by an appropriate intermediate host, either the larva of fleas or flour beetles (*Tenebrio spp.*), to continue the life cycle. In contrast to eggs of *H. nana*, *H. diminuta* ova are not infectious for humans. When eggs were experimentally fed to *Tenebrio molitor* larvae, some eggs passed through their gut tract, and were incorporated within the fecal pellets. There, they remained infective for 48 hours, allowing infection to spread among the remaining insect larvae.[15]

The egg hatches within the lumen of the insect gut, and the oncosphere penetrates into the hemocoel and develops into the cysticercoid, the infective stage for humans. The life cycle is completed when a human inadvertently eats an infected insect. Other vertebrates (e.g., rats, mice, and dogs) also serve as definitive hosts.

Cellular and Molecular Pathogenesis

Hymenolepis diminuta is a well-studied tapeworm,[16] and continues to serve as a model for all adult tapeworms infecting warm-blooded mammals.[17] Despite the wealth of knowledge accumulated on this cestode, little is known of its pathophysiology in humans.

Clinical Disease

H. diminuta induces no tissue damage. Usually there are no clinical symptoms attributable to this infection,[18] although infections with more than ten worms have been associated with abdominal pains, anorexia, and irritability.[19, 20] In experimental infection in rats, *H. diminuta* has subtle effects on gut transit time and the myoelectric potential,[21] but whether this is the case in human infection has yet to be demonstrated.

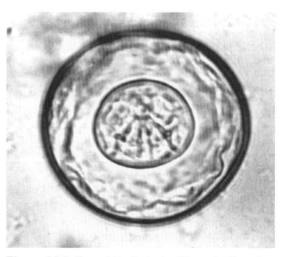

Figure 31.6. Egg of *H. diminuta.* 75 μm in diameter.

Diagnosis

Identification of eggs (see Fig. 31.6; Fig. C.61., Appendix C) in the stool is the definitive method of diagnosis. Occasionally, whole segments of adult worms, which can be identified directly, are also passed in the feces. It is possible to extract eggs from such gravid segments and identify them.

Treatment

Praziquantel or niclosamide are the drugs of choice. Repeated treatments may be necessary. The adaptation of *H. diminuta* to the golden hamster allows for the in vivo testing of new anti-cestode drugs.[22]

Prevention and Control

H. diminuta, like *H. nana,* must be controlled both in the infected individual and in the reservoir host, but the latter is an unrealistic goal in most rural and suburban situations in less-developed countries. Community efforts are aimed at curtailing contamination of food, especially whole grains and processed flour, by insects that could harbor the intermediate stage of the worm.

Dipylidium caninum (Linnaeus 1758)

Introduction

Dipylidium caninum lives in the lumen of the small intestine of the dog, cat, fox, hyena, and occasionally human. The name of the genus is of Greek origin, and means "double pore" or "double opening."

Life Cycle

The infection is acquired by ingesting an infected adult flea, usually *Ctenocephalides canis* or *C. felis* (see scanning EM, Fig. 38.23). The cysticercoid is released from the flea by the digestive enzymes of the host. The scolex (Fig. 32.7) attaches to the villous surface of the small intestine, and within 25 days, the adult worm begins passing gravid proglottids (Fig. 32.8). These segments disintegrate and release eggs (Fig. 31.9), which pass in feces to the external environment. Eggs are ingested by flea larvae. As with *H. diminuta,* the oncosphere penetrates the hemocoel of the immature flea, and develops into the cysticercoid. This stage is infective for humans. Children are frequently infected by coming in close contact with dogs or cats, inadvertently swallowing an infected adult flea.

Clinical Disease

D. caninum does not cause any recognized clinical disease. Attempts to link symptoms, such as mild

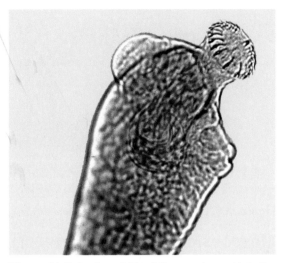

Figure 31.7. Scolex of *Dipylidium caninum.* Note the four suckers and hooks.

abdominal pain, diarrhea, pruritus ani, failure to thrive, and irritability, have failed to show an association with infection.[23] Most *D. caninum* infections occur in children less than 8 years of age.[24]

Diagnosis

The diagnosis is made by microscopically identifying the characteristic egg clusters in the patient's stool. If proglottids are available, they, too, are readily identifiable.

Treatment

Praziquantel or niclosamide are the drugs of choice.

Prevention and Control

Eradication of fleas in pets and treating infected animals with niclosamide greatly reduce the chances of human infection.

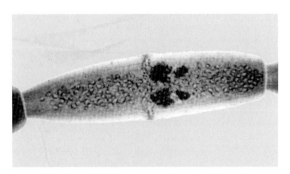

Figure 31.8. Double-pored gravid proglottid of *Dipylidium caninum.* 200 µm in width.

Figure 31.9. Egg cluster of *Dipylidium caninum*.

Mesocestoides spp. (Valliant 1863)

Introduction

Cestodes, in the genus Mesocestoides, infect numerous species of mammals and birds. Human infections have been reported.[25] Most of the cases reported from the U.S. were caused by *Mesocestoides variabiis*.[26] The life cycle of Mesocestoides is complex, involving a coprophagous arthropod as the first intermediate host, and birds, snakes, lizards, amphibians, rodents, or other mammalian carnivores as the second intermediate host. The infective stage, known as a tetrathyridium, develops in the second intermediate host. Tetrathyridia are usually about 1 cm long and contain an invaginated scolex with four suckers. Humans acquire the parasite by eating the tetrathyridia, which can develop to an adult worm in the gut or migrate to the peritoneal cavity. Cases of Mesocestoides infection have been described in the United States,[25] but the mode of acquisition is not known. However, a recent case of Mesocestoides infection from a 19 month-old boy in Alexandria, Louisiana, has led to the suggestion that the infection is food-borne, possibly in association with the culinary customs of the Acadian and Creole communities in this region. Treatment of the adult tapeworm with praziquantel or niclosamide is effective.[26]

References

1. Gomez-Priego A. Godinez-Hana AL. Gutierrez-Quiroz M. Detection of serum antibodies in human Hymenolepis infection by enzyme immunoassay. Trans R Soc Trop Med Hyg 85:645-647. 1991.
2. Mirdha BR. Samantray JC. *Hymenolepis nana*: a common cause of paediatric diarrhea in urban slum dwellers in India. J Trop Pediatr 48: 331-4. 2002.
3. Sirivichayakul C. Radomyos P. et al. *Hymenolepis nana* infection in Thai children. J Med Assoc Thai 83:1035-8. 2000.
4. Macnish MG. Ryan UM. Behnke JM. Thompson RC. Detection of the rodent tapeworm Rodentolepis (=Hymenolepis) microstoma in humans. A new zoonosis? Int J Parasitol 33: 1079-85. 2003.
5. Bilharz T. Em Beitrag zur Helminographia humana. Z Wissenschr Zool 4:53-76. 1852.
6. Andreassen J. Intestinal Tapeworms. In: Topley and Wilson's Microbiology and Microbial Infections. Collier L. Balows A. and Sussman M, ed. Volume 5 Parasiology (Cox FEG. Kreier JP. Wakelin D, ed). 9th edition Arnold Pub., London. pp. 520-537. 1998.
7. Niwa A. Asano K. Ito A. Eosinophil chemotactic factors from cysticercoids of *Hymenolepis nana*. J Helminthol. 72:273-5.1998.
8. Niwa A. Miyazato T. Reactive oxygen intermediates from eosinophils in mice infected with *Hymenolepis nana*. Parasite Immunol. 18:285-95. 1996.
9. Conchedda M. Bortoletti G. et al. Immune response to the cestode *Hymenolepis nana*: cytokine production during infection with eggs or cysts. Int J Parasitol. 27:321-7. 1997.
10. Asano K. Muramatsu K. Importance of interferon-gamma in protective immunity against *Hymenolepis nana* cysticercoids derived from challenge infection with eggs in BALB/c mice. Int J Parasitol. 27:1437-43. 1997.
11. Watanabe N. Nawa Y. Okamoto K. Kobayashi A. Expulsion of *Hymenolepis nana* from mice with congenital deficiencies of IgE production or of mast cell development. Parasite Immunol.16:137-44. 1994.
12. Diaz E. Mondragon J. Ramirez E. Bernal R. Epidemiology and control of intestinal parasites with nitazoxanide in children in Mexico. Am J Trop Med Hyg 68: 384-5. 2003.
13. Rudolphi CA. Entozoorum Synopsis cui Accedunt Mantissa Duplex et Indeces Locuplet. Issimi. Berolini. 1819.
14. Weinland DF. An Essay on the Tapeworms of Man. Cambridge, MA, 1858.
15. Pappas PW. Barley AJ. Beetle-to-beetle transmission and dispersal of *Hymenolepis diminuta* (Cestoda) eggs via the feces of *Tenebrio molitor*. J Parasitol. 85:384-5. 1999.
16. Arai HP. Biology of the Tapeworm *Hymenolepis diminuta*. Academic Press Pubs. New York, London. pp.733. 1980.
17. Andreassen J. Bennet-Jenkins EM. Bryant C. Immunology and biochemistry of *Hymenolepis diminuta*. Adv Parasitol. 42: 223-75. 1999.
18. Wiwanitkit V. Overview of *Hymenolepis diminuta* infection among Thai patients. MedGenMed 6:7. 2004.
19. Hamrick HI. Bowdre JH. Church SM: Rat tapeworm (*Hymenolepis diminuta*) infection in a child. Pediatr Infect Dis 1 9:216-219. 1990.
20. Tena D. Perez Simon M. et al. Human infection with *Hymenolepis diminuta*: case report from Spain. J Clin Microbiol. 36:2375-6. 1998.
21. Dwinell MB. Bass P. Schaefer DM. Oaks JA. Tapeworm infection decreases intestinal transit and enteric aerobic bacterial populations. Am J Physiol. 273:G480-5. 1997.
22. Ostlind DA. Mickle WG. et al. The *Hymenolepis diminuta*-golden hamster (*Mesocricetus auratus*) model for the evaluation of gastrointestinal cestode activity. J Parasitol 90: 898-9. 2004.
23. Hamrick HJ. Drake R. et at. Two cases of dipylidiasis (dog tapeworm infection) in children: update of an old problem. Pediatrics 72:114-117.1983.
24. Molina CP. Ogburn J. Adegboyega P. Infection by *Dipylidium caninum* in an infant. Arch Pathol Lab Med 127: e157-9. 2003.
25. Schultz LF. Roberto RR. et al. Mesocestoides (Cestoda) infection in a California child. Ped Infect Dis J 11:332-334. 1992.
26. Fuentes MV. Galan-Puchades MT. Malone JB. Short report: a new case report of human Mesocestoides infection in the United States. Am J Trop Med Hyg 68: 566-7. 2003.

32. Juvenile Tapeworm Infections

Introduction

Many cestodes that infect wild and domestic animals use other mammals as their intermediate hosts. In many instances, humans become "dead-end" intermediate hosts of these parasites by inadvertently ingesting the ova. Infection with the oncospheres of *Taenia solium, Taenia multiceps, Taenia serialis, Taenia brauni, Echinococcus granulosus, Echinococcus multilocularis,* and a group of related tapeworms in the genus Spirometra lead to space-filling lesions induced by the resulting metacestodes. Some cause serious disease: for example, neurocysticercosis due to infection with *T. solium,* and hydatid cyst due to infection with *Echinococcus granulosus.* Both cysticercosis and echinococcosis are considered emerging infections.

The juvenile tapeworm infections occasionally result in clinical conditions in which their lesions must be distinguished from other non-parasitic space-filling entities.[1] Fortunately, newer imaging techniques and confirmatory serologic assays have been extremely helpful in resolving the diagnosis of larval tapeworm infections.[2]

For additional information on larval cestode infections, the reader can refer to two excellent and comprehensive clinical reviews on cysticercosis by Garcia and colleagues,[3] and echinococcosis by McManus and colleagues.[4]

Taenia solium (Linnaeus 1758)

Introduction

Infection with the cysticercus (i.e., juvenile stage) of the pork tapeworm, *T. solium,* exists in regions where the following conditions are present: (1) the incidence of *T. solium* adult infections is high; (2) pigs are allowed to roam freely within human habitats; and (3) improper disposal of human feces is the rule (Fig. 32.6). These three situations occur together in impoverished regions of South America (especially the Andean Region), Central America, Mexico, Asia (especially China and Southeast Asia), and sub-Saharan Africa (particularly South Africa) (see www.promedmail.org 05/06/05, Neurocysticercosis Outbreak in the Village of Coza), where families frequently keep one or more pigs and permit them to roam free, feeding on garbage and human feces.[3, 5-7] In these regions, cysticerci in the brain,[8] leading to neurocysticercosis, is a leading cause of epilepsy in children. Within the last two decades,

neurocysticercosis also emerged in U.S. cities near the border with Mexico, including Los Angeles, San Diego, Tuscon, Phoenix, Albuquerque, El Paso, San Antonio, and Houston.[9] Neurocysticercosis in the U.S. is especially common among Hispanic populations in which a family member or other close contact harbors an adult *T. solium* tapeworm.

Aberrant Life Cycle

Infection begins by ingesting embryonated eggs (Fig. 29.5), usually from a contaminated external environment. Patients harboring adult worms typically have eggs on their exteriors (e.g., under fingernails, between the toes and fingers), despite good personal hygiene. Thus, they have plenty of opportunities to acquire cysticerci through autoinfection, as well as to contaminate others in their immediate surroundings.[10] When individuals ingest *T. solium* eggs, the larvae (oncospheres) inside survive the gastric acid of the stomach and enter the small intestine. They are stimulated to hatch, and then they penetrate the intestinal wall and enter the bloodstream. Eventually, the oncospheres could penetrate into one of many tissues (e.g., striated muscles, heart, brain, eye) and encyst there. The oncosphere rapidly differentiates into a cysticercus (juvenile stage) (Fig. 32.1), grows and develops, and creates a space-filling lesion within 2-3 months, typically measuring approximately 10 mm.[3] Cysticerci achieve maximum growth about three weeks after entering a given tissue, and then cease growing. Unlike adult pork tapeworm infection, cysticercosis and neurocysticercosis does not involve ingestion of uncooked pork, but rather the ingestion of eggs shed by individuals who harbor the adult pork tapeworm.

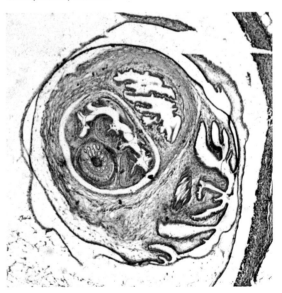

Figure 32.1. Cysticercus of *Taenia solium.*

Cysticercosis
(Taenia solium)

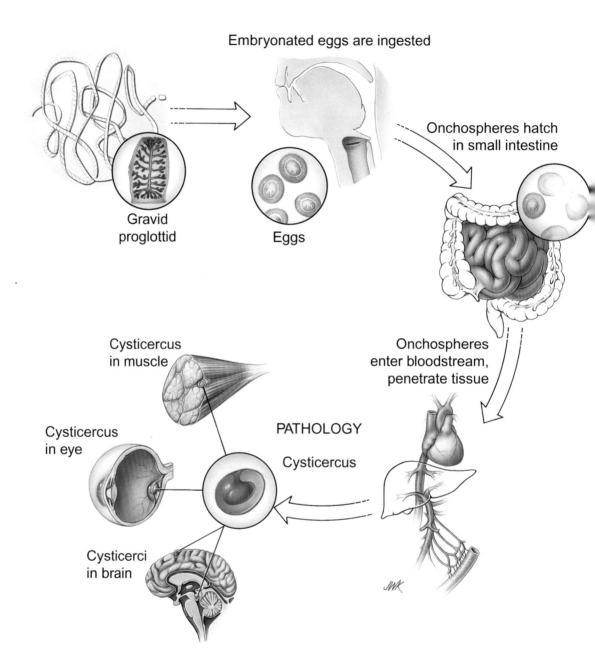

Embryonated eggs are ingested

Gravid proglottid

Eggs

Onchospheres hatch in small intestine

Onchospheres enter bloodstream, penetrate tissue

Cysticercus in muscle

Cysticercus in eye

PATHOLOGY

Cysticercus

Cysticerci in brain

JWK

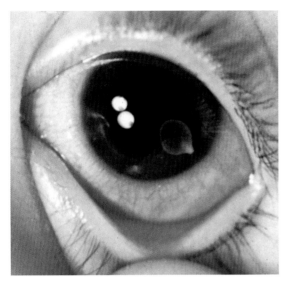

Figure 32.2. Cysticercus of *Taenia solium* floating free in the anterior chamber of the eye.

Cellular and Molecular Pathogenesis

The immunological and molecular aspects of the pathogenesis of cysticercosis have been reviewed by White and colleagues.[11] Pathological consequences are those of a space-occupying lesion.[1] Oncospheres that lodge in the CNS [i.e., eye (Fig. 32.2) or brain (Fig. 32.3)] grow up in an immunologically "privileged" site, and avoid immune attack. These cysts tend to grow to a larger size than those in other tissues.

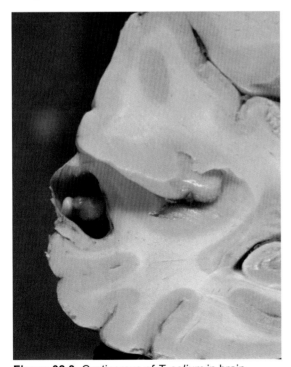

Figure 32.3. Cysticercus of *T. solium* in brain.

Oncospheres arriving from the circulation to sites other than CNS are presumably susceptible to the host's immune system, but rapid development to the cysticercus stage may account for the high rate of survival, at least during a primary infection. Cysticercus development is coincident with modulation of host immune responses, favoring expression of parasite immune evasion mechanisms that interfere with Th-2-type protective immune responses.[11] Immunomodulatory substances have been identified and partially characterized: for example, taeniastatin, a protease inhibitor,[12] and paramyosin.[13] Both molecules can inhibit different aspects of the complement cascade.[14]

Ultimately, cysticerci die of old age and become calcified, usually within two years after infection. Dying parasites release their suppressive hold on protective host immune responses, and are accompanied by release of antigens. When cellular reactions are present, they are the result of interleukin signaling from T cells. Specific IgM antibodies and NK+ cells are also present in these infiltrates.[15] An acute local inflammatory reaction follows, consisting of lymphocytes, plasma cells, and eosinophils, which may be clinically significant in neurocysticercosis.[11] Many investigators believe that this host inflammatory response around degenerating cysticerci, when it occurs in the brain, is responsible for eliciting seizures and intracranial hypertension. On neuroimaging studies (CT with contrast or MRI), the inflammation encircles the lesion, giving rise to the appearance of "ring-enhancement." In addition, cysticerci occurring in anatomically sensitive sites in the central nervous system can cause mass effect or block the circulation of cerebrospinal fluid leading to hydrocephalus.[3]

Strong, protective immunity to invasion of tissues by oncospheres can be induced in a variety of animals, and offers hope for developing a vaccine for use in pigs.[16]

Clinical Disease

There are two major clinical presentations: extraneural (subcutaneous and intramuscular) cysticercosis and neurocysticercosis.[3] These two conditions are not mutually exclusive, as most of the patients with neurocysticercosis also have evidence for subcutaneous disease.[3]

Extraneural cysticercosis is usually asymptomatic, but patients may notice painless subcutaneous nodules in the arms or chest,[17] or small, discrete swellings of particular muscles (Fig. 32.4), in which cysticerci have lodged. After several months, the nodules become swollen and tender, presumably because of the host inflammatory response to the cysticerci. Sub-

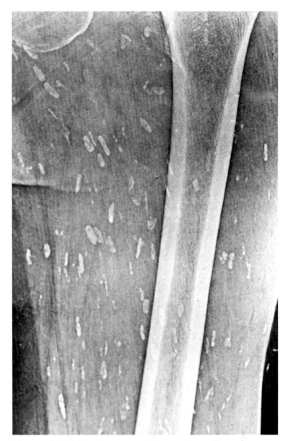

Figure 32.4. Radiogram of lower leg with numerous cysticerci of *Taenia solium*.

sequently, the nodules disappear. There may be geographic variation in this clinical presentation because subcutaneous cysticercosis is common in Asia and Africa, but rare in Latin America.[3] Ultimately, these lesions will calcify after death. The calcifications can persist for years. Some patients with extraneural cysticercosis can also harbor cardiac cysticercosis, which is usually also asymptomatic.[3]

Neurocysticercosis (cysticercosis in the central nervous system) is the most severe manifestation that follows the ingestion of *T. solium* eggs; the signs and symptoms vary greatly with the number and distribution of cysts (Fig. 32.2 – 32.7).[17] It often presents as a space-occupying lesion, and in many respects mimics a tumor.[1] Thus seizures, hydrocephalus, epilepsy,[18] and focal neurologic abnormalities may be the presenting signs. It has been estimated that seizures occur in 50-80 percent of patients with brain parenchymal cysts, which occur as a consequence of host inflammation around dead and degenerating parasites.[3] In endemic regions, teenage and young adults exhibit the highest rates of *T. solium* seizures.[3] These patients, especially females, can also develop an accompanying encephalitis.[3] Children immigrating to The United States from

endemic areas frequently present with a solitary mass and seizures[20] Usually, with those suffering seizures, the cysticercus has calcified to some extent (Fig. 32.7),[21] and possibly the parasite inside has died.

People still residing in endemic areas are often found to have more complex disease, and have a greater likelihood of presenting with multiple cysts, including cysts that locate in the subarachnoid space or the ventricles.[3] These patients present with elevated intracranial pressure, arachnoiditis, meningitis, encephalitis, or hydrocephalus.[22] They are also more likely to experience stroke.

There appear to be geographic differences in the presentation of clinical neurocysticercosis. In Asia, patients most commonly present with a single enhancing brain lesion, whereas in Latin America it is common to find multiple cysts without evidence of inflammation.[3]

Ophthalmic cysticercosis occurs in approximately 1-3 percent of all infections, and most typically manifest as intraocular cysts floating freely in the vitreous humor or the subretinal space. Patients complain of seeing shadows. Subsequent development of uveitis, retinitis, or choroidal atrophy can lead to visual loss.[3]

Diagnosis

Criteria for diagnosing cysticercosis have been reviewed by Dorny and colleagues.[22] The neuroimaging aspects of diagnosis have been reviewed by Leitte and colleagues,[23] and by Garcia and colleagues.[3]

Neuroimaging by CT or MRI is of critical importance in diagnosing neurocysticercosis. Because it is often not practical to biopsy cysticerci, the expert opinion by a consulting neuroradiologist is extremely helpful. On CT, the cysts appear as hypodense images containing a small hyperdense nodule that represents the parasite

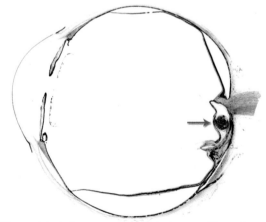

Figure 32. 5. Cross section of whole eye with cysticercus of *T. solium* (arrow) in retina at the level of the optic nerve.

scolex. As noted above, the inflammation surrounding dead and dying parasites will provide so-called ring-enhancement in the presence of contrast media. In the natural history of neurocysticercosis, the dead and dying cysts will calcify. Although MRI is more expensive and less available in developing countries, it often provides a clearer image of the cysticercus.[3]

Serologic testing provides important confirmatory data for patients with lesions suspicious for cysticerci on CT or MRI. The enzyme-linked immunoblot has replaced the older ELISA,[22, 24] and has a sensitivity in some settings of 98 percent and a specificity of 100 percent.[3, 24-26] However, for patients with a solitary lesion, the sensitivity is much lower, presumably because of the small amount of parasite antigen available to the host immune system. In an acute care setting, the enzyme-linked immunoblot test requires considerable interpretation because antibody titers can remain high long after the death of the parasites.[3]

Treatment

Because seizures most often occur in neurocysticercosis when the host inflammatory response is overcoming degenerating parasites, there is a controversy

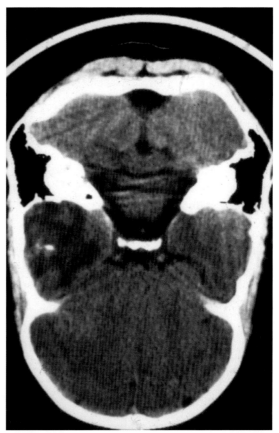

Figure 32.7. Radiogram of brain with calcified lesion due to infection with the metacestode of *T. solium*.

regarding the use of specific anthelminthic chemotherapeutic agents. Increasingly, the complexities of the medical and surgical management of neurocysticercosis require a team approach. Typically, this might include an infectious disease specialist, a neurologist, a neuroradiologist, an ophthalmologist and a neurosurgeon.[27]

Praziquantel and albendazole are the drugs of choice for neurocysticercosis.[28] Both antiparasitic agents are effective at destroying cysticerci in the brain, but parasite death occurs at the risk of inducing or exacerbating inflammation.[3] It is the inflammatory response in the brain that is largely responsible for seizures, encephalitis, and elevated intracranial pressure. The results of two double-blind, placebo-controlled trials in patients with a solitary enhancing lesion, and a third double-blind, placebo-controlled trial comparing the evolution of brain parenchymal lesions on CT after three months of treatment were recently summarized by Garcia.[3] Only one of these trials showed benefit from albendazole in terms of resolution of images and seizures. Therefore, the current recommendation is that therapeutic decisions on using either albendazole (15 mg/kg daily for 8 days) or praziquantel (50 mg/kg

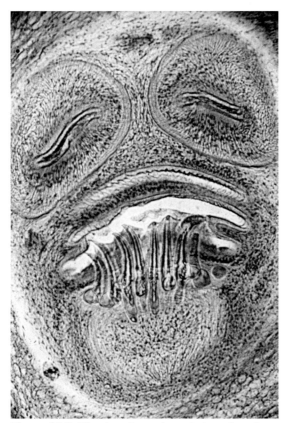

Figure 32.6. Alien invader: enlarged view of cysticercus from Figure 32.5.

daily for 15 days) need to be tailored to the individual patient, based on the number, location, and viability of the cysticerci.[3] All patients selected for treatment with anthelminthic drugs should undergo a prior ophthalmologic exam in order to rule out intraocular cysts.

Consensus guidlelines on the use of anthelminthic chemotherapy have been published.[29] Some clinicians are of the opinion that patients with single ring-enhancing lesions on CT scans often improve spontaneously without any therapy,[19, 30] but recommend that viable cysticerci should be treated with medical management, provided that the subsequent elevations in intracranial pressure and seizures can be monitored and controlled.[3] Also, patients with multiple viable cysts and enlarged cysts may benefit from therapy. For patients with a solitary lesion, shorter courses of anthelminthic chemotherapy (1 day of praziquantel or 3 days of

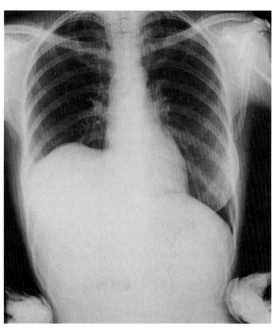

Figure 32.9. Radiogram of upper body showing elevation in right lobe of liver due to a large hydatid cyst.

albendazole) have also been reported to be effective.

Because both albendazole and praziquantel kill cysticerci and exacerbate brain inflammation and edema, patients being treated for neurocysticercosis also require steroids, usually dexamethasone, to reduce swelling. Dexamethasone affects the blood levels of both praziquantel and albendazole, so drug doses of either must usually be adjusted.[31] Additional medical management with anticonvulsants is also a critical component of the long-term management of *T. solium*-induced seizures; this should be undertaken with the consultation of a neurologist.

Neurosurgical management with placement of ventricular shunts is often required for complicated neurocysticercosis involving cerebrospinal obstruction and hydrocephalus. Surgical management may also be required for spinal lesions and eye lesions.

Prevention and Control

See Prevention and Control section for *Taenia solium* adults. In an endemic area of Guatemala, mass treatment of humans and pigs significantly reduced the incidence of infection in both hosts, and reduced the rate of neurocysticercosis, as well.[32] Vaccination of pigs with recombinant antigen might be possible in certain endemic situations,[16, 33, 34] but will not result in the elimination of neurocysticercosis in New Guinea and in other remote regions of the world, where vaccines could never benefit those who need them the most.

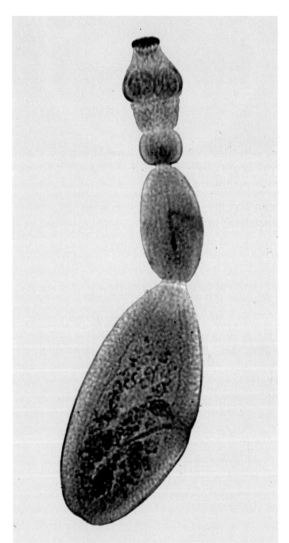

Figure 32.8. Adult of *Echinococcus granulosus*. Note four suckers and hooks on scolex. The worm is 5.5 mm long.

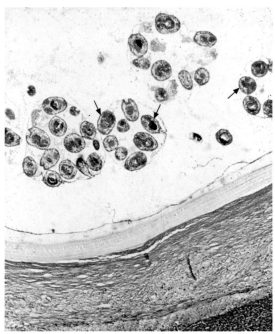

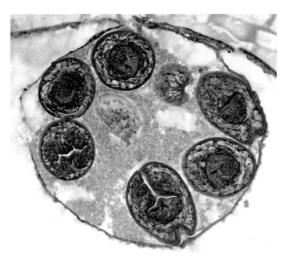

Figure 32.11. Brood capsule with protoscolices of *Echinococcus granulosus*.

Figure 32.10. Histological section of an hydatid cyst with capsules filled with protoscolices (arrows) of *Echinococcus granulosus*. Each protoscolex measures approx. 13-14 mm in length.

Echinococcus granulosus
(Batsch 1786)

Introduction

Echinococcus granulosus lives as an adult parasite in the small intestine of its definitive host – domestic dogs and other Canidae. It is one of the smallest cestodes, measuring 5 mm in length. The strobila consists of a scolex and three segments (Fig. 32.8). Sheep and other herbivores serve as intermediate hosts, acquiring infection by eating embryonated eggs that contaminate grazing pastures. Humans are also susceptible to the juvenile stage of the parasite, which may develop to a large, fluid filled cyst, often exceeding 40 cm in diameter. The condition is referred to as hydatid disease.

Distribution of *E. granulosus* coincides with sheep husbandry. Eurasia, especially the Russian Federation and Central Asia and China, Mediterranean countries (especially, Turkey, Lebanon and Syria), North and East Africa (especially, Egypt, Sudan, and Kenya), and Australia have the highest prevalence.[3] Infection has been totally eradicated from Iceland, but not from other island communities, such as Cyprus and New Zealand.[35]

Small, endemic areas of infection exist in the United States, primarily in California, Utah, and Arizona, where individuals of Basque descent and Native Americans

are rarely infected.[36] A number of cases have also been described in the lower Mississippi River Valley.[37]

Indigenous peoples of the Canadian Arctic, especially the Inuit, are infected with a northern variant of echinococcosis (*E. granulosus var. canadensis*), acquired in a sylvatic cycle involving moose and caribou (cervids), wolves, and sled dogs.[3, 38] Two cases recently reported from Alaska are unusually severe.[39] In Lapland (i.e., northern Scandinavian countries), herding of reindeer is associated with this infection.

Historical Information

Pallas, in 1766,[40] described the hydatid cyst of *Echi-*

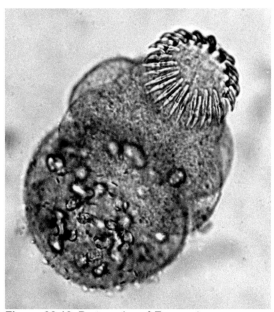

Figure 32.12. Protoscolex of *E. granulosus*.

Echinococcus granulosus

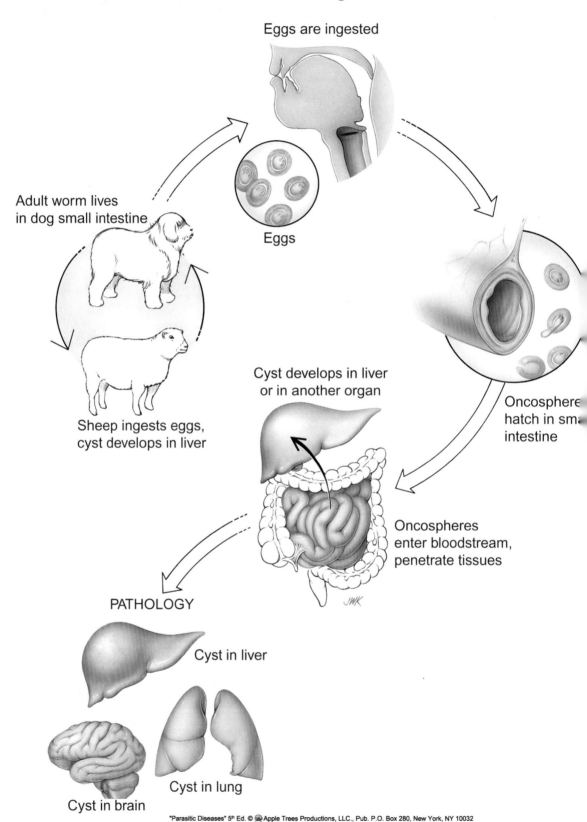

Eggs are ingested

Eggs

Adult worm lives in dog small intestine

Sheep ingests eggs, cyst develops in liver

Cyst develops in liver or in another organ

Oncospheres hatch in small intestine

Oncospheres enter bloodstream, penetrate tissues

PATHOLOGY

Cyst in liver

Cyst in lung

Cyst in brain

"Parasitic Diseases" 5th Ed. © Apple Trees Productions, LLC., Pub. P.O. Box 280, New York, NY 10032

Figure 32.13. Petri dish filled with daughter cysts of *Echinococcus granulosus*.

nococcus granulosus, in which he sketched cysts that he removed from the viscera of mice, and compared them with those recovered by others from human infections. Goeze, in 1782,[41] in his classic monograph, depicted the juveniles (i.e., protoscolices). Von Siebold, in 1853,[42] described the adult worms in the dog. Finally, Naunyn, in 1863,[43] fed the contents of hydatid cysts from a human infection to dogs, and recovered adult tapeworms. These experiments provided the essential link between the animal and human infection cycles.

Life Cycle

Echinococcus granulosus adults live in the canine

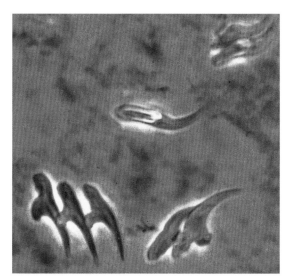

Figure 32.14. Hooklets of a protoscolex. Each hooklet measures approx. 2 μm in length.

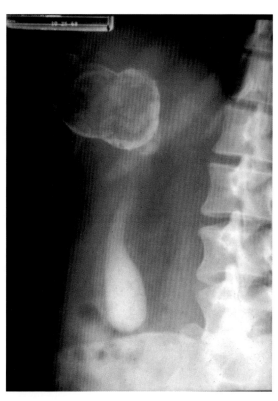

Figure 32.15. Radiogram of a calcified hydatid cyst of *Echinoccocus granulosus*.

small intestine. Multiple infection is the rule, with hundreds to thousands of adult worms occupying the greater portion of the upper half of the small intestine. The gravid segment (one per adult tapeworm) breaks off and disintegrates in the large bowel, releasing hundreds of infective eggs (Fig. 28.5; Fig. 29.5), which then pass out with the feces. Sheep, as well as other domestic animals (e.g., cattle, pigs, and horses), and humans acquire the larval stage by ingesting the embryonated egg. Each intermediate host species (sheep, cattle, pig, and horse) seems to have evolved a separate, genetically definable strain of parasite.[44] The oncosphere

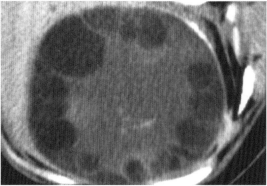

Figure 32.16. Radiogram of a liver infected with multiple hydatid cysts of *Echinoccocus granulosus*.

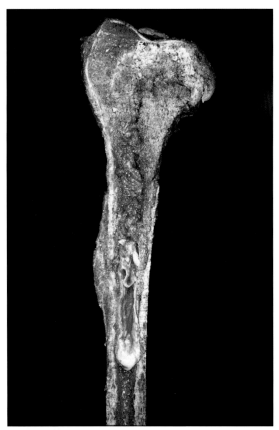

Figure 32.17. Femur from a patient who died of hydatid disease of the bone. Courtesy W. Johnson.

hatches in the small intestine, enters the blood stream, and in the vast majority of cases, reaches the liver via the portal circulation (Fig. 32.9). Other organs can also be invaded, including brain, lung, and kidney. Once in the tissue, the larva synthesizes a hyaline membrane, and becomes surrounded by it. This membrane differentiates into an outer, acellular laminate structure, and an inner, germinal layer (Fig. 32.10, 32.11). The inner surface of the germinal layer gives rise to protoscolices (Fig. 32.12) (i.e., the infectious stage for the definitive host), and more outer membrane material.

The hydatid cyst requires several months to years in order to develop, mature and fill with fluid (Fig. 32.13). The fluid is under pressure, and the wall, while substantial, can rupture if severely traumatized. The entire cyst can contain millions of protoscolices. The diameter of the mature outer cyst varies from 2 to 20 cm, and sometimes is even larger. The fluid portion of the cyst contains both host and parasite proteins. A canine host must ingest the hydatid cyst and its contents (i.e., the protoscolices) to complete the life cycle. This commonly occurs when infected sheep are slaughtered (Fig. 32.18), and organs containing hydatid cysts are discarded or fed to dogs.

The protoscolex, released from the hydatid cyst, attaches itself to the wall of the small intestine aided by its four suckers and a row of hooklets (Fig. 32.13). New gravid proglottids are produced within about 2 months. Dogs do not seem to become ill from the effects of even heavy intestinal infections, which may exceed a million adult worms.

Cellular and Molecular Pathogenesis

There is minimal host reaction to a living hydatid cyst, but little is known regarding the nature of the immune responses directed at the parasite and the antigens it secretes into the cyst fluid. Speculation favors the production of immunosuppressive substances by the parasite,[45, 46] which quell host responses for the life of the cyst. Cysts can remain alive for months to years. In contrast to the cysts, the eggs and their oncospheres of *E. granulosus* are immunogenic and can elicit protective immunity. This feature might provide a mechanism by which intermediate hosts, including humans, control the number of oncospheres that ultimately develop into hydatid cysts.[3]

Clinical Disease

Figure 32.18. Navajo butchering a sheep. The organs containing hydatid cysts are occasionally fed to their dogs, thus completing the life cycle. Courtesy P.M.Schantz.

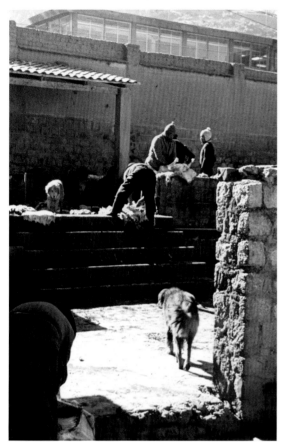

Figure 32.19. Peruvian slaughter house. Organs from sheep containing hydatid cysts are routinely fed to the numerous dogs that frequent these unsanitary, unsupervised rural establishments.

Hydatid disease develops as the result of rapid growth of the cyst (or cysts), and subsequent expansion of the cyst wall. The liver is the most common site of hydatid cyst development (Fig. 32.16), followed by the lungs. More than 90 percent of cysts develop in these two organs.[47] Cysts have been reported to infect almost all of the visceral organs, including the bone marrow (Fig. 32.17) or brain, the latter usually with fatal results.If a cyst ruptures, the entire contents (fluid and protoscolices) spill into the surrounding tissues or body cavity (e.g., peritoneum, pleural cavity). When such an event occurs, an immediate anaphylactic reaction may ensue. Moreover, cyst contents can seed the area, and invade new tissues to produce second-generation hydatid cysts (Fig. 32.17). Even a few cells from the germinal membrane can re-establish an entire hydatid cyst. In this sense, *E. granulosus* is a metastatic parasite. The overall case fatality rate has been estimated at just over 2 percent.[47]

Approximately 60 percent of hydatid cysts are asymptomatic.[47] Symptoms are those of a large space-occupying lesion. If the liver is involved, it becomes enlarged (Fig. 32.10). The cyst presents as a palpable, soft, non-tender, intrahepatic mass. The uninvolved bulk of the liver remains normal. Involvement of the lung is usually identified by chance on a radiograph, or by the presence of bloody sputum, in which protoscolices or hooklets (Fig. 32.14) can be found. Expansion and rupture of liver hydatid cysts into the biliary tree can result in secondary cholangitis, biliary obstruction, and intraperitoneal rupture. Lung cysts can rupture into the bronchial tree and cause the development of a bronchobiliary fistula.[47] Rupture of a cyst, wherever it is lodged, may occur even after relatively minor blunt trauma, and often leads to an allergic reaction. It may be mild and limited to urticaria, or may take the form of anaphylactic shock, requiring immediate intervention. Most patients with the northern variant of echinococcosis have asymptomatic lung cysts that are usually detected on chest radiographs obtained for other reasons (e.g., tuberculosis screening).[47]

Diagnosis

An accurate case history is essential to the diagnosis of hydatid disease. Ownership of dogs, life on a sheep farm – even during childhood, and especially in endemic areas – and/or a history of travel to endemic areas are important factors in ruling in this disease.

Within the last decade, the diagnostic algorithms for hydatid disease have been modified based on increasing experience with radiologic imaging modalities, including ultrasound, CT scanning, and magnetic resonance imaging. The major radiological criteria have been standardized.[47] Imaging by MRI frequently reveal a mixture of hyperdensities and hypodensities, with scattered calcifications (Fig. 32.15).[48] Internal septae and daughter cysts are often demonstrable, and such evidence is strongly suggestive of the diagnosis. Plain radiograms reveal only calcified cysts, which usually contain non-infective protoscolices.

Serodiagnosis is also useful both for primary diagnosis and following patients during and after their medical or surgical management.[49] ELISA, for the detection of Echinococcus antibodies, is the test of choice, and employs hydatid fluid antigen. In addition, efforts are underway to refine the ELISA using chemically-defined antigens, including two known as antigen 5 and lipoprotein antigen B.[50] Patients with intact cysts have a high false-negative rate; presumably because these patients do not experience sufficient antigen challenge to induce a detectable antibody response. Therefore, efforts are underway to develop tests that detect circulating Echinococcus antigens. Eosinophilia is found in less than one-third of patients with hydatid disease.[51]

The presence of a liver cyst may be associated with mildly elevated hepatic enzymes.

A definitive diagnosis of echinococcosis can be made by microscopically identifying hooklets (Fig. 32.14) in any sample, sputum being the most common. This is usually the case in long term infections, in which all cells within the cyst have died, and the only remaining evidence of infection are the hooklets and portions of the acellular, laminate outer membrane of the cyst wall. Biopsy of cysts is absolutely contra-indicated, due to their metastatic nature.

Treatment

Treatment of patients with hydatid cyst often requires both surgical and medical interventions. Surgical intervention is the usual approach to cure for patients with large cysts. Care must be taken to prevent inadvertent rupture of the cysts. Successful removal depends on the location of the cyst. Historically, a variety of strategies have been devised to prevent or minimize spillage of cyst contents.[47] This includes preoperative use of anthelminthic drugs (see below) and the use of protoscolicidal compounds such as 95% ethanol, hypertonic saline and cetrimide.[47]

Introduced in the mid-1980s, the PAIR technique (Puncture, Aspiration, Injection, Re-aspiration) with ultrasound guidance has replaced the need for laparotomy and surgery for some patients.[47,52,53] The risk of complications from PAIR appear to be greatly improved through the use of adjuvant anthelminthic chemotherapy (see below).[47]

Albendazole (400 mg bid x 1-6 months or, for children, 15 mg/kg/d [max. 800 mg] x 1-6 months) has been used successfully to treat hydatid disease, particularly when surgical removal was impossible. Chemotherapy can result in cyst regression or collapse, although prolonged courses of therapy are usually required.[51, 52, 53] It has been estimated that treatment can result in the disappearance of up to 48 percent of cysts and a substantial reduction in size of an additional 24 percent.[47,53] Albendazole is preferable to mebendazole because the former is metabolized to a sulfoxide derivative, which exhibits antiparasitic activity and is widely distributed in the tissues. Therapeutic responses can be monitored radiographically and serologically. Reversible liver toxicity has been reported with prolonged therapy with albendazole.[54, 55] As outlined in the section on Trichuriasis, the benzimidazole anthelminthics, including albendazole, are teratogenic and embryotoxic in laboratory animals. Both drugs are considered category C agents in the USA[47] therefore, before use in pregnancy, the risks versus benefits must be weighed.

Prevention and Control

Infection of domestic dogs with *E. granulosus* can be prevented. Control is best achieved by avoiding feeding dogs (Fig. 32.18, 32.19) any infected organs of slaughtered sheep, or other animals, and by periodically treating dogs prophylactically with niclosamide, arecoline hydrobromide, or praziquantel.[47, 53] An arecoline control program in dogs has resulted in the near-elimination of *E. granulosus* infection in New Zealand and Tasmania.[47] In Iceland, mass slaughter of infected sheep and dogs led to the total eradication of the disease;[56] however, attempts to duplicate that effort in Cyprus were unsuccessful. Strict regulations regarding the importation of animal products that might carry *E. granulosus* eggs (e.g., animal hides of various carnivores, fishing flies, etc.) is a requirement for this control strategy to be effective. A recombinant peptide vaccine, EG95,[57] induces high levels of protection in sheep, and may prove useful in situations where cost of production and ease of distribution are not important factors (i.e., the developed world).

Echinococcus multilocularis
(Leuckart 1863)

Echinoccocus multilocularis infects wild Caenidae, such as fox, and can also infect domestic dogs. The intermediate hosts are usually rodents (e.g., voles, field mice, ground squirrels). The biology of the infection in humans resembles the situation found in the intermediate hosts. *E. multilocularis* results in discrete cysts (alveolar echinococcosis) (Fig. 32.20) that metastasize from a single location. In rodents, protoscolices are found in each daughter cyst. *E. multilocularis* does not produce protoscolices in human infection, only membranes that grow and bisect whatever organ they happen to be in, confounding the diagnosis of this unusual parasitic disease.

This infection is prevalent among fur trappers and others whose occupations bring them in close contact with wild foxes. This includes urban areas where reservoir hosts could expand from foxes to domesticated dogs and cats.[47] Alveolar echinococcosis has emerged to the point where it is endemic in northern hemisphere including western Europe, where it is considered a re-emerging disease due, in part, to the banning of fox hunting in a number of Common Market countries. It is also prevalent in the Russian Federation and Central Asia, China (especially in western and central regions), and northern Japan (Hokkaido). In North America, human infections have been reported from Alaska and in the upper Midwest and Northern plains along the Canadian border.[47]

Infection begins when the intermediate host ingests the egg. The oncosphere hatches in the small intes-

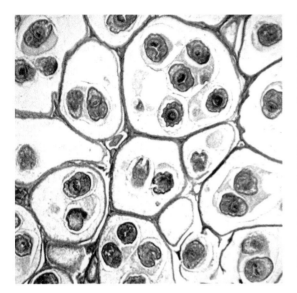

Figure 32.20. *Echinococcus multilocularis* alveolar cyst from an infected vole.

tine and invades the liver by the hematogenous route. It transforms, and then grows into an alveolar type of cyst, characterized by numerous daughter cysts, as compared to hydatid cysts, that grow as a single membrane-bounded unit. Foxes and dogs ingest infected liver containing numerous protoscolices, which leads to infection with the adult worm, thereby completing the life cycle.

In humans, the incubation period of larval infection with *E. multilocularis* is long, with incubation periods of 5-15 years.[47] The initial exposure often occurs during childhood, but the disease has been recognized mainly in older adults.[58] Alveolar disease produces a highly aggressive disease that specifically affects the liver as the primary target organ; the membrane proliferates indefinitely, and causes progressive destruction of the liver parenchyma, which can lead to hepatic failure. Hepatomegaly, jaundice, multiple palpable abdominal masses, epigastric pain, and weight loss have been described. In this sense, alveolar echinococcosis resembles a hepatic malignancy. In addition, metastatic alveolar disease via the hematogenous route is common.

HLA type may play a role in a given individual's risk of developing further disease after chemotherapy. Re-growth of the parasite was significantly more prevalent in patients with haplotype HLA-DQB1 *02 than those with haplotype HLA-DRB1 *1157.[59] Interleukin-10 production was also higher in infected individuals, and may relate to the lack of development of protective immunity.[60]

Diagnosis is based on radiographic imaging and serologic testing by ELISA with a species-specific pro-

tein known as Em2plus.[61]

No therapy has been fully effective. Radical surgery is sometimes effective; the entire larval mass is removed as part of a hepatic or pulmonary lobe resection. Long-term adjuvant chemotherapy with albendazole appears to improve the 10-year survival rate.[62]

Prevention relates to the handling of animal furs and subsequent oral contamination with eggs. Trappers and those involved in animal husbandry in the fur industry should exercise extreme caution when handling carcasses and processing furs. Oral baits laced with therapeutic doses of praziquantel for control of *E. multilocularis* infections in foxes has been attempted.[47] This approach has had remarkable success in controlling the spread of rabies when that vaccine was incorporated within.

Taenia spp.

Taenia spp. (e.g., *T. multiceps, T. brauni, T. serialis*) is a group of tapeworms that, as adults, infect dogs and other Canidae. Intermediate hosts include domestic cattle, horses, goats, and some wild herbivorous game animals of Africa. Humans become infected with the metacestode (juvenile stage), known as coenurus, which resembles cysts found in the intermediate hosts. Human infections have been largely confined to the African continent, but a few cases have been described from France, England, and North and South America.

The larva routinely invades the central nervous system (brain, eyes, spinal cord). Other space-occupying lesions resemble this infection, such as those caused by cysticerci and hydatid cysts.

Diagnosis is based on clinical, epidemiologic, and laboratory findings. No serologic tests are currently available.

Treatment involves surgery if the lesion is accessible. No chemotherapy is available. Prevention is not possible, because reservoir hosts include such a large number of species of wild animals.

Spirometra spp.

Spirometra mansonoides and other related *Spirometra spp.* cause a closely related series of metacestode infections in humans, referred to as sparganosis. Cases of sparganosis have been reported from Southeast Asia, Japan, China, Africa, and the United States. The definitive hosts for many of the species of Spirometra have not been identified. Cats and dogs, in experimental situations, can harbor adult *S. mansonoides*. Cats have also been experimentally infected with *S. ranorum*. The intermediate hosts represent a broad spectrum of vertebrates, including amphibians, reptiles, birds, and mammals, and all harbor the plero-cercoid, only.

Human infection results from ingestion of raw or undercooked flesh of any of the numerous intermediate hosts, and from application of such flesh as poultices. This practice is very common in some areas of the world, particularly on the island of Hianan, where over 30% of the frogs harbor the juvenile stage of spirometra.[63] It is interesting to note that the skin of numerous cold-blooded vertebrates contains a variety of closely related peptides, referred to as megainins.[64] These amphipathic peptides are related to gramicidin, and have potent anti-microbial activities.[65] Employing frog and fish skins for medical use has a chemotherapeutic basis.

However, as with any other therapy, the use of cold-blooded vertebrate skin as a poultice has "side effects." In this case, the user may develop a parasitic infection. The plerocercoid usually migrates out of the poultice into the subcutaneous tissues, stimulated by the rise in temperature from the human host. If the poultice is placed over an open wound, or the eye, the immature parasite enters the site and grows into irregular nodules. The surrounding tissues proliferate, becoming edematous and painful, because the larva secretes a version of growth hormone similar in activity to mammalian GH.[66]

In the case of early eye involvement, removal of the larva from the space between the lower lid and the eyeball results in complete remission. Unfortunately, larvae often migrate behind the eye, and even into the brain[67] via the optic nerve, making easy removal of the parasite impossible. In these instances, surgery is necessary. In some cases, death ensues. Subcutaneous lesions must also be removed by surgery;[67] there is no effective chemotherapy. Prevention is difficult, because of the effectiveness and popularity of poultice use for a variety of medical problems, including photophobia due to chickenpox.[68]

References

1. Silver SA. Erozan YS. Hruban RH. Cerebral cysticercosis mimicking malignant glioma: a case report. Acta Cytol. 40(2):351-7. 1996.
2. Tsuchiya K. Inaoka S. Mizutani Y. Hachiya J. Fast fluid-attenuated inversion-recovery MR of intracranial infections. AJNR Am J Neuroradiol.18:909-13. 1997.
3. Garcia HH. Gonzalez AE. Evans CAW. Gilman RH. for the Cysticercosis Working Group in Peru. Lancet 361: 547-56. 2003.
4. McManus. Zhang WB. Li J. Bartley PB. Echinococcosis. Lancet 362: 195- . 2003.
5. Flisser A. Larval Cestodes. In: Topley and Wilson's Microbiology and Microbial Infections (Collier L. Balows A. and Sussman M, eds). Volume 5. Parasitology (Cox FEG. Kreier JP. Wakelin D., volume eds.). 9th ed. Arnold Pubs., London. pp. 539-560. 1998.
6. Ruiz-Garcia M. Gonzalez-Astiazaran A. Rueda-Franco F. Neurocysticercosis in children. Clinical experience in 122 patients. Childs Nerv Syst. 13:608-12. 1997.
7. Cruz ME. Preux PM. et al. Epidemiology of cerebral cysticercosis in an Andean community in Ecuador. Bull Soc Pathol Exot. 92:38-41.1999.
8. Garcia HH. Del Brutto OH. Heavy nonencephalitic cerebral cysticercosis in tapeworm carriers. Neurology. 53:1582-4. 1999.
9. Sorvillo FJ. Waterman SH. Richards FO. Schantz PM. Cysticercosis surveillance: locally acquired and travel-related infections and detection of intestinal tapeworm carriers in Los Angeles County. Am J Trop Med Hyg 47:365-371. 1992.
10. Schantz PM. Moore AC. et al. Neurocysticercosis in an Orthodox Jewish community in New York City N Engl J Med. 327:692-5.1992.
11. White AC Jr. Robinson P. Kuhn R. *Taenia solium* cysticercosis: host-parasite interactions and the immune response. Chem Immunol. 66:209-30.1997.
12. Leid RW. Suquet CM. Tanogoshi L. Parasite defense mechanisms for evasion of host attack: A review. Vet Parasitol 25:147-162. 1987.
13. Laclette JP. Lnada A. et al. Paramyosin is the *Schistosoma mansoni* (Trematoda) homologue of antigen B from *Taenia solium* (Cestoda). Mol Biochem Parasitol 44:287-295. 1991.
14. Laclette JP. Shoemaker CB. et al. Paramyosin inhibits complement C1. J Immunol 148:124-128. 1992.
15. Restrepo BI. Llaguno P. et al. Analysis of immune lesions in neurocysticercosis patients: central nervous system response to helminth appears Th1-like instead of Th2. J Neuroimmunol. 89:64-72.1998.
16. Lightowlers MW. Eradication of *Taenia solium* cysticercosis: a role for vaccination of pigs. Int J Parasitol. 29:811-7. 1999.
17. Del Giudice P. Bernard E. et al. Cysticercose sous-cutanee. Ann Dermatol Venereol. 123:474-7. 1996.
18. Salgado P. Rojas R. Sotelo J. Cysticercosis. Clinical classification based on imaging studies Arch Intern Med. 157:1991-7. 1997.
19. Carpio A. Escobar A. Hauser WA. Cysticercosis and epilepsy: a critical 20. review. Epilepsia. 39:1025-40.1998.
20. Mitchell WH. Crawford TO: Intraparenchymal cysticercosis in children:diagnosis and treatment. Pediatrics 82:76-82. 1988.
21. Nash TE. Patronas NJ. Edema associated with calcified lesions in neurocysticercosis. Neurology. 53:777-81.1999.
22. Dorny P. Brandt J. Zoli A. Geerts S. Immunodiagnostic tools for human and porcine cysticercosis. Acta Trop. 87:79-86. 2003.
23. Leite CC. Jinkins JR. et al. MR imaging of intramedullary and intradural-extramedullary spinal cysticercosis. AJR Am J Roentgenol. 169:1713-7.1997.
24. Tsang VCW. Brand IA. Boyer AE. An enzyme-linked immunoelectrotransfer blot assay and glycoprotein antigens for diagnosing human cysticercosis (*Taenia solium*). J Infect Dis 159:50-59. 1989.
25. Proano-Narvaez JV. Meza-Lucas A. et al. Laboratory diagnosis of human neurocysticercosis: double-blind comparison of enzyme-

linked immunosorbent assay and electroimmunotransfer blot assay. J Clin Microbiol 40: 2115-18. 2002.

26. Gekeler F. Eichenlaub. S. et al. Sensitivity and specificity of ELISA and immunoblot for diagnosisng neurocysticercosis. Eur J Clin Microbiol Infect Dis 21: 227-9. 2002.

27. Wilson M. Bryan RT. et al. Clinical evaluation of the cysticercosis enzyme-linked immunotransfer blot in patients with neurocysticercosis. J Infect Dis 164:1007-1009. 1991.

28. Sotelo J. Del Brutto OH. Roman GC. Cysticercosis. Curr Clin Top Infect Dis. 16:240-59. 1996.

29. Garcia HH. Evans CAW. Nash TE et al. Current consensus guidelines for treatment of neurocysticercosis. Clin Microbiol Rev 15: 747-56.

30. Sotelo J. Del Brutto OH. et al. Comparison of therapeutic regimen of anticysticercal drugs for parenchymal brain cysticercosis. J Neurol 237:69-72. 1990.

31. Sotelo J. Jung H. Pharmacokinetic optimisation of the treatment of neurocysticercosis. Clin Pharmacokinet. 34:503-15. 1998.

32. Allan JC. Velasquez-Tohom M. et al. Mass chemotherapy for intestinal *Taenia solium* infection: effect on prevalence in humans and pigs. Trans R Soc Trop Med Hyg. 91:595-8. 1997.

33. Lightowlers MW. Jensen O. et al. Vaccination trials in Australia and Argentina confirm the effectiveness of the EG95 hydatid vaccine in sheep. Int J Parasitol. 29:531-4. 1999.

34. Plancarte A. Flisser A. Gauci CG. Lightowlers MW. Vaccination against *Taenia solium* cysticercosis in pigs using native and recombinant oncosphere antigens. Int J Parasitol. 29:643-7. 1999.

35. Economides P. Christofi G. Gemmell MA. Control of *Echinococcus granulosus* in Cyprus and comparison with other island models. Vet Parasitol. 79(2):151-63. 1998.

36. Schantz PM. Echinococcus in American Indians living in Arizona and New Mexico: a review of recent studies. Am J Epidemiol 106:370-379. 1977.

37. Daly JJ. McDaniel RC. Husted GS. Harmon H. Unilocular hydatid cyst disease in the mid-South. JAMA 251:932-933. 1984.

38. Finlay JC. Spreet D. Sylvatic hydatid disease in children: case reports and review of endemic *Echinococcus granulosus* infection in Canada and Alaska. Pedtri Infect Dis J 11:322-326 1992.

39. McManus DP. Zhang L. et al. Short report: molecular genetic characterization of an unusually severe case of hydatid disease in Alaska caused by the cervid strain of *Echinococcus granulosus*. Am J Trop Med Hyg 67: 296-8. 2002.

40. Pallas PS: Miscellanea Zoologica: Quibus Novae Imprimis Atque Obscure Animalium Species Describuntur Et Observationibus Iconibusque Illustrantur. Hagae Comitum Petrum van Cleff. 1766.

41. Goeze JAE. Versuch einer Naturgeschichte der Eingeweidewurme Thierische Korper. P.A.Pape, Blankenburg. 1782.

42. Von Seibold CT. Uber die Verwandlung der Echinococcus-brut in Taenia. Z Wissenshur Zool 4:409-424. 1853.

43. Naunyn B. Uber die zu Echinococcus *hominis* gehorige Taenia. Arch Anat Physiol Wissenschr Med 412-416. 1863.

44. Haag KL. Araujo AM. et al. Breeding systems in *Echinococcus granulosus* (Cestoda; Taeniidae): selfing or outcrossing? Parasitology. 118:63-71.1999.

45. Dixon JB. Echinococcosis. Comp Immunol Microbiol Infect Dis. 20:87-94 1997.

46. Gottstein B. Hemphill A. Immunopathology of Echinoccocus. In: Immunopathologic Aspects of Disease Induced by Helminth Parasites. Chem Immunol Basel, Karger 66:177-208. 1997.

47. Pawlowski I. Eckert J. et al. Echinococcosis in humans: clinical aspects, diagnosis and treatment. In: Eckert J, Gemmell M, Meslin F-X, Pawlowski Z, eds. WHOI/OIE manual on echinococcosis in humans and animals: a public health problem of global concern. Paris: World Organization for Animal Health, pp. 20-71. 2001.

48. Agildere AM. Aytekin C. et al. MRI of hydatid disease of the liver: a variety of sequences. J Comput Assist Tomogr. 22:718-24.1998.

49. Gottstein B. Molecular and immunological diagnosis of echinococosis. Clin Microbiol Rev 5:248-261. 1992.

50. Chemale G, Ferreira HB. et al. *Echinococcus granulosus* antigen B hydrophobic ligand binding properties. Biochim Biophys Acta.1747:189-94. 2005.

51. Schaefer JW. Yousuf Kahn M. Echinococcosis (hydatid disease). Lessons from experience with 59 patients. Rev Infect Dis 13:43-247. 1991.

52. Filice C. Brunetti E. Use of PAIR in human cystic echinococcosis. Acta Tropica 64: 95-107. 1997.

53. Pelaez V. Kugler C. et al. PAIR as percutaneous treatment of hydatid liver cysts. Acta Tropica 75: 197-202. 2000.

54. Horton R. Albendazole in treatment of human cystic echinococcosis: 12 years of experience Acta Tropica 64: 79-93. 1997.

55. Rowley AH. Shulman ST. Donaldson JS. Schantz PM. Albendazole treatment for recurrent echinococcosis. Pediatr Infect Dis 7:666-667. 1988.

56. Beard TC. The elimination of echinococcosis from Iceland. Bull WHO 48:653-660. 1973.

57. Woollard DJ. Gauci CG. Heath DD. Lightowlers MW. Epitope specificities and antibody responses to the EG95 hydatid vaccine. Parasite Immunol. 20:535-40. 1998.

58. Lukaschenko NP. Problems of epidemiology and prophylaxix of alveolar (multilocular echinococcosis): a general review – with particular reference to the U.S.S.R. Int J Parasitol 1:125-134. 1971.

59. Eiermann TH. Bettens F. et al. HLA and alveolar echinococcosis. Tissue Antigens. 52:124-9. 1998.

60. Godot V. Harraga S. et al. Increased basal production of interleukin-10 by peripheral blood mononuclear cells in human alveolar echinococcosis. Eur Cytokine Netw. 8:401-8.1997.

61. Gottstein B. Jacquier P. Bresson-Hadni S. Eckert J. Improved primary immunodiagnosis of alveolar echinococcosis in humans by an enzyme-linked immunosorbent assay using the Em2plus antigen. J Clin Microbiol 31: 373-76. 1993.

62. Schantz PM. Brandt FH. et al. Effect of albendazole on *Echinococcus multilocularis* infection in the Mongolian Jird. J Infect Dis 162:1403-1407. 1990.

63. Kean BH. Sun T. Ellsworth RM. Color Atlas / Text of Ophthalmic Parasitology. Igaku-Shoin, Pubs. New York and Tokyo. pp. 195-200. 1991.

VII. The Trematodes

For an excellent, comprehensive discussion of trematode biology, see Topley and Wilson.[1]

The class Trematoda, in the phylum Platyhelminthes, consists of two orders, Monogenea and Digenea. All are obligate parasites. Trematodes of medical importance only occur in the order Digenea, and include the blood flukes, the intestinal flukes, and the tissue flukes. They are mainly found throughout the tropics and subtropics, while a few species are encountered in temperate zones, as well.

Trematodes undergo complex developmental cycles in their intermediate and definitive hosts. But, as complex as trematode biology is, offering seemingly numerous opportunities for interrupting their life cycles, eradication of any medically important species has occurred to only a limited extent in specific geographic areas such as *Schistosoma mansoni* in China and *S. japonicum* in Japan.[2]

Trematodes maintain their site location within the host using their two suckers, one anterior and one ventral. The anterior sucker also serves as the opening to the oral cavity, into which host tissues are ingested. The outer surface of the adult is covered with a tegument similar in design and function to the tegument of cestodes. It serves as an absorbing surface for both large and small molecular weight molecules. The tegument is covered by membrane-bound microvilli, underneath which are mitochondria, pinocytes, and other structures facilitating nutrient acquisition.

In addition, trematodes have a functional blind gut into which they ingest tissues of the host. Ingested material is pumped down into the bifurcated intestinal tract, where digestion occurs, aided by enzymes (e.g., proteases, lipases, aminopeptidases, esterases). Since the gut has no exit, wastes are regurgitated into the host. Thus, these worms obtain a wide variety of nutrients in several different ways, making it difficult to develop drugs or immune-based therapies to interrupt metabolic processes.

Several layers of muscle lie just below the tegument, allowing trematodes to move about freely within the host. This activity can result in severe pathological consequences for the host, particularly in the case of *F. hepatica, P. westermani* and schistosomes.

A pair of dorsal ganglia gives rise to lateral peripheral nerves running the length of the body, and they innervate the muscle layers. Commissures from the lateral nerves also innervate various organs, including the gut, and reproductive organs. The flukes have no body cavity; rather, organs are embedded in the parenchyma.

In addition to solid wastes, trematodes excrete small molecular compounds using a network of tubules that connect to collecting organelles, known as flame cells. These, in turn, connect to the excretory pore at the tegumental surface of the parasite.

The digeneic trematodes employ one of three reproductive strategies: (1) Self-fertilization, in which the same worm possesses both sets of reproductive organs (e.g., *Fasciola hepatica*), (2) cross fertilization between two worms possessing both sets of reproductive organs (e.g., *Paragonimus westermani*), or (3) fertilization between worms of the opposite sex, as is the case among the schistosomes.

Egg production is complex, involving a series of specialized organs. The ovum, supplied with yolk from the vitelline glands, is fertilized within the uterus and becomes surrounded by a shell within the Mehlis' gland. It exits from the parasite through the genital pore, usually situated in between the anterior and ventral suckers.

Once the eggs reach fresh water, or, for some species, a suitable terrestrial niche, they are either stimulated to hatch in the external environment or they hatch after being ingested by the next host. There, they undergo asexual reproduction, eventually increasing in numbers many-fold, compared to the single entering miracidium. Intermediate hosts include snail species that live in fresh water or terrestrial habitats. In addition, other invertebrates, including ants and other insects, and a variety of cold blooded vertebrates, including fish and crabs, function as intermediate hosts for medically important species of trematodes. Plants (e.g., watercress and water chestnuts), are sites on which some species of metacercariae encyst.

Many species of adult trematodes are acquired by ingesting the intermediate stage (i.e., the metacercaria), but a few (notably the schistosomes) can actively penetrate unbroken skin.

Site selection by trematodes within the human host is poorly understood. It is determined by a complex interplay between chemical and physical niches, which represent environmental cues for the parasite, and the receiving and translation of those cues by the nervous system of the parasite. Some drugs interfere with trematode nervous system functions (e.g., praziquantel), resulting in profound changes in worm behavior. Under those conditions, elimination of the parasite is possible.

References

1. Topley and Wilson's Microbiology and Microbial Infections. 10th Edition. 2005 (*in press*).
2. Engels D, Chitsulo L, Montresor A, Savioli L. The global epidemiological situation of schistosomiasis and new approaches to control and research. Acta Trop. 82:139-46. 2002.

33. The Schistosomes:

Schistosoma mansoni
(Sambon 1907)

Schistosoma japonicum
(Katsurada 1904)

Schistosoma haematobium
(Bilharz 1852)

Schistosoma mekongi
(Bilharz 1852)

Introduction

Four trematode species in the genus Schistosoma; *Schistosoma mansoni, S. haematobium, S. japonicum,* and *S. mekongi,* cause a series of related diseases in humans referred to as schistosomiasis. *S. intercalatum,* a parasite of cattle in West Africa, also occasionally causes the disease in humans. Except for *S. haematobium* that produces urinary tract disease, the human schistosomes primarily affect the intestine and liver. Chronic schistosomiasis also causes physical growth and cognitive delays in children. The World Health Organization estimates that 85% of the 200 million people infected with one or more of these agents live in Africa, while another 600 million people are at risk worldwide. Their largely tropical distribution reflects the geographical distribution of their intermediate host snail species. Forced migration of people due to armed conflict throughout many parts of Africa, and encroachment into natural systems (e.g., constructing irrigation canals and dams), have resulted in regional increases in schistosomiasis.

Schistosoma mansoni is found throughout most

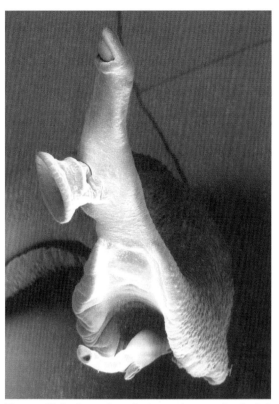

Figure 33.2. Scanning electron micrograph of adult schistosomes. Notice gynocophoral canal with female inside. Photo D. Scharf.

of sub-Saharan Africa, Egypt and Sudan, parts of the Middle East, some parts of South America (including Brazil and the Guyanas), and some islands in the Caribbean. Its intermediate hosts are aquatic snails in the genus Biomphalaria. Reservoir hosts for *S. mansoni* include baboons and monkeys in Africa. However, they play no significant role in the epidemiology of human disease.

Schistosoma haematobium is prevalent in most parts of Africa and in some parts of the Middle East. Its aquatic intermediate host snails are in the genus Bulinus. There are no important reservoir hosts for this trematode species, although during an epidemic of the infection in the Omo River Valley of Ethiopia, the origin of the outbreak was traced back to monkeys.[1]

Schistosoma intercalatum occasionally infects people in Cameroon, Gabon, Equatorial Guinea, Central African Republic, Chad, and Democratic Republic of Congo.[2]

Schistosoma japonicum occurs in China, Malaysia, the Philippines, and, to a small extent, Indonesia. It has been eradicated from Japan as of 1977.[3] Its amphibious intermediate host snails are in the genus Oncomelania. In contrast to the other schistosomes, zoonotic transmission occurs on a regular basis.

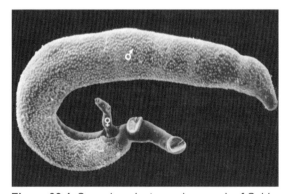

Figure 33.1. Scanning electron micrograph of *Schistosoma mansoni* adults. (From Kessel and Shih: Scanning Electron Microscopy in Biology. Springer-Verlag, 1976. Reproduced with permission).

Schistosoma mansoni

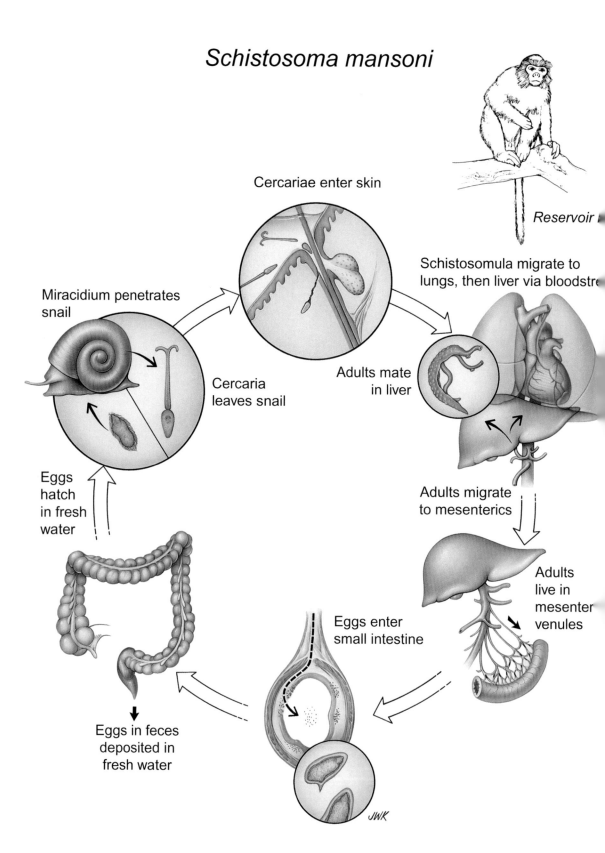

Cercariae enter skin

Reservoir

Schistosomula migrate to lungs, then liver via bloodstre

Miracidium penetrates snail

Cercaria leaves snail

Adults mate in liver

Eggs hatch in fresh water

Adults migrate to mesenterics

Adults live in mesenter venules

Eggs enter small intestine

Eggs in feces deposited in fresh water

JWK

"Parasitic Diseases" 5th Ed. © Apple Trees Productions, LLC., Pub. P.O. Box 280, New York, NY 10032

There are important reservoir hosts for *S. japonicum*, including water buffalo, cattle and pigs.[4] *S. mekongi,* a closely related species, is found in the Mekong River in southeast Asia. Some investigators consider this schistosome a member of the *S. japonicum* complex. There are no autochthonous infections in the United States with any of the above species of schistosomes because there are no appropriate species of intermediate host snails, and, most importantly, sanitary disposal of feces and urine is the general rule. However thousands of Caribbean and Southeast Asian immigrants may be infected, so clinicians who practice only in the United States must still be knowledgeable regarding this potentially life-threatening parasitic infection.

Historical Information

Ancient Egyptians believed that the advent of manhood was heralded by the appearance of blood in the urine, analogous to the onset of menstruation in women. Hematuria in males, in fact, represented a late manifestation of *S. haematobium* infection. Autopsies of mummies and microscopic examination of coprolites showed that schistosomiasis was quite prevalent throughout the lower Nile River valley more than 3,000 years ago. Bilharz, in letters to his friend and colleague, von Siebold, written between 1851 and 1853, described human cases of *Schistosoma haematobium*, a parasite of the venous plexus of the bladder, and whose eggs possessed a terminal spine. In 1902,

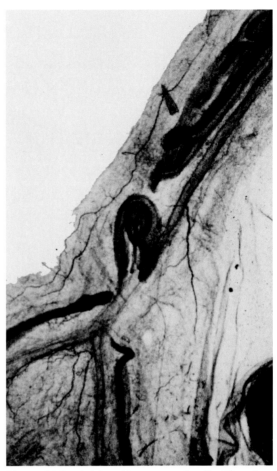

Figure 33.3a. Adult schistosomes *in situ*. The elongated worms appear dark due to the ingestion of hemaglobin.

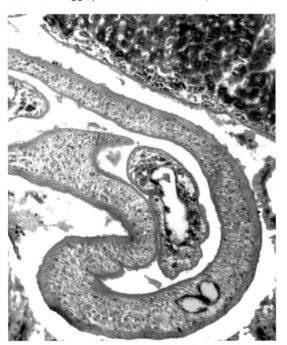

Figure 33.3b. Cross section of a pair of adult schistosomes *in situ* in a mesenteric venule.

Manson described a case of schistosomiasis in an Englishman who had traveled extensively throughout the Caribbean, and in whose stool, but not his urine, he found many eggs with lateral spines.[5] Sambon, in 1907,[6] recognized two blood flukes, on the basis of morphology and origin of the eggs in stool and urine. In tribute to Manson, Sambon named this new organism after him. Piraja de Silva, in 1908, also discovered *S. mansoni* in South America.[7] By 1918, Leiper[8] had conducted extensive investigations on schistosomiasis, and reported the life cycle of *S. mansoni*, in which he described its snail intermediate host, and morphology of the adult worms.

Katsurada, in 1904,[9] described *S. japonicum* adults from infected cats. Coincidentally, Catto, working in Singapore, described an identical adult worm in a patient who died of cholera.[10] He named it *S. cattoi*, but his publication was delayed, and the name *S. japonicum* was accepted instead. Earlier, in 1888, Majima[11] observed eggs of *S. japonicum* in a liver he examined at autopsy. He was unaware of the adult worms, but

Schistosoma japonicum

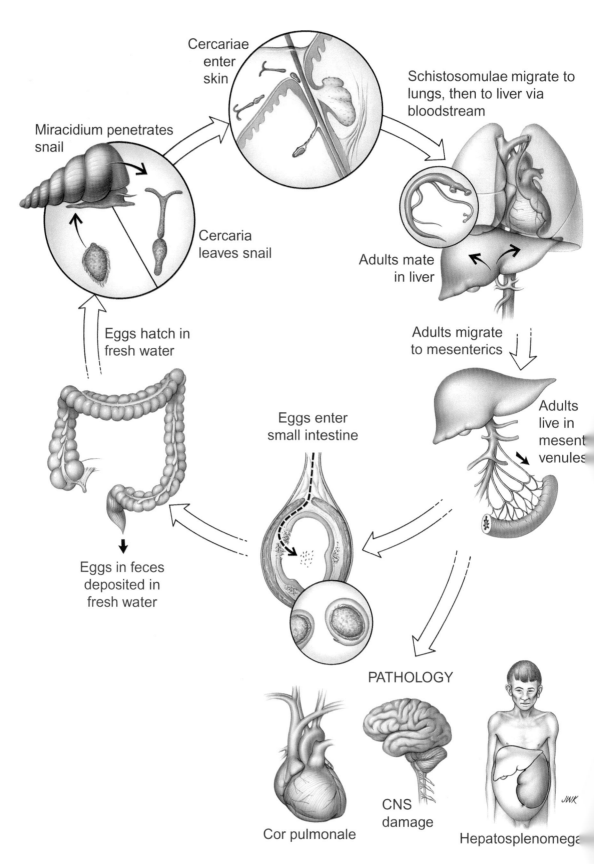

Cercariae enter skin

Miracidium penetrates snail

Cercaria leaves snail

Schistosomulae migrate to lungs, then to liver via bloodstream

Adults mate in liver

Eggs hatch in fresh water

Adults migrate to mesenterics

Eggs enter small intestine

Adults live in mesent venules

Eggs in feces deposited in fresh water

PATHOLOGY

Cor pulmonale

CNS damage

Hepatosplenomega

JWK

correctly ascertained that the eggs were responsible for the cirrhosis. Kawanishi, in 1904,[12] made the correlation between the clinical condition, Katayama fever (acute schistosomiasis), and the presence of *S. japonicum* adults, after finding eggs of this parasite in the stools of patients suffering from the acute phase of the infection. Fujinami and Nakamura in 1909,[13] and Miyagawa in 1912,[14] independently reported on the details of the life cycle. Miyairi and Suzuki, in 1914,[15] identified *Oncomelania spp.* snails as the vectors.

S. japonicum infection has had a major impact on the history of modern China. It is believed that Mao's troops were unable to launch an amphibious assault on Taiwan in the late 1940s because they developed Katayama fever while encamped along the Yangtze River. Later on during the great leap forward, Mao mobilized tens of thousands of peasants to either bury Oncomelania snails or even to remove them individually by hand.

Griesinger, in 1854,[16] described in detail the clinical disease and its pathology. He noted the relation of the infection to the involvement of the bladder and ureters. Leiper, in 1918,[8] described the life cycle of *S. haematobium*, its intermediate host, and its morphology. He also carried out experimental infections with *S. haematobium* in various indigenous animals of northern Egypt, and proved that rats and mice were susceptible.

Life Cycle

Schistosomes have separate sexes (Fig. 33.1); the female measures 15 mm in length, and the male is 10 mm long. Schistosome adults remain in copula (Fig. 33.2) during their life span, and live attached by their sucker disks to the endothelium of the veins (Figs. 33.3a, 33.3b) *S. mansoni* lives in the inferior mesenteric veins that drain the intestine, while *S. japonicum*

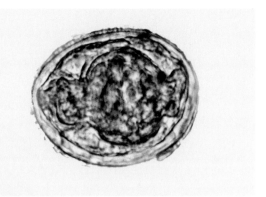

Figure 33.5a. Egg of *Schistosoma japonicum*. No spine can be seen. 85 μm x 60 μm.

and *S. mekongi* live in the superior mesenteric veins. *S. japonicum* adult worms can also find their way to the choroid plexus, the venules around the spinal column, and other ectopic locations. *S. haematobium* is found almost exclusively in the venus plexus that drain the urinary bladder. The routes by which adult schistosomes arrive at these sites is still considered controversial. Worms live 5-8 years, on the average, although some live as long as 37 years.[19] Schistosomes are facultative anaerobes, deriving energy primarily through the degradation of glucose and glycogen.

Adult schistosomes utilize hemoglobin[16] as a primary source of amino acids, which is ingested into their blind, bifurcated gut. They employ a hemoglobinase,[18] digesting the globin portion of the molecule, and detoxifying the heme moiety into a pigment before it is regurgitated back into the blood stream. The female lies within the gynecophoral canal of the male (Fig. 33.2). This muscular, tegumental fold extends down both sides of the male, and may enable the female to feed on blood, by assisting in pumping blood into their esophagus. Single sex infections with females, or females experimentally separated from males, then re-introduced into the same host, do not produce eggs, presumably due to their inability to obtain a blood meal.

Free amino acids and glucose are transported across the tegument by active transport mechanisms. They store excess glucose as glycogen. The tegumental surface of male *S. mansoni* are covered with finger-like projections, termed "papillae", while male *S. haematobium* have more widely spaced, shorter, finger-like projections, termed "tubercles". The purpose(s) of these projections is not known. In contrast, males of *S. japonicum* and *S. mekongi* are smooth.

Females in copula lay eggs throughout their lives. The eggs of *S. mansoni* are oval, and possess a lateral spine (Fig. 33.4); those of *S. japonicum* and *S. mekongi* are globular and lack a spine (Fig. 33.5a, 33.5b); those

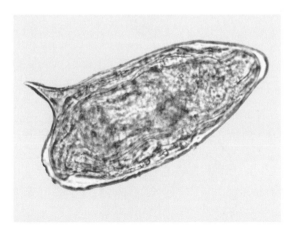

Figure 33.4. Egg of *Schistosoma mansoni*. Note lateral spine. 150 μm x 60 μm.

Schistosoma haematobium

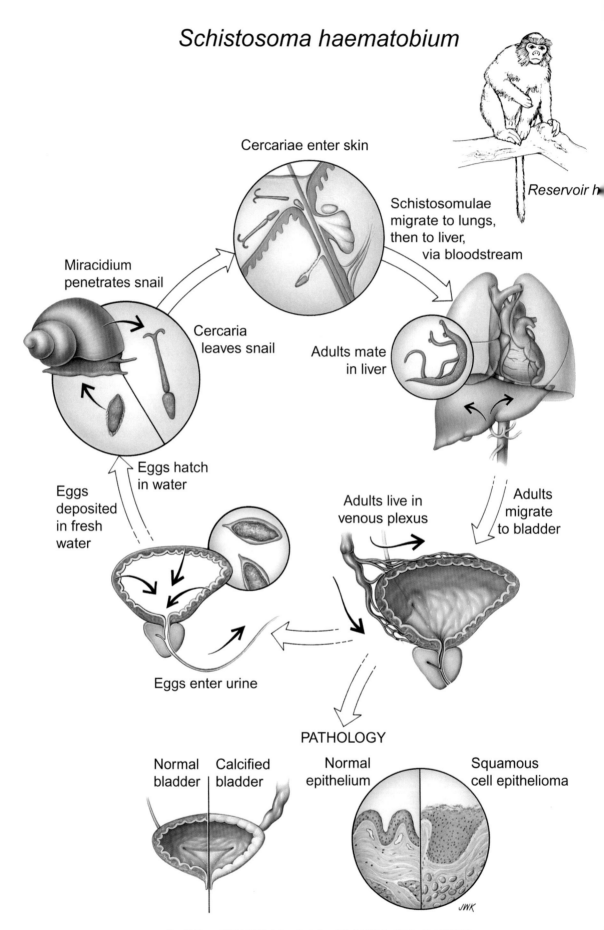

Cercariae enter skin

Schistosomulae migrate to lungs, then to liver, via bloodstream

Reservoir h

Miracidium penetrates snail

Cercaria leaves snail

Adults mate in liver

Eggs hatch in water

Eggs deposited in fresh water

Adults live in venous plexus

Adults migrate to bladder

Eggs enter urine

PATHOLOGY

Normal bladder | Calcified bladder

Normal epithelium

Squamous cell epithelioma

JWK

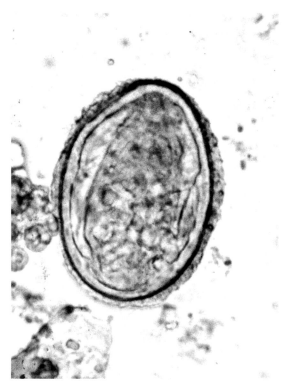

Figure 33.5b. Egg of *Schistosoma mekongi*. No spine can be seen. 65 μm x 50 μm.

of *S. haematobium* are oval, with a terminal spine (Fig. 33.6). *S. mansoni* females produce, on average, 300 eggs per day, while *S. japonicum* and *S. mekongi* shed some 1500-3000 eggs daily. Egg production of *S. haematobium* has not been determined. The eggs pass through the birth pore located above the posterior sucker. When the worm applies the sucker to the endothelial surface, the embryonated eggs secrete lytic enzymes, enabling them to enter the surrounding connective tissue. Eggs collect in the sub-mucosa (Fig. 33.7) before entering the lumen of either the small intestine, or for *S. haematobium*, the bladder.

When adult females raise their posterior suckers, eggs escape into the circulation, which carries them to the liver via the portal circulation. Nearly 50% of all *S. mansoni* eggs produced reach the liver. Eggs that reach the lumen of the small intestine are included in the fecal mass. Eggs of *S. haematobium* must traverse the wall of the bladder (Fig. 33.8) before exiting with the urine. In both cases, the egg's penchant for penetrating tissues causes the infected individual significant pathological consequences.

For the life cycle to continue, eggs in feces or urine must be deposited in fresh water. There, environmental cues trigger the larva stage, termed the miracidium, to hatch (Fig. 33.9). This ciliated, free-swimming stage (Fig. 33.10) seeks out its appropriate snail intermediate host, relying on a gradient of appropriate low molecular weight signal(s) emanating from the snail to do so. In essence, the snail becomes a chemical homing device for the parasite.

Upon finding the right snail (Fig. 33.11, 33.12), the miracidium enters the soft, fleshy parts, facilitated by a new set of proteolytic enzymes. The miracidium invades the snail's lymph spaces, and then its hepatopancreas.

A series of remarkable transformations then ensue, beginning with production of the sporocyst. This stage gives rise to daughter sporocysts, which, in turn, produce cercariae, the infectious stage for humans. During each stage of development, there is an increase in the number of individuals. A single miracidium of *S. mansoni* produces some 4,000 cercariae (Fig. 33.13). Throughout the process, the snail somehow manages to remain alive, even when it becomes infected with numerous miracidia. However, an infection that results in the production of more than 40,000 cercariae overwhelms the snail, and it dies. Each miracidium is either male or female, and the resulting cercariae are, also.

Cercariae exit from the snail aided by yet another set of proteolytic enzymes. Cercariae are positively phototropic and negatively geotropic. They accumulate at the surface of water, and swim about seeking their definitive host by following gradients of chemical cues, including linoleic acid, that emanate from human skin.

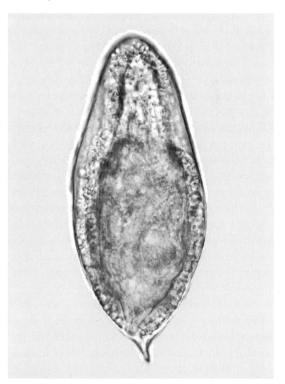

Figure 33.6. Egg of *Schistosoma haematobium*. Note terminal spine. 155 μm x 55 μm.

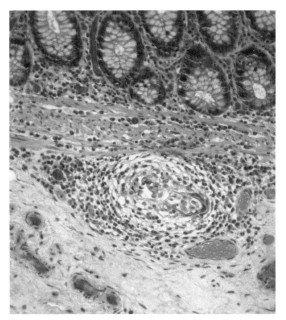

Figure 33.7. Schistosome egg in tissue of the small intestine. Note intense granuloma.

Cercariae must infect within 8 hours after emerging from its snail host; otherwise they exhaust their glycogen reserves and die.

Infection in the human host is initiated when the cercariae penetrate unbroken skin. With regards to *S. mansoni*, this step requires about 0.5 hour, but occurs much more rapidly with *S. japonicum*.[20] Skin penetration is usually through a hair follicle, and is facilitated by release of another set of proteases and eicasanoids.[21] Cercariae shed their tails, and rapidly transform within the dermal layer of skin into the schistosomula stage. After approximately 2 days, the schistosomulae migrate through the blood stream to the capillaries of the lung, where they remain for another several days. It is here that the immature worms acquire their ability to incorporate host serum proteins onto their tegumental surface. This "camouflage" has the profound effect of convincing the leukocytes that the worm is "self," enabling the parasite to live out a long, and prosperous life inside its new host. In addition, the worm possesses a β-2-microglobulin-like molecule that aids in confusing immune defense cells, particularly macrophages, in their attempt to recognize parasite antigens. Schistosomulae migrate from the lungs via the blood stream to the liver, where they mature to adult worms. Both sexes produce chemotactic agents that are mutually attractive, and eventually worms of opposite sex find each other in the vastness of the parenchymal tissue. They mate there, and migrate out into the mesenteric circulation. Egg production begins shortly thereafter. Other mammalian species, including baboons, rhesus monkeys, chimpanzees, mice, and rats, can be experimentally infected with the cercariae of *S. mansoni*. Few viable eggs are produced in the rat, however.

Cellular and Molecular Pathogenesis

Adult schistosomes usually do not cause significant pathological damage in the host. It is believed that the adult schistosome worm pair elicits remarkably little in the way of host immunopathologic responses as a consequence of unique antigen-masking properties. However, adult schistosomes living in the venous circulation have the capacity to harbor enteric bacteria affixed to their surface. This relationship can result in the introduction of enteric bacteria, such as Salmonella, directly into the bloodstream. As a result there is a well-described association between chronic schistosomiasis and so-called enteric fevers from non-typhoidal salmonellosis.[22]

In contrast to adults, the eggs produced by the worm pair result in profound immunopathologic responses. This phenomenon accounts for almost all of the pathology and clinical manifestations of schistosomiasis. For *S. japonicum* and *S. mansoni,* egg deposition occurs in the circulation of the small intestine and liver (Fig. 33.14) to produce intestinal and hepatic fibrosis, whereas *S. haematobium* egg deposition occurs in the circulation of the bladder to produce fibrosis leading to an obstructive uropathy. Heavy egg depo-

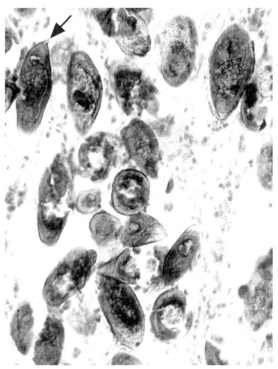

Figure 33.8. *S. haematobium* eggs in bladder wall. Note terminal spine (arrow).

sition occurs predominantly in individuals with large numbers of adult worms. Clinical illness caused by schistosomiasis generally occurs only in people who suffer from recurrent heavy worm burdens. Increasing evidence suggests that a component of this phenomenon depends on host genetic factors.[23] In this regard, the same genes specific for susceptibility to *Schistosoma mansoni* have been identified in people living in Africa and South America.[24] In a study in the Sudan, a specific gene locus was associated with advanced liver disease confirming epidemiologic observations of fibrosis occurring in families.[25] Furthermore, immunocompromised individuals with HIV shed fewer eggs in stool exams than similar individuals without HIV.[26] The soluble secretions from schistosome eggs, termed soluble egg antigens (SEAs), trigger host inflammatory and immune responses that result in granuloma formation,[27] and are T cell-dependent so as to include prominent Th2 components.[28] This Th2 bias can downregulate other host Th1 responses and result in altered patterns of host susceptibility to other infectious pathogens, possibly including the human immunodeficiency virus.[29, 30] The pathogenesis of granuloma formation also requires host-derived production of tumor necrosis factor.[31] The sizes of the granulomas vary with the age of the infection. In newly acquired infections, granulomas are large, causing displacement of normal tissue with fibrotic, epitheloid reactions. Over time, eggs elicit less and less volume of granulomatous tissue. This reaction appears to be under the regulation of IL-12.[32]

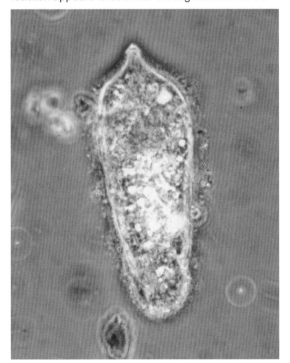

Figure 33.10. Miracidium of *S. mansoni*. Phase contrast.

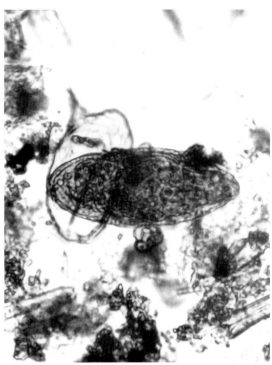

Figure 33.9. Miracidium of *S. mansoni* caught in the act of hatching.

Granulomas form around eggs that collect in the intestinal wall and result in fibrosis. Erosion of the submucosa and villous tissue also occurs, presumably by the action of secreted proteolytic enzymes from the eggs. In heavy infection, gastrointestinal hemorrhage results from damage to the submucosa.

Eggs swept back into the liver block pre-sinusoidal capillaries, and induce granulomas there, as well. The presence of granulomas causes tissue fibrosis, and eventually leads to obstruction of the hepatic vasculature. Fibrosis of most of the portal areas incorporating the blood vessels leads to pipe stem fibrosis (Symmer's Fibrosis) (Fig. 33.15), and, ultimately, to portal hypertension. Clinically, this is manifest as hepatosplenomegaly, the extent of which is dependent partially on host major histocompatibility class II alleles.[33] Development of collateral circulation follows, including esophageal varices. Parenchymal liver cells remain unaffected by granulomas, and, hence, liver function remains normal.

Portal hypertension forces eggs to bypass the liver, and many are carried to the spleen, which becomes enlarged, further contributing to increased pressure in portal circulation. Infection with *S. japonicum* results in a greater number of granulomas and consequently greater morbidity because this species produces, on average, five to ten times more eggs than *S. mansoni*. Collateral circulation may also wash eggs into the lung

Figure 33.11. *Biomphalaria grabrata*, the most common intermediate snail host for *S. mansoni*.

capillary beds, occasionally leading to pulmonary fibrosis and consequent cor pulmonale.

Accumulation of *S. haematobium* eggs around the bladder and ureters leads to granuloma formation and fibrosis. In addition, calcification of dead eggs in the bladder wall (Fig. 33.16) results in rigidity of the bladder and subsequent increased pressure in the ureters and kidneys. The bladder epithelium develops pseudopolyps (Fig. 33.17), which can transform into squamous cell carcinoma in untreated patients (Fig. 33.18).

In some patients with long-standing disease (in all four types of schistosomiasis), deposition of immune complexes in kidneys can lead to basement mem-

brane disease.[32]

Penetration of the skin by cercariae is dependent on the release of parasite-derived proteases and eicasanoids. The process of host entry typically causes no major reaction, but repeated exposure can lead to sensitization, and the development of a maculopapular rash (Fig. 33.19), characterized by IgE or IgG antibodies and an eosinophilic infiltrate. This is particularly true of accidental skin penetration by avian or bovine schistosomes. Many schistosomes specifically parasitic for animals can cause aberrant infections in humans. Avian schistosomes of the genera Austrobilharzia, Trichobilharzia, and Ornithobilharzia, and other mammalian schistosomes (*S. matthei* and *Schistosomatium douthitti*) are included in this group. The cercariae of these species cause a hypersensivity skin reaction (cercarial dermatitis), known as "clam digger's itch" or "swimmer's itch" (Fig. 33.20).

Cellular and humoral responses to both penetrating cercariae and migrating schistosomula are a critical

Figure 33.12. *Oncomelania nosophora*, a snail intermediate host for *S. japonicum*.

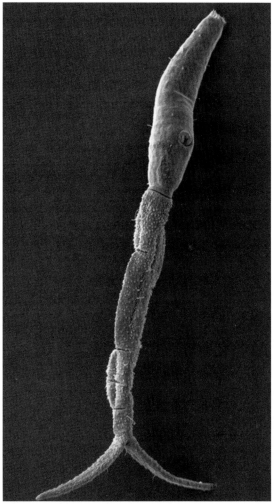

Figure 33.13. Scanning electron micrograph of a cercaria of *S. mansoni*. Photo D. Scharf.

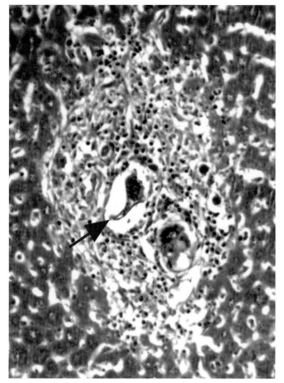

Figure 33.14. Granuloma in liver surrounding eggs of *S. mansoni*. Note the lateral spine (arrow).

component of naturally-acquired immunity to human schistosomiasis. This hypothesis derives from experimental evidence showing that cercariae attenuated by exposure to ionizing radiation (e.g., x-rays, gamma-rays or ultraviolet light), can penetrate skin and migrate through the tissues. In so doing they elicit protective immune responses, including IL-13.[35-37] These observations are the basis for an experimental vaccine in non-human primates. However, the cercariae must remain alive in order to secrete the antigens associated with vaccine protection. In humans living in endemic regions, this process may take years of exposure to cercariae. Until then, young children have a particular problem mounting an effective immune response to invading schistosomulae. The mechanism by which children during their early years of exposure to cercariae and invading schistosomulae are susceptible to the parasite but then become resistant over time is unclear. One widely held hypothesis is that young children respond initially to the parasite by producing IgG4 blocking antibodies.[38] It has been suggested that blocking antibodies delay the development of protective IgE that is needed for the resistance to infection that older people have in endemic areas.

Exploiting the current understanding of Th1 and Th2 immune responses elicited by different candidate antigens is the means by which vaccine researchers are attempting to bring a product to the field. Animal protection studies have used the protein paramyosin with good results in a mouse model although the mechanism of protection is still under study.[39] Studies in the Philippines in a population with risk of exposure to *S. japonicum* demonstrated that individuals with predominantly Th1 cellular immune responses appeared resistant to initial infection.[40, 41]

Clinical Disease

As in other helminth infections, clinical disease resulting from schistosomes usually occurs only in heavily-infected individuals. The clinical manifestations of acute schistosomiasis occur predominantly in *S. japonicum* and *S. mansoni* infections. This condition is sometimes known as "Katayama fever". The classical disease attributed to schistosomiasis occurs during chronic infections. Chronic infection with *S. haematobium* can also lead to squamous carcinoma of the bladder.

Acute schistosomiasis (Katayama fever)

The dramatic clinical manifestations of Katayama fever occur most commonly in new immigrants who experience intense levels of exposure to either *S.*

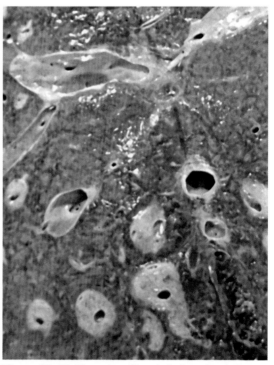

Figure 33.15. Pipe stem fibrosis in liver due to heavy infection with *S. mansoni*. Note normal liver tissue next to fibrotic vessels.

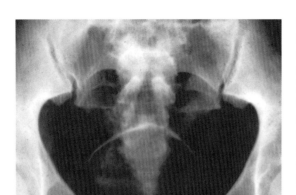

Figure 33.16. X-ray showing calcified dome of the bladder due to chronic infection with *S. haematobium.*

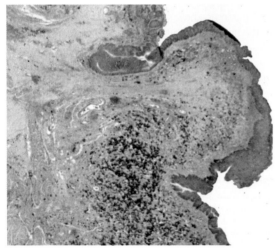

Figure 33.17. Histological section of bladder with pseudopolyp due to chronic infection with *S. haematobium.*

japonicum or *S. mansoni* cercariae. The name reflects the early descriptions of this syndrome in the Katayama Valley of Japan. The symptoms are often dramatic and appear approximately 4-8 weeks after initial exposure, when adult worm pairs begin releasing their eggs in the tissues. Some investigators believe that Katayama fever resembles some of the manifestations of serum sickness. There is also a clinical resemblance to typhoid fever. Patients experience hepatosplenomegaly and lymphadenopathy as well as an impressive eosinophilia. The affected individual is frequently febrile and has flu-like symptoms including cough and headache. At this stage of the illness, schistosome eggs may not yet have appeared in the feces.

Chronic schistosomiasis

This manifestation of infection occurs as a consequence of many years of progressive injury resulting from chronic egg deposition in the tissues and the resulting granuloma formation (Fig. 33.21). The injury has an immunopathological basis. In the case of *S. japonicum* and *S. mansoni* infection, the injury occurs when eggs are deposited in the wall of the intestine and in the liver parenchyma. With *S. haematobium,* injury occurs in the bladder. The extent of injury depends on chronic worm burden, so chronic schistosomiasis occurs predominantly in individuals who are predisposed to repeated heavy infections.[38] Generally speaking, heavy infections occur only in less than one-fourth of a given population under conditions of heavy exposure to cercariae, where up to 10% of individuals develop periportal fibrosis.

S. japonicum and *S. mansoni* infections result in chronic intestinal and hepatic dysfunction. Children with intestinal schistosomiasis develop intermittent abdominal pain, sometimes accompanied with bloody diarrhea. The blood loss and ulceration of intestinal schistosomiasis may result in iron deficiency and anemia. This may explain why chronic schistosomiasis during childhood can result in physical growth retardation similar to that described for intestinal nematode infections. Stunting becomes most prominent at the age of peak intensity (usually between 8 and 20 years).[42] It is partly reversible by specific anthelmintic therapy.[43]

Hepatomegaly results from portal fibrosis. Splenomegaly follows, and in advanced cases, the spleen may fill much of the left side of the abdomen. The patient may also develop symptoms of hypersplenism. Portal obstructive disease due to schistosomiasis is similar to other causes in that it leads to hematemesis from ruptured esophageal varices. As a result of portal hypertension, and the consequent development of a collateral circulation, schistosome eggs are washed into the lungs, where they induce granulomatous inflammation, leading to obstructive disease culminating in cor pulmonale. As noted above, long standing infections can cause nephrotic syndrome, resulting from the deposi-

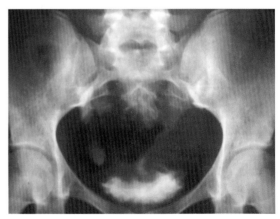

Figure 33.18. X-ray of bladder with a squamous cell tumor induced by *S. haematobium* eggs.

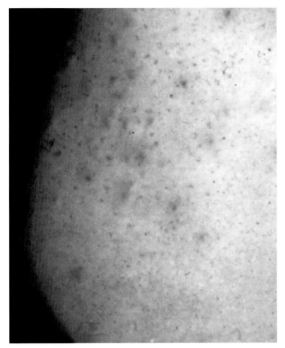

Figure 33.19. Thigh of a child suffering from a maculopapular rash ("swimmer's itch") due to the cercariae of a schistosome species that normally infects birds.

tion of immune complexes onto the glomerular membrane.

S. haematobium, unlike the other three major schistosomes, causes involvement of the urinary tract, which is characterized by an inflammation to the eggs as they are deposited in the wall of the bladder. Patients with chronic *S. haematobium* infection develop hematuria as well as symptoms that mimic urinary tract infections such as dysuria and increased urinary frequency. Over time the inflammatory changes in the bladder can result in fibrosis that can lead to an obstructive uropathy. This sometimes results in hydronephrosis or hydroureter. The resulting urinary stasis can sometimes lead to secondary bacterial urinary tract infections that may exacerbate the scarring and fibrosis.

Bladder carcinoma

A unique type of bladder carcinoma occurs in regions where *S. haematobium* is endemic. In contrast to adenocarcinoma, the most common type of bladder cancer in industrialized countries, some patients with chronic *S. haematobium* go on to develop squamous cell carcinoma. Squamous cell carcinoma is the most common type of bladder cancer in parts of Egypt as well as elsewhere in Africa. Possibly over time the *S. haematobium* eggs function as a human carcinogen that elicit metaplastic changes in the bladder.[44]

CNS schistosomiasis

Rarely, all three schistosomes induce focal inflammatory reactions within the central nervous system, caused by deposition of eggs in the spinal cord and the brain.[45] *S. mansoni* and *S. haematobium* are more likely to do so in the spinal cord, and *S. japonicum* in the brain. Inflammation due to eggs may result in focal transverse myelitis and encephalopathy.

Diagnosis

Definitive diagnosis is made by microscopically identifying schistosome eggs in stool or urine (Figs. 33.4, 33.5a, 33.5b, 33.6). If a single stool examination is negative, concentration of a specimen collected over a 24-hour period is required, because the number of eggs in stool can be few. Quantitative egg counts are sometimes useful for epidemiologic studies attempting to determine infection intensities. For light infections, or in patients from whom egg excretion is intermittent and from whom eggs cannot be found in stool, a rectal biopsy can be carried out (Fig. 33.22). The tissue is squashed between two microscope slides and examined under the low-power lens of a microscope. It is helpful to refer to the specimen as a "rectal snip," rather

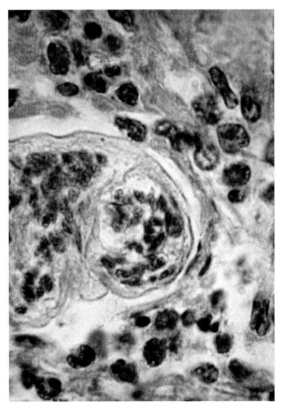

Figure 33.20. Cercaria of *S. mansoni* in skin surrounded by eosinophils.

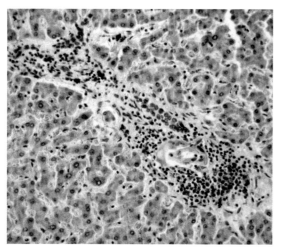

Figure 33.21. Granuloma surrounding an egg of *S. mansoni* in liver tissue.

than a biopsy, to preclude its fixation and subsequent sectioning, which would make identification of eggs more difficult.

Urine is examined for the presence of eggs of *S. haematobium*. The urine sample should generally be collected close to noon, when egg excretion is usually maximal. Urine may have to be concentrated by sedimentation to reveal the few eggs present. *S. haematobium* eggs may also be seen in stool and rectal snip specimens, but their numbers are typically small in these samples.

As an alternative to the current methods of diagnosis, two schistosome antigens known as CCA and CAA that circulate in the bloodstream of infected patients have been identified.[46] The detection of these antigens may someday provide the basis of a finger-stick dot-ELISA assay for the diagnosis of active infections. A positive serological test to detect anti-schisto-somal antibodies is indirect evidence of infection, and cannot distinguish current from past infection, or light versus heavy infection. Indirect immunofluorescence, ELISA, and circumoval precipitin tests are available. The reactions are positive in nearly all infected individuals. The ELISA test is particularly useful for conducting epidemiologic surveys or in recent travelers.

Portable ultrasound imaging has been shown to be clinically useful in the diagnosis of schistosomiasis. Ultrasound can define the extent of Symmer's fibrosis in patients with *S. mansoni* or *S. japonicum* infections, while the chronic obstructive changes associated with *S. haematobium* infection can also be detected.[47]

Treatment

Praziquantel is the drug of choice for most species of schistosomes. This drug is well-tolerated, is

associated with few side effects (nausea, epigastric pain, dizziness, and general malaise), has a very high therapeutic index, and a single dose is usually sufficient to kill all adult worms. Praziquantel allows for calcium ion influx across the tegument resulting in spastic paralysis and at higher doses, the worm tegument develops blebs and is unmasked, and is now susceptible to immune attack by the host.[48] In younger patients praziquantel may also reverse some of the pathology associated with Symmer's fibrosis.[49] There is evidence that part of its effectiveness is due to synergism with the host's humoral immune response.[50] Because it is effective in a single dose, it has been used in control programs (see below). In patients with CNS schistosomiasis, administration of the drug may elicit inflammation that may temporarily exacerbate pathology and worsen symptoms similar to that described in patients with neurocysticercosis. It is not recommended for pregnant patients.

Praziquantel is now available for $0.30 and the World Health assembly has endorsed community treatment of school-age children in endemic areas. Resistance has not occurred to any appreciable degree although this must be monitored closely.

Alternatives to praziquantel are limited in use due to a higher frequency of adverse reactions and differences in spectrum of activity. Oxamniquine is an alternate drug with good anti-parasitic activity. In some regions, oxamniquine is as effective as praziquantel for the treatment of infections with *S. mansoni*, and metrifonate is effective for the treatment of *S. haematobium* infections.[51] The anti-malarial drug artemether has been studied in China as a chemprophylactic agent in patients who anticipate high levels of exposure to *S. japonicum* and *S. mansoni* cercariae

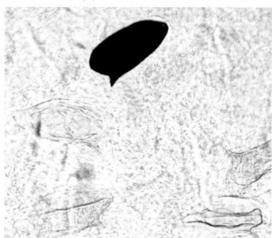

Figure 33.22. Biopsy of rectal tissue revealing eggs of *S. mansoni*. Note calcified egg, indicating that the infection was chronic.

Figure 33.23. Lake Nasser and the Aswan High Dam in Egypt. Photo S. Musgrave, astronaut *extraordinaire*.

during seasonal floods.[52] Chemoprophylactic activity of artemether was present but lower against *S. haematobium*.[53] The efficacy of praziquantel is enhanced when combined with artemether[54] and the combination might prevent the emergence of resistance to praziquantel when used in widespread and repeated community treatment.

Treatment should be carried out only in patients with active schistosome infections. Portocaval or splenorenal shunts should be avoided in untreated schistosomiasis, because they increase the probability of eggs reaching the lungs. If such a shunt is mandated by the intensity of portal hypertension, it should be carried out only after treating with any of the above mentioned drugs.

Prevention and Control

Schistosomes' success in carrying out their life cycles is dependent upon complex ecological interactions with a wide variety of invertebrate and vertebrate host species. Hence, they appear to have numerous weak points in their quest to complete their life cycles. Numerous control programs have attempted to take advantage of these "weak points." Control programs

in the Middle East and North Africa have nearly succeeded in schistosome elimination while programs in China and Brazil have also achieved remarkable success.[55, 56] The prospects for less-developed countries remain dismal because of a lack of adequate resources committed to health in general.

Prevention of schistosomiasis by individuals requires that they never come in contact with infested fresh water. This suggestion is impossible to carry out in much of the world because of many complex economic, cultural, and behavioral patterns. In addition, it may be necessary for many people to be in contact with fresh water for agricultural or other food-gathering purposes. Temporary visitors to endemic areas, however, can heed the advice to avoid potential sources of infection. Dam-building in Africa has helped increase the spread of schistosomiasis (Fig. 34.23).

Control of schistosomiasis at the community level has been directed at (1) eradication of snail vectors with molluscacides, and biologic agents[57]; (2) public health education; (3) sanitation,[58] or other engineering interventions concerning fresh water supplies; and (4) chemotherapy with praziquantel and oxamniquine. Control of *S. japonicum* is complicated by the occurrence of reservoir hosts, such as water buffalo and cattle, in many regions of Asia, particularly in China. The true extent of horizontal transmission from these animal reservoir hosts to people is not known.

Studies in endemic areas have shown that while praziquantel is effective at treating large populations, there is a high rate of post-treatment reinfection. This necessitates frequent administration of the drug, although this tactic is frequently not possible in poor, developing rural areas.[59] Therefore, control of the infection with anthelminthic drugs alone is difficult. There is also concern about the emergence of praziquantel drug resistance.[60]

Candidate antigens under study as potential vaccine candidates were largely discovered over 10 years ago. An *S. haematobium* vaccine has completed safety testing in humans.[61] Paramyosin combined with other peptides to prevent *S. mansoni* infection is likely to be the first candidate tested.[62] Human testing is needed to evaluate the experimental evidence from murine models.[63]

To learn more about the ecology of snail intermediate hosts important to the maintenance of schistosome infections in humans, as well as control programs that take advantage of their biology, see www.medicalecology.org/water/schistosomiasis/schistosomiasis.htm.

References

1. Fuller GK. Lemma A. Trinidad H. Schistosomiasis in Omo National Park of southwest Ethiopia. Am J Trop Med Hyg 28:467-471. 1979.

2. World Health Organization. Weekly Epidemiol Rec 64:171. 1989.

3. Minai M. Hosaka Y. Ohta N. Historical view of schistosomiasis japonica in Japan: implementation and evaluation of disease-control strategies in Yamanashi Prefectur. Parasitol Int. 52:321-6. 2003

4. Hotez PJ. Feng Z. et al. Emerging and re-emerging helminthiases and the public health of China. Emerg Infect Dis 3:303-310. 1997.

5. Manson P. Report of the case of bilharzia from the West Indies. BMJ 2:1894-1895. 1902.

6. Sambon LW. New or little known African entozoa. J Trop Med Hyg 10:117. 1907.

7. Piraja de Silva MA. Contribucao para o estudo da schistosomiasena Bahia. Brazil Med 2:281-283. 1908.

8. Leiper RT. Researches on Egyptian Bilharziosis. John Bale Sons and Danielsson. London. 1918.

9. Katsurada F. The etiology of a parasitic disease. Iji Shimbun 669:1325-1332. 1904.

10. Catto J. Schistosoma cattoi, a new blood fluke of man. BMJ 1:11-13. 1905.

11. Majima T. A strong case of liver cirrhosis caused by parasitic ova. Tokyo Ig Za 2:898-901. 1888.

12. Kawanishi K. A report on a study of the "Katayama disease" in Higo-No-Kuni. Tokyo Ig Za 18:31-48, 1904.

13. Fujinami K. Nakamura H. Katayama disease in Hiroshima prefecture: route of infection, development of the worm in the host and animals in Katayama disease in Hiroshima prefecture (Japanese blood sucking worm disease-schistosomiasis japonica). Kyoto Ig Za 6:224-252. 1909.

14. Miyagawa Y. Uber den Wanderungsweg des *Schistosomum japonicum* von der Haut bis zum Pfortadersystem und uber die Korperkonstitution der jungsten Wurmer zur Zeit der Hautinvasion. Zentralbl Bakteriol Parasit Lnfekt 66: 406-417. 1912.

15. Miyairi K. Suzuki M: Der Zwischenwirt der *Schistosoma japonicum* Katsurada. Mitt Med Fakultat Kaiserlichen Univ Kyushu 1:187-197. 1914.

16. Griesinger W: Klinische und anatomische Beobachtungen uber die Krankheiten von Aegypten. Arch Physiol Heilk 13:528-575. 1854.

17. Lawrence JD. The ingestion of red blood cells by *Schistosoma mansoni*. J Parasitol 59:60-63. 1973.

18. Chappell CL. Kalter DC. Dresden MH. The hypersensitivity response to the adult worm proteinase, Smw32, in *Schistosoma mansoni* infected mice. Am J Trop Med Hyg 39:463-468. 1988.

19. Vermund SH. Bradley DJ. Ruiz-Triben E. Survival of *Schistosoma mansoni* in the human host: estimates from a community-based prospective study in Puerto Rico. Am J Trop Med Hyg 32: 1040-1048.1983.

20. Ruppel A. Chlichlia K. Bahgat M. Invasion by schistosome cercariae: neglected aspects in *Schistosoma japonicum*. Trends Parasitol. 20:397-400. 2004.

21. Cohen FE. Gregoret LM. et al: Arresting tissue invasion of a parasite by protease inhibitors chosen with the aid of computer modeling. Biochemistry 30:11221-11229. 1991.

22. Gendrel D. Kombila M. Beaudoin-Leblevec. Richard-Lenoble D. Nontyphoidal salmonellal septicemia in Gabonese children infected with Schistosoma intercalatum. Clin Infect Dis 18:103-5, 1994.

23. Webster JP. Do hosts and parasites coevolve? Empirical support from the schistosoma system. Am Nat.164 Suppl 5:S33-51. 2004.

24. Chiarella JM. Goldberg AC. et al. Absence of linkage between MHC and a gene involved in susceptibility to human schistosomiasis. Brazil J Med Biol Res 31:665-70. 1998.

25. Dessein AJ. Hillaire D. et al. Severe hepatic fibrosis in *Schistosoma mansoni* infection is controlled by a major locus that is closely linked to the interferon-gamma receptor gene. Am J Hum Genet. 65:709-21. 1999.

26. Karanja DM. Boyer AE. et al. Studies on schistosomiasis in western Kenya: II. Efficacy of praziquantel for treatment of schistosomiasis in persons coinfected with human immunodeficiency virus-1. Am J Trop Med Hyg. 59:307-11. 1998.

27. Warren KS. The pathology of schistosome infections. Helminth Abstr Ser A 42:591-633. 1973.

28. King CL. Xianli J. et al. Mice with a targeted deletion of the IgE gene have increased worm burdens and reduced granulomatous inflammation following primary infection with *Schistosoma mansoni*. J Immunol 158:294-300. 1997.

29. Pearce EJ. Caspar P. et al. Down-regulation of Th1 cytokine production accompanies induction of Th2 responses by a parasitic helminth, *Schistosoma mansoni*. J Exp Med 173: 159-166. 1991.

30. Curry AJ. Else KJ. et al. Evidence that cytokine-mediated immune interactions induced by *Schistosoma mansoni* alter disease outcome in mice concurrently infected with *Trichuris muris*. J Exp Med 181:769-774. 1995.

31. Haseeb MA. Shirazian DJ. Preis J. Elevated serum levels of TNF-alpha, sTNF-RI and sTNF-RII in murine schistosomiasis correlate with schistosome oviposition and circumoval granuloma formation. Cytokine. 15:266-9. 2001.

32. Wynn TA. Development of an anti-pathology vaccine for schistosomiasis. Ann New York Acad Sci 797:191-5. 1996.

33. Secor WE. del Corral H. et al. Association of hepatosplenic schistosomiasis with HLA-DQB1*0201. J Infect Dis 174:1131-5. 1996.

34. Watt G. Long GW. et al. Prevalence of renal involvement in *Schistosoma japonicum* infection. Trans R Soc Med Hyg 82: 339-342.1991.

35. Bickle QD. Andrews BJ. et al. Resistance against *Schistosoma mansoni* induced by highly irradiated infections: studies on species specificity of immunization and attempts to transfer resistance. Parasitol 90:301-312. 1985.

36. Mangold BL. Dean DA. The role of IgG antibodies from irradiated cercaria-immunized rabbits in the passive transfer of immunity to *Schistosoma mansoni*-infected mice. Am J Trop Med Hyg 47: 821-829,1992.

37. Dessein A. Kouriba B. et al. Interleukin-13 in the skin and interferon-gamma in the liver are key players in immune protection in human schistosomiasis. Immunol Rev. 201:180-90. 2004.

38. Acosta LP. McManus DP. et al. Antigen-specific antibody isotype patterns to *Schistosoma japonicum* recombinant and native antigens in a defined population in Leyte, the Philippines. Am J Trop Med Hyg. 70:549-55. 2004.

39. Kojima S. Nara T. et al. A vaccine trial for controlling reservoir livestock against schistosomiasis japonica. In Tada, I Kojima S and Tsuji

M (eds), Proceedings of the 9th International Congress of Parasitology. Bologna, 489-494. 1998.

40. Acosta LP. Waine et al. Immune correlate study on human *Schistosoma japonicum* in a well-defined population in Leyte, Philippines: II. Cellular immune responses to *S. japonicum* recombinant and native antigens. Acta Trop. 84:137-49. 2002.

41. Acosta LP. Aligui A. et al. Immune correlate study on human *Schistosoma japonicum* in a well-defined population in Leyte, Philippines: I. Assessment of 'resistance' versus 'susceptibility' to *S. japonicum* infection. Acta Trop. 84:127-36. 2002.

42. McGarvey ST. Aligui G. et al. Child growth and schistosomiasis japonica in northeastern Leyte, Philippines. I. Cross sectional results. Am J Trop Med Hyg 46:571-581. 1992.

43. Stephenson LS. Latham MC. et al. Single dose metrifonate or praziquantel treatment in Kenyan children. II. Effects on growth in relation to *Schistosoma haematobium* and hookworm egg counts. Am J Trop Med Hyg 41:445-453. 1989.

44. Hodder SL. Mahmoud AA. et al. Predisposition to urinary tract epithelial metaplasia in *Schistosoma haematobium* infection. Am J Trop Med Hyg. 63:133-8. 2000.

45. Scrimgeour EM. Gaidusek CD. Involvement of the central nervous system in *Schistosoma mansoni* and *S. haematobium* infection. Brain 108:1023-1038.1985.

46. van Dam GJ, Wichers JH. et al. Diagnosis of schistosomiasis by reagent strip test for detection of circulating cathodic antigen. J Clin Microbiol. 42:545 61. 2004.

47. Ultrasound in Schistosomiasis (Hatz C. Jenkins JM. Tanner M, eds). Acta Tropica 51:1. 1992.

48. Greenberg RM. Are Ca2+ channels targets of praziquantel action? Int J Parasitol. 35:1-9. 2005.

49. Homeida MA. Tom JE. Nash T. Bennett JL. Association of the therapeutic activity of praziquantel with the reversal of Symmer's fibrosis induced by *Schistosoma mansoni*. Am J Trop Med Hyg 45:360-365. 1991.

50. Brindley PJ. Sher A. The chemotherapeutic effect of praziquantel against *Schistosoma mansoni* is dependent on host antibody response. J Immunol 139:215-220. 1987.

51. King CH. Lombardi G. et al. Chemotherapy-based control of schistosomiasis haematobia. II. Metrifonate vs. praziquantel in control of infection-associated morbidity. Am J Trop Med Hyg 42:587-595. 1990.

52. Xiao SH. Tanner M. Artemether in the chemopropylaxis against schistosomiasis in China. Parasitol. Today. 2000.

53. Utzinger J. Chollet J. et al. Effect of combined treatment with praziquantel and artemether on *Schistosoma japonicum* and *Schistosoma mansoni* in experimentally infected animals. Acta Trop. 80:9-18. 2001.

54. Ngoran EK. Utzinger J. et al. Randomized, double blind placebo controlled trial of oral artemether for the prevention of patent S. hematobium infections. Am J Trop Med Hyg, 68; 24-32. 2003.

55. Engels D. Chitsulo L. Montresor A. Savioli L. The global epidemiological situation of schistosomiasis and new approaches to control and research. Acta Trop. 82:139-46. 2002.

56. Jordan P. Schistosomiasis research to control. Am J Trop Med Hyg 26:877-885. 1977.

57. Jobin WR. Brown RA. et at. Biological control of *Biomphalaria glabrata* in major reservoirs of Puerto Rico. Am J Trop Med Hyg 26: 1018-1024.1977.

58. Unrau GO. Individual household water supplies in rural St. Lucia as a control measure against *Schistosoma mansoni*. Bull WHO 52:1-8. 1975.

59. Olveda RM. Daniel BL. et al. Schistosomiasis japonica in the Philippines: The long term impact of population based chemotherapy on infection, transmission and morbidity. J Infect Dis 174:163-72. 1996.

60. Herwaldt BL. Tao LF. et al. Persistence of *Schistosoma haematobium* infection despite multiple courses of therapy with praziquantel. Clin Infect Dis 20:309-15. 1995.

61. Capron A. Capron M. Dombrowicz D. Riveau E. Vaccine strategies against schistosomiasis: from concepts to clinical trials. Int Arch Allergy Immunol Jan 124:9-15. 2001.

62. Pearce EJ. Progress towards a vaccine for schistosomiasis. Acta Trop. 86:309-13. 2003.

63. Bergquist R. Al-Sherbiny M. Barakat R. Olds R. Blueprint for schistosomiasis vaccine development. Acta Trop. 82:183-92. 2002.

34. *Clonorchis sinensis*
(Loos 1907)

Introduction

Clonorchis sinensis is endemic in Japan, Korea, Cambodia, Laos, Vietnam, and China,[1] and is acquired by eating raw or undercooked fresh water fish. *C. sinensis* has numerous reservoir hosts, including dogs and cats. Two other closely related species deserve mention, due to their high prevalence in some regions. *Opisthorchis felineus* occurs throughout the Philippines, India, Japan, Vietnam, and eastern Europe, particularly Poland and western Russia. It has a similar range of reservoir hosts. *O. viverini* is found in northern Thailand[2] and in Laos.[3] The biology, pathogenesis, and

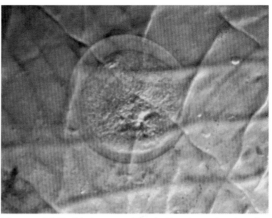

Figure 34.2. Metacercaria of *C. sinensis*, *in situ*, under the scales of a grass carp. 165 μm.

clinical disease of all three species are similar, hence, only *C. sinensis* will be presented.

More than 25 million people in the Far East are infected with *C. sinensis*, and up to one fourth of Chinese immigrants to the United States harbor this fluke.[1,4] Approximately 10 million people in northern Thailand are infected with *O. viverini*,[5] and 16 million in the former USSR with *O. felineus*.[6]

Historical information

McConnell, in 1875,[7] described the adult *C. sinensis*, and Loos named it. Ijima, in 1887,[8] demonstrated that *C. sinensis* infects animals, establishing the concept of reservoir hosts for this parasite. Kobayashi, in 1914,[9] found that fresh water fish were the intermediate vertebrate hosts. Muto, in 1918,[10] extended these studies in Japan by identifying snails in the genus Bulimus as the first intermediate hosts. It is now known the genus of snail responsible for harboring the intermediate stages of *C. sinensis* varies from region to region.

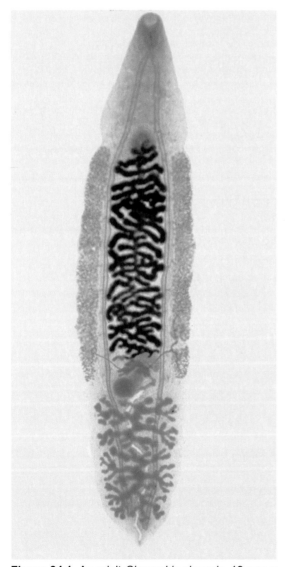

Figure 34.1. An adult *Clonorchis sinensis*. 19 mm x 3.5 mm.

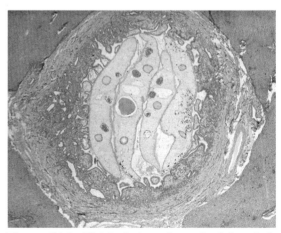

Figure 34.3. Histological section of adults of *C. sinensis* in bile duct.

Clonorchis sinensis

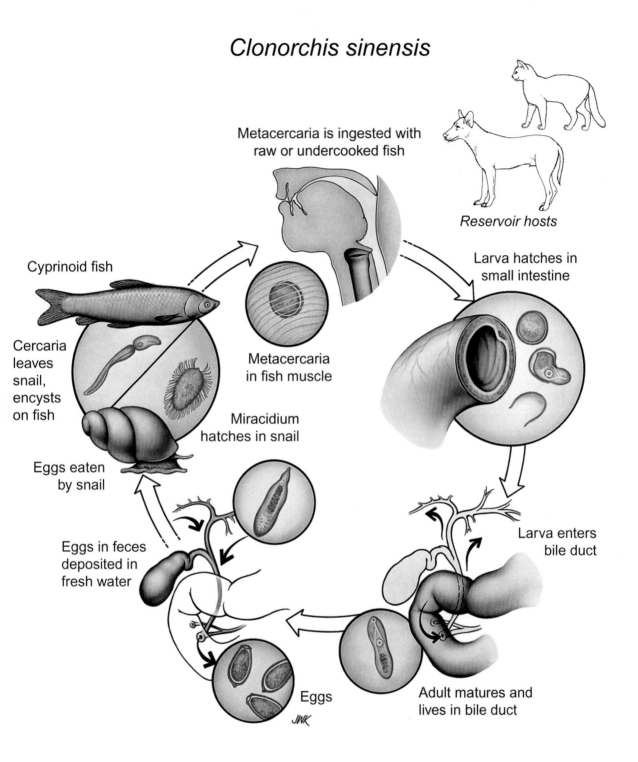

Metacercaria is ingested with raw or undercooked fish

Reservoir hosts

Larva hatches in small intestine

Cyprinoid fish

Cercaria leaves snail, encysts on fish

Metacercaria in fish muscle

Miracidium hatches in snail

Larva enters bile duct

Eggs eaten by snail

Eggs in feces deposited in fresh water

Eggs

JWK

Adult matures and lives in bile duct

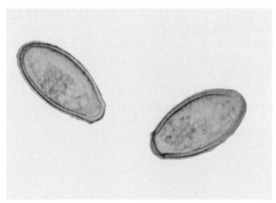

Figure 34.4. Eggs of *C. sinensis*. 30 μm x 15 μm.

Life Cycle

Infection begins when the definitive host ingests a raw or undercooked fish or crab harboring the metacercaria (Fig. 34.2). This larval stage excysts in the small intestine and transforms to the immature fluke. It then crawls up the bile duct (Fig. 34.3) and remains there, growing to adulthood within several weeks. The mature parasite (Fig. 34.1) measures 20 mm by 3.5 mm, and lives in the lumen of the bile duct, feeding on epithelium. Since each worm has both male and female reproductive organs, self-fertilization is the norm. Egg production follows self-fertilization. Embryonated eggs (Fig. 34.4) pass from the common bile duct into the small intestine and are excreted with the feces. They must reach fresh water in order to continue the life cycle. In experimental infections, adult worms produce 1000-4000 eggs per day; there is no corresponding information for human infections.

Eggs are eaten by the intermediate host snail, (in most of Asia, *Parafossarulus spp.*), stimulating the miracidium to hatch. The parasite penetrates the hepatopancreas and undergoes development to the sporocyst, then the redia stage. Cercariae emerge from the snail some twenty days later. This stage is highly motile, and when it encounters an appropriate fish (Family: Cyprinidae), it encysts under the scales, transforming to the metacercaria. Encystment can also occur under the exoskeleton of various fresh-water crustacea (e.g., crabs and crayfish), completing the life cycle.

Cellular and Molecular Pathogenesis

Adult worms induce eosinophilic inflammatory reactions[11,12] after they attach to the bile duct and begin feeding. In heavy infection, these changes usually lead to desquamation of the biliary epithelium, formation of crypts, and metaplasia.[13, 14] *C. sinensis* elicits

the production of specific IgE antibody in serum and bile.[15] Chronic Clonorchis and Opisthorchis elicit reactions results in intermittent obstruction of the biliary tree, as well introducing pyogenic bacteria into the infection site.[16] Through this process, chronic liver fluke infection can result in recurrent ascending cholangitis and pancreatitis.[17-21] Over time, the presence of either Clonorchis or Opisthorchis in the biliary tree results in squamous metaplastic changes that lead to cholangiocarcinoma. This is particularly true of heavy *O. viverini* infections in Thailand that can be associated with a 15-fold increase in risk of developing this unusual form of cancer. A much higher percentage of patients who died of cholangiocarcinoma had coexistent opisthorchiasis than did those who died of other causes.[14] It is suspected that high levels of N-nitrosoamines in the northern Thai diet may contribute to this condition.

Clinical Disease

Light infections do not cause disease, although moderate and heavy chronic infections can result in liver enlargement, right upper quadrant tenderness, and eosinophilia.[20] Very heavy infections can lead to anorexia, cachexia and weight loss. Similarly heavy infections can facilitate the introduction of pyogenic bacteria to cause recurrent ascending cholangitis and pancreatitis.[17-21] These are often associated with the production of pigmented stones in the left lobe of the liver. Possibly some of these stones have a fluke or a fluke remnant as a nidus. These patients can also go on to develop multiple pyogenic abscesses with subsequent enlargement of the left lobe of the liver.

Diagnosis

Eggs of *Clonorchis sinensis* are present in stool, so a microscopic examination of a concentrated sample of feces is the definitive test. The presence of flukes in the biliary tract can be determined by radiogram,[22] then confirmed by stool examination. A variety of serological tests, including Western blot and ELISA, and CT[23, 24] are available, but most only indicate whether or not the patient has even been infected. Use of recombinant antigens offers some promise for increasing the specificity of serological testing.[24]

Treatment

Praziquantel is the drug of choice for treating *Clonorchis sinensis* and also for *Opisthorchis viverini*.[25] Albendazole is also effective.[26]

Prevention and Control

Ingestion of contaminated raw, undercooked, pickled, frozen, salted, or dried fresh water fish or crustaceans is the source of infection with *Clonorchis sinensis* and its close relatives. Therefore, thoroughly cooking contaminated fish and crustaceans is the most effective way of eliminating the parasite on an individual basis.[20] Thus, at least one form of biliary carcinoma is preventable by changes in eating habits. Unfortunately, centuries-old culinary preferences in most endemic areas do not allow for this possibility.

The advent of large-scale aquaculture of grass carp, and related fishes in areas where fecal contamination of the ponds from infected hosts occurs on a regular basis, results in the establishment of infection in the fish population.[20, 21] Thus, animal reservoirs make control of this parasite difficult at best. Ammonium sulfate kills the eggs of Clonorchis, and so it is recommended as a treatment for human feces destined to be used as fertilizer.

Molluscicides, alone, have not been used successfully for eradicating the intermediate snail hosts. However, in combination with regular draining of ponds, they have been moderately effective in controlling infection in fish.

References

1. Stauffer WM. Sellman JS. Walker PF. Biliary liver flukes (Opisthorchiasis and Clonorchiasis) in immigrants in the United States: often subtle and diagnosed years after arrival. J Travel Med. 11:157-9. 2004.
2. Kruthong S. Lerdverasirikul P. et al. *Opisthorchis viverini* infection in rural communities in northeast Thailand. Trans R Soc Med Hyg 81:41 1-414. 1987.
3. Giboda M. Ditrich O. et al. Human Opisthorchis and Haplorchis infections in Laos. Trans R Soc Trop Med Hyg 85:538-540. 1991.
4. Case Records of the Massachusetts General Hospital: Case 33-1990.
5. Schwartz DA. Cholangiocarciroma associated with liver fluke infection: a preventable source of morbidity in Asian immigrants. Am J Gastroenterol 81:76-79. 1986.
6. Control of food-borne trematode infections: Report of a WHO study group. WHO Technical Report Series No. 849. Geneva, World Health Organization 1995.
7. McConnell JFP. Anatomy and pathological relations of a new species of liver fluke. Lancet 2: 271-274.1875.
8. Ijima I. Notes on Diastoma endemicum. Baelz J Coll Sci Imperial Univ Jpn 1:47-50. 1887.
9. Kobayashi H. On the life cycle and morphology of *Clonorchis sinensis*. Centr Bakter-Parasit Infect-Krank. 75: 299-317. 1914.
10. Muto S. On the primary intermediate host of *Clonorchis sinensis*. Chuo Igakakai Zasshi 25:49-52. 1918.
11. Sun T. Pathology and immunology of *Clonorchis sinensis* infection in the liver. Am Clin Lab Sci 14:208-215. 1984.
12. Yen C-M. Chen E-R. Hou M-F. Antibodies of different immunoglobulin isotypes in serum and bile of patients with clonorchiasis. Ann Trop Med Parasitol 86:263-269. 1992.
13. Pungpak S. Akai PS. et al: Tumor markers in the detection of opisthorchiasis-associated cholangiocarcinoma. Trans R Soc Trop Med Hyg 85:277-279. 1991.
14. Srivatanakul P. Sriplung H. Deerasamee S. Epidemiology of liver cancer: an overview. Asian Pac J Cancer Prev. 5:118-25. 2004.
15. Yong TS, Park SJ. et al. Identification of IgE-reacting *Clonorchis sinensis* antigens. Yonsei Med J. 40:178-83. 1999.
16. Ho CS. Wesson DE. Recurrent pyogenic cholangitis in Chinese immigrants. Am J Roentgenol Radium Ther Nucl Med.122:368-74. 1974.
17. McFadzen AJS, Yeung RTT: Acute pancreatitis due to *Clonorchis sinensis*. Trans R Soc Trop Med Hyg 60:466, 1966.
18. Haswell-Elkins MR. Mairiang E. et al. Cross-sectional study of Opisthorchis viverini infection and cholangiocarcinoma in communities within a high-risk area in Northeast Thailand. Int J Cancer 59:505. 1994.
19. Thamavit W. Bharmarapravati N. et al. Effects of dimethylnitrosamine on induction of cholangiocarcinoma in Opisthorchis viverini-infected Syrian Golden Hamsters. Cancer Res 38:1634. 1978.
20. Lun ZR, Gasser RB. et al. Clonorchiasis: a key foodborne zoonosis in China. Lancet Infect Dis. 5:31-41. 2005.
21. Wang KX. Zhang RB, et al. Clinical and epidemiological features of patients with clonorchiasis. World J Gastroenterol.1:446-8. 2004.
22. Choi BI. Han JK. Hong ST. Lee KH. Clonorchiasis and cholangiocarcinoma: etiologic relationship and imaging diagnosis. Clin Microbiol Rev. 7:540-52. 2004.
23. Kim SI. A *Clonorchis sinensis*-specific antigen that detects active human clonorchiasis. Korean J Parasitol 36:37-45. 1998.
24. Kim CS. Min DY. et al. Immunodiagnosis of clonorchiasis using a recombinant antigen. Korean J Parasitol 36:183-90. 1998.
25. Hsu CCS. Kron MA. Clonorchiasis and praziquantel. Arch Intern Med 145:1002-1003. 1985.
26. Liu YH. Wang XG. Gao P. et al. Experimental and clinical trial of albendazole in the treatment of clonorchiasis sinensis. Chin Med J (Engl) 104:27. 1991.

35. *Fasciola hepatica*
(Linnaeus 1758)

Introduction

Fasciola hepatica, the sheep liver fluke, is acquired by eating contaminated leafy wild plants (e.g., watercress) that grow at the littoral zone of standing bodies of fresh water. It is a zoonosis, infecting wild animals and livestock of all kinds, and is prevalent throughout Latin America, the British Isles, southeastern United States, Africa, Europe, China, and South America.[1] It is a frequent parasite of sheep and bovines, but humans also become infected with the adult parasite. Intensity of infection in humans is always associated with intensity of animal husbandry.[2] The highest prevalence is believed to occur in the northwestern altiplano of Bolivia, near Lake Titicaca.[3] *Fasciola gigantica* is a closely related species infecting cattle and wild herbivores in Africa and Asia.

Historical Information

The writings of de Brie, in 1379, indicate that shepherds not only knew of the infection, but also known that contaminated watercress was a source of the

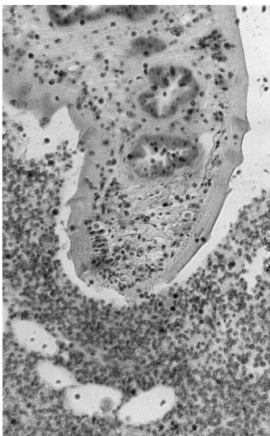

Figure 35.2. Histological section of an adult *F. hepatica* in liver.

parasite.[4] Redi, in 1684,[5] described the adult parasite he obtained from a rabbit. Linnaeus, in 1758, named it *Fasciola hepatica*, and Leuckart[6] and Thomas, in 1881,[7] discovered aspects of its life cycle. Lutz, in 1892,[8] reported that the adult parasite was acquired by swallowing the infective stage, a fact that could probably have been deduced from the early description by de Brie.

Life Cycle

Infection begins by ingestion of encysted metacercariae that are firmly attached to littoral vegetation, particularly watercress, in standing bodies of fresh water (e.g., farm ponds). They excyst in the small intestine, penetrate the intestinal wall, and migrate in the peritoneal cavity to the surface of the liver. They then penetrate Glisson's capsule and enter the parenchymal tissue of the liver. Maturation to reproductive adults takes up to 4 months. The adult fluke is large, measuring 35 mm by 15 mm (Fig. 36.1).

Both the immature worms and adults feed on liver parenchymal tissue and epithelial cells lining the bile ducts (Fig. 35.2). Self-fertilization leads to egg production. These large worms spend their lives burrowing

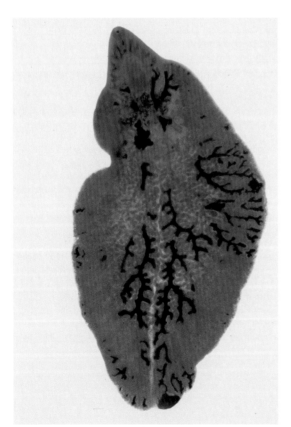

Figure 35.1. An adult of *Fasciola hepatica*. 30mm x 14 mm.

Fasciola hepatica

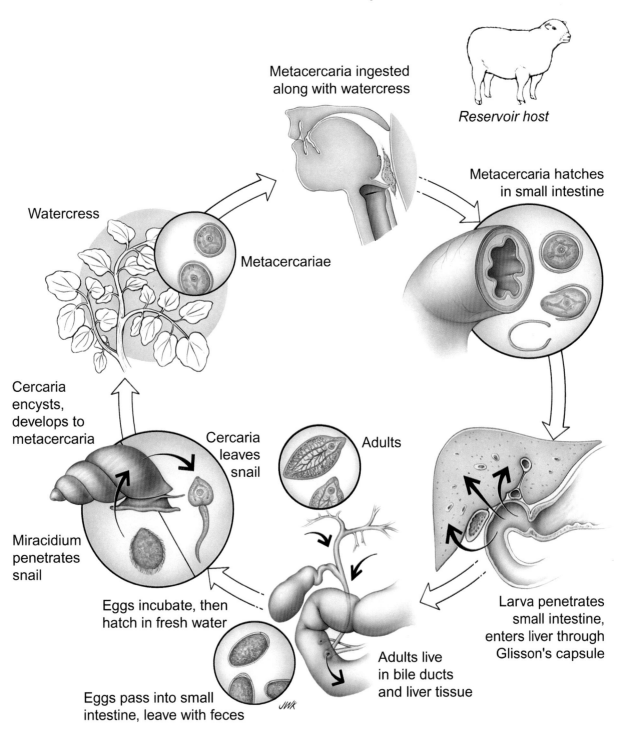

Metacercaria ingested along with watercress

Reservoir host

Metacercaria hatches in small intestine

Watercress

Metacercariae

Cercaria encysts, develops to metacercaria

Cercaria leaves snail

Adults

Miracidium penetrates snail

Larva penetrates small intestine, enters liver through Glisson's capsule

Eggs incubate, then hatch in fresh water

Adults live in bile ducts and liver tissue

Eggs pass into small intestine, leave with feces

JWK

through the liver, aided by their muscular oral suckers, creating tunnels into which are deposited eggs and waste products.

Fertilized, unembryonated eggs (Fig. 35.3) pass out of the liver through the common duct, enter the small intestine, and become included in the fecal mass.

Eggs must be deposited in fresh water in order to embryonate, which may take as long as 9-15 days. The miracidium is stimulated to hatch by exposure to direct sunlight, and after emerging from the egg it is a free-swimming organism until it finds its snail host. The most common snail species for *F. hepatica* is *Lymnea truncatula*, but, due to its worldwide distribution, many other species of Lymneid snails (e.g., *Fossaria modicella*) also support the growth and development of this fluke. The miracidium penetrates the snail's body wall, and finds its way to the hepatopancreas. After sequential development, first into sporocysts, then into rediae, the cercariae (Fig. 35.4) emerge from the snail and attach themselves to the surfaces of littoral vegetation, where they become encysted. Within the cyst they transform into the environmentally resistant, infective stage, the metacercariae. This stage can live and remain infective for several months.

Ingested metacercariae sometimes find their way to tissues other than the liver (e.g., brain, kidney).[9, 10] In this case, they become aberrant infections, and pass eggs that cannot find their way out of the body.

Cellular and Molecular Pathogenesis

Adult *Fasciola hepatica* secrete large quantities of proline[11] which stimulates the bile epithelial cells to divide and hypertrophy, creating the "lawn" of cells on which the fluke periodically grazes, presumably with the aid of its secreted proteases.[12] Essentially, the parasite grows its own food by "fertilizing" the epithelium downstream from itself. Moving through liver tissue creates trauma - tunnels and abscesses filled with necrotic cell debris, worm excreta, and fertilized eggs. Fascioliasis induces high levels of circulating eosinophils throughout the infection period.[13, 15]

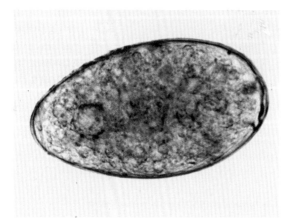

Figure 35.3. Egg of *F. hepatica*. 140 μm x 85 μm.

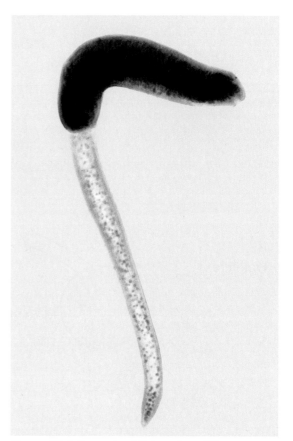

Figure 35.4. Cercaria of *F. hepatica*. 100 μm.

Halzoun (pharyngitis and laryngeal edema) is limited to the Middle East. It is a condition associated with consumption of raw, infected sheep liver.[14] It is caused by an adult Fasciola adhering to the posterior pharyngeal wall causing partial blockage of the pharynx.

Clinical Disease

Clinical aspects of infection with *F. hepatica* have been reviewed.[15] Individuals may develop symptoms related to the migration of the immature worms within a month after becoming infected. Many infected persons are asymptomatic during this early phase, while others complain of fever, pain in the right upper quadrant of the abdomen, and general malaise of varying degree, including myalgia and urticaria. In heavy infections, the liver is enlarged and tender, but often subsides within a month. The mature worms in bile ducts cause disease proportional to the number of worms. Dull pain and obstruction of bile ducts occur, but these are not common symptoms. There are usually no changes in liver function tests, and jaundice is not present. The gallbladder may become severely damaged in heavy infection. Fasciola in sites other than liver may cause no symptoms, or it may be present as a small tumor mass; if the parasite invades the brain, it can induce focal neurological abnormalities. Halzoun causes intense pain in the back of the throat. Extensive edema may lead to laryngeal obstruction.

Diagnosis

Microscopic identification of eggs is the definitive method of diagnosis. However, worms present in ectopic locations do not pass eggs into feces, and the diagnosis may be missed. Ultrasonography is the procedure of choice for the diagnosis of biliary fascioliasis.[16] CT scans and other imaging methods are also helpful in the differential diagnosis of fascioliasis. On CT scans, small nodules and linear tracts are seen in infected liver.

If no eggs have been found in the stool, one can resort to immunodiagnosis. An ELISA employing cathepsin L1 antigen from the adult worm gives excellent results regarding specificity and sensitivity.[17, 18] ELISA is rapid and is usually positive during the acute phase of infection (i.e., between the 5th and 20th weeks).[17] There are cross reactions with antibodies to group-specific antigens of trematodes, which can confuse the diagnosis. An elevated level of circulating eosinophils is present in most patients.[15]

Treatment

Either bithionol or triclabendazole is the drug of choice for *Fasciola hepatica*.[15, 19] Praziquantel, which is excellent for treating infections with other flukes, is not effective against Fasciola.[20]

Prevention and Control

Fasciola can best be controlled by periodic draining of ponds, reducing littoral plant growth to a minimum. Further control of the spread of fascioliasis in domestic animals can be achieved by protecting water supplies, and regularly surveying herds and herders for the presence of the parasites. In this regard, an ELISA test detected experimentally and naturally-infected calves, with a high degree of sensitivity and specificity.[18] When infections are detected, appropriate treatment in both groups is warranted. Use of molluscacides and drug treatment of livestock, alone, comprises effective environmentally-based control programs. Education of farm personnel regarding the mode of acquisition of the infection is essential to eliminating transmission due to human fecal contamination of fresh water aquatic habitats.

A novel saposin-like molecule has been expressed and used in an experimental trial in rabbits as a test for efficacy as a molecular vaccine candidate.[21] It elicited strong protection, reducing worm burdens by 82%. This recombinant protein has the potential to become the first practical vaccine for cattle and sheep.

References

1. Esteban JG. Bargues MD. Mas-Coma S. Geographical distribution, diagnosis and treatment of human fascioliasis: a review. Res Rev Parasitol 58: 13–42. 1998.
2. Esteban JG. Gonzalez C. et al. Hyperendemic fascioliasis associated with schistosomiasis in villages in the Nile Delta of Egypt. Am J Trop Med Hyg. 69:429-37. 2003.
3. Hillyer GV. Soler DE. et al. Use of the Falcon assay screening test-enzyme-linked immunosorbent assay (Fast-ELISA) and the enzyme-linked immunoelectrotransfer blot (EJIB) to determine the prevalence of human fascioliasis in the Bolivian altiplano. Am J Trop Med Hyg 46:603-609. 1992
4. de Brie J. Le Bon Berger ou le Vray Regime et Gouvenement de Bergers et Bergeres: Compose par le Rustique Jehan de Brie le Bon Berger (1379). Isidor Liseux, Paris. 1879.
5. Redi F. Osservazioni di Francesco Redi. Intorno Agli Animali Viventi che si Trovano Negli Animali Viventi. Piero Matini, Florence. 1684.
6. Leuckart FR. Zur Entwicklungsgeschichte des Lerberegels. Zool Anz 4:641-646. 1881.
7. Thomas APW. Report of experiments on the development of the liver fluke, *Fasciola hepatica*. J R Agric Soc Engi 17:1-28. 1881.
8. Lutz A. Zur Lebensgeschichte des Distoma hepaticum. Zentralbi Bakteriol Parasit 11:783-796. 1892.
9. Catchpole BN. Snow D. Human ectopic fascioliasis. Lancet 2:711-712. 1952.
10. Arjona R. Riancho JA. et al. Fascioliasis in developed countries: a review of classic and aberrant forms of the disease. Medicine (Baltimore). 74:13-23. 1995.
11. Modavi S. Isseroff H. *Fasciola hepatica*: collagen deposition and other histopathology in the rat host's bile duct caused by the parasite and by proline infusion. Exp Parasitol. 58:239-44.1984.
12. Wijffels GL. Panaccio M. et al. The secreted cathepsin L-like proteinases of the trematode, *Fasciola hepatica*, contain 3-hydroxyproline residues. Biochem J. 299:781-90. 1994.
13. Demirci M. Korkmaz M. et al. Diagnostic importance of serological methods and eosinophilia in tissue parasites. J Health Popul Nutr. 20:352-5. 2002.
14. Saleha AA. Liver fluke disease (fascioliasis): epidemiology, economic impact and public health significance. Southeast Asian J Trop Med Public Health. 22 Suppl:361-4. 1991.
15. Saba R. Korkmaz M. et al. Human fascioliasis. Clin Microbiol Infect. 10:385-7. 2004.
16. Zali MR. Ghaziani T. et al. Liver, spleen, pancreas and kidney involvement by human fascioliasis: imaging findings. BMC Gastroenterol. 4:15. 2004.
17. O'Neill SM. Parkinson M. et al. Short report: Immunodiagnosis of human fascioliasis using recombinant *Fasciola hepatica* cathepsin L1 cysteine proteinase. Am J Trop Med Hyg. 60(5):749-51. 1999.
18. Rokni MB. Massoud J. et al. Diagnosis of human fasciolosis in the Gilan province of Northern Iran: application of cathepsin L-ELISA. Diagn Microbiol Infect Dis. 44:175-9. 2002.
19. el-Karaksy H. Hassanein B. et al. Human fascioliasis in Egyptian children: successful treatment with triclabendazole. J Trop Pediatr 45:135-8. 1999.
20. Fand Z. Kamal M. Mansour N: Praziquantel and *Fasciola hepatica* infection. Trans R Soc Trop Med Hyg 83:813. 1989.
21. Espino AM. Hillyer GV. A novel *Fasciola hepatica* saposin-like recombinant protein with immunoprophylactic potential. J Parasitol 90:876-9. 2004.

36. *Paragonimus westermani*
(Kerbert 1878)

Introduction

Paragonimus westermani lives typically as pairs of worms, usually in lung tissue. It occurs throughout Japan, China, Korea,[1] Vietnam, Thailand, Cambodia, India,[2] Micronesia, Irian Jaya, Papua New Guinea,[3] and the Philippines. *P. westermani* infects a wide range of reservoir hosts, including the fox, civet, tiger, leopard, panther, mongoose, wolf, pig, dog, and cat. It employs numerous crustaceans as intermediate hosts, making it one of the most widely-distributed trematode infections of humans.

The genus Paragonimus is diverse.[4, 5] Several other species routinely infect humans: *P. skrjabini* and *P. miyazakii* in Japan, *P. africanus* in Cameroon, *P. uterobilateralis* in Liberia and Nigeria, and *P. mexicanus* and *P. ecuadoriensis* in Latin America.[5] *P. kellicoti*, a lung fluke of mink and opossums in the United States, has also caused infection in humans.[6]

Historical Information

Kerbert, in 1878,[7] described the adult worm that he isolated at autopsy from a Bengal tiger. Nakahama had

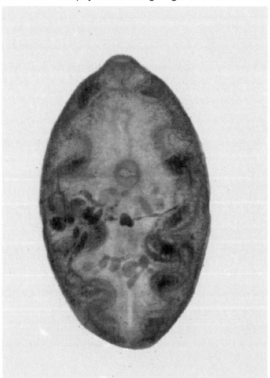

Figure 36.1. An adult of *Paragonimus westermani*. 10mm x 5 mm.

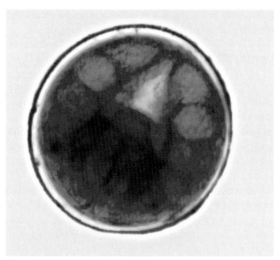

Figure 36.2. Metacercaria of *P. westermani*. 34 μm.

previously described an identical trematode from a human autopsy case. The life cycle of *P. westermani* was determined by Japanese parasitologists. Nakagawa, in 1916,[8] implicated the crab as the intermediate host in the transmission of *P. westermani*, and Yokagawa, in 1915,[9] deciphered the correct route of migration of the immature adult fluke in the mammalian host. von Baelz and Manson, in 1880,[10, 11] reported on most of the clinical features of the disease, and also identified eggs of *P. westermani* in the sputum of patients with hemoptysis.

Life Cycle

The adult of *P. westermani* measures 10-12 mm in length and 5-7 mm in width (Fig. 36.1). It induces a fibrotic capsule of tissue at the periphery of the lung and lives there, usually as a pair of worms. Fresh water crabs (e.g., *Eriocheir spp.*, *Potamon spp.*, *Potamiscus spp.*) are most common sources of infection throughout most of the Far East. In many Asian countries, crabs are eaten raw or undercooked.

Infection begins by ingesting the metacercariae (Fig. 36.2), that excyst in the small intestine, penetrate into the abdominal cavity, and within several days, develop to immature flukes. The worms migrate to the lungs by penetrating the diaphragm, and mature to reproductive adults within 8-12 weeks (Fig. 36.3). Worms also locate to aberrant sites, including brain, liver, intestines, muscle, skin, and testes. In these sites, passage of eggs to the external environment is impossible.

The pair of adults usually cross-fertilize each other. Both diploid and triploid forms of the adult *P. westermani* exist.[4] The triploid form produces eggs via parthenogenesis. Egg production begins about 30 days after ingestion of the metacercariae. Eggs (Fig. 36.4)

Paragonimus westermani

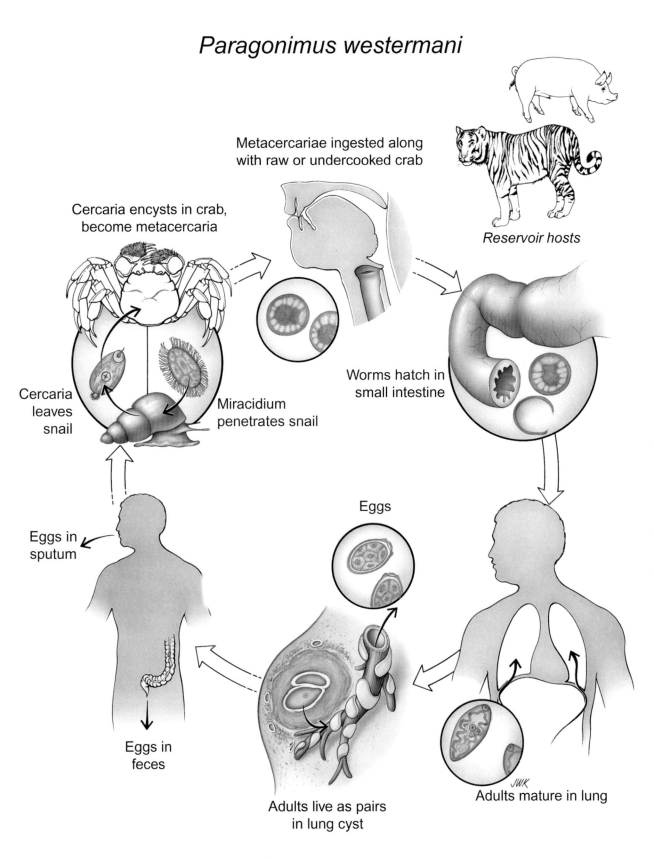

Metacercariae ingested along with raw or undercooked crab

Cercaria encysts in crab, become metacercaria

Reservoir hosts

Worms hatch in small intestine

Cercaria leaves snail

Miracidium penetrates snail

Eggs

Eggs in sputum

Eggs in feces

Adults live as pairs in lung cyst

Adults mature in lung

pass fertilized, but unembryonated, into the surrounding tissue. Eventually, they reach the bronchioles and are included in the sputum, which also contains blood and debris from the necrotic lesions created by the adults. The number of eggs produced by each worm is unknown. Because some of the sputum is swallowed, eggs can be recovered from feces. The eggs must reach fresh water to embryonate. The miracidium develops over a 3-week period, after which it hatches and seeks out its intermediate host snail (e.g., *Melania spp., Semisulcospira spp.,* and *Thiara spp.*). They develop through the sporocyst and redia stages into cercariae, which then exit from the snail and encyst upon and within crustacean intermediate hosts. In the case of the crab, the metacercariae infect all organs.

Cellular and Molecular Pathogenesis

Immature worms of *P. westermani* do not cause clinical disease, either on their way from the small intestine to the abdominal cavity, or during the last leg of their journey to the lung tissue. In contrast, mature adult worms in the lung form cysts that eventually communicate with the bronchioles.[12] Triploid forms of the parasite are considered more pathogenic than diploid forms. The diploid forms are smaller and will form cysts only if sexual partners are found.[12] The inflammatory responses to Paragonimus cysts are characterized by a variety of cells, but eosinophils usually predominate. Charcot-Leyden crystals can frequently be found in the sputum of infected individuals. Specific IgG and IgE antibodies are produced throughout the infection, but appear to have no protective function.[13] Several stages of

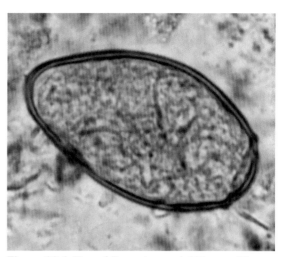

Figure 36.4. Egg of *P. westermani.* 110 μm x 60 μm.

P. westermani secrete cysteine proteases that cleave IgG molecules, and the worm may employ this strategy to avoid immune damage by the host.[14] Infections last somewhat longer than a year, after which adult worms die and become calcified.

Larval stages of several zoonotic species of Paragonimus such as *P. skrjabini* and *P. miyazakii* can cause extensive damage to the tissues as they migrate throughout the viscera.[12]

Clinical Disease

The disease caused by *P. westermani* can be progressive, and begins with a nonspecific cough that becomes chronic and is productive of blood-tinged sputum. This condition is known as endemic hemoptysis. Pleural pain and dyspnea are associated with patent infection, and is complicated by recurrent bacterial pneumonitis and lung abscess. Depending on the severity of the infection and the frequency of bacterial superinfections, there may be pneumothorax and pleural effusion, with consequent pleural adhesions.

Larval migration of *P. skrjabini* usually results in the formation of subcutaneous nodules,[12] which often contain juvenile flukes. Aberrant infection can also lead to the migration of worms into various parts of the brain, occasionally causing seizures.

Diagnosis

Definitive diagnosis is by microscopic identification of eggs in the sputum, and more rarely in stool. Indirect evidence of infection is obtained by serological tests, such as ELISA[15] and Western blot.[16, 17] There is also a simple and rapid intradermal test, performed by injecting diluted Paragonimus antigen into the skin.[12] Using

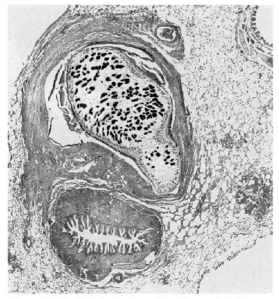

Figure 36.3. Histological section of an adult *P. westermani* in lung.

this procedure, over 2 million people have been tested in China to date, with an overall positivity rate of 20%.[12, 18] Both the serologic and intradermal assays indicate either current or past exposure to the infection. However, a clinical diagnosis depends on suspicion of paragonimiasis in any patient from an endemic area who has the characteristic pulmonary disease. Pulmonary paragonimiasis[2, 19] must be distinguished from chronic bronchiectasis, lung abscess due to other causes, and tuberculosis. Cerebral paragonimiasis must be distinguished from the more likely brain tumors, and lesions caused by other helminths (i.e., juvenile tapeworms and *Fasciola hepatica*). The subcutaneous nodules of *P. skrjabini* must be differentiated from other forms of cutaneous larva migrans and gnathostomiasis.[12]

Treatment

The drug of choice against *Paragonimus westermani* is praziquantel.[19] The drug is also effective against extra-pulmonary forms. An alternative drug, tri-clabendazole, is also effective in patients with *P. mexicanus* infections, as well as some *Paragonimus spp.* infections in Africa.[12, 20, 21] The complications of pleural effusions and subsequent fibrosis may sometimes require surgical management, including decortication.

Prevention and Control

Because of its numerous reservoir hosts, its worldwide distribution, and cultural eating habits favoring the acquisition of this parasite, control of Paragonimus infection is difficult and would require a comprehensive approach including treatment of infected individuals, sanitation changes, and behavioral changes in handling and cooking intermediate crustacean hosts. The metacercariae can be killed by boiling the invertebrate host for several minutes until the meat has congealed and turned opaque. Marinating and salting of crabs or other crustaceans does not reliably kill these infective stages.[12]

References

1. Kim EA. Juhng SK. et al. Imaging findings of hepatic paragonimiasis: a case report. J Korean Med Sci.19:759-62. 2004.
2. Singh TN. Singh HR. et al. Indian J Chest Dis Allied Sci. 46:225-7. Pulmonary paragonimiasis. 2004.
3. Owen IL. Parasitic zoonoses in Papua New Guinea. J Helminthol. 79:1-14. 2005.
4. Blair, D. Genomes of *Paragonimus westermani* and related species: current state of knowledge. Int. J. Parasitol. 30, pp. 421–426. 2000.
5. Iwagami M. Monroy C. et al. A molecular phylogeographic study based on DNA sequences from individual metacercariae of Paragonimus mexicanus from Guatemala and Ecuador. J. Helminthol 77:33–38. 2003.
6. Mariano EU. Borja SR. Vruno Mi. A human infection with *Paragonimus kellicotti* (lung fluke) in the United States. Am J Clin Pathol 86:685-687. 1986.
7. Kerbert C. Zur Trematodenkenntnis. Zool Anz 1:271-273. 1878.
8. Nakagawa K. The mode of infection in pulmonary distomiasis: certain fresh water crabs as intermediate hosts of *Paragonimus westermani*. J Infect Dis 18:131-142. 1916.
9. Yokogawa S. On the route of migration of *Paragonimus westermani* in the definitive host. aiwan Igakkai Zasshi 152:685-700. 1915.
10. Von Baelz EOE. Uber Parasitare Haemoptoe (gregarinosis pulmonum). Zentralbl Med Wissenschr 18:721-722. 1880.
11. Manson P. Distoma ringeri: Medical Report for the Half Year Ended 30 September 1880. Published by order of the Inspector General Shanghai; Imperial Maritime Customs (China). Special Series No. 2, 20th issue, pp. 10-12. 1880.
12. Blair D. Xu ZB. Paragonimiasis and the genus Paragonimus. Adv Parasitol 42:113-222. 1999.
13. Kong Y. Ito A. et al. Immunoglobulin G (IgG) subclass and IgE responses in human paragonimiases caused by three different species. Clin Diag Lab Immunol 5:474-8. 1998.
14. Chung YB. Yang HJ. et al. Activities of different cysteine proteases of *Paragonimus westermani* in cleaving human IgG. Korean J Parasitol 35:139-42. 1997.
15. Ikeda T. Cystatin capture enzyme-linked immunosorbent assay for immunodiagnosis of human paragonimiasis and fascioliasis. Am J Trop Med Hyg 59:286-90. 1998.
16. Slemenda SB. Maddison SE. et al. Diagnosis of paragonimiasis by immunoblot. Am J Trop Med Hyg 39:469-471. 1988.
17. Dekumyoy P. Waikagul J. Eom KS. Human lung fluke *Paragonimus heterotremus*: differential diagnosis between *Paragonimus heterotremus* and *Paragonimus westermani* infections by EITB. Trop Med Internat Health 3:52-6. 1998.
18. Johnson RJ. Johnson JR. Paragonimiasis in Indochinese refugees: roentgenographic findings in clinical correlations. Am Rev Respir Dis 128:534-538. 1983.
19. Johnson Ri. Jong EC. Paragonimiasis: diagnosis and the use of praziquantel in treatment. Rev Infect Dis 7:200-206, 1985.
20. Ripert C. Couprie B. Moyou R. et al. Therapeutic effect of triclabendazole in patients with paragonimiasis in Cameroon: a pilot study. Trans R Soc Trop Med Hyg 86:417. 1992.
21. Keiser J. Utzinger J. Chemotherapy for major food-borne trematodes: a review. Expert Opin Pharmacother. 5:1711-26. 2004.

37. Trematodes of Minor Medical Importance

Besides the trematode infections described in the previous chapters as major causes of human disease throughout the world, other trematode species continue to have a negative impact on the human condition, but not quite to the extent of schistosomiasis, for example. Nonetheless, a few of these "rare" infections are actually not so rare in some geographic regions and deserve more than a mention, since cases of exotic infections are becoming more common in western clinics due to increased immigration from those regions. Many of them are zoonotic and classify as emerging infections in some locales. For a comprehensive review, see Fried et al. 2004.[1]

Fasciolopsis buski
(Lankaster 1857)

Fasciolopsis buski is a large trematode (Fig.

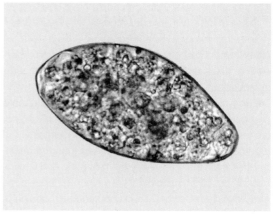

Figure 37.2. Egg of *F. buski*. 140 μm x 80 μm.

37.1), similar in morphology to *Fasciola hepatica*, that lives attached to the columnar epithelium of the small intestine. Infection occurs in China, Taiwan, Vietnam, Thailand,[2] and India.[3] Reservoir hosts include dogs and rabbits.

Life Cycle

The infectious stage for mammals is the metacercaria, which is found on the husks of the seeds of littoral plants (e.g., lotus, water chestnut, water caltrop and other commercial crops in which human feces is used as fertilizer). Once eaten, the metacercaria excysts in the small intestine and attaches to the luminal surface. The adult matures within 2-4 months, and measures 20-30 mm by 10 mm. After self-fertilization, egg-laying begins. The large, ovoid, unembryonated eggs (Fig. 37.2) are passed out with the fecal mass. If they reach warm (i.e., 25°–30°C), fresh water, they immediately undergo embryogenesis, and hatch within 5-8 weeks. The miracidium that emerges penetrates a snail (e.g., *Segmentina spp.* and *Heppentis spp.*), and develops sequentially first into sporocysts, then rediae, and finally into cercariae. After leaving the snail, the cercariae swim about and come to rest on littoral vegetation. The metaceracaria develops and then encysts there, awaiting ingestion by an unsuspecting host.

Clinical Disease

The worm feeds on columnar epithelial cells, injuring the tissue. Light infection does not cause clinical disease, although intermittent diarrhea may result. Heavy infection (i.e., hundreds of worms), produces continuous diarrhea, intestinal hemorrhage,

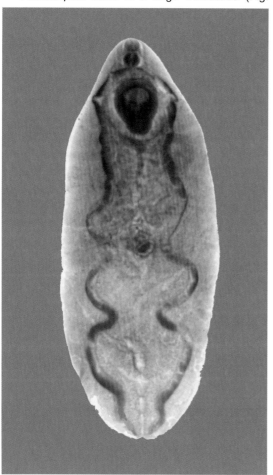

Figure 37.1. An adult of *Fasciolopsis buski*. 25 mm x 10mm.

obstruction of the ampula of Vater, blockage of the common bile duct, and in extreme cases blockage of the small intestine. Abdominal pain is a common complaint, simulating that due to peptic ulcer. Hypoproteinemia, vomiting, and weight loss have been described in heavily-infected children.[4] Elevated levels of circulating eosinophils is a common feature of even light infection with *F. buski.*

Diagnosis

Definitive diagnosis is by microscopic identification of the egg in stool.

Treatment

The drug of choice is praziquantel.[5]

Prevention and control

Proper disposal of human feces is the primary method of control. Reservoir hosts apparently play only a minor role in the maintenance of this parasite in endemic regions. The habit of shucking water chestnuts by placing the seed pod in one's mouth and biting through the tough, outer husk, exposes

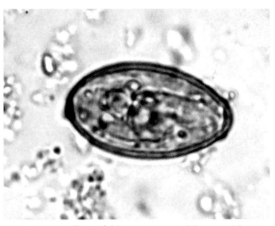

Figure 37.5. Egg of *M. yokogawai*. 25 μm x 15 μm.

one to the infection. This activity is still common in some areas, but public health education programs have helped reduce infection.[6]

Echinostomes

The genus Echinostoma has at least 15 members that are capable of infecting humans.[1] These trematodes occur in the Republic of Korea,[7] throughout Asia, and in Southeast Asia.[8] Their life cycles are similar to that of Fasciolopsis, except that the metacercariae encyst in various species of snails, tadpoles, or fresh water fish.[9] Adults live in the small intestine, and the symptoms they induce depend on the degree of infection. Diarrhea, nausea, vomiting, and abdominal pain are commonly experienced, usually accompanied by fever. The full pathogenic extent of human echinostomiasis has not been sufficiently described.

Heterophyes heterophyes
(Siebold 1852)

Metagonimus yokogawai
(Katsurada 1912)

Heterophyes heterophyes (Fig. 37.3) and *Metagonimus yokogawai* (Fig. 37.4) are small flukes that live primarily in the small intestine. They cause little damage there. *H. heterophyes* is found throughout Asia, the Middle East, and Africa. *M. yokogawai* is also common in Asia, but foci of infections have been reported in Spain and Russia. A few human infections with *H. nocens* have been reported from the Republic of Korea.[10]

Figure 37.3. An adult of *Heterophyes heterophyes*. 2 mm x 0.5 mm.

Life Cycles

Infection begins with the ingestion of encysted metacercariae that live just under the skin of certain fresh water fishes (e.g., grass carp).[11] The metacercariae excyst in the small intestine and develop into adult worms. Although a rare event, instead of remaining in the small intestine the adult worms can migrate to other organs, such as the heart or brain, where they cause focal granulomas, with variable clinical consequences. Both species of trematodes self-fertilize, and egg production ensues shortly thereafter. The fully-embryonated eggs pass out with the fecal mass into fresh or brackish water.

H. heterophyes primarily infect snails of the genus Cerithidia, while those of *M. yokogawai* infect

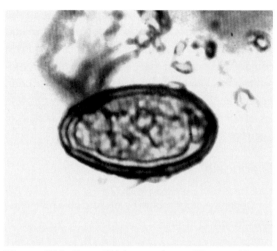

Figure 37.6. Egg of *H. heterophyes*. 25 μm x 13 μm.

snails in the genera Semisulcospira and Thiara. The embryonated eggs are ingested by their respective snail hosts, and hatch inside, releasing the miracidia. This stage undergoes sequential development in the snail, first to sporocysts, then to rediae, and finally to cercariae. The cercariae penetrate out of the snail, and like those of *Clonorchis sinensis*, encyst under the skin of fresh water fish. The species of intermediate hosts for both of these parasites varies widely with the geographic locale. In Asia, the intermediate hosts are cyprinoid and salmonid fishes, and in the Middle East, mullet and tilapia are primarily involved with the life cycle.

Clinical Disease

Epigastric distress, fatigue, and malaise have been reported for heavy infection with *Metagonimus yokogawai*.[10]

Diagnosis

The eggs (Fig. 37.5, 37.6) of *H. heterophyes* and *M. yokogawai* resemble those of *C. sinensis*. They must be carefully differentiated by their absence of a terminal knob and a collar at the operculum.

Treatment

The drug of choice is praziquantel.

Prevention and control

Both parasites can be prevented by eating only cooked fish, and by controlling the indiscriminate use of untreated human feces as fertilizer.[1, 9, 11]

Figure 37.4. An adult of *Metagonimus yokogawai*. 2.5 mm x 0.6 mm.

Nanophyetus salmincola
(Chapin 1927)

Nanophyetus salmincola infects dogs, foxes, and coyotes in eastern Siberia and in the Pacific Northwest of the United States, where it produces "salmon poisoning" or "elokomin fluke fever" as a result of a rickettsia, *Neorickettsia helmintheca*, which is co-transmitted with the parasite. Human infection has also been described,[12] resulting in diarrhea, nausea, vomiting, cachexia, anorexia, and elevated levels of circulating eosinophils. *N. salmincola* infection is diagnosed by the presence of characteristic eggs in the stools along with a history of ingestion of raw or poorly cooked salmon.

References

1. Fried B. Graczyk TK. Tamang L. Food-borne intestinal trematodiases in humans. Parasitol Res. 93:159-70. 2004.
2. Wiwanitkit V. Suwansaksri J. Chaiyakhun Y. High prevalence of *Fasciolopsis buski* in an endemic area of liver fluke infection in Thailand. Med Gen Med. 4:6. 2002.
3. Bhatti HS. Malla N. et al. Fasciolopsiasis – a re-emerging infection in Azamgarh (Uttar Pradesh). Indian J Pathol Microbiol. 43:73-6. 2000.
4. Gupta A, Xess A. et al. *Fasciolopsis buski* (giant intestinal fluke) – a case report. Indian J Pathol Microbiol. 42:359-60. 1999.
5. Taraschewski H. Mehlhorn H. et al. Effects of praziquantel on human intestinal flukes (*Fasciolopsis buski* and Heterophyes heterophyes). Zentralbl Bakteriol Mikrobiol Hyg [A]. 262:542-50. 1986.
6. Graczyk TK. Gilman RH. Fried B. Fasciolopsiasis: is it a controllable food-borne disease? Parasitol Res. 87:80-3. 2001.
7. Park SK, Kim DH. et al. Status of intestinal parasite infections among children in Bat Dambang, Cambodia. Korean J Parasitol. 42:201-3. 2004.
8. Huffman JE. Fried B. Echinostoma and echinostomiasis. Adv Parasitol 29:215-269. 1990.
9. Anantaphruti MT. Parasitic contaminants in food. Southeast Asian J Trop Med Public Health 32 Suppl 2:218-28. 2001.
10. Chai JY. Park JH. et al. Prevalence of *Heterophyes nocens* and *Pygydiopsis summa* infections among residents of the western and southern coastal islands of the Republic of Korea. Am J Trop Med Hyg 71:617-22. 2004.
11. Chai JY. Lee SH. Food-borne intestinal trematode infections in the Republic of Korea. Parasitol Int. 51:129-54. 2002.
12. Eastburn RL. Fritsche TR. Terhune CA. Human intestinal infection with *Nanophyetus salmincola* from salmonid fishes. Am J Trop Med Hyg 36: 586-59. 1987.

VIII. The Arthropods

Arthropods directly influence humans' well-being, not only because they are hosts of parasitic organisms and vectors of a wide variety of pathogens, but also by causing tissue damage and disease. They also affect human health by reducing the availability of food. Insects destroy an estimated 20% of all food crops, and this destruction continues despite the increasing use of pesticides in fields and storage areas. Livestock are also affected by arthropod-borne infections. Vast areas of Africa are short of protein foods because cattle suffer a number of vector-borne diseases, including trypanosomiasis transmitted by tsetse flies and a variety of tick-transmitted diseases.

Although the pathogenic effects of arthropods are most pronounced in the tropics, they are by no means negligible in the United States and other temperate areas. Lyme disease[1,2] and anaplasmosis,[3,4] which are transmitted by ticks, have spread rapidly throughout the United States. *Aedes albopictus*, the Asian tiger mosquito, has been introduced in shipments of used automobile tires into the southern United States and has spread as far north as central Ohio, Indiana, and Illinois; moreover, the introduced strain of the mosquito is apparently able to survive the winter in the egg stage in temperate climates.[5,6] The same species has been introduced into Europe[7] and South America. *Ae. albopictus* can be an efficient vector of dengue. In 1999, reports surfaced about the introduction and rapid spread across the Eastern United States of another pest mosquito, *Ochlerotatus japonicus*. Introductions of new species should not be unexpected and point to the ease with which such introductions can occur. The unexpected appearance in New York City in 1999 of mosquito-transmitted human infections of the West Nile virus, and its subsequent spread throughout the United States, should reinforce our awareness of vulnerability to invasion by both pathogens and vectors.[8, 9]

Although fear has been expressed that blood-feeding arthropods, especially mosquitoes, could transmit the AIDS virus, a large body of epidemiological and experimental evidence fails to support this hypothesis.[10, 11]

Even though arthropods cause problems for humans and livestock, they are also beneficial as pollinators, producers of honey, natural regulators of harmful insects, and essential members of food chains. Wholesale destruction of entire communities of arthropods in programs designed to control pests can result in serious modification of the environment, with consequences far more deleterious than the original problem.

The phylum Arthropoda contains an enormous diversity of members, with the number of species exceeding that of all other phyla combined. The arthropods share a number of characteristics that distinguish them from all other animal groups, although some of these features are absent in a particular species or group at some period of development. Nevertheless, all species in the phylum are identifiable.

Among the morphologic characteristics are bilateral symmetry, a hard exoskeleton, a segmented body, and paired, jointed appendages. The term arthropod, derived from Greek, means "jointed foot."

Growth by metamorphosis is another characteristic of the arthropods. In some groups, growth is gradual; each change from one stage to the next is known as a molt, and gives rise to a stage somewhat larger but morphologically similar to its predecessor. Among the spiders, eight or nine immature stages may precede the final molt to the sexually mature adult.

The application of the tools of molecular biology to the study of arthropods is pervasive. Most dramatic are the various "genome" projects. The genome of *Anopheles gambiae*, the most important of the African malaria vectors, is complete,[12] and work on *An. funestus* has begun. There are ongoing genome projects for *Aedes aegypti*, *Culex pipiens* and *Ixodes scapularis*. Projects for *Rhodnius prolixus* and the sand flies are planned. The value of these programs and their use in eventual control of the diseases these vectors transmit remains to be determined.

References

1. Spielman A. Wilson ML. Levine J. et al. Ecology of *Ixodes dammini* born human babesiosis and Lyme disease. Annu Rev Entomol 30:439-460, 1985.
2. Lane RS. Piesman J. Burgdorfer W. Lyme borreliosis: relation of its causative agents to its vectors and hosts in North America and Europe. Annu Rev Entomol 36:587-609, 1991.
3. McQuiston JH. Paddock CD. Holman RC. Childs JE. The human ehrlichioses in the United States. Emerg Inf Dis 5:635-642, 1999.
4. Ijdo JW. Meek JI. Cartter ML. Magnerelli L. et al. The emergence of another tick-borne infection in the 12-town area around Lyme, Connecticut: Human Granulocytic Ehrlichiosis. J Infect Dis 4:181, 2000.
5. Hawley WA. Reiter P. Copeland PS. et al. *Aedes albopictus* in North America: probable introduction in used tires from northern Asia. Science 236:1114-1116, 1987.
6. Moore CG. *Aedes albopictus* in the United States: current status and prospects for further spread. J Am Mosq Control Assoc 15:221-227, 1999.
7. Romi R. Di Luca M. Majori G. Current status of *Aedes albopictus* and Aedes atropalpus in Italy. J Am Mosq Control Assoc 15:425-427, 1999.
8. Lanciotti RS. Roehrig JT. Deubel V. et al. Origin of the West Nile virus responsible for an outbreak of encephalitis in the northeastern United States. Science 286:2333-2337, 1999.
9. Despommier, D. West Nile Story. Apple Trees Productions, LLC, NY. 2001.
10. Piat P. Schofield CJ. No evidence for arthropod transmission of AIDS. Parasitol Today 2:294-295, 1986.
11. Iqbal MM. Can we get AIDS from mosquito bites? J La State Med Soc 151:429-433, 1999.
12. Toure YT, Oduola AM, Morel CM. The *Anopheles gambiae* genome: next steps for malaria vector control. Trends Parasitol 20:142-149, 2004.

38. Insects

Introduction

The insects have two distinct types of development. The more primitive insect orders pass through a series of stages by incomplete metamorphosis (Fig. 38.1). A typical life cycle involves the egg, a (usually) fixed number of immature nymph stages, and the mature adult stage. The insect molts between stages, sheds its old exoskeleton, and reveals a new skin within. Nymphs are similar to the adult, but lack wings and are sexually immature.

In contrast, complete metamorphosis is characteristic of some of the more advanced insect orders, including the Diptera (Fig. 38.2) and the Siphonaptera (Fig 38.3). The life cycle of an insect exhibiting complete metamorphosis includes the egg, larval stages, a pupa stage, and the adult stage.

Table 38.1 lists arthropods of importance to human health, the pathogens they harbor and transmit, and the diseases they cause. The methods by which the arthropod vectors transmit pathogens vary. Some pathogens, unchanged by any interaction with the vector, are transmitted mechanically from one host to another on contaminated legs or mouthparts of the arthropod or in its feces. Other pathogens require passage through the arthropod as part of their life cycle. In such cases, the pathogens undergo specific developmental changes, which usually include multiplication, within the arthropod.

Arthropods can also be pathogens themselves. They can infest the host, migrating through the body or developing in situ while feeding on host tissue. Other arthropods cause mechanical injury through bites, chemical injury through injection of toxins, or allergic reactions to the materials they transmit via the bite or sting.[1] Moreover, entomophobia and arachnophobia (i.e., fear of insects and arachnids, particularly spiders) are not uncommon psychological conditions.[2]

The salivary secretions of arthropods in general, and insects in particular, have proven to be extraordinarily complex. These secretions serve as potent immunogens and stimulate the bothersome allergic reactions to the insect's bite. They also serve, in many cases, to carry the viral, bacterial, protozoal or nematode pathogens for which so many arthropods serve as vectors. These salivary secretions evolved not to cause allergic responses or convey pathogens, but for a much more basic reason. They facilitate the capacity of the arthropod to take blood from a host whose physiology and defense mechanisms are designed to prevent the loss of blood.

In almost all blood-sucking arthropods studied to date, the saliva of each species has a least one an-ticlotting, one vasodilator and one antiplatelet compound. However, the molecular diversity of these compounds is great, even among closely related genera of blood feeders.[3]

Diptera: The Flies

No single group of insects has so affected human evolution, development, or history as the Diptera, the order of insects comprised of flies and mosquitoes. Malaria, yellow fever, elephantiasis, sleeping sickness, dengue, and river blindness are among the more serious diseases carried by members of this large order. Notorious as vectors of pathogenic organisms of humans and animals, dipterans are also important for the mechanical damage (i.e., myiasis) caused by their larvae and the allergic responses caused by the bites of some adults.

Flies develop by complete metamorphosis and thus have distinct larval, pupal, and adult forms. Larvae are usually vermiform, often living in water or damp places or developing in living or dead tissue. Pupae represent a non-feeding transitional stage. Adult dipterans, which usually possess wings, have only one pair (*diptera* means "two wings"). The mouthparts of the adults may be adapted for biting, piercing flesh, and sucking blood, or only for sucking fluids.

Diptera is a large order, divided into three suborders containing over 100 families. Only nine families are of medical concern. The most primitive suborder, the Nematocera, contains four medically important families: Ceratopogonidae, Psychodidae, Simuliidae, and Culicidae. In the suborder Brachycera, only the Tabanidae are of any medical significance; in the third suborder, Cyclorrhapha, the Muscidae, Gasterophilidae, Cuterebridae, and Oestridae are of major concern.

Ceratopogonidae: The Biting Midges

Ceratopogonids, commonly called punkies, no-see-ums, sand flies, or midges, are minute (0.4-5.0 mm long), slender, blood-sucking dipterans. They constitute a serious pest problem in many areas of the tropics, the temperate zones, and in the Arctic. Most of the species that affect humans belong to two genera, Culicoides and Leptoconops, which act as vectors of several filariids that infect humans in Africa and the New World. Species of Culicoides may also serve as vectors of filariids and viruses that infect animals including humans.

Life Cycle

Ceratopogonid larvae develop in aquatic or semi-aquatic habitats, often in fresh water, but usually in

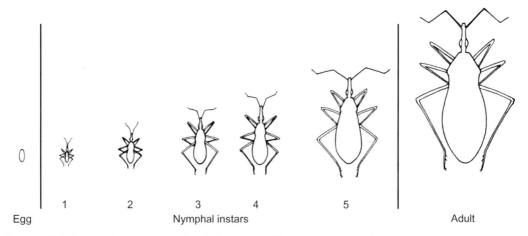

Figure 38.1. Incomplete metamorphosis in insects. Typical example of incomplete metamorphosis is the kissing bug, *Rhodnius prolixus*. Immature stages are wingless, smaller versions of the winged adult. All stages, except the egg, have three pairs of legs. The number of nymphal stages varies with the species.

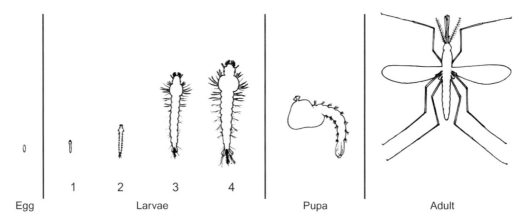

Figure 38.2. Complete metamorphosis in an insect with aquatic immature stages. The Anopheles mosquito begins as an egg laid on the surface of water and develops through four larval stages and a single pupal stage to a sexually mature, winged adult.

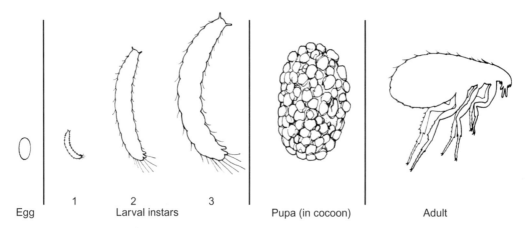

Figure 38.3. Complete metamorphosis in an insect with terrestrial immature stages. The flea begins as an egg laid on the fur of the host or in the nest area. Several maggot-like larval stages are followed by a single pupal stage,encased in a sand-covered cocoon, from which a wingless, sexually mature adult flea emerges.

Table 38.1. Arthropods of medical importance.

Order and representative species	Common name	Geographic distribution	Effects on humans
Insecta			
Anoplura (sucking lice)			
Pediculus humanus humanus	Body louse	Worldwide	Skin reactions to bites, vectors of rickettsiae and spirochetes
P. humanus capitis	Head louse	Worldwide	Skin reaction to bites
Phthirus pubis	Crab louse	Worldwide	Skin reaction to bites
Heteroptera (true bugs)			
Cimex lectularius	Bedbug	Worldwide	Skin reaction to bites
C. hemipterus	Tropical bedbug	Tropical and subtropical	
Triatoma infestans	Kissing bug, cone-nosed bug	Tropical and subtropical regions of the New World	Skin reaction to bites, vectors of *Trypanosoma cruzi*, the cause of Chagas disease
Rhodnius prolixus			
Panstrongylus megistus			
Hymenoptera (bees, wasps, ants)			
Apis mellifera	Honeybee	Worldwide	Painful sting, potential anaphylaxis
Bombus spp.	Bumblebee	Worldwide	Painful sting, potential anaphylaxis
Various genera and species of the family Vespidae	Wasp, hornet, yellow jacket	Worldwide	Painful sting, potential anaphylaxis
Solenopsis spp.	Fire ant	Tropical America, southeastern United States	Painful bite and multiple stings, potential anaphylaxis
Diptera (flies, mosquitoes, and their relatives)			
Ceratopogonidae	No-see-um, Sand fly	Worldwide	Serious biting pest, skin reaction to bites, vectors of several filariid nematodes
Culicoides spp.			
Leptoconops spp.			
Psychodidae	Sand fly	Worldwide	Skin reaction to bites, vectors of *Leishmania*, Pappataci fever, and Carrion's disease
Phlebotomus spp.			
Lutzomyia spp.			
Simuliidae	Blackfly, buffalo gnat	Worldwide	Serious biting pests, skin reaction to bites, vectors of *Onchocerca* and *Mansonella*
Simulium spp.			
Culicidae	Mosquito	Worldwide	Serious biting pests, skin reaction to bites, vectors of viruses, protozoa, and filaria
Aedes spp.			
Anopheles spp.			
Culex spp.			
Culiseta spp.			
Mansonia spp.			
Tabanidae			
Tabanus spp.	Horsefly	Worldwide	Biting pests, painful bite followed by skin reaction
Chrysops spp.	Deerfly	Worldwide	Biting pests, vectors of tularemia and *Loa loa*.
Muscidae			
Musca domestica	Housefly	Worldwide	Mechanical disseminator of pathogens
Stomoxys calcitrans	Stablefly	Worldwide	Serious biting pest
Glossina spp.	Tsetse fly	Africa	Vector of trypanosomes of humans and animals
Calliphoridae			
Cuterebridae			
Sarcophagidae			
Larvae of various genera and species	Maggots	Worldwide	Myiasis, accidental or obligate development of larval flies in human tissue
Siphonaptera (fleas)			
Xenopsylla cheopis	Oriental rat flea	Worldwide	Vector of bubonic plague
Ctenocephalides felis	Cat flea	Worldwide	Biting pest
C. canis	Dog flea		
Pulex irritans	Human flea	Worldwide	Biting pest, plague vector
Tunga penetrans	Chigoe flea	Africa and South America	Infestation of toes, feet and legs, causing severe pain and secondary infection

brackish water or tidal flats. Some important species are associated with the highly-polluted runoff from livestock holding areas. Larval stages are long, slender, and maggot-like; in some species they undergo diapause, a state of arrested development, for as long as three years while awaiting optimal environmental conditions. Adult female ceratopogonids require blood for the production of their eggs. They typically feed at dusk and may attack in large numbers.[4]

Pathogenesis

The mouthparts of ceratopogonids are short and lancet-like, producing a painful bite.[5] Because of their large numbers, they can be important pests, particularly in beach and resort areas near salt marshes. Bites can produce local lesions that persist for hours or days. Sensitized individuals develop allergic reactions.[6]

Midges of the genus Culicoides are the main vectors of the filariid nematodes: *Mansonella perstans* and *M. streptocerca* in Africa, and *M. ozzardi* in the New World tropics.

Control

Ceratopogonids develop in a wide range of habitats, and each species presents its own special problems with respect to control. Salt marsh habitats can be drained or channeled and other breeding sites modified, but treatment of breeding sites with insecticides remains the most effective short-term control measure. Window screens are ineffective unless they are treated with insecticides, because they allow these minute insects easy entry. Commercial mosquito repellents containing diethyltoluamide (DEET) may be useful against some of the common species of these pests.[6]

Psychodidae: Mothflies or Sand flies

A single subfamily of the Psychodidae – the Phlebotominae, of tropical, subtropical, and temperate regions – contains members that suck blood. Phlebotomine sand flies are small (1-3 mm), hairy, delicate, weak-flying insects that feed on a wide range of cold- and warm-blooded animals, and transmit a number of viral, bacterial, and protozoan infections. Flies of the genera Phlebotomus and Lutzomyia are important as vectors of the leishmaniae.

Historical Information

The role of phlebotomine flies in the transmission of leishmaniasis was suggested by Sergent.[7]

Fig. 38.4. Adult female phlebotomine sand fly, *Lutzomyia anthophora*. Courtesy J. Ribeiro

Life Cycle

Phlebotomine larvae develop in non-aquatic habitats such as moist soil, animal burrows, termite nests, loose masonry, stonewalls, or rubbish heaps. The four larval stages are completed within 2-6 weeks; the pupa stage may last 8-14 days. The adults (Fig. 38.4) are weak fliers, exhibiting a hopping movement rather than sustained flight. Only female phlebotomines require blood, feeding usually at night. Some species prefer to feed on humans, but none are exclusively anthropophilic; they feed on dogs and rodents as well.[8, 9]

Pathogenesis

The mouthparts of the female phlebotomine are short and adapted for piercing and sucking. The bite may be painful, producing an itchy local lesion. Sensitized individuals may show severe allergic reactions. The saliva of the Sand fly is particularly complex and contains a number of potent compounds that can influence the susceptibility of human macrophages to invasion by promastigotes of Leishmania introduced by the feeding vector. The use of components of Sand fly saliva as a vaccine to prevent infection is being actively pursued and has received encouraging preliminary results.[10]

Although phlebotomines cause problems in some areas as pests, they are of particular concern as vectors of a number of diseases. Bartonellosis (also called Carrion's disease, Oroya fever, or verruga peruana) is a South American disease transmitted from human to human by *Lutzomyia verrucarum* and related species. It is caused by the bacterium *Bartonella bacilliformis*, which invades erythrocytes and reticuloendothelial cells. The organism can produce a severe febrile illness, complicated by profound anemia. Untreated, bartonellosis is fatal in 50% of cases. There is no known animal reservoir.

Sand fly fever, also called papatasi fever, is a viral disease seen in the Mediterranean region, central Asia, Sri Lanka, India, and China. *Phlebotomus papatasii* is the main vector for this acute febrile disease, which is characterized by severe frontal headaches, malaise, retro-orbital pain, anorexia, and nausea. Female flies become infected when they feed on viremic individuals. After an incubation period of 7-10 days, the flies become infective and remain so for the rest of their lives.

Leishmaniasis is transmitted by a number of phlebotomine species.[9] Flies initially pick up the parasite while feeding on infected humans or animals. In the fly, the parasite undergoes asexual multiplication, eventually accumulating in the mouthparts, from where it is transmitted to the host when the insect feeds.

Control

Phlebotomine sand flies are particularly sensitive to insecticides, and the use of DDT in campaigns against malaria coincidentally controlled these flies and virtually eliminated Sand fly-borne diseases in many regions. In areas where malaria has been eliminated or where malaria control programs have been abandoned, the phlebotomine flies have reestablished themselves, and the Sand fly-borne diseases have returned.

Sand flies may be controlled with residual or short-lived insecticides applied to breeding sites or houses. Treatment of window screens with insecticides may also be effective. Mosquito repellents can be used to reduce the frequency of Sand fly bites.

Simuliidae: Blackflies

Members of the family Simuliidae, commonly called blackflies, buffalo gnats, or turkey gnats, are small (1-5 mm long), hump-backed, blood-sucking dipterans that usually breed in fast-flowing streams and rivers. Simuliids are important as vectors of *Onchocerca volvulus*, the causative agent of onchocerciasis. In addition, they present a serious pest problem in many temperate and Arctic areas. Blackflies may also serve as vectors of bovine onchocerciasis and protozoan parasites of various species of birds.

Historical information

Blackflies first stimulated medical interest in 1910, when they were incorrectly considered vectors of pellagra.[11] Their role in the transmission of Onchocerca was demonstrated in 1926.[12]

Figure 38.5. Black fly adult feeding on a human host

Life Cycle

Adult female simuliids (Fig. 38.5) lay eggs at or below the surface of moving, well-oxygenated water. Larvae and pupae, equipped with gills for respiration, remain attached to objects below the surface. Larvae are nourished by food filtered from the passing water. They undergo development in five stages. The non-feeding pupae gradually assume adult characteristics while they are enclosed within a cocoon. Adult female simuliids require blood for egg production. They feed primarily during daylight hours. Male simuliids do not feed on blood.[13]

Adult blackflies in temperate areas may emerge synchronously in large numbers. Their bites cause serious damage to humans and animals. Blackflies often reach such high population densities that they can kill livestock and wild animals, torment campers and fishermen, and render large areas uninhabitable by humans and animals for long periods of time.

Pathogenesis

The bite of the female simuliid is particularly painful. The insect's mouthparts consist of six blades in the shape of lancets, which tear the skin surface to induce bleeding. The fly feeds from the resulting pool of blood, and the bite wound continues to bleed for some time after the fly has departed. Simuliid bites leave a characteristic point of dried blood at the wound site. The extreme pain of the initial bite is followed by itching and swelling due to reactions to the injected salivary secretions. Blood loss from multiple bites can be considerable. Allergic reactions in previously sensitized individuals are common, and can sometimes reach serious levels, including anaphylaxis.

Control

Control of blackflies is most effectively achieved by the slow-dripping of insecticides into rivers or streams. Mass control programs using insecticides applied by fixed-wing aircraft and helicopters have been successful in West Africa. Clearing debris from streambeds can also reduce breeding. Repellents containing DEET are recommended for personal protection.

Culicidae: The Mosquitoes

Mosquitoes constitute one of the largest dipteran families and are of major significance as vectors of disease and as biting pests. Their economic, cultural, and evolutionary impact has been devastating.[14, 15] Mosquitoes develop in a wide range of aquatic larval habitats and in all climates from the arctic to the tropics. Adult mosquitoes are generally similar in appearance. They are usually small and have delicate legs, a single pair of wings, long antennae, and elongated mouth parts capable of piercing flesh and sucking blood. Larvae and pupae are aquatic and their development proceeds through complete metamorphosis (Fig. 38.2).

Historical Information

The association between mosquitoes and various tropical fevers had been suggested by numerous writers in the past. The association of these fevers with mosquitoes was finally recognized during the nineteenth century. The proof that mosquitoes could transmit diseases was provided by Manson in 1878, when he showed that mosquitoes were intermediate hosts of *Wuchereria bancrofti*.

Transmission of malaria by mosquitoes was suggested by Manson as early as 1884, but Ross and Italian investigators under the direction of Grassi were the first to prove that mosquitoes transmitted malaria.[16] The incrimination of *Aedes aegypti* in the transmission of yellow fever was suggested by Finlay in 1880, and proved by Reed and his co-workers in 1900.[17]

Figure 38.6. *Anopheles dirus*, one of the major malaria vectors in Southeast Asia, performing "plasmapheresis".

Figure 38.7. *Anopheles stephensi*, a malaria vector found in Asia, particularly India and Pakistan.

Life Cycle

Both major subfamilies of the Culicidae – the Anophelinae and the Culicinae – are involved in transmission of diseases. Members of these subfamilies share a number of basic similarities in their life cycles and development. They lay eggs on or near water or on surfaces that become flooded. Their larvae are always aquatic. The four larval stages are elongate, active "wigglers" that feed by filtering particulate matter from water; they must remain in contact with the surface for respiration. The pupae, known as "tumblers," are comma-shaped and aquatic. They remain at the surface unless disturbed. Adult mosquitoes of most species are good fliers. Males and females feed on nectars and sugars, although females of most species also feed on blood. They require a blood meal for each clutch of eggs, which may contain 100-200 eggs. A female may produce six or more clutches during her lifetime. Eggs require 48-72 hours to develop within the female. They may be deposited almost as soon as they mature. Consequently, a female may take a blood meal every 2-4 days and contact a number of hosts during that period, thus providing an excellent opportunity for the dissemination of pathogens.[18]

Subfamily Anophelinae

The genus Anopheles contains the species responsible for the transmission of human malaria. The anopheline female lays eggs singly, each equipped with floats, usually on the surface of water. Eggs hatch 2-4 days after they are laid. The aquatic larvae attach to the surface and assume a horizontal position. The larval period may last 1-3 weeks, depending on environmental temperature. Anopheline pupae are superficially similar to the pupae of other mosquitoes. The pupal stage lasts 1-3 days. Adult anophelines (Fig. 38.6) are delicate, long-legged mosquitoes. Although some species are capable of extended flight and dispersion

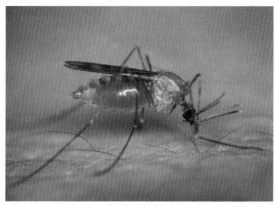

Figure 38.8. *Anopheles freeborni*, a potential malaria vector in California.

from breeding sites, anophelines typically remain close to their food supplies and breeding habitats.

Most anophelines are night feeders, with characteristic peaks of biting activity for each species. Some species are exclusively zoophilic, some are anthropophilic, and others are nonspecific biters. Feeding habits also vary between species. Certain species readily enter houses and feed on sleeping individuals; others feed only outdoors.

In temperate areas, anophelines spend the winter as inseminated adult females. In the tropics, these mosquitoes breed continually, although their population levels may fluctuate drastically in relation to rainfall and dry seasons.[19]

Approximately 300 species of Anopheles mosquitoes have been described. However, only a small number of species are important as malaria vectors within any geographic area (e.g., *An. gambiae* and *An. funestus* in sub-Saharan Africa, *An. culicifacies* and *An. stephensi* (Fig. 38.7) on the Indian subcontinent, and *An. quadrimaculatus* and *An. freeborni* (Fig. 38.8) in North America). Moreover, populations vary within each species with respect to their competence as vectors and capacity for transmission.

Intense study has led to the division of several well-established species of vectors into morphologically similar but genetically distinct groups or complexes of species. The important vector of malaria in Africa, *An. gambiae*, consists of at least six discrete but cryptic species, most of which are not major vectors. Similar revision of species has resulted in a clearer definition of the members of the European complex and the Southeast Asian group (Fig. 38.6). It appears that reexamination of most of the anopheline species that occupy large or ecologically diverse geographic areas will lead to the description of closely related but genetically divergent species.

Anophelines also play an important role as vectors of filarial nematodes. An. gambiae and *An. funestus* are

the main vectors of *Wuchereria bancrofti* in Africa, and *An. hyrcanus* in China and *An. barbirostris* in Southeast Asia are vectors of both *W. bancrofti* and *Brugia malayi*. Although anophelines are not usually involved in the transmission of viruses, *An. gambiae* and *An. funestus* are the vectors of O'nyong-nyong fever.

To learn more about the ecology of anopheline mosquitoes and control programs that take advantage of their biology, see www.medicalecology.org/diseases/malaria/malaria.htm.

Subfamily Culicinae

The subfamily Culicinae consists of more than 1500 species distributed among 20 genera, six of which (Aedes, Ochlerotatus, Culex, Mansonia, Psorophora, and Culiseta) are of major importance to human health. Culicine mosquitoes are primary vectors of a number of viruses and filariae and pose a serious problem as pest insects in many parts of the world.

Several species formerly recognized as members of the genus Aedes, the largest of the Culicine genera, have been undergoing a major reorganization. In 2000, the genus was divided into two genera, Aedes and Ochlerotatus, on the basis of consistent primary characters of the female and male genitalia.[20] These changes have been generally accepted. A more dramatic renaming was suggested where common mosquitoes such as *Aedes aegypti* would be called *Stegomyia aegypti* and *Aedes albopictus* renamed *Stegomyia albopicta*.[21] These changes are being hotly debated.

Mosquitoes of the genera Aedes and Ochlerotatus remain in the "tribe" Aedini, and are found in all habitats, ranging from the tropics to the Arctic. The typical aedine mosquito (Fig. 38.9) is robust, a strong flier, and usually a vicious biter. Its eggs are laid singly, without floats, on or near the surface of water or in areas likely to be flooded periodically. Unlike the eggs of Anopheles or Culex mosquitoes, which usually hatch within a few days of deposition, aedine eggs have the capacity for an extended period of dormancy. This dormancy allows the eggs to survive the winter or to delay hatching until conditions are ideal for development. Aedine mosquitoes occupy salt marsh habitats, flood plains, tree holes, irrigated pasturelands, and man-made containers.

Aedine larvae are nourished by food filtered from water. They develop and feed while suspended from the surface of water by a breathing tube. Larvae develop by progressing through four stages over a period of 6-10 days, or longer at lower temperatures. Aedine pupae are typical of those of most mosquitoes; this stage usually lasts less than three days. Adults usually emerge from breeding sites synchronously, followed by mass migrations of females in search of blood.

Aedine species may develop overwhelming populations in salt marshes, tundras, pastures, and floodwater, and they have a severe impact on wildlife, livestock, and humans. If left uncontrolled, the salt-marsh mosquitoes of the East Coast of the United States, *Ochlerotatus. sollicitans* and *Oc. taeniorhynchus*, could deny vast areas of seashore to development and tourism. The floodwater mosquito, *Ae. vexans*, develops after spring rain and flooding; the Arctic species begin hatching with the first melting snows. Populations of Arctic Aedes become so great at times that humans and larger mammals do not venture into the tundra area.

Aedines, breeding in tree holes in the populated areas of temperate zones (e.g., *Oc. triseriatus*), seldom produce large populations, but can become local pests and important vectors of various viral infections. In tropical regions, populations of aedine mosquitoes are usually much smaller than in the Arctic. *Aedes aegypti* (Fig. 38.9), the yellow fever mosquito, occurs alongside humans throughout the tropics and subtropics. *Ae. aegypti* usually breeds in man-made containers such as discarded auto tires, flower pots, blocked gutters, water jugs, rain barrels, cemetery urns, and tin cans. The mosquito lays eggs above the waterline in these containers, and the eggs remain dormant there, often as long as six months, until the container becomes filled with water. Because this mosquito is closely associated with humans and is almost exclusively anthropophilic, it has most of the characteristics of a good vector. *Ae. aegypti* is the primary vector of yellow fever and dengue in urban environments throughout the world.[22] In the South Pacific, container-breeding members of the *Ae. scutellaris* complex are vectors of certain viruses and *W. bancrofti*. The introduction of *Ae. albopictus* into the United States has added a new species with the potential for transmitting dengue. *Ae. albopictus* is proving to be a serious biting pest, particularly in urban and suburban areas of the Eastern and Southeastern

US. *Ae. albopictus* appears to be out-competing *Ae. aegypti* in many areas, which is not an altogether undesirable effect, since *Ae. aegypti* is much more efficient at transmitting yellow fever and dengue.

The genus Culex is the second largest group in the subfamily, best represented by *Cx. pipiens pipiens*, the northern house mosquito found in temperate areas, and *Cx. pipiens quinquefasciatus* (formerly known as *Cx. fatigans*), the southern house mosquito found throughout the sub-tropics and tropics.

Culex mosquitoes deposit their eggs in rafts, which usually contain 50-200 eggs cemented together. The eggs float perpendicular to the water surface and hatch within 2-3 days. The four larval stages develop and feed on nutrients in the water, much like aedine mosquitoes. The siphons of larval Culex mosquitoes are usually longer and more slender than those of aedines. The larval period lasts less than two weeks and the pupal stage less than two days. Adults usually feed at night. Many show a preference for avian blood, but most members also feed on humans or other mammals. *Cx. p. quinquefasciatus* is the major vector of *W. bancrofti* throughout the tropics. The species is particularly well-adapted to development in polluted waters, breeding in or near population centers and readily biting humans.

The genus Mansonia includes a number of species important as vectors of Brugian filariasis. This genus differs in its development from most other mosquitoes in that its larvae and pupae affix themselves below the surface of water to the stems and roots of aquatic plants and derive oxygen from these plants. Mosquitoes of the genus Psorophora can be important biting pests. Culiseta includes several species involved in the transmission of arboviruses to humans.

Pathogenesis of the Mosquito Bite

The mouthparts of the adult female mosquito are adapted for piercing flesh and sucking the blood needed by the female for the production of eggs. During the act of feeding, the female repeatedly injects saliva, which produces the reaction that follows the bite.[23]

Although the mechanical damage induced by the feeding mosquito can cause pain and irritation, the immediate and delayed immune reactions are of greater concern. Individuals with no previous exposure to mosquitoes show neither immediate nor delayed reactions. However, after sensitization, a bite is followed by a small, flat wheal surrounded by a red flare, which appears within a few minutes and lasts about 1 hour, and is mediated by antibodies. The delayed reaction consists of itching, swelling, and reddening of the wound region. It may persist for days. Repeated exposure can lead to loss of the delayed reaction and perhaps

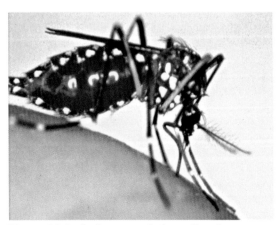

Figure 38.9. *Aedes aegypti*, the yellow fever mosquito, in a typical feeding position.

eventual desensitization. Desensitization to one species does not necessarily extend to other members of the same genus and usually does not include protection against the bites of mosquitoes of other genera.[24-26] The intense itching, primarily associated with the delayed reaction, encourages scratching and secondary infection of the wound site. Local anesthetics are useful for treating reactions to mosquito bites.

Mosquito-Borne Viral Diseases

Yellow fever is a severe hemorrhagic disease, characterized by high fever, jaundice, and prostration. Case fatality during epidemics may exceed 10%. The yellow fever virus naturally infects monkeys and is maintained in a monkey-to-monkey sylvatic cycle by forest-dwelling mosquitoes. When the sylvatic cycle is disturbed (e.g., by wood cutters), humans can be bitten by one of the monkey-feeding vectors. When these individuals return to their villages and become viremic, the ubiquitous *Ae. aegypti* is able to initiate the urban cycle of transmission from person to person. An effective vaccine for yellow fever is available, and is usually required for travelers to endemic areas.

Dengue is an acute, usually non-fatal viral disease characterized by high fever, severe headache, backache, and arthralgia, hence the common name "breakbone fever." A hemorrhagic form of dengue is frequently fatal. *Ae. aegypti* is the usual vector of both the typical and the hemorrhagic forms of dengue, although other aedine mosquitoes may transmit the organism. There is no verified animal reservoir for dengue; several vaccine candidates are being evaluated.

In the United States, the mosquito-borne viral encephalitides include St. Louis encephalitis (SLE), eastern equine encephalitis (EEE), and western equine encephalitis (WEE). They are viral diseases of wild birds transmitted by mosquitoes. Under certain conditions, normally ornithophilic mosquito species that had previously fed on viremic birds feed on humans or other mammals. St. Louis encephalitis may be transmitted by members of the *Culex pipiens* complex in urban areas, by *Cx. tarsalis* in rural areas in the western states, and by *Cx. nigripalpus* in Florida. *Cx. tarsalis* is the main vector of WEE in the West, and *Culiseta melanura* is one of the major vectors of EEE in the East.

Japanese encephalitis is transmitted by *Cx. tritaniorhynchus* and *Ae. togoi* in the Orient. In Australia and New Guinea, Murray Valley encephalitis is transmitted by various Culex species. Rift Valley fever (RVF), an East African disease usually associated with wild animals and livestock, caused a serious epidemic in Egypt in 1977-1978, infecting millions. The viral agent of RVF has been assigned to the Sand fly fever group of viruses and is probably transmitted in Egypt by *Cx. pipiens*

and by other Culex and Aedes mosquitoes throughout the rest of Africa.

California group viruses, including LaCrosse virus, rarely cause epidemics. They are transmitted by the tree-hole breeding species *Oc. triseriatus* in the Midwestern United States.

West Nile virus is a member of the flavivirus group (e.g., Yellow fever, dengue) responsible for regular epidemics in human populations in Europe and Africa. It can also cause significant epizootics in birds. The 1999 outbreak of human encephalitis in New York associated with the West Nile (WNV) virus was the first isolation of this agent in the New World, and was concurrent with extensive mortality in crows. The vectors that transmit WNV to people in the New York City environs have yet to be identified, although *C. pipiens* is suspected to be among the most likely candidates. *Culex pipiens* is the probable vector for bird-to-bird transmission. WNV has remained endemic in the US, and outbreaks in 2003-2004 were the largest on record, infecting an estimated 2 million people and killing countless wild birds. It is hypothesized that dry, hot spells of weather of more than two weeks favor such outbreaks in humans.[9]

To learn more about the ecology of West Nile virus and the vectors that transmits it, see www.medicalecology.org/diseases/westnile/westnile.htm.

Mosquito Control

The most effective method of mosquito control is reduction at the source (i.e., the elimination or modification of the aquatic sites at which the mosquitoes breed). Control may take the form of drainage, impoundment, or level control of large bodies of water, the clearing or filling of ditches, or the elimination of man-made containers. Methodology must be tailored to the specific breeding requirements of the species. The general use of chemical insecticides has obvious potential for deleterious side effects. However, given the serious nature of many of the mosquito-borne diseases, insecticide use may be required where reduction at the source is inadequate. Larvicides can be applied to breeding sites. Under extreme conditions, pesticides can be directed against adult mosquitoes.

The most common and effective method of malaria control employs insecticides applied to the walls of houses. Anopheline malaria vectors tend to rest on walls after feeding; they then come in contact with the residual insecticide and die. Consequently, insecticides applied to the insides of walls affect only those mosquitoes that have fed on humans and are potentially infected. This scheme does little to reduce mosquito populations and usually has little environmental impact; it does, however, reduce the incidence of malaria by interrupting transmission of the disease.[27] DDT was effectively used in house spraying programs for several decades. In addition to toxicity to resting mosquitoes, this insecticide produced a repellant effect that discouraged mosquitoes from entering treated houses. Bed nets, with or without insecticide impregnation, can provide significant protection from feeding mosquitoes.

A number of effective mosquito repellents are available as sprays or lotions. When applied according to direction, they can reduce the annoyance caused by the insects. The most effective repellents usually contain DEET.

Tabanidae: Horse and Deerflies

The Tabanidae are a large family of blood-sucking dipterans with a cosmopolitan distribution. They are robust flies, ranging in size from 7 to 30 mm in length, and are locally referred to as horseflies, deerflies, mango flies, or greenheads. Tabanids are strong fliers, capable of inflicting painful bites, and in some areas of the world are considered serious pests of humans and animals. Flies of the genus Chrysops act as vectors of the filarial eye worm *Loa loa* in Africa and may be involved in the mechanical transmission of anthrax, tularemia, and *Trypanosoma evansi*.

Historical Information

Tabanids were implicated in the transmission of anthrax as early as 1874, and of *T. evansi* in 1913. The role of tabanids as intermediate hosts and vectors of *Loa loa* was verified, in 1914, by Leiper.[28]

Life Cycle

Tabanids usually lay eggs on vegetation near moist areas. Their larvae develop in water or wet earth and pass through four to nine stages. In some species the larvae remain dormant during the winter. Pupation occurs in dry earth, and the quiescent pupal stage may last 2-3 weeks. Adult females feed on blood and the males on plant juices.

Pathogenesis

Tabanid mouthparts are short and blade-like. During the act of biting, the insect inflicts a deep, painful wound, causing blood to flow. The fly then laps up blood from the freshly-formed pool. Individuals can become sensitized to tabanid bites and suffer severe allergic reactions after attack.

Tabanids act as efficient mechanical vectors of several pathogens. They are easily disturbed during feeding. They fly to another host and begin the process anew. Consequently, the fly's mouthparts can readily transfer organisms to the next host after contamination on the first. Bacteria causing anthrax and tularemia, the protozoan *T. evansi*, and the retrovirus agents of bovine leukemia and equine infectious anemia may be transmitted by the tabanid flies, which act as mechanical vectors.

Loa loa is transmitted by African tabanids of the genus Chrysops, which include *C. silacea* and *C. dimidiata*. Microfilariae of the worm, ingested by female flies with the blood meal, develop in the flight muscles. When they reach maturity, they migrate to the mouthparts and are deposited on the skin of a new host when the fly feeds again. Infectious larvae burrow into the skin of the host after the fly has abandoned the bite wound.

Control

Tabanids are difficult to control because of their diverse breeding sites. Larvae are sensitive to DDT and other insecticides, but these compounds are seldom used. Sensitive individuals should consider using repellents to avoid bites. Mosquito repellents containing DEET are usually effective.

Muscidae: The Housefly and Its Relatives

The muscoid flies include insects that are important as blood-sucking pests, vectors of diseases, and mechanical vectors of a variety of pathogenic organisms.[29, 30] Some better-known members of this family are the housefly *Musca domestica*, the stable fly *Stomoxys calcitrans*, and the tsetse flies of the genus Glossina.

Most muscoids are fairly large, robust dipterans. They develop from eggs to maggots (larvae), non-motile pupae, and adults by complete metamorphosis. Only the tsetse flies differ, in that their larvae develop singly within the female and are deposited fully developed and ready for pupation.

Historical Information

One of the plagues of Egypt described in the Old Testament consisted of swarms of flies. It appears that humans have been troubled by these insects throughout history. The role of the tsetse fly as the vector of African trypanosomiasis was demonstrated by Bruce in 1895,[31] and the importance of houseflies as disseminators of various pathogens was outlined in 1898 by Veeder.[30]

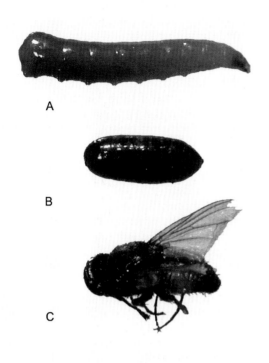

Figure 38.10. *Musca domestica*, the housefly. A. Larva. B. Pupa. C. Adult. The larvae of flies are referred to as maggots.

Life Cycle

Musca domestica (Fig. 38.10), the ubiquitous housefly, lays her eggs on any matter that will serve as food for the developing maggots. Animal or human feces, garbage, decaying plant material, and sewage all provide suitable substrates. A single fly lays more than 1,000 eggs during her life span. The development from eggs to adults requires less than 10 days at summer temperatures. As a result of this reproductive potential, summer fly populations can be enormous. These flies can carry viruses, bacteria, protozoa, and the eggs of parasitic worms and are thus a serious public health problem.[30] The presence of large fly populations is a clear indicator of poor sanitation.

Stableflies

Stomoxys calcitrans is a serious biting pest usually associated with domestic animal husbandry. The fly lays her eggs in moist, decaying vegetable material (e.g., hay, alfalfa, and straw). In suburban communities, moist piles of grass clippings and weeds provide ideal

sites for larval development. The egg-to-adult period during the summer lasts about 4 weeks, and a female may lay as many as 400 eggs during her life span.

Although superficially similar in appearance to houseflies, stable flies have a prominent proboscis, which both sexes use effectively for sucking blood. The bite of the stable fly is initially painful but usually causes little delayed reaction. Sensitized individuals develop allergic responses to repeated bites. Stomoxys serves as a mechanical vector for anthrax and some trypanosomes of animals.[31]

Tsetse Flies

Tsetse flies of the genus Glossina occur in sub-Saharan Africa, where they are the intermediate hosts and vectors of a number of trypanosomes infecting humans and animals (Fig. 38.11). Tsetse flies differ markedly from muscoid flies, and indeed from most insects, in that they produce only one egg at a time. This single egg is retained within the "uterus" of the female, where it hatches. The larva develops in three stages "in utero" while feeding on "milk" produced by accessory glands of the female. Eventually, a fully mature larva is deposited in a shady location, and it pupates immediately. The pupal stage can last up to 30 days and the resulting adult remains inactive for 1-2 days after emerging before seeking its first blood meal. Both male and female tsetse flies are exclusively hematophagous, and both sexes are capable of transmitting trypanosomes.[32, 33]

A female tsetse produces 10-15 larvae during her life span. Tsetse populations are relatively small and dispersed. Glossina hunt by sight and follow animals, humans, or even vehicles for long distances. They feed during the day, usually along paths or riverbanks. *G. palpalis* and *G. tachinoides* are the main vectors of *Trypanosoma brucei gambiense*; *G. morsitans*, *G. swynnertoni*, and *G. pallidipes* are the primary vectors of *T. b. rhodesiense*.[33]

Figure 38.11. *Glossina spp.* tsetse fly feeding on blood. Courtesy of J. Gingrich

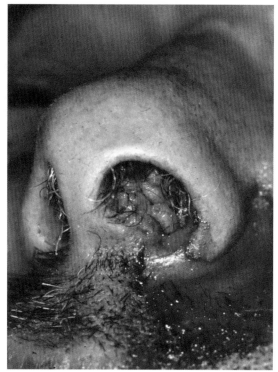

Figure 38.12. *Sarcophaga* larvae *in situ* (Courtesy of Y. Mumcouglu. In Mumcouglu Y, Rufli Th: Dermatologische Entomologie. Perimed Fachbuch, Erlangen, 1982).

Calliphoridae, Cuterebridae, and Sarcophagidae:

Myiasis-Causing Flies

Not all dipterans inflict damage by the bite of adult flies seeking blood. The larvae of several families are pathogenic during their development within the tissues of the infested host. This infestation with larvae, or maggots, is known as myiasis.[34] Certain species of flies are obligate parasites and require living tissue for development. Other species develop facultatively in either living or dead tissues. A third group can cause accidental myiasis when their eggs, deposited on foodstuffs, are ingested. Cheese-skippers of the family Piophilidae, rat-tailed larvae of the Syrphidae, soldier fly larvae of the Stratiomyidae, and several species of the Muscidae cause gastrointestinal myiasis. Symptoms are proportional to the number of larvae developing and include nausea and vomiting. Diagnosis requires the finding of living or dead maggots in the vomitus, aspirates of gastrointestinal contents, or stool specimens.[35]

Species of flies that normally favor decaying flesh for larval development occasionally deposit eggs or larvae on wounds or ulcers (Fig. 38.12).

Maggot therapy is the use of the larvae of certain fly species for selectively debriding non-healing necrotic skin and soft tissue wounds.36 In 2004, the US Food and Drug Administration (FDA) gave permission to market maggots for medical use.[37] In Europe, approximately 30,000 maggot treatments are applied annually.

The flesh flies of the family Sarcophagidae contain several members of the genera Wohlfahrtia and Sarcophaga, which cause myiasis. Female flies in this family do not lay eggs, but deposit freshly hatched first-stage larvae directly in wounds, ulcers, or even unbroken skin. These feeding larvae may cause considerable tissue damage.

Flies of the family Cuterebridae are obligate parasites, usually of wild and domestic animals. Human myiasis due to infestation with maggots of Cuterebra, normally associated with rodents, is not uncommon in the United States. This condition usually presents as individual larvae developing on various parts of the body (Fig. 38.13). *Dermatobia hominis*, the human botfly, parasitizes a number of mammals and is a serious pest of cattle in Central and South America. Flies of this species cause infestation in a unique manner. Female Dermatobia flies capture various blood-sucking arthropods (usually mosquitoes or other flies), lay their eggs on the abdomens of their prey, and release these insects. When the fly or the mosquito carrying the eggs alights on a warm-blooded host, the eggs hatch, immediately liberating larvae onto the skin of the host. These maggots penetrate the skin and develop in the subcutaneous tissue, maintaining contact with the surface through a small opening in the center of an abscess-like swelling (Fig. 38.13). When the larvae complete their development after 6-12 weeks, they emerge, fall to the ground, and pupate. During the phase within the tissues, the maggots can cause intermittent pain and

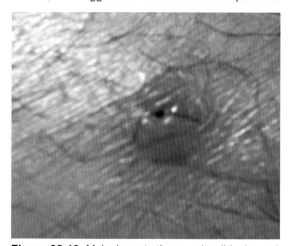

Figure 38.13. Myiasis: note the opening (black spot) in the skin which permits the maggot, burrowing in the tissue below, to breathe.

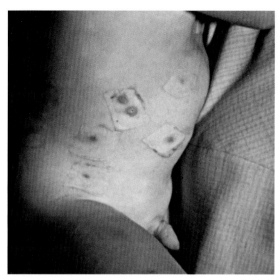

Figure 38.14. Myiasis. Maggots of *Cordylobia anthropophaga* in the flesh of an infant. Note the raised area and opening for the larvae to breath.

secrete a foul-smelling material from the opening in the skin.

For human infestations, each maggot should be removed surgically. Particular care must be taken not to damage it during the procedure because the patient has usually become sensitized to the antigens of the maggot. The maggots can also be removed by coating their external spiracles with petroleum jelly, which blocks access to oxygen. They are thus forced to crawl to the surface. They may then have to be removed surgically, under local anesthesia, and the wound sutured.[37]

Several species of the family Calliphoridae are obligate parasites, whereas others cause only accidental myiasis. , *Cordylobia anthropophaga,* the tumbu fly, is a larval parasite of humans and other animals, especially rats, in Africa. These flies lay eggs on soil contaminated with urine or feces or on similarly soiled bedding or clothing that is set out to dry. The emerging larvae attach themselves to any host with whom they come in contact and penetrate the skin. After penetration, larvae cause individual tender abscess-like swellings from which serous fluid exudes, particularly when pressure is applied to the lesion (Fig. 38.14). Treatment consists in covering the wound with petroleum jelly to force the maggot to the surface in search of oxygen. The maggot can then be gently squeezed out. Surgical excision is necessary for some infestations.

Another African species, the Congo floor maggot, *Auchmeromyia luteola,* feeds preferentially on humans. The fly lays eggs on the floor of huts. The maggots come out of the soil at night to feed on the blood of the inhabitants of the hut who sleep on the floor. The larvae lacerate the victim and suck blood but do not

penetrate tissues, returning to the soil after taking their blood meal.

Two species of Cochliomyia, the New World screw worm, occasionally cause myiasis in humans in North and South America, although these flies are primarily parasites of animals. Adult females lay their eggs around the edges of wounds, and the larvae invade the wounds and macerate the traumatized tissues. Large numbers of maggots can infest a single wound. Because infestations of the nose can be fatal, the maggots should be removed surgically as soon as they are detected.

Flies of the genus Chrysomyia, the Old World screw worm, are important causes of human and animal myiasis throughout Asia and Africa. Chrysomyia larvae penetrate wounds or mucous membranes, primarily affecting areas around the eyes, ears, mouth, and nose.

Green bottle flies (Lucilia *spp.*) and blue bottle flies (Calliphora *spp.*) sometimes infest wounds of humans in Asia, Africa, and the Americas. The larvae of these species prefer dead tissue; in the past, these maggots, reared free of pathogens, were used therapeutically for cleansing septic wounds.[36, 37] A number of flies whose larvae are primarily parasites of domestic animals occasionally infest humans. Larvae of the sheep bot (*Oestrus ovis*) may invade nasal cavities of shepherds and cause severe frontal headaches. Such larvae do not complete their development because humans are aberrant hosts, so the larvae usually exit spontaneously before maturation.

Cattle warbles of the genus Hypoderma occasionally infest humans, causing a condition similar to creeping eruption. Larvae penetrate exposed skin and wander aimlessly, causing severe itching, pain, and sleeplessness. Surgical removal of the larvae from the ends of their burrows is recommended.[38]

Larvae of various flies, particularly Calliphora, Phaenicia, and Cochliomyia, infest a cadaver in a pre-

Figure 38.15. Body lice after feeding, resting on cloth.

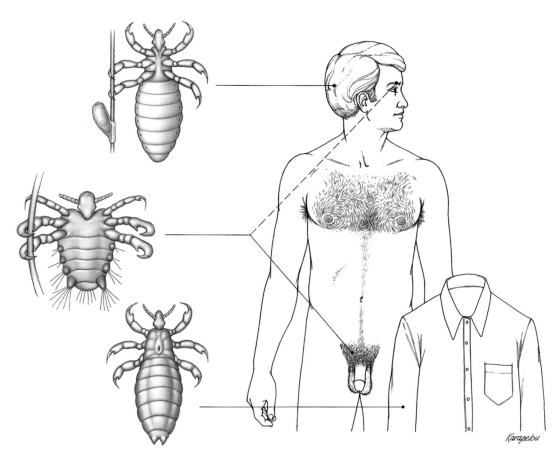

Figure 38.17. Preferred feeding and resting sites of the three species of louse affecting humans. *Pediculus humanus capitis*, the head louse, resides, feeds, and reproduces on the hairs of the head. Eggs are laid individually on hair shafts. *Phthirus pubis*, the crab louse, prefers hair of the pubic regions but is occasionally found on the eyebrows, eyelashes, beard,or moustache. Eggs are attached to the individual hairs. *Pediculus humanus humanus*, the body louse, is usually found on clothing,moving to the body of the human host only to feed. Eggs are laid in masses in the seams of the clothing of the host.

dictable succession. The science of forensic entomology has developed the use of flies and, to a lesser extent, beetle larvae to determine the manner, time, and place of death; it uses entomologic information to support pathologic findings in legal proceedings.[39, 40]

Anoplura: Sucking Lice

Three species of lice infest humans as obligate, blood-feeding ectoparasites. Only one of them, the body louse, is important in human medicine as the vector of the rickettsiae of epidemic typhus and trench fever and the spirochetes of relapsing fever. Louse infestation is known as pediculosis.[41]

The body louse, *Pediculus humanus humanus* (Fig. 38.15), and its close relative, the head louse, *P. humanis capitis*, are wingless, elongate, dorsoventrally flattened insects, 2.5-4.0 mm long. They have three pairs of legs of about equal length. Their mouthparts are adapted for piercing flesh and sucking blood. The crab louse, *Phthirus pubis* (Fig. 38.16), is shorter (0.8-1.2 mm) and, as its common name implies, resembles a crab. Crab lice have somewhat reduced front legs, with the second and third leg pairs stout and strongly clawed. All lice undergo development characterized by incomplete metamorphosis.

Historical Information

The association between humans and lice is an ancient one and probably represents an evolutionary relationship begun by lice and ancestral hominids. Closely related species of lice infest gorillas and monkeys. Humans have certainly been aware of the discomforts of louse infestation from the earliest times, and the condition has been recorded by poets and artists as well as by early writers on science and medicine. However, the recognition of body lice as disease vectors is more

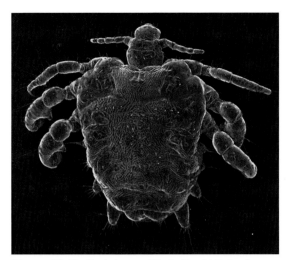

Figure 38.16. Crab louse. Photo David Scharf.

recent. Transmission of typhus and relapsing fever by lice was not demonstrated until the early 1900s.

Lice have been considered variously as unwelcome pests or a sign of unclean habits. They have often been accepted as one of life's unavoidable afflictions. As vectors of diseases, body lice have, on numerous occasions determined the outcome of human history. Zinsser, in 1935,[42] and Busvine, in 1976,[43] chronicled empires and even entire civilizations that were profoundly changed by epidemics of louse-borne typhus.

Life Cycles

The life cycles of the human lice are depicted in Figure 38.17. The crab louse, *P. pubis*, sometimes referred to as papillion d'amour, usually inhabits the hairs of the pubic and perianal regions of the body but can also be found on axillary hair or on moustaches, beards, eyebrows, or eyelashes. Adult crab lice are sedentary, often clutching the same hairs for days while feeding for hours at a time. Lice of all stages and both sexes feed solely on blood. They must obtain daily blood meals to survive. The female lays individual eggs or nits (approximately 0.6 mm in length) and attaches them to hairs of the host (Fig. 38.18). They embryonate and hatch over 6-8 days. The louse has three nymphal (pre-adult) stages, lasting 15-17 days, before the final molt to the adult stage. Nymphs are tiny, sexually immature versions of the adults. Adult crab lice live less than one month, and the females usually lay fewer than 50 eggs during her lifetime. The entire life cycle (i.e., egg-to-egg interval) lasts 22-27 days.[44, 45]

Crab lice are most frequently transmitted from one person to another by sexual contact. However, general physical contact or contact with a variety of contaminated objects such as toilet seats, clothing, or bedding can also result in infestation.

The head louse, *P. humanus capitis*, inhabits the hairs of the head, particularly behind the ears and around the occiput. Heavy infestations may force head lice to establish themselves on other hairy parts of the body. Like the crab lice, the head lice are relatively sedentary, feeding for hours at a time while clutching firmly to hair; like the crab lice, they seldom leave the hairy regions voluntarily. The eggs are attached to hair shafts and hatch within approximately one week; the three nymphal stages are completed within less than 14 days. The egg-to-egg cycle lasts about three weeks. A head louse lays 50-150 eggs during her lifetime. Head lice are disseminated by physical contact, by sharing of hats, scarves, combs, or brushes, or by the common storage of garments that contain nits or lice of various stages.

Although head lice have been shown to be capable of transmitting rickettsiae and spirochetes in the laboratory, they are usually not involved in the transmission of these organisms under natural conditions.[46]

The life cycle of the body louse, *P. humanus humanus*, differs significantly from those of the other two in that body lice spend much of their lives on the clothing of infested individuals. Body lice (commonly referred to as "cooties") are usually found on clothing wherever it comes into close contact with the body. Although body lice in all stages of their development must move to the body for regular blood meals, they return to the cloth-

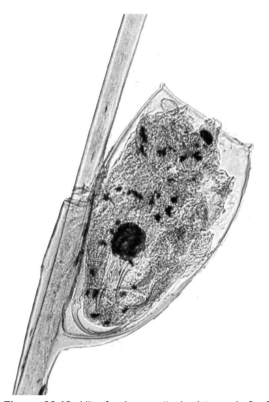

Figure 38.18. Nit of a louse attached to a shaft of hair.

Figure 38.19. Body lice eggs on fabric.

ing after feeding. The lice lay eggs along the seams of garments attached to cloth fibers and sometimes attach the eggs to some of the coarser body hairs (Fig. 38.19). Eggs kept near the body hatch within 5-7 days. Nymphs require about 18 days to mature, and the adult lice live for about a month. A body louse lays more than 300 eggs during her lifetime.

Body lice are readily transmitted between individuals by physical contact, exchanges of clothing, or the common storage of infested garments. They are the only vectors of louse-borne relapsing fever, trench fever, and epidemic typhus.

Pathogenesis

Lice inject salivary fluids into the wound during ingestion of blood. These secretions induce varying degrees of sensitization in the human host.

Clinical Disease

The usual characteristic of infestation by all types of lice is intense itching. Constant scratching can lead to secondary bacterial infection of the wound. Crab lice produce characteristic "blue spots," which are often seen around the eyes of individuals with infested lashes. The bites of head lice result in inflammatory papules and impetiginous lesions often associated with lymphadenopathy (Fig. 39.20). Heavy infestations of head lice can cause a condition in which hair, eggs, louse feces, and exudates of bite wounds form a cap-like mass teeming with lice. There may be secondary fungal infection within the mass.[47] Children infested with head lice often appear restless.

Bites by body lice cause pinpoint macules, excoriations, and pigmentation of the skin. "Vagabond's disease" is an extreme condition caused by a combination of persistent heavy infestation and poor personal hygiene. Affected individuals show a generalized bronze pigmentation and hardening of the skin.[47]

Diagnosis

The diagnosis depends on identification of lice or eggs in the hair or in the seams of garments. In the latter, they may be difficult to find. The eggs must be identified by microscopy.

Treatment

There are several formulations available as dusts, shampoos, lotions, and creams. Some may be obtained as over-the-counter preparations, and others require a prescription. All of the effective products contain low concentrations of insecticides such as benzene hexachloride, pyrethrum, or synthetic pyrethrum analogues.[48]

Head and crab lice can be treated similarly. Infested individuals should remove all clothing, apply the pediculicide, and put on clean clothing after treatment. The procedure should be repeated after 10 days to kill any newly hatched lice, as most treatments do not kill eggs. To prevent re-infestation, the clothing and bedding of infested individuals should be dry-cleaned or washed and dried by exposure to heat. Exposure of infested clothing to temperatures of 70° C for 30 minutes kills lice and eggs. Combs and brushes should also be treated by heat to prevent re-infestation by head lice. Simply washing the head or affected areas with soap does not kill lice or destroy the nits. Benzene hexachloride (lindane, Kwell) remains one of the most effective treatments for head lice but should be used with caution[48] and with strict adherence to instructions for use.

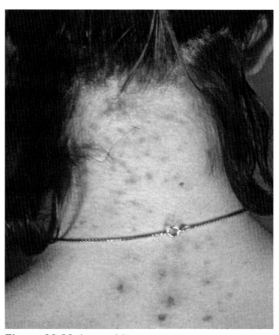

Figure 38.20. Louse bites

Oral ivermectin as a systemic insecticide has been suggested for use in cases where all else fails, and should be used with caution.[49, 50] Insecticides should not be used on crab lice infesting eyebrows or lashes. Petrolatum should be applied thickly and individual lice removed with forceps.

Because body lice inhabit and lay eggs on clothing, regularly changing underwear and garments significantly reduces the infestation. Garments infested by lice should be treated as indicated above. Blankets, bedding, sleeping bags, and other items that might be contaminated should be similarly treated.

Various powdered formulations of pediculicides can be applied directly to clothed individuals. Several of these compounds have been used effectively for mass treatment of large groups of infested individuals to control epidemic typhus. Nit combs, hair combs with teeth spaced closely enough to scrape the louse eggs (nits) from the hair, can be effective if used thoroughly and repeatedly. All nits must be removed to prevent re-infestation.

Epidemiology

The three species of human lice can be considered cosmopolitan in distribution, with infestations recorded throughout tropical, temperate, and Arctic regions. The absence of lice in a population is a result of social or hygienic habits rather than of geographic or climatic factors.

The rates of infestations with crab lice are usually much lower than those for head or body lice. Infestations with head lice can reach epidemic proportions, particularly among schoolchildren.[51, 52]

Infestations with body lice are usually associated with poverty, crowded conditions, social upheavals such as wars, or natural disasters. Because body lice reside and deposit eggs on clothing, conditions that prevent changing and cleaning garments coupled with close contact and crowding foster the spread of these insects.

Louse-Borne Diseases

Body lice are the only vectors involved in infecting humans with *Rickettsia prowazeki*, which causes epidemic typhus, *Rochalimaea quintana*, the rickettsial agent of trench fever; and *Borrelia recurrentis*, the spirochete that causes louse-borne relapsing fever.[53]

The rickettsiae multiply within the louse in the epithelial cells of the midgut, which ultimately rupture, releasing large numbers of these microorganisms. Human infections occur by rubbing infected louse feces into skin abrasions caused by the original louse bites. These abrasions are often extended by scratching. In-halation of fomites containing rickettsiae also causes human infection. Rickettsiae survive dehydration and remain infective for over two months at warm temperatures.

Humans are the usual reservoir for the rickettsiae of epidemic typhus. The organism can remain latent for years, occasionally giving rise to a mild recrudescent form of typhus termed Brill-Zinsser disease. Lice feeding on people with this form of typhus can become infected with the rickettsiae and transmit them to non-immune individuals, giving rise to the primary epidemic form of the disease. Studies have demonstrated a sylvan cycle of R. prowazeki in flying squirrels in the United States,[54] but the importance of this rodent reservoir in the spread of typhus is yet to be determined.

Trench fever is a self-limiting disease caused by *R. quintana*. Transmission to humans is similar to that of epidemic typhus. Individuals with trench fever can infect lice from the third day of illness and sometimes for months thereafter. The rickettsiae develop only within the cuticular margin of the louse gut (i.e., not intracellularly) and cause no disease in the insect. Infected feces and crushed lice are the usual sources of infection. The human is the only animal in which this rickettsia causes disease.

Louse-borne relapsing fever is caused by the spirochete *B. recurrentis*, and the body louse is the only vector of *B. recurrentis*, although similar spirochetes cause tick-borne relapsing fevers. Lice are infected when feeding on infected individuals during febrile periods. The spirochetes invade the epithelium of the gut and ultimately the blood of the louse. Transmission can occur only when crushed lice are rubbed into a wound or are inhaled. Lice do not pass the spirochete by biting and do not excrete it in feces.[55]

Siphonaptera: The Fleas

The siphonaptera comprise a small order of insects of generally similar appearance and habits. The adult fleas exist as ectoparasites on warm-blooded animals. The typical adult flea is a brown, laterally compressed, wingless insect with a tough skin, usually less than 3 mm long. Its third pair of legs is adapted for jumping, and it has mouthparts designed for blood-sucking.

Fleas undergo complete metamorphosis in their development, exhibiting markedly different larva, pupa, and adult stages. The larvae are delicate, motile, vermiform creatures; the pupae are encapsulated and quiescent.

Fleas cause diseases in humans as serious biting pests and as vectors of a number of infectious agents, most notably the agent of bubonic plague, *Yersinia pestis*. Fleas usually feed quickly and to repletion at a single site.

Historical Information

Humans have evolved with these "lair" parasites of domestic animals and fellow cave dwellers. Literature is replete with songs, poems, and stories extolling the virtues and vices of fleas and the miseries they cause. The importance of fleas as vectors was not recognized until the final years of the nineteenth century, when they were implicated in the transmission of plague. The historical impact of flea-borne bubonic plague, or Black Death, in the development of civilization, has been well documented.[42]

Life Cycle

The life cycle of a typical flea is shown in Figure 38.3. Fleas are usually parasites of animals inhabiting nests, dens, or caves. The adult flea is an obligate parasite of its warm-blooded host, feeding only on blood. The flea scatters its eggs in and around the nest of its host. Larval fleas are active, yellowish-white creatures with biting mouthparts. They feed on host feces or on dried blood defected by adult fleas. Under ideal conditions of temperature and humidity, eggs can embryonate and hatch in less than a week; larvae develop to adults in less than two weeks. After the flea has developed through three larval stages, it spins a cocoon and forms a quiescent pupa. The period of pupation, during which the insect gradually develops its adult characteristics, may last from a week to a year depending on the species and the environmental conditions. The pupa, encased in its cocoon, can remain dormant for months. The quiescent adult, encased in the pupal cocoon is stimulated to emerge by detecting vibrations in the local environment, thus giving rise to a hungry adult flea.[56]

Although many species of fleas bite humans if the insects are sufficiently hungry, only a small number are

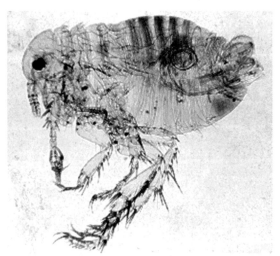

Figure 38.21. *Pulex irritans*

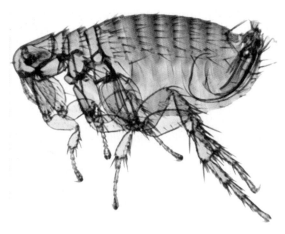

Figure 38.22. *Xenopsylla cheopis,* an important vector of Bubonic Plague.

consistent human pests. The combless fleas, so called because they lack prominent spines (ctenidia) on their heads, include several species that regularly feed on humans.

The human flea *Pulex irritans* (Fig. 38.21) is an ectoparasite of humans and animals, particularly swine. *P. irritans* is cosmopolitan in distribution and is the most common flea affecting humans. A closely related species, *P. simulans*, is restricted to the New World. Both species are capable of transmitting plague, but are considered minor vectors of this disease.

The oriental rat flea, *Xenopsylla cheopis* (Fig. 38.22), as the vector of *Y. pestis*, has long been considered one of the great killers of humankind. It is an ectoparasite of rats, feeding on humans only when its customary host is unavailable. Classically, human bubonic plague is a consequence of an epizootic of plague in the rat population. As rats die in massive numbers, infected fleas leave their dead hosts and seek fresh sources of blood. Under these circumstances, humans are readily attacked and infected.

Xenopsylla acts as an efficient vector because of its association with reservoir rats and its readiness to feed on humans. When a flea takes a blood meal from an infected rat, the plague organism rapidly multiplies within the flea's proventriculus, an organ of the intestinal tract lined with spiny projections. Within three days, the proventriculus is blocked by a gelatinous mass of partially digested blood and bacteria. When the flea feeds again, it is unable to engorge and is forced to regurgitate the blood and bacteria from the proventriculus into the host. Because the flea is unable to feed completely, it moves from host to host, repeatedly attempting to feed without attaining satisfaction, and transmitting the plague organism as it goes. The flea eventually dies of starvation, but not before its role as a vector of plague has been discharged.

The combed fleas also include species that affect

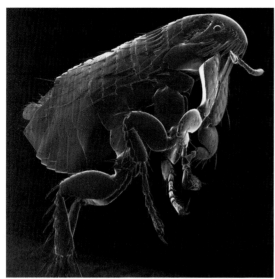

Figure 38.23. *Ctenocephalides felis.* Photo D. Scharf.

humans. The dog and cat fleas, *Ctenocephalides canis* and *C. felis* (Fig. 38.23), are closely related, morphologically similar species, with two sets of prominent combs on the head. Both species feed equally well on dogs and cats, and both bite humans if given the opportunity. Their larvae and pupae are usually found in the places where the animals rest. The fleas can prove particularly annoying when the pet leaves the household and the fleas have humans as their only source of blood. Raccoons can also bring dog or cat fleas into homes, often by building their nests in chimneys.[57]

The northern rat flea, *Nosopsyllus fasciatus*, and the squirrel flea, *Diamanus montanus*, are common combed fleas of rodents in North America. They readily bite humans and may be involved in transmission of plague from wild rodents to rats or humans.

Tunga penetrans, known as the chigger flea or chigoe, is a serious pest in the tropical and subtropical regions of the Americas, Africa, and the Indian subcontinent.[58] This flea originated in South America and was introduced into Africa during the late nineteenth century. Adult chigoes are less than 1 mm long. Both sexes feed regularly on blood. After insemination, the female flea attaches itself to the skin of the toes, soles of the feet, or the legs, and becomes enveloped by host tissue (Fig. 38.24). Thus protected, the female swells to the size of a pea, produces 150-200 eggs (Fig. 38.25), and dies still embedded in the tissue.[59, 60] The infested tissue can become ulcerated and infected by bacteria, possibly including the clostridia, and cause tetanus or gas gangrene. Auto-amputation of toes is not uncommon. Infection can be avoided by wearing shoes in areas when *T. penetrans* occurs. Treatment consists in removing the flea with a sterile instrument and treating the wound locally to prevent infection.

Pathogenesis

The response to repeated flea bites is typical of reactions to most insect bites Initial exposure produces little or no reaction, but after an individual is sensitized to the salivary antigens of the flea, first delayed reactions and then primary reactions develop.[61]

Clinical Disease

Intense irritation that leads to scratching and secondary bacterial infections[62] is the main manifestation of flea bites. The major health problem caused by fleas is the transmission of infectious agents for which the fleas are vectors.

Diagnosis

The typical flea bite first appears as a single papule. However, with heavy flea infestations, papules may be grouped along the arms and legs, on the face and neck, or where clothing fits snugly. Precise incrimination of fleas requires capture of one of the offending insects. The species of the flea can be determined with the aid of a dissecting microscope and a key to identifying fleas that affect humans.

Treatment

Pruritus can be treated symptomatically. Secondary bacterial infection is medicated as appropriate.

Control

Fleas can be controlled at the source of the infestation by various commercially available insecticides. Dusts should be applied to the fur and beds of dogs and cats. These dusts are particularly effective against

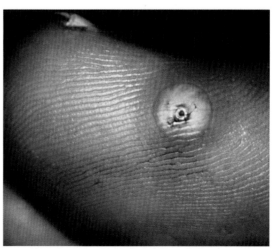

Figure 38.24. *T. penetrans* in skin. Courtesy G. Zalar.

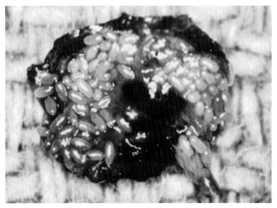

Figure 38.25. *Tunga penetrans* eggs. Photo G. Zalar

the fleas that dwell in nests, whose larvae feed on particles. Space sprays can be effective against adult fleas. Pets can be treated for flea infestations topically or with systemic compounds that are lethal to the feeding insect. A number of topically-applied repellents can protect individuals against flea bites for short periods.[63]

Epidemiology of Flea-Borne Diseases

Fleas serve as primary vectors of *Yersinia pestis*, the agent of the plague, and *Rickettsia mooseri*, which causes murine or endemic typhus. Moreover, fleas can serve as intermediate hosts of various cestodes and nematodes that infect mammals, including humans.

Yersinia pestis persists in nature in a so-called sylvan or campestral cycle in which wild rodents are constantly infected by various species of fleas. Foci of naturally infected rodents occur in central Asia, South Africa, South America, and the Russian steppes. In western North America, plague is maintained in a ground squirrel reservoir with the squirrel flea, *Diamanus montanus*, as the vector. A number of other rodent species and flea vectors may also be involved. The United States reports 5-10 autochthonous cases of bubonic plague each year, usually among campers, hunters, and farmers in the western states. As long as plague exists as a disease of field rodents, human cases are rare. However, when the plague is transferred from wild rodents to peridomestic rats and becomes established in a rat-rat flea cycle, the potential for human infection increases markedly. The epidemiology of murine typhus has been clarified with the demonstration that *R. mooseri* can be transmitted transovarially from an infected flea to her progeny.[64]

Heteroptera: Bugs

Heteroptera are known as true bugs. This large order contains two families of medical importance.

Adults of most heteropterans are winged; the wingless bed bugs, the Cimicidae, are an exception. Bugs have mouthparts modified for piercing and sucking. Their long, slender, segmented beak is usually held along the ventral surface of the body when it is not in use. Most heteropterans are plant feeders, and some are predaceous on other insects; the ones that affect humans, the Reduviidae and Cimicidae are hematophagous. Heteroptera develop by incomplete metamorphosis.

Cimicidae: Bed Bugs

Three closely related species of bed bugs are blood-feeding ectoparasites of humans.[65] The common bed bug (*Cimex lectularius*) and the tropical bed bugs (*C. hemipterus* and *C. boueti*) are morphologically similar; they are oval, flattened, reddish-brown insects with mouth parts well-adapted for piercing flesh and sucking blood. Adult bed bugs (Fig. 38.26) have non-functional reduced wings. They are approximately 5 mm long and 3 mm wide. Their five nymphal stages are smaller, sexually immature copies of the adults.[66]

Bed bugs are cosmopolitan in distribution. *C. lectularius* is widespread throughout temperate and tropical regions. The Indian bed bug, *C. hemipterus*, is restricted to tropical and sub-tropical climates, and *C. boueti* is found in the tropical regions of Africa and South America.

Historical Information

Bed bugs evolved from ectoparasites of cave-dwelling mammals, probably bats, at the time when humans were cave dwellers. They were first recorded as a problem in the Mediterranean region by early Greek and Roman writers. In northern Europe they were identified much later (e.g., during the eleventh century in England).[41] Bed bugs have been suspected of transmitting a number of human diseases, but no direct evidence of involvement exists. Epidemiologic associations with hepatitis B virus transmission have not been verified experimentally.[67, 68]

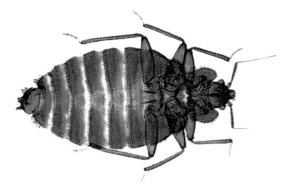

Figure 38.26. Bed bug.

Life Cycle

Bed bugs are found in a variety of human habitations, including homes, hotels, dormitories, prisons, barracks, and hospitals. They remain hidden in cracks and crevices in walls, floors, and furniture, usually appearing at night or in dim light to feed on a sleeping host. Humans are the preferred source of blood, but bed bugs feed on a variety of animals if humans are unavailable. They characteristically bite two or three times in succession over a period of a few minutes to engorge themselves.

Adult females lay 2-3 eggs per day for a total of 200-500 during a lifetime. The pearly white eggs are 1 mm long. They are laid individually in crevices, behind loose wallpaper, in cracks in woodwork or furniture, or in mattresses. Hatching depends on temperature but usually occurs after 9-10 days of embryonation. There are five nymphal stages, each requiring a blood meal before molting to the next. The egg-to-egg period, depending on temperature, varies from 7 to 19 weeks, which allows the development of several generations of bugs within a year. Availability of a blood source also influences generation time. Adult bugs feed weekly during the summer, less frequently during the cooler months, and starve during the winter, reappearing to feed again in the spring.

Pathogenesis

Feeding bed bugs inject salivary fluids to sensitize the host. Primary exposure produces little or no reaction. After repeated exposures a severe delayed reaction may develop; continued exposure produces an additional primary reaction. Finally, after a course of regular exposures to bites, the host can become desensitized.

Clinical Disease

Reactions to bites can be mild or severe. Large hemorrhagic bullae form on some sensitized individuals, whereas others develop erythema and local edema, and may experience severe, prolonged pruritus. Scratching can lead to secondary bacterial infections. Heavy bedbug infestations can interfere with sleep.

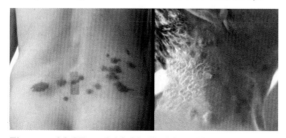

Figures 38.27 and 38.28. Bed bug bites: note hemorrhagic bullae and paired bitemarks.

Diagnosis

The bite wounds are firm, closely spaced papules, appearing as two or three lesions together (Fig. 38.27, 38.28). This grouping can be used to differentiate predation by bedbugs from the typically single bites of other insects. The final determination that bedbugs are involved depends on finding living or dead bugs or the circumstantial evidence of a characteristically pungent odor associated with the alarm glands of these insects and trails of blood droplets near the hiding places of the bugs.

Treatment

The itching associated with the bites of bed bugs responds to symptomatic therapy.

Control

Control in dwellings is best achieved with chemical insecticides. Residual compounds such as DDT and BHC are effective and long lasting, though generally not recommended. Resistance to these compounds has been reported in a number of areas, particularly in the tropics. Diazinon has been used successfully to treat infested surfaces. Removal of old furniture, mattresses, and loose wallpaper, as well as the patching of wall cracks can deny the bugs resting and breeding places.

Reduviidae: Assassin Bugs

Reduviidae is a large family of predaceous insects collectively referred to as assassin bugs, most members of which are insectivorous. One subfamily, the Triatominae, is found mainly in the New World and is of particular importance because its members are hematophagous and are vectors of Chagas' disease.

Bugs of the Triatominae (Fig. 38.29), the so-called kissing bugs, cone-nosed bugs, or vinchucas, are large insects with distinct elongate cone-shaped heads. They possess a long, three-segment proboscis that has been well-developed for piercing skin; all developmental stages feed exclusively on blood. Adults are winged and are good fliers, whereas the nymphal stages are wingless, sexually immature miniatures of the adults, developing through the various stages by incomplete metamorphosis (Fig. 38.1).

Historical Information

The Triatominae received little attention from entomologists before 1909, at which point Chagas identified them as the vectors of *Trypanosoma cruzi*.[69]

Life Cycle

Three species of Triatominae serve as major vectors of Chagas' disease, although several species are important as vectors in restricted areas and a large number of species have been found naturally infected with the parasite. *Panstrongylus megistus, Triatoma infestans,* and *Rhodnius prolixus* are large bugs that feed on humans as well as on wild or domestic animals whenever they are available. These insects abound in the cracks and crevices of the mud and timber houses typical of rural areas in the Latin American tropics.[69] Kissing bugs are usually found in resting places near their source of blood meals. Domestic or peridomestic species that prey on humans are found in cracks and crevices of walls and floors, particularly in sleeping areas.

Adult females require a blood meal before producing a clutch of eggs. They lay eggs singly within the same cracks that harbor the nymphs and adults. The eggs hatch within 10-30 days, and each of the five nymphal stages requires a full blood meal before molting to the next. Kissing bugs are prodigious feeders. First-stage nymphs can imbibe 12 times their weight in blood; subsequent stages drink relatively less. Fifth-stage nymphs of *R. prolixus* may suck in more than 300 μl of blood, and adult females may ingest more than 200 μl for each egg batch. The five nymphal stages may last several months before their final molt to the adult stage. Most species have one generation per year.[70, 71]

Pathogenesis

Intense, persistent pain is associated with the bites of some insectivorous assassin bugs, a result of injection of various toxins. The bites of most of the blood-feeding Triatominae are notably painless, enabling these insects to feed undisturbed on sleeping individuals. The habit of feeding around the mouth or eyes of a sleeper accounts for the designation "kissing bug." After sensitization to the salivary fluids of feeding bugs, individuals can develop delayed reactions characterized by itching, swelling, redness, nausea, and, in rare cases, anaphylaxis. Anaphylactic responses to xenodiagnosis, usually with *R. prolixus,* have been reported.[72]

Both nymphs and adult bugs act as vectors of *T. cruzi.* Although bugs may be infected by feeding on human hosts and can transmit the organism from human to human, the usual sources of bug infection are wild and peridomestic animals (e.g., dogs, cats, mice, armadillos, and opossums). *T. cruzi* develops in the hindgut of the bug and does not invade the salivary glands. Thus, the bite of the bug does not cause in-

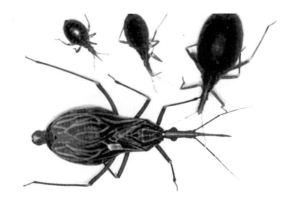

Figure 38.29. Kissing bug family of *Rhodnius prolixus.*

fection. Rather, infectious parasites are passed in the feces of the bug while it feeds. The victim reacts to the irritation of the bite, then rubs the infected feces into the eyes, mouth, or the wound made by the bite. Various triatomine species regularly feed on infected animals, supporting growth of the parasite, but do not defecate until they leave the host. These species usually are not involved in transmission to humans, but may serve to maintain the parasite in an animal reservoir where infected bugs may be eaten by the animal host, which thus becomes infected. *T. cruzi* is naturally maintained in wood rats in southern California by such a cycle. Although transmission of *T. cruzi* to humans is rare in the United States, infected animals are found regularly, and autochthonous cases have been reported.

Clinical Disease

Except for the allergic reaction to the bite, the bite itself is innocuous. The importance of these bugs lies in their acting as vectors in Chagas' disease.

Diagnosis

The night-feeding kissing bugs are insidious, leaving little initial evidence of their blood meal. Kissing bugs normally feed from one puncture, leaving a single papule. This point distinguishes the lesion from those caused by bedbugs, which also feed at night but whose bites are usually clustered in groups of two or three.

Most of the entomophagous bugs likely to bite humans are large insects; the wheel bug, a common offender with a distinctive cog-like crest on its thorax, is more than 30 mm long. Because they bite during the day, usually when handled, they can be readily identified.

Treatment

Reactions to the bites of kissing bugs require, at most, local symptomatic therapy.

Control

Insecticides applied to houses have been effective for the control of some species of kissing bugs. However, environmental control programs work better than even prudent and appropriate application of insecticides. For example, improved housing, in which thatched roofing and adobe walls and flooring are eliminated, helps to greatly reduce breeding sites for the bugs. Indoors, smooth walls with little in the way of pictures, etc. hanging on them also favors the elimination of reduviiidae from the local environment. These latter two approaches have been used in many parts of Brazil with a high degree of success. An aggressive vector control program now underway offers the promise of interruption of transmission of Chagas' disease throughout most of South America.[72-74]

Hymenoptera: The Stinging Insects

The stinging insects, including the bees, wasps, hornets (Fig. 38.30), and ants (Fig. 38.31), are members of the Hymenoptera, a large order of highly developed species. Complex social systems, castes, and elaborate hive and nest structures have evolved among the Hymenoptera. The only other insect group to achieve such a level of social development is the termite. In the Hymenoptera, the ovipositor (the apparatus used for egg laying) has been modified to serve as a stinging organ and is used by adult females to capture prey for food or for defense.

The stinging apparati of honeybees, bumblebees, wasps, and hornets are generally similar in structure. They consist of paired acid glands, a single alkaline gland, a poison sac with muscular neck, and the piercing apparatus itself, which includes a pair of stylets and a stylet sheath. The stylets or darts of the honeybee stinger are barbed (Fig. 39.32) and, once inserted by the insect, cannot be withdrawn. Consequently, when a honeybee stings and attempts to fly away, it leaves behind the complete stinging apparatus, virtually disemboweling itself and suffering a mortal wound. The

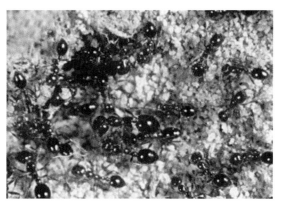

Figure 38.31. Fire ants, *Solenopsis invicta*.

self-contained stinger with its attached poison sac and musculature continues to pump venom into the wound long after the bee has departed.[75] The stingers of most hymenopterans are not barbed (Fig. 39.33) and are withdrawn after stinging. Wasps, hornets, bumblebees, and ants are capable of multiple stings without losing their stinging apparatus.

It is estimated that in the United States 50-100 people die each year from reactions to stings of the hymenopterans, and even then, there is probably substantial underreporting and some misdiagnosis. Yellow jackets and honeybees are the major causes of such reactions.[76]

Certain behavioral characteristics of bees and yellow jackets result in increased aggressiveness. Honeybees are generally benign unless they are individually molested or provoked to defend their hive. Their venom contains the pheromone isopentyl acetate, which acts as an alarm signal and draws other bees to the site of the original sting, which in turn leads to multiple stings.[77] Dramatic reports of the so-called African killer bees are often exaggerations of reality, although these bees tend to be more aggressive and less predictable than the common bees found in most domestic hives.[78,79] The range of these "Africanized" honeybees has extended from South America through Central America and Mexico into the southern United States. The ultimate distribution into the United States will be limited by the bees' ability to survive killing temperatures.[79-81]

Yellow jackets are particularly aggressive when their nest areas are approached, at which point they sting without provocation or warning. Their aggressive behavior increases during the late summer and early fall. Gardeners and picnickers are particularly at risk.

Historical Information

The honeybee, *Apis mellifera*, was one of the first insects recorded by humans in writings and art. Bees have long been recognized as sources of honey, and their role as plant pollinators is crucial to agriculture.

Figure 38.30. Stinging Insects: wasp, yellow jacket, honey bee.

Figure 38.32. Bee stinger – note barbs.

Life Cycle

Hymenopterans develop by complete metamorphosis with distinct larva, pupa, and adult stages. Larvae are vermiform and resemble maggots. They are dependent upon adults for food. Pupae, encased in a cocoon, represent an inactive, non-feeding transitional phase. The adults usually have wings and are good fliers. Certain groups with highly developed social systems have evolved non-reproducing worker and soldier castes. Other groups, such as the ants, are wingless as adults except during reproductive periods. Four families of the Hymenoptera contain medically important species, the stings of which can cause severe reactions in humans: Apidae, Vespidae, Formicidae, and Mutillidae.

The bees, or Apidae, include some species that live in complex social organizations such as hives or in less-structured subterranean nests, although most species in this family live as solitary insects. Only the honeybees and bumblebees among the Apidae are of concern to humans because of their ability to sting. The honeybee, *Apis mellifera*, originally an Old World species, is now found worldwide in domestic and wild hives. Bees of this species are raised commercially for their honey and for their role as pollinators of a wide range of plants, including most fruits and legume crops. They construct elaborate hives wherein a single non-foraging queen lays eggs in wax cells. Larvae develop within these cells while being fed by non-reproductive female workers. Adult workers tend the hives and forage for nectar and pollen. The bees tend to sting when their hive or individual insects are disturbed.

Bumblebees of the genus Bombus are large, hairy, ungainly, less organized social bees that build simple underground nests. They sting under the same circumstances as do honeybees.

The Vespidae include the wasps, hornets, and yellow jackets, all of which are capable of inflicting painful stings. Many species in this family build elaborate nests of masticated wood fibers or mud, whereas others construct simple nests underground. The yellow jackets are social hymenopterans with distinctive yellow and black bands on the abdomen, and are often mistaken for bees. They are aggressive insects and a major cause of stings in humans.[82]

Ants belong to the family Formicidae, some members of which can cause damage by biting or stinging. They have a variety of complex social systems, with elaborate behavior patterns, intricate nests, and castes of workers, soldiers, and reproducing insects. Two groups of ants are of concern in the United States.

The harvester ants of the genus Pogonomyrmex readily attack humans and other animals and are capable of inflicting painful stings. They build underground nests, topped by mounds, in warm, dry, sandy areas. When a nest is disturbed, ants come out and swarm over the invader; their stings are repeated and vigorous.

Fire ants of the genus Solenopsis are so named because of their sharp, fiery sting. Several native US species are of medical importance, but the imported fire ant, *Solenopsis invicta* (Fig. 38.31), is a particularly dangerous species.[83] It was introduced into the United States around 1930 and since then has spread throughout the southeastern states, where it presents a serious hazard to humans and livestock. These ants build large, hard-crusted mounds, which are well camouflaged and often not seen until they are disturbed. When fire ants attack, they first bite their victim with strong mandibles, and then sting their victim repeatedly. The result is a circle of painful stings around a central bite.

Certain species of tropical ants are notorious for their ability to ravage plants and animals alike as they travel from place to place in colonies or armies num-

Figure 38.33. Wasp stinger - barbs absent.

bering millions of individuals.

The so-called velvet ants are not true ants, but wingless wasps of the family Mutillidae. These large, hairy, often brightly-colored insects are capable of inflicting a painful sting if they are disturbed. A large black mutillid with scarlet hairs is common in the central United States, where it can cause considerable distress by stinging barefoot bathers. Several other groups of the Hymenoptera have the capacity to sting.

Pathogenesis

During the act of stinging, the aroused insect first inserts the sheath, inflicting a wound, then follows immediately with the inward thrust of the stylets and injection of the venom. The combination of the acid and alkaline venom fluids, designed to kill insect prey, causes extreme pain and inflammation. Venom from 500 stings received within a few minutes can cause death. The inhabitants of a single disturbed beehive can inflict at least that number of stings within a matter of minutes. Sensitization to the venom can result in severe allergic reactions. A number of antigenically-active compounds has been identified in venom, phospholipase A being the most important. Others include hyaluronidase, melittin, and apamin.[84]

Clinical Disease

The primary manifestations of the sting are due to mechanical damage and the direct action of the venom. The pain, edema, pruritus, and warmth produced at the site of the sting are transitory. Severe toxic reactions can be caused by as few as 10 stings within a period of a few minutes. Muscle cramps, drowsiness, fever, and headache are characteristic.

Allergic reactions are by far the most serious consequence of the stings of hymenopterans. They may develop in previously sensitized individuals and include three symptom patterns: (1) urticaria associated with pruritus; (2) edematous skin and mucous membranes; and (3) simultaneous bronchospasm and anaphylaxis, followed sometimes by death. In sensitized individuals, even a single sting may bring the most severe reaction. A delayed reaction characterized by urticaria, fever, and arthralgia may occur hours or weeks after a sting.

Although the stinging hymenopterans share a number of common antigens, each possesses one or more unique antigens. Sensitization to stings of one species does not always produce sensitivity to those of other species.[85-88]

Diagnosis

Individuals with suspected sting sensitivities can undergo skin testing with specific venoms to determine the level of risk. Identification of the species posing the greatest threat to an individual may be critical.[89]

Treatment

Initial treatment for a honeybee sting must include removal of its stinger and the attached venom sac. Removal can be accomplished with a knife blade, a needle, or a fingernail. It is important not to squeeze the site, because such pressure releases more venom from the sac. A non-allergic primary reaction may be treated with ice to lessen edema and pain, and with various local anti-pruritics.

Individuals with known sting sensitivity must be prepared to act quickly to prevent serious reactions. Upon being stung, the individual should remove the stinger immediately and, if the sting is on an arm or leg, apply a tourniquet above it.

Emergency kits are available by prescription, and sensitive individuals should be familiar with their use. Such kits contain epinephrine in a syringe, antihistamine tablets, and a tourniquet.

Emergency treatment consists of injections of epinephrine, half of the calculated dose injected intramuscularly and half intravenously, and an antihistamine. Obviously, use of these measures presupposes planning; the sensitized person and his or her next of kin must be prepared to carry out at least the intramuscular injection of epinephrine. In addition, the potential victim must carry isoproterenol for sublingual administration and an oral, non-enteric, coated antihistaminic.

Desensitization using whole-body extracts of the insects has been attempted but is ineffective. Purified venoms have been used successfully for desensitization.[90, 91] Successful treatment for severe reactions to fire ant stings has been reported.[92]

Control

Wasp, hornet, and ant nests can be destroyed with a number of commercially available insecticidal compounds, such as carbamates, malathion, and resmithrin. Aerial nests can be destroyed at night, when the insects are quiescent. General avoidance of areas where stinging hymenopterans occur should be a rule for sensitive individuals. There are no effective repellents against these insects.

References

1. Jongi BS. Centipede venoms and poisoning. In: Insect Poisons, Allergens, and Other Invertebrate Venoms. (Tu AT. ed). Marcel Dekker, New York pp. 333- 368, 1984.
2. Koo J. Lee CS. Delusions of parasitosis,. A dermatologist's guide to diagnosis and treatment. Am J Clin Dermatol. 2:285-290. 2001
3. Ribeiro JMC. Francischetti IMB. Role of arthropod saliva in blood feeding: Sialome and post-sialome perspectives. Annu Rev Entomol. 48:73-88. 2002
4. Blanton FS. Wirth WW. The sand flies (Culicoides) of Florida. Arthropods Florida 10:1-204. 1979.
5. Downes JA. The ecology of blood-sucking diptera: an evolutionary perspective. In: Ecology and Physiology of Parasites. (Fallis AM, ed.) University of Toronto Press, Toronto. pp. 2-258. 1971.
6. Kettle. DS. The biology and bionomics of blood-sucking ceratopogonids. Annu Rev Entomol 22:3-51.1977.
7. Theodorides J. Note historique sur la decouverte de la transmission de la leishmaniose cutanee par les phlebotomes. Bull Soc Pathol Exot. 90:177-180. 1997.
8. Wenyon CM. Some recent advances in our knowledge of leishmaniasis. J London School Trop Med 1:93-98. 1912.
9. Lewis DJ. The biology of Phlebotomidae in relation to leishmaniasis. Annu Rev Entomol 19:363-384.1974.
10. Valenzuela JG. et al. Identification of the most abundant secreted proteins from the salivary glands of the Sand fly *Lutzomyia longipalps*, a vector of *Leishmania chagasi*. J Ex Biol 207:3717-3729. 2004
11. Sambon LW. Progress report of investigations of pellagra. J Trop Med 13:271-287. 1910.
12. Blacklock DB. The development of *Onchocerca volvulus* in *Simulium damnosum*. Ann Trop Med Parasitol 20:1-48.1926.
13. Dalmat HT. The Black Flies (Diptera, Simuliidae) of Guatemala and Their Role as Vectors of Onchocerciasis. Smithsonian Institution, Washington, DC, 1955.
14. Mattingly PF. The Science of Biology. Series 1. The Biology of Mosquito-Borne Disease. George Allen & Unwin, London. 1969.
15. Harrison G: Mosquitoes, Malaria and Man: A History of the Hostilities Since 1880. Dutton, New York. 1978.
16. Ross R: Memoirs. John Murray, London. 1923.
17. Reed W. Carroll J. Agremonte A. et al: Etiology of yellow fever, a preliminary note. Philos Med J 6:790-796. 1900.
18. Clements AN. The Biology of Mosquitoes. Vol 1.Development, Nutrition and Reproduction. Chapman & Hall, London. 1992.
19. Bates M: The Natural History of Mosquitoes. Harper & Row, New York. 1965.
20. Reinert JF. New classification for the composite genus Aedes (Diptera:Culicidae: Aedini), elevation of subgenus Ochlerotatus to generic range, reclassification of the other subgenera, and notes on certain subgenera and species. J Am Mosq Control Assoc 16:175-188. 2000
21. Reinert JF. Karbach RE. Kitching IJ. Phylogeny and classification of Aedini (Diptera:Culicidae), based on morphological characters of all life stages. Zool J Linnean Soc 142:289-368. 2004.
22. Christophers SR. Aedes aegypti, the Yellow Fever Mosquito: Its Life History, Bionomics, and Structure. Cambridge University Press, Cambridge. 1960.
23. Mellanby K. Man's reaction to mosquito bites. Nature 158:554. 1946.
24. Beard RL. Insect toxins and venoms. Annu Rev Ent 8:1-18. 1963.
25. Wilson AB. Clements AN. The nature of the skin reaction to mosquito bites in laboratory animals. Int Arch Allergy 26:294-314. 1965.
26. Feingold BF. Benjamini E. Micheali D. The allergic responses to insect bites. Annu Rev Entomol 13:137-158. 1968.
27. Russell PF. West LS. et al. Practical Malariology. London, Oxford University Press, London. 1963.
28. Leiper RT. Report of the Helminthologist for the Half -Year Ending 30 April, 1913. Report of the Adv Commission on Tropical Disease Research Fund. 1913-1914.
29. Linda DR. Scudder Hl. Non-biting flies and disease. Annu Rev Entomol 1:323-346. 1956.
30. Greenberg B. Flies and Disease (Vol II). Princeton University Press, Princeton. 1973.
31. Bruce D. Further report on sleeping sickness in Uganda: report of the Sleeping Sickness Com-mission. R Soc Lond 1:1-88. 1895.
32. Buxton PA. The Natural History of Tsetse Flies. H.K. Lewis, London. 1955.
33. Ford J. The Role of the Trypanosomiases in African Ecology. The Study of the Tsetse Fly Problem. Clarendon Press, Oxford. 1971.
34. Zumpt F. Myiasis. Butterworth, London, 1965.
35. Catts EP. Biology of New World bot flies: Cuterebridae. Annu Rev Entomol 27:313-338. 1982.
36. Sherman RA. Hall MJ. Thomas S. Medicinal maggots: an ancient remedy for some contemporary afflictions. Annu Rev Entomol 45:55-81. 2000.
37. Greer KA. In the spotlight: Age-old therapy gets new approval. Adv Skin Wound Care 18(1) 12-15. 2005
38. Greenberg B. Forensic entomology: case studies. Bull Entomol Soc Am 31:25-28. 1985.
39. Lord WD. Burger J. Collection and preservation of forensically important entomological materials. J Forensic Sci 28:936-944. 1983.
40. Chosidow O: Scabies and pediculosis. Lancet 355:819-826. 2000.
41. Zinsser H. Rats, Lice and History. Little, Brown, Boston. 1935.
42. Busvine JR: Insects, Hygiene, and History. Athlone Press, London. 1976.
43. Buxton PA: The Louse. Williams & Wilkins, Baltimore. 1946.
44. Ackerman, AB: Crabs-the resurgence of *Phthirus pubis*. N Engl J Med 278:950-951. 1968.
45. Morley WM. Body infestations. Scott Med J 22:211-216. 1977.
46. Epstein E Sr. Orkin M. Pediculosis: clinical aspects. In: Cutaneous Infestations and Insect Bites. (Orkin M. Maibach Hl., eds.) Marcel Dekker, New York. pp. 175-186. 1985.
47. Orkin M. Maibach Hl. Treatment of today's pediculosis. In: Cutaneous Infestations and Insect Bites. (Orkin M, Maibach Hl., eds.) Marcel Dekker, New York. pp. 213-217. 1985.
48. Orion E. Matz H. Wolf R. Ectoparasitic sexually transmitted diseases: Scabies and pediculosis. Clinics Dermatol 22:513-519. 2004

49. Hall RC. Hall RC. Long-term psychological and neurological complications of lindane poisoning. Psychosomatics 40:513-517. 1999.

50. Elgart ML. Current treatment for scabies and pediculosis. Skin Therapy Lett 5:1-3. 2000.

51. Juranek DD. *Pediculus capitis* in school children. In: Cutaneous Infestations and Insect Bites. (Orkin M, Maibach HI., eds.). Marcel Dekker, New York. pp. 199-211. 1985.

52. Slonka GF. Fleisner ML. et al. An epidemic of *Pediculus capitis*. J Parasitol 63:377-383. 1977.

53. Raoult D. Roux V. The body louse as a vector of re-emerging human diseases. Clin Infect Dis 29:888-911. 1999.

54. Sonenshine DE. Bozman FM. et al. Epizootiology of epidemic typhus (*Rickettsia prowazekii*) in flying squirrels. Am J Trop Med Hyg 27:339-349. 1978.

55. Burgdorfer W: The epidemiology of relapsing fevers. In: The Biology of Parasitic Spirochetes (Johnson RC., ed.). Academic Press, Orlando, FL. pp. 191-200. 1976.

56. Jellison WL. Fleas and Disease. Annu Rev Ent 4:389-414. 1959.

57. Hunter KW Jr. Campbell AR. Sayles PC. Human infestation by cat fleas: *Ctenocephalides felis* (Siphonaptera: Pulicidae). J Med Entomol 16:547. 1979.

58. Grunwald MH. Shai A. Mosovich B. Avinoach I. Tungiasis. Australas J Dermatol 41:46-47. 2000.

59. Goldman L. Tungiasis in travellers from tropical Africa. JAMA 236:1386. 1976.

60. Zalar GL. Walther. RR. Infestation by *Tunga penetrans*. Arch Dermatol 116:80-81. 1980.

61. Benjamini E. Feingold BF. Kartman L. Skin reactivity in guinea pigs sensitized to flea bites: the sequence of reactions. Proc Soc Exp Biol Med 108:700-702. 1961.

62. Lee SE. Johnstone IP. Lee RP. Opdebeeck JP. Putative salivary allergens of the cat flea *Ctenocephalides felis felis*. Vet Immunol Immunopathol 69:229-237. 1999.

63. Marsella R: Advances in flea control. Vet Clin North Am Small Anim Pract 29:1407-1424. 1999.

64. Farhang-Azad A. Traub R. Baqar S. Transovarial transmission of murine typhus rickettsiae in Xenopsylla cheopis fleas. Science 227:543-545. 1985.

65. Huntley AC: Cimex lectularius. What is this insect and how does it affect man? Dermatol Online J 5:6. 1999.

66. Usinger RL. Monograph of Cimicidae (Vol VII). Thomas Say Foundation, Entomology Society of America, Washington, DC. 1966.

67. Jupp PG. Purcell RH. et al. Attempts to transmit hepatitis B virus to chimpanzees by arthropods. S Afr Med J 79:320-322. 1991.

68. Mayans MV. Hall AJ. et al. Do bedbugs transmit hepatitis B? Lancet 343:761-763. 1999.

69. Chagas C. Nova trypanozomiaze humans: estudos sobre a morfolojiia e o ciclo evalutivo do *Schizotripanum cruzi*. n. genl., n. sp., ajente etiolojico de nova entidade morbida do homen. Mem Inst Oswaldo Cruz 1:159-218. 1909.

70. Usinger RL. The Triatominae of North and Central America and the West Indies and their public health significance. Public Health Bull 288:1-88. 1944.

71. Buxton PA. Biology of a blood-sucking bug, Rhodnius prolixus. Trans Entomol Soc Lond 78:227-236. 1930.

72. Costa ZHN. Costa MT. et at. Skin reactions to bites as a result of xenodiagnosis. Trans R Soc Trop Med Hyg 75:405-408. 1981.

73. Morel CM: Chagas' disease, from discovery to control and beyond: history, myths and lessons to take home. Mem Inst Oswaldo Cruz 94 Suppl 1:3-16. 1999.

74. Ebrahim GJ. Eradication of American trypanosomiasis (Chagas' disease): an achievable goal? J Trop Pediatr 50;320-321. 2004

75. Maschwitz UW. Kloft W. Morphology and function of the venom apparatus of insects - bees, wasps, ants, and caterpillars. In: Venomous Animals and Their Venom. Vol III. Venomous Invertebrates. (Bucherl W, Buckley EE., eds.) Academic Press, Orlando, FL. pp. 1-60. 1971.

76. Kemp ED. Bites and stings of the arthropod kind: Treating reactions that can range from annoying to menacing. Postgrad Med 103: 88-90, 93-96, 102. 1998.

77. Koeniger N. Weiss J. Maschwitz U. Alarm pheromones of the sting in the genus Apis. J Insect Physiol 25:467-476. 1979.

78. Winston ML. The biology and management of Africanized honey bees, Annu Rev Entomol 37:173-193. 1992.

79. Tunget CL. Clark RF. Invasion of the 'killer' bees. Separating fact from fiction. Postgrad Med 94: 92-94, 97-98, 101-102. 1993.

80. Taylor OR Jr. African bees: potential impact in the United States. Bull Entomol Soc Am 31:14-24. 1985.

81. Kim KT. Oguro J. Update on the status of africanized honey bees in the western states. West J Med 170:220-222. 1999.

82. Akre RP. Davis HG. Biology and pest status of venomous wasps. Annu Rev Entomol 23:215-238.1978.

83. Lofgren CS. Banks WA. Glancy BM. Biology and control of imported fire ants. Annu Rev Entomol 20:1-30. 1975.

84. Hoffman DR. Insect venom allergy, immunology and immunotherapy. In: Insect Poisons, Allergens, and Other Invertebrate Venoms. (Tu AT., ed.) Marcel Dekker, New York. pp. 187-223. 1984.

85. Shulman S. Allergic responses to insects. Annu Rev Entomol 12:323-346. 1967.

86. Lockey RF. Systemic reaction to stinging ants. J Allergy Clin Immunol 54:132-146. 1974.

87. Caplan EL et al. Fire ants represent an important risk for anaphylaxis among residents of an endemic region. J Allergy Clin Immunol 111:1274-1277. 2003

88. Stafford CT. Hypersensitivity to fire ant venom. Ann Allergy Asthma Immunol 77:87-95. 1996.

89. Wong HC. Importance of proper identification of stinging insects. Ann Intern Med 132:418. 2000.

90. Hunt KJ. Valentine MD. et al. A controlled trial of immunotherapy in insect hypersensitivity. N Engl J Med 299:157-161. 1978.

91. Jones RG. Corteling RL. Bhogal G. Landon J. A novel Fab-based antivenom for the treatment of mass bee attacks. Am J Trop Med Hyg 61:361-366. 1999.

92. Duplantier JE. Freeman TM. Bahna SL. et al. Successful rush immunotherapy for anaphylaxis to imported fire ants. J Allergy Clin Immunol 101:855-856. 1998.

39. Arachnids

Introduction

The arachnids comprise a class of arthropods that includes the ticks, mites, scorpions, and spiders. The characteristics of the Arachnida clearly differentiate it from the class Insecta. All arachnids are wingless, have four pairs of legs as adults, and usually show only two distinct body regions: a cephalothorax and an abdomen. Metamorphosis among the arachnids is of the incomplete type. The immature, non-reproductive stages are smaller but morphologically similar to the adults. In many groups, arachnids in the first, or larval, stage may have only three pairs of legs.

The class Arachnida comprises three orders: Acarina, Araneida, and Scorpionida. The order Acarina includes mites and ticks. Ticks are exclusively hematophagous, whereas mites feed on a variety of substances, including cells and blood. The spiders (order Araneida) are mainly insectivorous, feeding on body fluids of captured insects. Scorpions (order Scorpionida) feed on arthropods or small animals that they have immobilized with their stinging apparatus, which is located at the tip of the abdomen.

Most members of these three orders do not affect human health directly. Each order, however, includes some members of medical importance. Ticks and mites injure their victims by their feeding habits and serve as vectors for a number of important diseases (Table 39.1). Spiders inject toxins that can cause severe systemic or tissue reactions, and the toxins injected by the stings of certain species of scorpions can cause severe reactions in affected individuals.

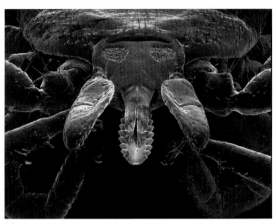

Figure 39.2. Deer tick, *Ixodes scapularis*. Photo D. Scharf

Acarina (Ticks and Mites)

Ticks

The ticks comprise two large families: the Ixodidae (hard ticks) and the Argasidae (soft ticks). Ticks are responsible for damage to livestock, causing considerable weight loss, and for providing opportunities for secondary infection by bacteria or infestation by flies. Many species are capable of transmitting pathogens to domestic animals and humans. The salivary secretions of some species can cause paralysis (tick paralysis) and even death in humans or animals.

The consequences of infestations by ticks are enormous in terms of yearly losses in dairy and meat production. In areas of the world where sources of protein are already scarce, tick infestations have created a crisis situation. Humans are seldom the natural host for any species of tick, but many species will feed on

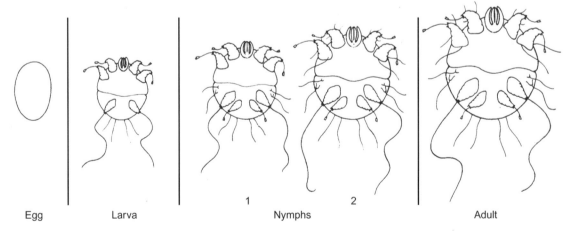

| Egg | Larva | 1   Nymphs   2 | Adult |

Figure 39.3 Incomplete metamorphosis in the arachnida. Ticks and mites undergo incomplete metamorhosis as typified by the itch mite, *Sarcoptes scabiei*. Larvae have three pair of legs; adults and nymphal stages have four pairs of legs.

human blood if given the opportunity, and have the opportunity to become vectors of human infections.

Homer recorded the feeding of ticks on humans during the ninth century BC, as did Aristotle during the fourth century BC. One of the earliest references to ticks as a possible cause of disease was the suggestion by a 12th-century Persian physician that a fever (probably Crimean-Congo hemorrhagic fever) was transmitted by ticks.[1]

Smith and Kilborne were the first to demonstrate that ticks could transmit disease.[2] They reported that the tick *Boophilus annulatus* carried the bovine protozoan parasite *Babesia bigemina*, a serious pathogen of cattle in the western United States. They further demonstrated that the parasite was not passed from cow to cow by a single infected tick; rather, it was transmitted from an infected cow through a female tick to the tick's offspring, transovarially. This mechanism, referred to as vertical transmission, resulted in infection of larval ticks capable of transmitting the parasite at the time of the first feeding. These authors reported their findings in 1893, four years before Ross completed his studies on the transmission of malaria by mosquitoes. The role of ticks as vectors of spirochetes was shown first with an avian parasite by Marchoux and Salimbeni in 1903,[3] and a year later with the spirochete causing human relapsing fever by Ross and Milne.[4]

Hard Ticks: Family Ixodidae

Hard ticks (Fig 39.1) (family Ixodidae) are found throughout the world as ectoparasites of a variety of animals. Their name derives from the characteristic tough, leather-like integument that covers most of their body. Their mouthparts are included in a capitulum (Fig. 39.2), but there is no defined head. Members of both sexes feed exclusively on blood.

The typical hard tick develops by gradual metamorphosis from the egg through the larva and nymph to the adult (Fig. 39.3). Larvae have three pairs of legs; the nymphs and adults have four pairs. Each stage takes a single blood meal. The larvae and nymphs feed prior to molting and the adult females prior to producing a single batch of eggs. The female tick dies after oviposition.[5]

Hard ticks exhibit one of three life cycles and may be classified as one-, two-, or three-host ticks. A one-host tick spends its life on a single animal. It attaches to the skin of its host as a larva, feeds, and then molts to the nymph stage. After feeding again, it molts a second time, developing into the adult. The adults mate, after which the female engorges with blood, falls to the ground, and lays her eggs. Larvae begin to hatch within 30 days, and await a new host to begin the cycle anew.

Two-host ticks usually spend their larva and nymph stages on one host, drop to the ground, molt, and await a second host of another species for completion of the adult phase of the cycle. Each of the three stages of a three-host tick develops on a separate host. The immature stages are usually found on small rodents. The adults feed and mate on larger animals.

Hard ticks display remarkable longevity, with adults of many species surviving up to two years without a blood meal. One-host ticks have the shortest egg-to-egg life cycles, sometimes lasting less than a year. Three-host ticks require 2-3 years to complete their life cycles.

Hard ticks feed slowly, requiring 7-9 days to become completely engorged. After attaching to a suitable host, the tick searches for a feeding site often well concealed by hair. Once in place, it inserts its mouthparts armed with re-curved teeth, secretes a cement-like substance, and begins to feed. After engorging it easily detaches and moves away. In general, the act of feeding is painless to the host, who is often unaware of the tick.[5, 6]

There are 11 genera within the Ixodidae, some of which include species of ticks that feed on humans, and so are of medical importance. *Amblyomma americanum* and *A. cajennense* prey on a variety of animals, feed avidly on humans, and are serious pests in the southern and southwestern states of the United States and in Mexico. They are capable of transmitting the rickettsiae that cause Rocky Mountain spotted fever.

Dermacentor variabilis (Fig. 39.4), the American dog tick, is the major vector of Rocky Mountain spotted fever in the eastern and central United States. It is involved in the transmission of tularemia and can cause tick paralysis in humans and dogs. *D. variabilis* is a three-host tick. The larvae and nymphs feed on small rodents, and the adults feed and mate on larger mammals. The dog is the most common host for adults of this species, but humans are readily targeted as well.

Dermacentor andersoni (Fig. 39.5), the Rocky Mountain wood tick, is a common species in the western and northern United States. It transmits Rocky Mountain spotted fever and Colorado tick fever, and it causes tick paralysis in humans. This three-host tick feeds on a variety of small mammals as a larva or nymph. As an adult, it feeds on large wild or domestic animals and humans. Both nymphs and adults are capable of over-wintering, and therefore the life cycle of this species is usually greater than two years. *D. albipictus* and *D. occidentalis*, found in the western United States, are capable of transmitting Rocky Mountain spotted fever and Colorado tick fever, but they attack humans only infrequently.

Ixodes scapularis (Fig. 39.6) is a three-host tick

Table 39.1. Arthropods of medical importance.

Order and representative species	Common name	Geographic distribution	Effects on humans
Acarina (ticks and mites)			
Argasidae: various genera and species	Soft ticks	Worldwide	Skin reactions to bite, tick paralysis, vectors of relapsing fever
Ixodidae: various genera and species	Hard ticks	Worldwide	Skin reactions to bite; tick paralysis; vectors of rickettsia, viruses, bacteria, and protozoa
Dermanyssidae *Allodermanyssus sanguineus*	House mouse mite	Worldwide	Vector of *Rickettsia akari*, the cause of rickettsial pox
Various genera and	Mites	Worldwide	Occasional dermatitis from bite species
Demodicidae *Demodex folliculorum*	Follicle mite	Worldwide	Found in sebaceous glands and hair follicles, occasional skin reactions
Trombiculidae *Trombicula spp.*	Chigger, red bug	Worldwide	Intense itching at site of attachment
Trombicula akamushi		Southeast Asia, India, Pacific Islands	Vector of *Rickettsia tsutsugamushi*, the cause of scrub typhus
Sarcoptiae *Sarcoptes scabiei*	Human itch mite	Worldwide	Burrows in skin causing severe itching
Araneidae (spiders)			
Latrodectus mactans	Black widow spider	Americas	Bite usually painless; delayed systemic reaction
Latrodectus spp.	Widow spider	Worldwide	
Loxoceles reclusa	Brown recluse spider	North America	Initial blister at wound site followed by sometimes-extensive necrosis and slow healing
Loxoceles laeta		South American	
Scorpionida (scorpions)			
Various genera and species	Scorpion	Tropics and subtropics	Initially painful sting often followed by systemic reactions

common throughout the eastern United States. It readily attacks humans and can inflict painful bites. In New England, it had been suggested that a distinct species, *I. dammini*, was responsible for the transmission of human babesiosis[7] and later for being the vector of Lyme disease.[8] Subsequent studies determined that a single species, *I. scapularis*, was involved throughout the area.[9] *I. pacificus* is a common pest of deer and cattle in California; it readily bites humans as well, and has been implicated in the transmission of the Lyme spirochete.[10] *I. holocyclus* is an important cause of tick paralysis in Australia.

Rhipicephalus sanguineus, the brown dog tick, is a cosmopolitan ectoparasite of dogs. Although this species does not readily bite humans, it can be a serious nuisance around homes. Female ticks recently engorged on the blood of domestic dogs drop off and deposit eggs in houses or kennels. The newly hatched larvae tend to crawl up vertical surfaces, literally covering walls or furniture. *R. sanguineus* is considered the major vector of the rickettsia that causes boutonneuse fever.

Hyalomma and Boophilus are genera of ticks whose members are ectoparasites of animals and play important roles in transmitting pathogens in animal populations. Occasionally, these ticks act as vectors of human diseases.

Soft Ticks: Family Argasidae

Ticks of the family Argasidae are soft-bodied arthropods covered by a wrinkled, often granulated tegument (Fig. 39.1). They do not have a distinct head region, and their mouthparts are located on the ventral surface, not visible from above. Soft ticks are found throughout the world, usually as ectoparasites of birds, although some species normally feed on bats and other small mammals. Several species attack humans if given the opportunity.

Soft ticks differ from the hard ticks in their feeding behavior, habitat, and life cycles. Soft ticks normally inhabit the nesting site of their hosts, moving onto the host to feed and returning to the nest when satisfied. They are completely engorged within a matter of minutes or a few hours at most, usually feeding at night while the host is asleep.

The typical life cycle of a soft tick consists of a single six-legged larval stage, two or more eight-legged nymph stages, and the eight-legged adult stage. Some species require several blood meals before each molt,

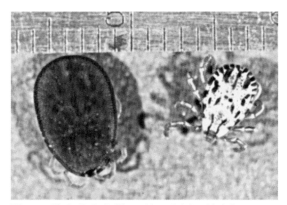

Figure 39.1. Soft (left) and hard ticks (right)

and adult females feed repeatedly, producing a small batch of eggs after each meal.

Three genera of soft ticks affect humans as pests or as vectors of pathogens. The fowl tick *Argas persicus* is an important cosmopolitan ectoparasite that preys on poultry. It bites humans as well, particularly if the normal fowl hosts are unavailable. Ticks of the genus Otobius occasionally infest human ears.

Ticks of the genus Ornithodorus are important pests and vectors of the spirochetes, causing tick-borne relapsing fevers. *O. moubata* attacks a number of wild and domestic animals, but humans are its major host. This tick inhabits huts, feeding at night on the sleeping inhabitants. It is found throughout southern and central Africa reaching as far north as Ethiopia, and it is the major vector of African relapsing fever caused by various *Borrelia spp.* Epidemiologic evidence suggests that *0. moubata*, the tampan tick, may be involved in the transmission of Hepatitis B virus in Africa, but direct experimental evidence is lacking.[11]

Several species of Ornithodorus are vectors of relapsing fevers in both the New World and the Old World. Most of these species, however, are ectoparasites of rodents and other mammals, feeding on humans only occasionally.

Pathogenesis and Treatment of Tick Bites

Most ticks attach themselves firmly to the skin of the host before beginning the blood meal. The mouthparts and injected salivary secretions provoke inflammation of the surrounding tissue, characterized by local hyperemia, edema, hemorrhage, and thickening of the stratum corneum.[12] Although the initial bite and insertion of the mouthparts may be painless, irritation often develops later, followed by necrosis and secondary infection at the wound site.

It is important to remove ticks from the skin of the host as soon as they are detected, as early removal often prevents firm attachment and makes transmission of the pathogens less likely. It also limits the infusion of toxins that cause tick paralysis, as these toxins are released slowly.

Numerous methods have been suggested for the removal of firmly attached ticks. Traditionally, ticks have been treated with chloroform, ether, benzene, turpentine, or petrolatum, each of which, it has been suggested, irritates the tick, causing it to withdraw. The US Public Health Service recommends mechanical removal without chemical aids. Many genera of ticks, especially Dermacentor, may be removed by gently but firmly, pulling the tick away from its attachment. Ixodes and Amblyomma, which have longer mouthparts that do not detach easily, may require the use of instruments for removal. These ticks should be pulled gently away from the host so the skin surrounding the mouthparts forms a tent. A sterile needle or scalpel can then be inserted under the mouthparts and used to tease them away from the tissue. In all cases, care should be taken to avoid leaving any tissue from the tick, as it will induce intense inflammation. The tick should not be crushed or damaged, thereby preventing the release of pathogenic organisms onto the wound site. Subsequent thorough cleaning of the wound is recommended.

Tick Paralysis

More than 40 species in 10 genera of both hard and soft ticks secrete salivary toxins that cause paralysis in humans and a number of other animals. It is not a universal property of any one species, though, suggesting that salivary secretions are characteristic of individual ticks.[13-17]

Figure 39.4. Blood-engorged adult female American dog tick, *Dermacentor variabilis*. Courtesy W. Burgdorfer.

Figure 39.6. *Ixodes scapularis* – adult of the species feeds on deer. The nymphs transmit spirochetes and Babesia to humans.

The affected patient becomes irritable, is restless, and experiences numbness and tingling in the extremities, face, lips, and throat. Soon, the patient develops symmetric, flaccid paralysis that is ascending in nature and can lead to bulbar palsy. Sensory loss is rare. There is no fever. Death results from respiratory paralysis. The laboratory findings (complete blood count, urinalysis, and cerebrospinal fluid examination) are normal. Differential diagnosis includes poliomyelitis, Guillain-Barre syndrome, transverse myelitis, and spinal cord tumors. The diagnosis depends on the patient's clinical history and finding the tick. Treatment consists in removing the feeding tick. Recovery follows rapidly. The usual causes of human tick paralysis are *D. andersoni* and *D. variabilis* in the United States and *I. holocylus* in Australia. A number of species of Dermacentor, Ixodes, Amblyomma, Rhipicephalus, Argas, and Ornithodorus often cause paralysis in animals but only occasionally affect humans. A vaccine for tick paralysis is under development.

Tick-Borne Diseases in Humans

Ticks transmit a broad array of viruses, rickettsiae, bacteria, and protozoa, which may cause disease in their human hosts.

Viral Diseases

Colorado tick fever is the only tick-borne viral disease in humans in the United States. A benign disease transmitted by the bite of *D. andersoni*, it is maintained in nature as an enzootic infection of rodents spread by the same vector. Transovarial (vertical) transmission of the virus has not been demonstrated. Colorado tick fever is characterized by sudden onset of chills, headache, severe myalgia, and fever.[18]

In the Old World, hard ticks are vectors of a number of viral diseases grouped as hemorrhagic fevers or tick-borne encephalitides. Among them are Russian spring-summer encephalitis, Kyasanur Forest disease, Crimean-Congo hemorrhagic fever, and Omsk hemorrhagic fever.[18, 19]

Rickettsial Diseases

Rocky Mountain spotted fever is an acute, sometimes fatal, febrile, exanthematous disease caused by *Rickettsia rickettsii*. It most frequently affects children and is characterized by fever, headache, musculoskeletal pain, and a generalized rash that appears first on the wrists and ankles and often becomes hemorrhagic.

Although initially described from the Rocky Mountain region of the United States and distributed throughout much of North and South America, the infection is of particular importance in the " tick belt" states of Maryland, Virginia, North Carolina, South Carolina, and Georgia. In these states, the incidence of the disease has been rising steadily over the last 10 years (see www.cdc.gov/ncidod/dvrd/rmsf.htm). The main vector in the eastern United States is *D. variabilis*, the American dog tick; in the western states it is *D. andersoni*. Other tick species that are considered minor vectors have the capacity to transmit the organism to humans, but may be primarily important as vectors that infect reservoir hosts.

In areas where Rocky Mountain spotted fever is prevalent, regular inspection for ticks should be undertaken. Children especially should be examined twice

Figure 39.5. *Dermacentor andersoni*: an adult female on vegetation, awaiting a host. Courtesy W. Burgdorfer.

Figure 39.7. Adult female and nymph of *Ixodes scapularis* (formerly *I. dammini*). Courtesy of A. Spielman and P. Rossignol.

daily. The tick must be attached to the host for several hours before it transmits the pathogen; therefore its expeditious removal can prevent infection. No vaccine against Rocky Mountain spotted fever is currently available,[20] but infections can easily be treated with tetracycline. Untreated cases have a mortality rate of 2-5%.

Old World tick-borne typhus has different regional names: boutonneuse fever, Kenya typhus, and South African tick bite fever. It is a relatively mild disease, presenting with chills, fever, and generalized body rash.

Rhipicephalus sanguineus, the brown dog tick, is the main vector of boutonneuse fever in the Mediterranean region; other hard ticks are involved elsewhere.

Q fever is a self-limited infection. The disease consists of fever, headache, constitutional symptoms, and often pneumonitis. Caused by the rickettsia *Coxiella burnetii*, it is usually contracted by inhalation. Ticks are involved in maintaining the infection in the animal reservoir host and can transmit the organism to humans.

Anaplasmosis (formerly referred to as Ehrlichiosis) is a tick-borne rickettsiosis, first described in Japan in 1954, that resembles other tick-borne diseases such as "spotless" Rocky Mountain spotted fever. This generally mild infection may be mistaken for pyelonephritis, hepatitis-C or D, gastroenteritis, or unexplained febrile illnesses with leukopenia or thrombocytopenia. Treatment is similar to that for other rickettsial diseases.[21, 22]

Bacterial Diseases

Tularemia is a bacterial disease caused by *Franciscella tularensis* and characterized by a focal ulcer at the site of entry of the organism, enlargement of regional lymph nodes, fever, prostration, myalgia, and headache. *D. andersoni* and *D. variabilis* are the ticks most frequently involved in the transmission of this infection from small mammals, particularly rabbits, to humans.

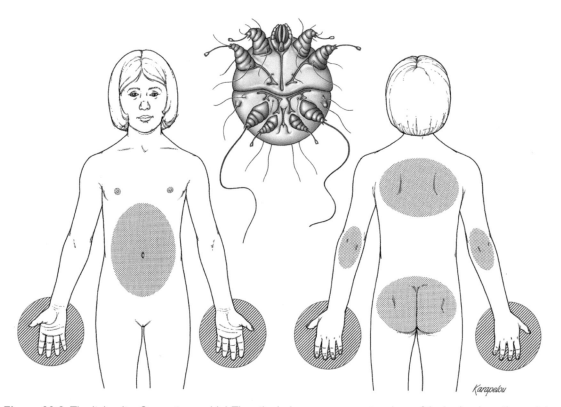

Figure 39.8. The itch mite, *Sarcoptes scabiei.* The stippled areas represent regions of the body where the rash is found. The mites themselves are found predominantly between the fingers and on the wrists (hatched areas).

A number of tick species maintain the infection in the reservoir population.

The relapsing fevers form a group of diseases with a similar clinical pattern; they are caused by spirochetes of the genus Borrelia, all of which are transmitted by arthropod vectors. Lice transmit epidemic louseborne relapsing fever, and soft ticks transmit endemic tick-borne relapsing fever. The human relapsing fevers are described as acute infections with toxemia and febrile periods that subside and recur over a period of weeks. Tick-borne relapsing fevers are transmitted by ticks of the genus Ornithodoros. In the Western Hemisphere, *O. hermsi*, *O. turicata*, and *O. rudis* are the most important vectors. A close association between humans, vector ticks, and rodents infected with spirochetes, usually in a rural setting, is the typical condition necessary for human infections. In Africa, *O. moubata*, which feeds primarily on humans and lives in human dwellings, maintains transmission of relapsing fever from human to human.[23]

Lyme arthritis and erythema chronicum migrans, or Lyme disease, as these conditions are known collectively, is caused by the spirochete *Borrelia burgdorferi*,[24] which is transmitted by a number of ixodid ticks. *I. scapularis* [25] (Fig. 39.7) is the primary vector in the eastern United States, while *I. pacificus* is the main vector on the West Coast, and *I. ricinus* is primarily responsible for transmission in Europe.[26, 27]

The spirochete is commonly found in rodents, especially white-footed mice. In its immature stages, the tick vector feeds on this rodent reservoir host, and on deer in its adult state. The range of the tick is limited by the range of the deer populations (see www.medicalecology.org/diseases/lyme/lyme_disease.htm).

Human infection with this spirochete usually results from a bite of the nymphal tick, though adult ticks are also capable of transmitting it. Before the tick has fed, the spirochete is found in its gut. After the tick has attached to a host and has begun feeding, the spirochetes disseminate throughout the hemocele, invade the salivary glands, and infect the host. This process takes about a day, so prompt removal of the tick reduces the chance of infection.[28]

Protozoal Diseases.

Babesiosis, a protozoal disease, is seen in a variety of animals but rarely appears in humans (see page 95).

Prevention and Control of Tick-Transmitted Infections

The best measure of tick control is avoidance of

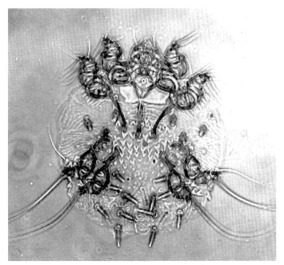

Figure 39.9. Adult female itch mite. *Sarcoptes scabiei.*

areas where ticks are known to exist. Wide-scale chemical control of tick populations is impractical, although various compounds have been used. Tick control on dogs can be achieved with systemic compounds, topically applied chemicals, or available tick collars; dusts have proved useful for preventing the introduction of brown or American dog ticks into homes. Permethrin, sprayed on clothing, appears to be most effective and may last at least a week or more.[29] Diethyltoluamide (DEET) has been shown to be generally ineffective as a tick repellent. However, careful examination for ticks is still necessary after traveling through infested areas.

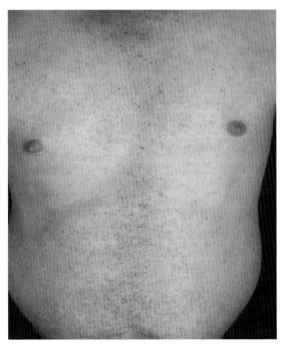

Figure 39.10. Scabies rash.

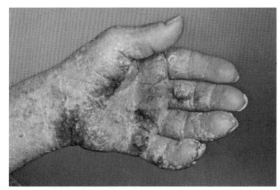

Figure 39.11. Patient with Norwegian scabies showing numerous lesions. Millions of mites may be present. Courtesy of Y. Mumcouglu.

Mites

Within the Order Acarina, the term "mite" is applied to members of several large families of minute arthropods, most free-living but many existing as ecto- or endoparasites of vertebrates and invertebrates. Mites affect humans by causing dermatitis; they serve as vectors of a number of diseases and as a source of allergens that can lead to serious hypersensitivity reactions.

Mites, as described by Aristotle, were well known to ancient civilizations. Their function as ectoparasites was not recognized until about the year 1000 AD, when scabies was first recorded. Although scabies continued to be described in the early medical literature and the association of a mite with this skin condition was repeatedly noted by physicians and naturalists, the causal relation was largely ignored by the medical profession. The unequivocal demonstration that a mite was indeed the cause of scabies took place in 1834 when a Corsican medical student recovered mites from affected individuals.[30]

Human Itch Mite: *Sarcoptes scabiei*

Scabies is a human skin disease caused by the mite *Sarcoptes scabiei* (Fig. 39.8). It is usually associated with crowded living conditions, and its outbreaks often accompany wars, famine, and human migrations. Currently, scabies has reached pandemic proportions.[30-33]

The condition first presents as nocturnal itching, usually on the webbing and sides of the fingers, later spreading to the wrists, elbows, and the rest of the body. The buttocks, breasts of females, and genitalia of men are occasionally affected. Lesions appear as short, sinuous, slightly raised, cutaneous burrows.

Infections begin when fertile female mites (Fig. 39.9) are transferred from infected individuals by direct contact. The female mite finds a suitable site, burrows into the skin, and tunnels through the upper layers of the epidermis, depositing fertile eggs. Six-legged larvae hatch from these eggs, leave the tunnel, and wander about the skin before re-invading it and starting new burrows. Once in place, the larvae eat, molt, and transform into eight-legged nymphs. Larvae destined to become females molt again into a second nymph stage; those destined to become males molt directly to the adult form. After fertilization, young adult females begin construction of a new tunnel. The egg-to-egg life cycle may be as short as two weeks. A typical infection usually involves only 10-15 adult female mites.[34]

With primary infections, itching and skin eruption are usually delayed for several weeks. As sensitization develops, the typical scabies rash appears on various parts of the body that do not necessarily correspond to the location of active adult female mites, but represent a generalized response to the allergens (Fig. 39.10).

The face and scalp may be affected in infants and children, whereas adults seldom have lesions in these areas. A rare condition known as Norwegian, or crusted, scabies may result from hyper-infection with thousands to millions of mites (Fig. 39.11). The consequence is a crusted dermatosis of the hands and feet and often much of the body. This condition is characteristic of infected individuals who cannot take care of themselves and is often reported in custodial institutions such as mental hospitals.[35, 36] It is highly contagious because of the large number of loosely attached, easily transferred mites present in the exfoliating skin. Crusted scabies has also been reported in individuals treated with immunosuppressive drugs (Fig. 39.12). Secondary infections of lesions, particularly as a result of scratching, are common; and post-streptococcal glomerulonephritis has been reported.[37]

A diagnosis of scabies can be confirmed by picking up adult female mites at the ends of their burrows or by

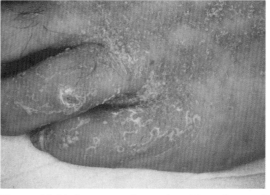

Figure 39.12. Large numbers of scabies mites and lesions on an immunosupressed patient.

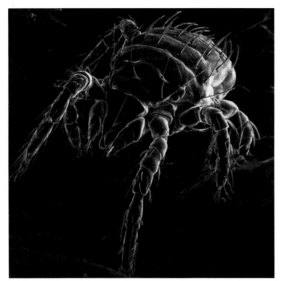

Figure 39.13. Larval stage of the common chigger *Trombicula alfreddugesi*. It is the larva, with three pairs of legs, that feeds on vertebrates. Photo by D. Scharf.

scraping the affected skin lightly covered with mineral oil. The scrapings are then examined under a microscope for immature or adult mites or for eggs. Skin biopsy reveals mites in tissue sections. The presence of infection in several members of a family is reasonable circumstantial evidence for a diagnosis of scabies in those not yet examined.

Lindane, the γ-isomer of benzene hexachloride, is the most effective compound available for treatment of scabies. It is available as a lotion or cream, which is applied once to the affected areas. Benzyl benzoate in a 25% emulsion is an alternative drug, but must be applied to the whole body. Treatment of all members of a family may be necessary to prevent reinfection.[35] Systemic treatment with ivermectin has proven particularly efficacious, but should still be used carefully.[38-42]

Animal Scabies

The itch and mange mites of various domestic animals (horses, pigs, dogs, cats, camels) can infest humans. These mites are often morphologically indistinguishable from the human parasites and are fully capable of penetrating human skin. The infection is usually self-limited, however, because these mites do not form tunnels and cannot complete their life cycles. Nevertheless, humans may react with severe papular urticaria to these transitory infestations.

Chigger Mites

The chiggers, or redbugs, (Fig. 39.13) of the family Trombiculidae comprise an important group of annoying human ectoparasites. In some geographic areas, they act as vectors of the rickettsiae, causing scrub typhus.

In the United States, the chigger mites include three species of Trombicula. Among the chiggers, only the six-legged larvae feed on humans and other mammals, whereas the nymphs and adults usually feed on arthropods or arthropod eggs. Chigger larvae are usually picked up in brush frequented by rodents or other small mammals, which serve as normal hosts of the larvae. These mites tend to attach to skin where clothing is tight or restricted. The ankles, waistline, armpits, and perineal skin are common areas of infestation. Chiggers insert their capitula but do not burrow into the skin. The host reacts to the mouthparts and the injected saliva by forming a tube-like "stylosome" partially engulfing the feeding mites. The chigger does not feed on blood, rather, it ingests a mixture of partially digested cells and fluids formed within the stylosome. After feeding for several days, the engorged chigger withdraws and drops to the ground.[43]

The intense itching and discomfort associated with chigger "bites" often begins after the chiggers have withdrawn and departed. Irritation may be so severe as to cause fever and loss of sleep. Local anesthetics may be useful for relieving itching, and antibiotics may be needed to treat secondary bacterial skin infections.

In areas where chiggers are common, repellents containing DEET applied to skin and clothing can be effective. Scrubbing exposed or infested areas of the body with soap and water removes even well-attached chiggers.

Scrub typhus (tsutsugamushi fever) is a chigger-borne rickettsial zoonotic disease found in Southeast Asia, certain islands in the Indian and Pacific Oceans, and Australia. The causative agent is *Rickettsia tsutsugamushi*, and the usual vectors are larvae of the chigger *Trombicula akamushi* and *T. deliensis*. Rodents are the normal reservoir hosts for this pathogen.[44]

Follicle Mites

The ubiquitous follicle mite *Demodex folliculorum* are normal inhabitants of our sebaceous glands and hair follicles, particularly around the nose and eyelids. Follicle mites are minute (<0.4 mm long), atypically vermiform arthropods that seldom cause discomfort. In rare cases, the skin of the scalp becomes heavily infected. Treatment consists of a single application of γ-benzene hexachloride. Closely related species of Demodex, which cause mange in dogs and other mammals, may cause a transitory burning reaction in individuals handling heavily infested animals.

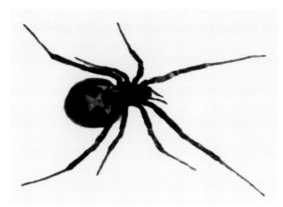

Figure 39.14. Black Widow Spider. Ventral view.

Mites and Dermatitis

A number of species of mites, either parasitic for animals or free living, occasionally infest humans and cause dermatitis. Mites associated with straw, flour, grain, dried fruits, vanilla, copra, and cheese can produce serious but transitory skin irritation in persons contracting large numbers of these acarines. Bird and rodent mites may also cause serious annoyance when they attempt to feed on humans, but they do so only occasionally. Bird mites may be particularly bothersome if their normal avian hosts depart and they are forced to forage for food.

The tropical rat mite, *Ornithonyssus bacoti,* is a parasite of rodents that can attack humans and cause dermatitis.[44] The house mite *Allodermanyssus sanguineus* is a common ectoparasite of mice, but readily feeds on humans. These mites have been shown to transmit rickettsial pox, a mild exanthematous disease related to Rocky Mountain spotted fever found in the eastern United States and Russia. The causative agent is *Rickettsia akari.*[46]

Allergies Caused by Mites

Certain mites of the genus Dermatophagoides have been incriminated as sources of antigens associated with allergies to house dust.[47] House dust mite allergens area common cause of asthma attacks in sensitized individuals, particularly children. Desensitization has been successful.[48]

Araneida (Spiders)

The spiders constitute a large, distinctive order of arachnids whose bodies are divided into two regions: cephalothorax and abdomen. Four pairs of walking legs, pedipalps, and chelicerae with poison fangs all arise from the cephalothorax. All spiders produce a venom in anterior venom glands that is capable of immobilizing prey. Although most species are unable to pierce human skin, several groups of spiders do occasionally bite humans. The consequences of these bites may include transitory pain, necrotic lesions, systemic reactions, or even death.

Tarantulas

The name tarantula is loosely applied to a number of large, hairy spiders, some of which belong to the family Theraphosidae. These spiders are common in tropical and subtropical regions. Although they are much feared, few tarantulas bite humans. Those that do may inflict a painful wound, but the symptoms are not long lasting, and no fatalities have been reported.[49]

Black Widow Spiders

Spiders of the genus Latrodectus are found throughout the world, primarily in warm climates. At least six species that bite humans have been reported. They inflict painful and sometimes fatal wounds (mostly in children).

Latrodectus mactans, the black widow, hourglass, or shoe-button spider, (Fig. 39.14) is widespread through the United States and southern Canada. Related species are found throughout the temperate and tropical regions of all continents. The adult female black widow spider is usually black with a characteristic crimson hourglass marking on the underside of its globose abdomen. The coloration (various shades of black, gray, or brown) and the shape of the hourglass may vary. The typical mature female is about 40 mm

Figure 39.15. *Loxoceles reclusa,* the brown recluse spider. Dorsal view. Note "fiddle" pattern.

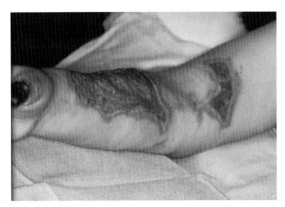

Figure 39.16. Spider bite - Loxoceles species, initial bite on the tip of the thumb.

long with its legs extended.[50] Black widow spiders are normally reclusive in behavior, but females bite if disturbed and are particularly aggressive when they are gravid or defending their egg cases. These spiders frequent wood and brush piles, old wooden buildings, cellars, hollow logs, and vacant rodent burrows. The pit privy is a preferred site for webs, and a significant number of human spider bites have taken place in these locations.

Bites of the black widow spider may be initially painless, sometimes appearing only as two small red puncture marks at the site. Thereafter, pain at the site increases and spreads, reaching a maximum within 1-3 hours and later subsiding. Generalized muscle pain, abdominal rigidity, tightness in the chest, difficulty with breathing and speaking, nausea, and sweating may occur within an hour of the bite. Most symptoms pass after 2-3 days without treatment. In severe cases, paralysis and coma may precede cardiac or respiratory failure. The toxin has been identified as a low-molecular-weight protein.[51, 52] Its mode of action involves the inhibition of fusion of neurotransmitter vesicles with membranes leading to depolarization of synapses.[53] Treatment usually consists of measures designed to relieve pain and reduce muscle spasms. An anti-venom is available in locales where bites are common. Control of black widow spiders with the use of insecticides such as malathion, particularly in privies, is effective.

Nectrotic Arachnidism

Five species of the genus Loxoceles in the New World attack when they are disturbed. Their bites may produce severe tissue reactions. *Loxoceles reclusa* (Fig. 39.15) is found in the southern and central United States; *L. unicolor* and *L. arizonica* are found in the western states; and *L. laeta* and *L. intermedia* are seen in South America. These spiders are of medium size, are yellow to brown in color, and have a body length of 10-15 mm.[54-58]

Loxoceles reclusa, the brown recluse spider of the United States, is a non-aggressive arachnid found outdoors in woodpiles and debris in warm climates, and in basements or storage areas in cooler regions. Humans are typically bitten only when they disturb them (e,g., when entering a sleeping bag, or putting on shoes or clothing).[59]

The South American brown spiders, *L. laeta* and *L. intermedia*, are common domestic species found in closets, corners of rooms, or behind pictures. Humans are often bitten while sleeping or dressing, but only when the spider is threatened or disturbed. *L. laeta* has been introduced into the United States on at least one occasion.[60]

The bite of Loxoceles tends to be initially painless. Several hours later, itching, swelling, and tenderness may develop in the area of the bite. The wound site may turn violaceous and then black and dry. In other cases, a blister may form over the bite. Necrosis may begin within 3-4 days, and tissue destruction may be extensive (Fig. 39.16). Healing may take eight weeks or longer. Some of the more serious lesions require surgery and skin grafts. The venom of Loxoceles appears to work by inactivating hemolytic components of complement.[61] An antiserum for treatment of Loxoceles bites is being evaluated in Brazil.[62] Loxoceles spiders may be controlled in dwellings with insecticide compounds containing γ-benzene hexachloride or malathion.

Figure 39.17. Scorpion.

Chiracanthium mildei is the most common spider found in houses in the eastern United States; usually in bathrooms, kitchens, and bedrooms. It attacks when disturbed, and its bite can cause a mild necrotizing skin lesion.[63] Spiders of the genera Phoneutria in Brazil and Chile are capable of inflicting severe bites, sometimes with fatal results.[64]

The spider fauna of Australia is a particularly robust and dangerous species,[65-68] but only the male Atrax spider is capable of inflicting a lethal bite in humans. The venom is neurotoxic and causes nausea, vomiting, abdominal pain, diarrhea, profuse sweating, salivation, and lacrimation. There may also be severe hypertension and cardiac arrest.

Scorpionida (Scorpions)

The scorpions belong to the order Scorpionida of the class Arachnida, with all members generally similar in appearance (Fig. 39.17). The typical scorpion is an elongate arthropod with stout, crab-like claws (pedipalps), four pairs of walking legs, and a distinctly segmented abdomen ending in a hooked stinger.

Scorpions are reclusive, nocturnal animals in behavior that feed primarily on other arthropods and sometimes on small rodents. While feeding, the scorpion holds its prey with its pedipalps and repeatedly stings its victim with over-the-back thrusts of its stinger. When the scorpion is disturbed, it uses the stinger for defense, which is the manner in which humans are stung.[69, 70] Most species of scorpions are unable either to penetrate human skin or inject sufficient toxin to cause damage. The few species that do sting humans are capable of inflicting a painful wound, precipitating a severe reaction and sometimes causing death. These species present a significant hazard to public health in many tropical and sub-tropical regions.[69]

Scorpions produce two types of venom: hemolytic and neurotoxic. The first induces local reactions characterized by a burning sensation, swelling, and necrosis at the wound site. The second produces intense pain at the site of the sting and causes chills, cold perspiration, thirst, excessive salivation, and vomiting. Other systemic symptoms may include generalized numbness, difficulty with speech and swallowing, paralysis, convulsions, tachycardia, and myocarditis. Death may result from respiratory paralysis, often within two hours of the sting.[71]

Children under five years of age are particularly susceptible to the adverse effects of scorpion stings, and case fatality rates of 5% in Mexico, 25% in Trinidad, and 60% in the Sudan have been reported. Multiple stings, stings around the head, and stings of debilitated individuals are also particularly serious.[72]

Since the venom is injected into the subcutaneous tissues, initial treatment of scorpion stings should be designed to delay absorption of the toxin into the lymphatic vessels. A tourniquet is applied above the wound with care taken to release pressure every 20-30 minutes. Ice should be applied to the wound site and the patient kept calm. Specific scorpion anti-sera are available in areas where stings are common.

Programs to reduce scorpion populations with wide-scale or focal application of persistent chemical pesticides have met with limited success. Elimination of rubbish piles around dwellings can reduce favored hiding and breeding places of scorpions.

References

1. Hoogstraal H. The epidemiology of tick-borne Crimean-Congo hemorrhagic fever in Asia, Europe, and Africa. J Med Entomol 15:307-417. 1979.
2. Smith T. Kilborne FL. Investigations into the nature, causation, and prevention of Texas, or southern cattle fever. USDA Bureau Anim Ind Bull 1:1-301. 1893.
3. Marchoux E. Salimbeni A. La spirillose des poules. Ann Inst Pasteur Paris 17:569-580. 1903.
4. Ross PH. Milne AO. Tick fever. BMJ 2:1453-1454. 1904.
5. Arthur DR. Ticks and Disease. Row, Peterson, Evanston, IL. 1961.
6. Sen SK. The mechanism of feeding in ticks. Parasitology 27:355-368. 1935.
7. Spielman A. Clifford CM. Piesman J. Corwin MD. Human babesiosis on Nantucket Island, USA: description of the vector, *Ixodes dammini*, n.sp. (Acarina:Ixodidae). J Med Entomol 15:218-234. 1979.
8. Spielman A. Wilson ML. Levitne JF. et al. Ecology of *Ixodes dammini*-borne human babesiosis and Lyme disease. Annu Rev Entomol 30:439-460. 1985.
9. Oliver JH Jr. Owsley MR. Hutcheson HJ. et al. Conspecificity of the ticks Ixodes scapularis and I. dammini (Acari: Ixodidae). J Med Entomol 30:54-63. 1993.
10. Burgdorfer W. Lane RS. Barbour AG. et al. The western black-legged tick, *Ixodes pacificus*: a vector of *Borrelia burgdorferi*. Am J Trop Med Hyg 34:925-930. 1985.
11. Jupp PG. Purcell RH. et al. Attempts to transmit hepatitis B virus to chimpanzees by arthropods. S Afr Med J 79:320-322. 1991.
12. Nelson WA. Bell J. Clifford CM. et al. Interaction of ectoparasites and their hosts. J Med Entomol 13:389-428. 1977.
13. Dworkin MS. Shoemaker PC. Anderson DE. Tick paralysis: 33 cases in Washington in 1996. Clin Infect Dis 29:1435-1439. 1999.
14. Schaumberg HH. Herskovitz S. The weak child-a cautionary tale. N Engl J Med. 342:127-129. 2000.
15. Felz MW. Smith CD. Swift TR. A six-year-old girl with tick paralysis. N Engl J Med 342: 90-94. 2000.
16. Greenstein P. Tick paralysis. Med Clin North Am 86: 441-446. 2002.
17. Vedanarayanan v et. Al. Tick paralysis Semin Neurol 24: 181-184. 2004.
18. Burgdorfer W. Tick-borne diseases in the United States: Rocky Mountain spotted fever and Colorado tick fever. Acta Trop (Basel) 34:103-126. 1977.
19. Hoogstrall H. Ticks in relation to human diseases caused by viruses. Annu Rev Entomol 11:261-308. 1966.

20. Burgdorfer W. A review of Rocky Mountain spotted fever (tick-borne typhus), its agent, and its tick vectors in the United States. J Med Ento-mol 12:269-278. 1979.

21. McDade JF. Olson JG. Ehrlichiosis, Q fever, typhus, rickettsialpox, and other rickettsioses. In: Infectious Diseases. 2nd ed. (Gorbach SL, Bartlett JG, Blacklow NR (eds) Saunders, Philadelphia. pp. 1599-1611. 1998.

22. Ijdo JW. Meek JI. et al. The emergence of another tickborne infection in the 12-town area around Lyme, Connecticut: Human granulocytic ehrlichiosis. J Infect Dis 181:1388-1393. 2000

23. Burgdorfer W. The epidemiology of the relapsing fevers. In: The Biology of Parasitic Spirochetes. (Russell C, Johnson C.,eds.). Academic Press, Orlando, FL. pp. 191-200. 1976.

24. Burgdorfer W. Barbour AG. et al. Lyme disease-a tick-borne spirochetosis? Science 216:1317-1319. 1982.

25. Basler EM. Coleman JL. et at. Natural distribution of *Ixodes dammini* spirochete. Science 220:321-322. 1983.

26. Burgdorfer W. Barbour AG. et al. Erythema chronicum migrans-a tick borne spirochetosis. Acta Trop (Basel) 40:79-83. 1983.

27. Lane RS. Piesman J. Burgdorfer W. Lyme borreliosis: relation of its causative agent to its vectors and hosts in North America and Europe. Annu Rev Entomol 36:587-609. 1991.

28. Steere AC. Grodzicki RL. et al. The spirochetal etiology of Lyme disease. N Engl J Med 308:733-740. 1983.

29. McMahon C, Krober T. et al. in vitro assays for repellants and deterrents for ticks: differing effects of products when tested with attractant or arrestment stimuli. Med Vet Entomol 17: 370. 2003.

30. Busvine JR. Insects, Hygiene, and History. Athlone Press, London. 1976.

31. Orion E. et al. Ectoparasitic sexually transmitted diseases: Scabies and pediculosis. Clincs Dermatol 22: 513-519. 2004.

32. Orkin M. Maibach HI. This scabies pandemic. N Engl J Med 298:496-498. 1978.

33. Arlian LG. Biology, host relations, and epidemiology of *Sarcoptes scabiei*. Annu Rev Entomol 34:139-161. 1989.

34. Mellanby K. Biology of the parasite. In: Scabies and Pediculosis. (Orkin M, Maibach HI, Parish LC, et al., eds.). J.B. Lippincott, Philadelphia. pp 8-16. 1977.

35. Epstein E Sr. Orkin M. Scabies: clinical aspects. In: Scabies and Pediculosis. (Orkin M, Maibach HI, Parish LC, et at., eds.). J.B. Lippincott, Philadelphia. pp. 17-22. 1977.

36. Walton SF. Holt DC. et al. Scabies: New future for a neglected disease. Adv Parasitol 57: 309-376. 2004.

37. Potter EV. Earle OP. et al. Acute glomerulonephritis as a complication of scabies. In: Cutaneous Infestations and Insect Bites. (Orkin M, Maibach HI., eds.). Marcel Dekker, New York. pp. 49-61. 1985.

38. Orkin M. Maibach HI. Treatment of today's scabies. In: Cutaneous Infestations and Insect Bites. (Orkin M, Maibach HI (eds). Marcel Dekker, New York. pp. 103-108. 1985.

39. Bigby M. A systematic review of the treatment of scabies. Arch Dermatol 136:387-389. 2000.

40. Walton SF. Myerscough MR. Currie BJ. Studies in vitro on the relative efficacy of current acaracides for *Sarcoptes scabiei* var. *hominis*. Trans R Soc Trop med Hyg 94:92-96. 2000.

41. Burkhart CH. Burkhart CG. Ivermectin: a few caveats are warranted before initiating therapy for scabies. Arch Dermatol 135:1549-1550. 1999.

42. Karthikeyan K. Treatment of scabies: newer perspectives Postgaduate Med J. 81: 7-11. 2005.

43. Sasa M. Biology of chiggers. Annu Rev Entomol 6:221-244. 1961.

44. Audy JR. Red Mites and Typhus. Athlone Press, London. 1968.

45. Busvine JR. Dermatoses due to arthropods other than the scabies mite. In: Scabies and Pediculosis. (Orkin M, Maibach, HI, Parish LC, et at., eds.) J.B. Lippincott, Philadelphia. pp. 132-138. 1977.

46. Fuller HS. Studies of rickettsial pox. III. Life cycle of the mite vector, *Allodermanyssus sanguineus*. Am J Hyg 59:236-239. 1954.

47. Arlien LG. Morgan MS. Biology, ecology, and prevelance of dust mites. Immunol Allergy Clin North Am 23: 443-468. 2003.

48. Milian E. Diaz AM. Allergy to house dust mites and asthma. P R Health Sci J 23: 47-57. 2004.

49. Bucherl W. Spiders. In: Venomous Animals and Their Venoms. Vol III. Venomous Invertebrates. (Bucherl W, Buckley EE., eds.). New York, Academic Press, Orlando, FL. pp. 197-277.1971.

50. Maretic Z. Latrodectism in Mediterranean countries, including south Russia, Israel, North Africa. In: Venomous Animals and Their Venoms. Vol III. Venomous Invertebrates. (Bucherl W, Buckley EE., eds.) Academic Press, Orlando, Fl. pp. 299-309. 1971.

51. McCrone JD. Hatala RJ. Isolation and characterization of a lethal component from the venom of Latrodectus mactans mactans. In: Animal Toxins. (Russell FE, Saunders PR., eds.). Pergamon Press, New York, , pp. 29-34. 1967.

52. Russell FE. Venom poisoning. Rational Drug Ther 5:l-7. 1971.

53. Sudhof TC. alpha-Latrotoxin and its receptors: neurexins and CIRL/latrophilins. Annu Rev Neurosci. 24:933-62. 2001.

54. Vetter R. Identifying and misidentifying the brown recluse spider. Dermatol Online J 5:7. 1999.

55. Lyon WF. Brown recluse spider. Ohio State University Extension Fact Sheet. Hyg-2061-97. 1997.

56. Zeglin D. Brown recluse spider bites. Am J Nurs 105: 64-68. 2005.

57. Sams HH. King LE Jr. Brown recluse spider bites. Dermatol Nurs 11:427-433. 1999.

58. Swanson DL. Vetter RS. Bites of brown recluse spiders and suspected necrotic arachnidism. N Eng J Med 352:700-707. 2005.

59. Foil LD. Norment BR. Envenomization by *Loxosceles reclusa*. J Med Entomol 16:18-25. 1979.

60. Levi HW. Spielman A. Biology and control of the South American brown spider *Loxosceles laeta* (Nicolet) in a North American focus. Am J Trop Med Hyg 13:132-136. 1964.

61. Williams ST. Khare VK. Johnston GA. Blackall DP. Severe intra-vascular hemolysis associated with brown recluse spider envenomization. A report of two cases and review of the literature. Am J Clin Pathol 104:463-467. 1995.

62. Braz A. Minozzo J. Abreu JC et al. Development and evaluation of the neutralizing capacity of horse antivenom against the Brazilian spider *Loxoceles intermedia*. Toxicon 37:13423-1328. 1999.

63. Spielman A. Levy HW. Probable envenomation by *Chiracanthium mildei*; a spider found in houses. Am J Trop Med Hyg 19: 729-732. 1970.

64. Ori M. Biology and poisonings by spiders. In Insect Poisons, Allergens, and Other Invertebrate Venoms. (Tu AT., ed.). Marcel Dekker, New York. pp. 397-440. 1984.

65. Atkinson RK. A comparison of the toxicity of the venoms of twelve common Australian spider species on rodent vital organ systems. Comp Biochem Physiol C 106:639-642. 1993.

66. Sheumack DD. Comis A. et al. An endogenous anti-toxin to the lethal venom of the funnel web spider, *Atrax robustus*, in rabbit sera. Comp Biochem Physiol C 99:157-161. 1991.

67. White J. Envenoming and antivenom use in Australia Toxicon 36:1483-1492. 1998.

68. Currie BJ. Clinical toxicology: a tropical Australian perspective. Ther Drug Monit 22:73-78. 2000.

69. Keegan HL. Scopions of medical importance. University Press of Mississippi, Jackson. 1980

70. Bucherl W. Classification, biology, and venom extraction of scorpions. In: Venomous Animals and Their Venoms. Vol III. Venomous Invertebrates. (Bucherl W, Buckley EE., eds.) Academic Press, Orlando, FL. pp. 317-347. 1971.

71. Balozet L. Scorpionism in the Old World. In: Venomous Animals and Their Venoms. Vol III. Venomous Invertebrates. (Bucherl W, Buckley EE., eds.). Academic Press, Orlando, FL. pp. 349-371. 1971.

72. Possani LD. Fletcher PL. et al: Purification and characterization of a mammalian toxin from venom of the Mexican scorpion Centruroides limpidus tecomanus Hoffman. Toxicon 18:175-183. 1980.

40. Arthropods of Minor Medical Importance

Butterflies and Moths: Order Lepidoptera

Several species of larvae or caterpillars of the order Lepidoptera are covered with hollow, sharply pointed hairs containing a toxin that may cause severe dermatitis. Contact occurs when an individual handles the caterpillars or inhales the "hairs," which are blown about after the larva molts. In the northeastern United States, the gypsy moth, *Lymantria dispar*, has been responsible for defoliation of enormous areas of forest. The "population explosion" of the caterpillars of this species has led to periodic outbreaks of pruritic dermatitis, primarily among school children. Similar outbreaks of dermatitis have been reported from the southeastern and south central states, attributed to the caterpillars of the puss moth *Megalopyge opercalis*.[1, 2] In a Mexican outbreak, severe dermatitis was initially attributed to scabies, but eventually associated with contact with adult moths of the species *Hylesia alinda*. Populations of this normally rare species rapidly expanded after its natural predators were killed by a hurricane sweeping the island.[3]

Individuals working with lepidopterans may become sensitized to the scales of adult moths or butterflies. Repeated exposure may produce severe bronchospasm and even asthma.[4] There is an increasing awareness of the ubiquity and potential serious consequences of exposure to a wide range of these larvae.[5]

Beetles: Order Coleoptera

Within the order Coleoptera, which comprises a large group of insects, only a few families contain members of medical importance. Certain scavenger beetles of the families Dermestidae, Silphidae, and Staphylinidae feed on feces and carrion and mechanically transmit pathogenic organism. Adult beetles of the family Meloidae, the blister beetles, produce a vesicant (cantharidin) that may cause blistering or a severe burning sensation on contact with the skin or mucous membranes. Inadvertent ingestion of beetle larvae, a condition termed canthariasis, may produce transient gastrointestinal discomfort.

Many beetles, particularly those that feed on feces, act as intermediate hosts for helminthic parasites of humans and other animals. Members of the family Scarabaeidae are intermediate hosts of the spiny-headed worm *Macracanthorhynchus hirudinaceus*, a parasite of pigs, which rarely infects humans. The tapeworms *Hymenolepis nana* and *H. diminuta* develop in grain beetles of the family Tenebrionidae.

Cockroaches: Order Orthoptera

Orthoptera is a large, diverse order of primitive, successful insects (over 4,000 species, worldwide) that includes the grasshoppers and crickets as well as cockroaches. The cockroaches are included in a single family, the Blattidae, with several members closely associated with human habitations. All members of this group have non-biting mouthparts.

The female cockroach encloses her eggs in a bean-shaped case called an ootheca. Some species retain the ootheca internally until the eggs hatch, others carry it externally for several weeks, and still others drop the ootheca soon after it is formed. After hatching, the young, wingless, feeding nymphs begin to undergo staged development. Some species progress through as many as 13 nymph stages, each being wingless and somewhat larger than its predecessor, until the final molt produces the winged adult. With its series of wingless nymph stages, the cockroach is a classic example of an insect developing by incomplete metamorphosis.

Most cockroach species do not invade homes, confining themselves to outdoor habitats, although in the United States five species of cockroaches do invade human habitats. The most common is the German cockroach or croton bug, *Blatella germanica*, a small (<16 mm), light brown species. The American cockroach or palmetto bug, *Periplaneta americana*, is in fact an African species now found worldwide. It is a large (30-40 mm) reddish-brown insect with long wings. It is found in and around homes, farms, restaurants, stores, and warehouses. Other species that may infest homes are the Oriental cockroach *Blatta orientalis*, the Australian cockroach *P. australasiae*, and the brown-banded cockroach, *Supella supellectilium*.

Most of these species are cosmopolitan, having been distributed by ship traffic starting with the earliest voyages. In general, domestic species are omnivorous. They feed on a wide variety of nutrients, paper, book bindings, and human and animal feces. They serve as mechanical vectors of pathogens, carrying infectious agents from feces to food.[6, 7]

The presence of cockroaches is usually associated with a breakdown of general sanitation. Exposed foods or poor packaging and storage, open garbage, darkness and moisture are all conducive to the development of large cockroach populations. Initial infestations may be introduced with foodstuffs or migration from adjoining dwellings. In apartment buildings, the insecticide treatment of one apartment may cause the migration of cockroaches to adjoining, untreated apartments.

Although cockroaches are resistant to a number of insecticides in some areas, compounds for control are commercially available. Coupled with improved house-keeping, treatment with these agents can be sufficient, although heavy infestations require repeated treatments by professional exterminators.

Cockroaches, because of their close association with sewage and garbage, may serve as paratenic hosts for various pathogens, and may, upon long-term exposure to them, induce an asthma-like condition.[8]

Centipedes: Class Chilopoda

The centipedes of the class Chilopoda are worm-like, segmented creatures with a distinct head and paired appendages on each of 15-100 or more segments. They have a pair of poisonous claws, or maxillipeds, on the first segment after the head, which are used for capturing prey. Most centipedes are predaceous insectivores, and humans are sometimes bitten accidentally. Centipede bites may be locally painful, causing transient swelling at the site of the bite. No complications are associated with these bites.[9]

Crustacea

The crustacea include many species that serve as intermediate hosts of parasites of humans and animals.

These organisms are discussed in the other, relevant chapters.

Tongue Worms: Class Pentastomida

The pentastomids, or tongue worms, of the class Pentastomida are a small group of parasites of uncertain origin and affinity. Because their larvae superficially resemble the larvae of mites, they have been included among the Arthropoda, but they probably evolved early from annelid or arthropod ancestral stocks. They were first noted in the nasal cavities of dogs and horses during the eighteenth century and were later described in human autopsy material as insect larvae.

The adult tongue worms are blood-sucking, endo-parasitic, legless vermiform inhabitants of the respiratory system of reptiles, birds, and mammals. Eggs fertilized within the host emerge through the respiratory tract. After being eaten by an intermediate host, they hatch in the gut, yielding a migratory larva that pierces the stomach wall and encysts in host tissue. When the intermediate host is eaten by the definitive host, the larvae mature.[10]

In humans, encysted larvae have been found in the lungs,[11, 12] liver, intestine, spleen, and other internal organs. There is no evidence that any human disease results from infection with tongue worms. They are usually identified at autopsy.

References

1. Kawamoto F. Kumada N. Biology of and venoms of Lepidoptera. In: (Poisons, Allergens and Other Invertebrate Venoms. (Tu AT. ed). Marcel Dekker, New York. pp 291-330. 1984.
2. Wirtz RA. Allergic and toxic reactions to non-stinging arthropods. Annu Rev Entomol 29:47-69. 1984.
3. Fernandez G. Morales E. et al. Epidemic dermatitis due to contact with a moth in Cozumel, Mexico. Am J Trop Med Hyg 46: 560-563.1992.
4. Pesce H. Delgado A. Poisoning from adult moths and caterpillars. In: Venomous Animals and Their Venoms. Vol III. Venomous Invertebrates (Bucherl W. Buckley EE., eds.) Academic Press, Orlando, FL. pp. 119-156. 1971.
5. Diaz JH. The evolving global epidemiology, syndromic classification, management, and prevention of caterpillar envenoming. Am J Trop Med Hyg 72: 347-357. 2005.
6. Miller P. Peters B. Overview of the public health implications of cockroaches and their management. N S W Public Health Bulol. 15: 208-211. 2004
7. Mechanical transmission of human protozoan parasites by insects. Clin Microbiol Rev. 18: 128-132. 2005
8. Miller P, Peters B. Overview of the public health implications of cockroaches and their management. N S W Public Health Bull.15:208-11. 2004.
9. Jongi BS. Centipede venoms and poisoning. In: Insect Poisons, Allergens and Other Invertebrate Venoms. (Tu AT. ed.) Marcel Dekker, New York. pp. 333-368. 1984.
10. Drabick JJ Pentastomiasis Rev Infect Dis 9: 1087-1094. 1987.
11. Roberts PP. Parasitic infections of the pleural space. Semin Respir Infect. 3(4):362-82. 1988.
12. Maleky F. A case report of Linguatula serrata in human throat from Tehran, central Iran. Indian J Med Sci. 55:439-41. 2001.

IX. Medical Ecology of Parasitic Diseases

How are parasitic diseases maintained in the environment, and why are many of us - some 2-3 billion at any one time - harboring so many different species of parasites? A simple answer to this complex question is that we choose to live everywhere, and in doing so, we eat and drink whatever nature offers to us in those myriad ecological settings. That is our evolutionary heritage, and in attempting to combat parasitic diseases throughout the 3-5 millions years of our brief history on this planet, our immune systems have been selected for life with them. In contrast, western medicine adheres to the tenant that we should live our lives without them! Therein lies the conflict. The scientific community, through the deployment of a global research and development effort, continues to pursue this ideal of a disease-free life style by inventing newer and newer strategies for alleviating suffering. This is all to the good, but our small successes have come with a heavy price tag.

Meanwhile, the relentless process of natural selection continues to re-shuffle the mix of plant and animal species, attempting to achieve ecological balance between all life forms within a given ecosystem. Humans, for the most part, are immobilized in the headlights of this process. We are, like it or not, as natural a part of any ecosystem we live in as any of the rest of the life forms that define a given region on earth. In denying this fact, we have created a new generation of health-related problems that can be traced back to our desire to divorce ourselves from the natural settings of our ancestors through the process of urbanization and modern agricultural practices. For example, following the industrialization of antibiotics manufacture, we attempted to use these "miracle" drugs to eradicate a number of troublesome pathogens; tuberculosis, bacterial pneumonia, staphylococcus, syphilis, malaria. Predictably, and most regrettably, mutants arose for each and every one of them to foil our best intentions.[1] This is the struggle that every practicing physician faces every day of their life. The same thing happened when we attempted to eradicate all noxious arthropods using DDT. Vaccines have fared somewhat better, particularly for a few important viral infections, but are totally missing from our armamentarium against eukaryotic parasites.

We must look to other means of avoiding infection if we are to live long and prosper. This is not to say that we should return to a more primitive (i.e., naturalistic) life style. To do so would be quite impossible, given our current level of dependency on technology. Nonetheless, understanding the forces that shape our world

with regard to mechanisms that facilitate the spread of infectious diseases empowers all levels of health professionals, enabling them to offer some hope to their consumer groups regarding avoidance of illnesses caused by them.[2, 3]

The brief look at disease ecology offered to the medical student and practitioner in this chapter will hopefully serve as the opening sentence or two in an endless dialogue between humans, their environment, and the causes of suffering inflicted upon them by parasites of all kinds.

Understanding the biology of disease transmission requires intimate knowledge of the host, the organism, and the environmental context in which they encounter one another (i.e., the medical ecology of the disease in question. See www.medicalecology.org).[2-5] If vectors are involved in their transmission, then their biology must also be taken into account.[6] Sorting out patterns of disease emergence and re-emergence has proven difficult at best, for even those infectious agents about which we know a great deal (e.g., human influenza and cholera).[7] It is a daunting task, even when the correct approach is taken, due to the very nature of the complexity of issues surrounding this subject. Often, in attempting to solve one problem, the answer comes back in the form of another set of equally difficult to answer questions. The deeper we probe into the ecology of infectious diseases, the more we come to realize that, indeed, we are not separated from natural systems simply because we now choose to live in urban and suburban environments of our own design.

Parasites of all varieties somehow manage to find us and detract from our pursuit of happiness. What is even more sobering is the fact that no two parasites are alike. Each has gained its hold on us following a unique set of evolutionary circumstances driven by natural selection and environmental change. Studying the factors that contribute to the overall pattern of disease transmission is a relatively new field that takes advantage of a wide variety of applied and basic sciences.[2] Applying the sciences of epidemiology and many of the ecological sciences, particularly population, ecosystem, and landscape ecology, to an outbreak event, especially a zoonotic one,[5, 6] requires a new generation of public health-trained professionals, in which teams of experts from these fields combine their efforts to unravel the biological complexities of a given entity.[2, 7-9]

Often, the answer lies in understanding the effect humans have had on a given region, due to activities related to the production of food and the creation of reliable water supplies.[7, 8] However, assessing the "health" of an ecosystem is a difficult process, requiring integration of measures of attributes that include its vigor, organization, and resilience.[10] The functions of any natural system are dependent upon countless interactions among the numerous assemblages of plants and animals that live there. Many examples of environmental disturbance have been identified which favor the transmission of certain groups of parasites, and in particular, those that are either zoonotic, vector-borne, or both.

A complete description of the ecological consequences of altering an ecosystem is not yet possible.[10] Nonetheless, once the general nature of a given disturbance is identified and understood, remediation of the damage can help reduce the transmission of a given entity (e.g., the routine draining of irrigation ditches to eliminate breeding sites for mosquitoes and snails that transmit malaria and schistosomiasis, respectively).

From a strictly ecological perspective, the transmission of a parasite from one host to another depends upon a number of complex elements, all of which, when taken together, define the parasite's essential niche.[11] Parasitism is a central theme throughout nature, and is essentially responsible for the population dynamics for almost all the creatures that harbor them.[12, 13]

Sexually transmitted parasites (*Trichomonas vaginalis*, and occasionally *Trypanosoma cruzi*) take advantage of a normal human behavior to move from one person to another. In this case, disturbance of the environment plays, at most, a minor role in the process. But over-population and crowding can enhance the chances for transmission.

Parasites that spread from one individual to another by the direct route usually depend upon fecal or urine contamination of the environment. Parasites with environmentally resistant stages (most geohelminths and some protozoans) are successful in this situation. The spread of untreated human feces into drinking water supplies and onto foodstuffs (e.g., the use of "night soil" for fertilizer) creates conditions that maintain endemic foci of infection. In regions of the world where over-population and unsanitary conditions are coincident, rates of more than 90% exist for some infections caused by geohelminths.

Fragmentation of ecosystems creates numerous ecotones. These unique zones define the edges where two or more ecosystems meet.[14] In these narrow areas the diversity of life is higher than in ecosystems that contribute to them. A variety of infectious agents are transmitted within these narrow regions; rabies, leishmaniasis,[15] schistosomiasis, and malaria, to name but a few. Unfortunately, encroachment into natural systems is the norm throughout most of the world. Urbanization,[16] the construction of dams, deforestation, agriculture, aquaculture, mining, political instability, civil unrest, and war are human activities that lead to the formation of ecotones. In addition, pesticide resistance

in vectors, and drug resistance in a few important parasitic organisms are two other factors that help explain why some parasitic infections continue to be so successful,[17, 18] despite numerous attempts by international and in-country health organizations to control or eradicate them.

Urbanization

As of May 10th, 2005, there were some 6.44 billion people on earth,[19] the majority of whom live in tropical and sub-tropical regions. In Africa, the population of most countries is still on the rise despite political instability, civil unrest, wars, and diseases that have claimed so many lives.[20] The same is true, to a lesser extent, for Central America, where geohelminths and malaria continue to take their toll. In tropical zones, wherever large populations live next to rivers, lakes, and wetlands, parasitic diseases such as malaria, African trypanosomiasis, lymphatic filariasis, onchocerciasis, and schistosomiasis flourish.[3] Regrettably, most urbanization, even in the developed world, is unplanned, resulting in sprawling, slum-like settlements in many regions of South and Central America, India, the Middle East, and Africa. Vector-borne illnesses such as leishmaniasis, Chagas' disease, lymphatic filariasis and malaria have burgeoned in these unfortunate communities.

Dams

There are an estimated 800,000 dams impeding the progress of thousands of rivers throughout the world,[21] many of which lie within the tropics. Each creates a lake whose surface area and depth depend upon the gradient and size of the feeder river. Dams produce hydroelectric power, water for irrigation and drinking, and help control floods. It is obvious to all that have access to a clean supply of water that it is a highly valued commodity.[22] It is also true that maintaining a pathogen-free water supply requires constant vigilance and capital; two things that can only co-exist in countries that have stable governments.

Of the 12 million children in the world under five years of age who die each year, it is estimated that over 2 million succumb to diarrheal diseases, most of which is spread through contaminated water.[23] In tropical zones, dams create lentic environments in which snails, black flies and mosquitoes breed. The incidence of vector-borne diseases that are dependent upon these kinds of invertebrates have increased, for the most part, after each dam was constructed. The Aswan High Dam in Egypt (see Fig. 33.23) is an excellent example of an altered ecological setting resulting in increased health risks for those living along the Nile

River. Before the dam was completed in 1968, the distribution of *Schistosoma mansoni* was confined to lower Egypt.[24] Now, both *S. mansoni* and *S. haematobium* are found along the entire length of the Nile, due in large part to a slow river current, increased numbers of irrigation ditches, and the lack of annual flooding. The absence of floods also allows more people to live close to the Nile, compromising the health of large numbers of children who swim unaware in that ancient body of water. Dam construction is on the increase throughout the tropical and sub-tropical world, especially in West Africa.[25] For example, several in central Côte d'Ivoire have resulted in a dramatically increased incidence of *S. haematobium*,[26] while in Senegal, the incidence of *S. mansoni* increased at a remarkable rate after construction of dams in the region of the Senegal River delta.[27] In China, the Three Gorges dam across the Yangtze River is the world's largest construction project ever attempted. *S. japonicum* will undoubtedly increase in the surrounding area due to irrigation projects associated with this new source of water.[28, 29]

Deforestation

Cutting down and/or burning of trees to clear land for farming, urbanization, fuel, and various wood products has already permanently altered the global carbon cycle,[30, 31] and contributed in a major way to the depletion of the ozone layer in both the northern and southern hemispheres.[32] Bromine is the primary offending chemical released by combustion of organic matter; it eventually reaches the stratosphere where it interacts with ozone in much the same way as chlorine.[33] This activity has resulted in much speculation about the causes of global climate change - including increases in ambient temperature and UV-B radiation, and their potential effects on human health.[34-38] In addition, the clearing of forests in tropical zones has depleted the biological diversity of those impacted regions, and probably eliminated many natural products that may have proven useful in a number of medical and industrial situations.[39, 40] Clear-cutting creates huge ecotonal zones.

The amount of deforestation for farming and mining is at a new high in the dense forest in the central portion of the Mato Grosso in Brazil. An area of rain forest about the size of Belgium disappears each year.[40] With each new road into the jungle, humans encroach deeper into the rainforest. Mammals indigenous to specific regions of that vast ecosystem harboring their own species of leishmania serve as the source of new infections in newly established human settlements.[15]

Since high levels of precipitation is the defining feature of rain forests, it is reasonable to assume that standing water accumulating in ecotonal zones created by deforestation serves as an opportunistic breeding site for many species of mosquitoes. Endemic foci of malaria sometimes develop in these situations.[41]

Agriculture

The clearing of land for agriculture in most tropical forested regions offers little in the way of sustainable resource. These soils are thin, little carbon storage is possible, and thus they are nutrient-poor.[30] Subsistence farming is largely of the slash and burn variety.

Swaths of forest are removed by setting fires, or by first felling trees, then burning them. In either case, the ash fertilizes the soil. These kinds of farms become established for only several years. After cultivation of food crops, which extract all the inorganic nutrients from the ash, farmers and their families have to move to another patch of forest and repeat the process.

Trees perform many ecosystem services that include the absorption of rainwater and prevention of soil erosion. In Haiti, deforestation has had an indirect effect on the prevalence of hookworm infection.[42] Most of the forests have been cut down to accommodate an ever-increasing human population. Excess siltation from flooding of rivers has changed the soil types along the banks of some of those rivers. What were once hard-packed clays are now loosely-packed sandy soils. This change has resulted in an altered environment, ideal for the survival of hookworm larvae. The incidence of hookworm disease along these rivers in Haiti has risen dramatically over the last several years. Despite these negative health-related effects of deforestation, sometimes, albeit rarely, a positive effect is the outcome. In one instance, removal of forest from some regions of Côte d'Ivoire has eliminated breeding sites for *Glossina palpalis*, the primary vector of *Tyrpanosoma brucei gambiense*.[43] However, removal of forest as a control measure for infectious tropical diseases is not an ecologically sound solution, as other unrelated health hazards undoubtedly emerge, as already documented. Fungi are essential detritivores for the re-cycling of leaf litter. Burning rainforest kills fungi in the understory and in their shallow soils, making rainforest recovery a very slow process, often taking hundreds of years.

Rice farming is water-intensive, and has a long history of association with transmission of schistosomiasis[44] and malaria.[45] In addition, rice paddies, when filled with water, function as miniature, temporary aquatic ecosystems. Many species of amphibians and poisonous and non-poisonous snakes take advantage of these seasonal ponds, using them as feeding stations and breeding sites. A variety of wild *Rattus spp.* feed on the maturing rice crops. Russell's viper, a widely distributed, highly poisonous snake, eats both small mammals and amphibians, and is a severe health risk throughout the rice growing regions of the Far East, South East Asia, and South Asia, particularly Sri Lanka, where the overall incidence of bites exceeds 400 per 100,000 annually.[46]

On a brighter note, Japan has eliminated *Schistosoma japonicum* from all their territories, and serves as a model for the employment of control strategies that require a deep understanding regarding the biology of the parasite. By employing numerous steps, most of which were ecologically based, to eliminate both the snail intermediate hosts and the reservoirs,[47] Japan has declared itself schistosome-free. Replacing susceptible bovines with relatively non-susceptible horses in the rice fields greatly reduced the role of the reservoirs in spreading the infection to humans. Cementing over the earthen banks of irrigation ditches eliminated littoral breeding sites for *Oncomelania nosophora* (Figure 34.12), the dominant intermediate snail host species. Human and animal feces collected for use as fertilizer was first treated with lime, killing the eggs of *S. japonicum,* prior to using it in the fields, further reducing the rate of transmission. The last human case was reported in 1977. The control programs to eradicate schistosomiasis in Japan were implemented after World War II, but prior to the advent of praziquantel. Japan's economy flourished in the post-war years, with a stable government, and none of the economic burdens associated with maintaining a fully equipped, standing army. The Marshall Plan provided extensive financial aid that helped insure that full economic recovery was achieved. Japan now could concentrate on domestic life issues in a systematic, logical fashion, including public health. The military situation has remained stable in Japan for some 65 years; time enough for that country to once again rise in prominence to a world power. Only this time, it is through the relatively peaceful conduit of world markets and economics.

Aquaculture

The ever-increasing demand for reliable sources of high protein foods has given rise to a new wave of high tech freshwater aquaculture. Numerous species of fish and shrimp have been domesticated with the advent of new advances in diets and parasite control. However, this diverse industry is not without its drawbacks. For example, tilapia farming in Africa has resulted in the construction of numerous fresh water fishponds. In places where fish production was not successful, due largely to over-crowding and subsequent stunting of fish, the ponds were abandoned, creating new breeding sites for mosquitoes, with a resulting increase in

malaria.[48]

Carp of various species constitute the main source of protein for many hundreds of thousands of people living throughout the Far East. Raising fish in large, shallow, permanent artificial lakes has created lentic ecosystems in which the proper snail intermediate hosts for a wide variety of trematodes have become established. *Clonorchis sinenesis, Fasciolopsis buski* and their relatives are prevalent in human populations living adjacent to these aquatic settings.[49]

Mining

In recent years, mining for gold in many parts of the Brazilian rain forest has drawn tens of thousands of people from all over South and Central America to that region. Mining creates numerous ecotonal situations. Those who seek out their fortunes there are at risk from acquiring leishmaniasis, malaria,[50] Chagas' disease, schistosomiasis, and wide variety of rare virus infections.[51] HIV is also rampant among the miners. Holes dug in the forest floor from which the gold-enriched earth is removed rapidly fills up with water, and serve as additional points of dissemination for water-borne diseases, including typhoid, Amoebiasis, and malaria. In addition, non-native people have brought their own communities of microbes with them that can pose serious health risks for indigenous Amerindian populations. Neither group is immunologically adapted to the other's pathogens, so both often suffer greatly from the encroachment. Much the same pattern occurred on a larger scale when droves of Spanish soldiers first arrived in the New World and "conquered" the native peoples with their diseases of smallpox, influenza, and the common cold virus. Finally, rain forest patches damaged by mining activities do not recover quickly, sometimes taking 20-40 years to repair the damage.

Disease transmission of vector-borne agents lingers in these environments for many years, often discouraging further settlement. Dams create the possibility for hydroelectric power that is essential for many countries that do not have ready access to fossil fuels. However, in many cases, most of the electricity generated is used in large-scale, mechanized mining operations to smelt aluminum from the thin tropical soils, further damaging those regions, and creating more opportunities for standing bodies of water to develop. Political instability, civil unrest, and war exacerbate these already beleaguered situations.

There can never be enough space allocated in any text to convey the full extent of the devastation to a given ecological region caused by widespread civil unrest and war. The effect that forced migration of people and their domestic animals has on intact biomes creates ecological chaos of major proportions. Africa appears to be the continent most impacted in recent years by political upheaval. Sleeping sickness has become, once again, epidemic in many of the more unstable central and West African countries.[52, 53] This is due largely to the disruption of ongoing control programs, and the translocation of large numbers of people and their domestic animals, who are squeezed into transmission zones that otherwise would remain sparsely populated.[54]

In the 1960s, the Vietnam War produced extensive ecological destruction, resulting in the spread of drug-resistant malaria that still plagues that region.[55] Chloroquine resistance in *Plasmodium falciparum* developed during the height of that conflict, and continues today as one of the most intractable health problems facing those living in Southeast Asia. Biological recovery of damaged Vietnamese rain forests has been slow.

Operation Desert Storm placed thousands of soldiers at risk from a visceralizing strain of leishmaniasis.[56, 57] As the result, none of the more than 600,000 US troops who participated in that military action can donate blood.

Malaria, typhoid, dengue, schistosomiasis, tuberculosis, and a wide array of exotic mycoses are medical problems commonly encountered in refugee camps in tropical climates, exacerbated by these inhumane conditions. In addition, crowding thousands of individuals into inadequate facilities, then subjecting them to contaminated water, lack of food, vector-borne illnesses, and the constant threat of invasion from whom ever they were running from, significantly lowers their ability to fight off agents that otherwise would cause them little or no harm. Under these circumstances, many die unnecessarily.

Conclusions

Damaged ecosystems, overcrowding of people into tropical ecotonal zones, and the spread of tropical diseases are inexorably linked. These interrelated, complex health problems require equally complex solutions, that address controlling the size of human populations, raising the educational and economic level of those in greatest need, and applying creative, ecologically sound regional control practices to specific parasitic diseases. Four cases which serve as examples of the results of concerted efforts that helped control such infections are: the eradication of *Schsitosoma japonicum* from Japan, the elimination of *Dracunculus medinensis* throughout most of the world except for Africa;[58] the control of onchocerciasis in most of West Africa;[59] and the elimination of transmission of Chagas' disease in the Southern Cone region of South America.[60] Unfortunately, apart from these few exceptions, ecologically damaged regions throughout the world still pose major health threats to hundreds of millions of people living in them.

To learn more about medical ecology and the role of damaged ecosystems in the spread of infectious diseases, log onto www.medicalecology.org.

References

1. Bush K. Antibacterial drug discovery in the 21st Century. Clin Microbiol Infect.10 Suppl 4:10-7. 2004.
2. Medical Ecology web site: www.medicalecology.org
3. Guernier V. Hochberg ME. Guegan JF. Ecology drives the worldwide distribution of human diseases. PLoS Biol. 2:e141. 2004.
4. Nature's Services (Daily G., ed.). Island Press, Washington, D.C. pp. 392. 1997.
5. Baskin Y. The Work of Nature. Island Press, Washington D.C. pp. 263. 1997.
6. Slingenbergh JI. Gilbert M. de Balogh KI. Wint W. Ecological sources of zoonotic diseases. Rev Sci Tech. 23:467-84. 2004.
7. Daszak P. Tabor GM. et al. Conservation medicine and a new agenda for emerging diseases. Ann N Y Acad Sci. 1026:1-11. 2004.
8. De Rycke J. Chomel B. Foreword. Vet Res. 36:265-6. 2005.
9. Patz JA. Daszak P. et al. Unhealthy landscapes: Policy recommendations on land use change and infectious disease emergence. Working Group on Land Use Change and Disease Emergence. Environ Health Perspect. 112:1092-8. 2004.
10. Rapport DJ. Constanza R. McMichael AJ. Assessing ecosystem health. Trends Ecol Evol 13:397-402. 1998.
11. Hutchinson GE. Concluding remarks. Population studies: animal ecology and demography. Cold Spring Harbor Symp Quant Biol 22:415-427. 1957.
12. Bowers RG. Turner J. Community structure and the interplay between interspecific infection and competition. J Theor Biol 187:95-109. 1997.
13. Hudson P. Greenman J. Competition mediated by parasites: biological and theoretical progress. Trends Ecol Evol 13:387-390. 1998.
14. Odum EP. Ecology: A Bridge Between Science and Society. Sinauer Associates, Inc. Pubs. Sunderland, Mass. pp. 331. 1997.
15. Peterson AT. Shaw J. Lutzomyia vectors for cutaneous leishmaniasis in Southern Brazil: ecological niche models, predicted geographic distributions, and climate change effects. Int J Parasitol. 33:919-31. 2003.
16. Pimentel D. On the ecology of increasing disease: population growth and environmental degradation. Willey D. Medicine, Con-fl ict & Survival 15:291-4. 1999.
17. Molyneux DH. Patterns of change in vector-borne diseases. Ann Trop Med Parasitol 91:827-839. 1997.
18. Anderson RM. May RM. The invasion, persistence, and spread of infectious diseases within animal and plant communities. Philo Trans R Soc London Ser B 314:533-570. 1986.
19. www.census.gov/main/www/popclock.html

20. Gwatkin DR. Poverty and inequalities in health within developing countries: filling the informaton gap In: D. Leon and B. Watt, Editors, Poverty, Inequality and Health. An International Perspective, Oxford University Press, Oxford. pp. 217–246. 2001.

21. Joyce S. Is it worth a dam? Env Health Persp 105: 1050-1055. 1997.

22. Steiner TS. Thielman NM. Guerrant RL. Protozoal agents: what are the dangers for the public water supply? Annu Rev Med 48:329-40. 1997.

23. Nataro JP. Vaccines against diarrheal diseases. Semin Pediatr Infect Dis. 15:272-9. 2004.

24. Khalil SB. Mansour NS. Soliman GN. Biological and biochemical comparative studies on *Schistosoma mansoni* from two localities in Egypt where *Schistosoma haematobium* is endemic. Ann Trop Med Parasitol 89:645-652. 1995.

25. United States Agency for International Development, 2000

26. N'Goran EK. Diabate S. Utzinger J. Sellin B. Changes in human schistosomiasis levels after the construction of two large hydroelectric dams in central Cote d'Ivoire. Bull WHO 75:541-545. 1997.

27. Ernould JC. Ba K. Sellin B. The impact of the local water-development programme on the abundance of the intermediate hosts of schistosomiasis in three villages of the Senegal River delta. Ann Trop Med Parasitol 93:135-145. 1999.

28. Ross AG, Li Y. et al. Dam worms. Biologist (London). 48:121-4. 2001.

29. McManus DP. Bartley PB. A vaccine against Asian schistosomiasis. Parasitol Int. 53:163-73. 2004.

30. Houghton RA. Skole DL. et al. Annual fluxes of carbon from deforestation and re-growth in the Brazilian Amazon. Nature. 403:301-4. 2000.

31. Cramer W. Bondeau A. et al. Tropical forests and the global carbon cycle: impacts of atmospheric carbon dioxide, climate change and rate of deforestation. Philos Trans R Soc Lond B Biol Sci. 359:331-43. 2004.

32. Pennington DW. Potting J. et al. Life cycle assessment part 2: current impact assessment practice. Environ Int. 30:721-39. 2004.

33. Keppler F. Eiden R. et al. Halocarbons produced by natural oxidation processes during degradation of organic matter Nature 403:298-301. 2000.

34. Patz JA. Climate change and health: new research challenges. Ecosystem Health 6:52-58. 2000.

35. Booth S. Zeller D. Mercury, food webs, and marine mammals: implications of diet and climate change for human health. Environ Health Perspect.113:521-6. 2005.

36. Watson RT. Turning science into policy: challenges and experiences from the science-policy interface. Philos Trans R Soc Lond B Biol Sci. 360:471-7. 2005.

37. Kovats RS. Haines A. Global climate change and health: recent findings and future steps. CMAJ. 172:501-2. 2005.

38. Gewin V. Ecosystem health: The state of the planet Nature 417:112 - 113 2002.

39. Stokstad E. Ecology. Ecosystem services. Science. 308:41-3. 2005.

40. Laurance WF. Mark A. et al. The future of the Brazilian Amazon. Science 291:438-439. 2001.

41. Molyneux DH. Common themes in changing vector-borne disease scenarios. Trans R Soc Trop Med Hyg. 97:129-32. 2003.

42. Lilley B. Lammie P. Dickerson J. Eberhard M. An increase in hookworm infection temporally associated with ecologic change. Emerg Infect Dis. 3(3):391-3. 1997.

43. Dagnogo M. Yapi Y. Traore G. Kone M. Redistribution des glossines dans une zone forestiere ivoirienne? Med Trop (Mars). 57:265-8. 1997.

44. Zheng J. Gu X. Qiu Z. Hua Z. Transmission factors of schistosomiasis japonica in the mountainous regions with type of plateau canyon and plateau basin. Chin Med J (Engl). 110:86-9. 1997.

45. Mouchet J. L'origine des epidemies de paludisme sur les Plateaux de Madagascar et les montagnes d'Afrique de l'Est et du Sud. Bull Soc Pathol Exot. 91:64-6. 1998.

46. Ariaratnam CA. Meyer WP. et al. A new monospecific ovine FAB fragment antivenom for treatment of envenoming by the Sri Lankan Russell's viper (Daboia russelii russelii); a preliminary dose-finding and pharmacokinetic study. Am J Trop Med Hyg 61:259-265. 1999.

47. Tanaka H. Tsuji M. From discovery to eradication of schistosomiasis in japan:1847-1996. Int J Parasitol 27:1465-1480. 1997.

48. Desowitz RS. New Guinea Tapeworms and Jewish Grandmothers: A Tale of Parasites and People. W. W. Norton, Co., Pubs. 1981.

49. Ooi HK. Chen CI. et al. Metacercariae in fishes of Sun Moon lake which is an endemic area for *Clonorchis sinensis* in Taiwan. Southeast Asian J Trop Med Public Health. 28 Suppl 1:222-3. 1997.

50. Zalis MG. Pang L. et al. Characterization of *Plasmodium falciparum* isolated from the Amazon region of Brazil: evidence for quinine resistance. Am J Trop Med Hyg 58:630-7. 1998.

51. Vasconcelos PF. Travassos da Rosa AP. et al. Inadequate management of natural ecosystem in the Brazilian Amazon region results in the emergence and reemergence of arboviruses. Cad Saude Publica.17 Suppl:155-64. 2001.

52. Moore A. Richer M. Re-emergence of epidemic sleeping sickness in southern Sudan. Trop Med Int Health. 6:342-7. 2001.

53. Hutchinson OC. Fevre EM. Carrington M. Welburn SC. Lessons learned from the emergence of a new *Trypanosoma brucei* rhodesiense sleeping sickness focus in Uganda. Lancet Infect Dis. 3:42-5. 2003.

54. Smith DH. Pepin J. Stich AH. Human African trypanosomiasis: an emerging public health crisis. Br. Med Bull 54:341-355. 1998.

55. Kidson C. Indaratna K. Ecology, economics and political will: the vicissitudes of malaria strategies in Asia. Parasitologia 40: 39-46. 1998.

56. Anonymous. From the Centers for Disease Control. Viscerotropic leishmaniasis in persons returning from Operation Desert Storm–1990-1991. JAMA. 267:1444-6. 1992.

57. Magill AJ. Drogi M. et al. Visceral infection caused by Leishmania tropica in veterans of Operation Desert Storm. N Engl J Med 328:1383-1387. 1993.

58. Hopkins DR. Ruiz-Tiben E. et al. Dracunculaisis eradication: delayed, not denied. Am J Trop Med Hyg 62:163-168. 2000.

59. Boussinesq M. Hougard JM. La lutte contre l'onchocercose en Afrique: aspects actuels. Med Trop (Mars). 58:285-96. 1998.

60. Moncayo A. Chagas disease: current epidemiological trends after the interruption of vectorial and transfusional transmission in the Southern Cone countries. Mem Inst Oswaldo Cruz. 98:577-91. 2003.

X. Travel Medicine: Advice for the Clinician

Medical students taking elective study time in tropical and subtropical ecozones and practicing clinicians specializing in infectious diseases are likely to have the opportunity to travel and work in developing countries that lie within these broad geographic regions. This chapter is intended to outline for the medically-informed reader the background of the morbidity and mortality associated with travel. We encourage even the experienced traveler to seek pre-travel advice for themselves and for any companions with whom they plan to travel.

Travel medicine specialists are comfortable with an overall approach to travel advice. A personal enthusiasm for travel often gives the specialist a first-hand knowledge of various destinations and the ability to individualize the assessment of the travelers' risk. Knowledge of clinical guidelines and a continuous review of multiple sources of information allow the travel medicine specialist to give personalized advice to protect travelers against the many hazards they may encounter. A critical component of the travel consult is educating travelers about all facets of travel related danger and ensuring that individuals know where to seek help abroad if needed. The information and references in this chapter will lead readers to additional sources of information.

History

The prehistoric record of the human species is punctuated with migration events starting with the Olduvai Gorge in East Africa. Travel seems to be in our genetic makeup. The distribution of humans some 40,000 years ago includes groups of hunter-gatherer tribes on every continent and Australia. It appears as though whenever we could, we took off for parts unknown. Historical records are filled with tantalizing glimpses of what the world looked like to wayfaring nations (e.g., the Phoenicians, the Norse, and the Greeks and Romans). Travel was often necessary because of plagues, war, or economic circumstances, but sometimes curiosity was the principal motivating factor. Peril during actual or mythical travel is vividly described in original biblical sources and in the struggles facing Jason as he pursued the golden fleece and Homer's characters in the Odyssey. Later, efficient travel arrangements allowed Ghengis Khan to create the Mongol empire, which eventually became the greatest land based dynasty of all time. The success of the Mongols was due largely to an elaborate organizational hierarchy of traveling. The terror produced in villages by the

approach of the Mongol horsemen is legendary. The fact that these traveling units, called tumens, were comprised of 10,000 warriors and an additional 40,000 accompanying family members, including children, is a less well-known piece of trivia.[1]

Travel today is logistically simpler (airport security procedures aside), although the hazards may be significant for those working in the developing world. Journeys to any part of the world can be made in hours, whereas many destinations would have required year-long expeditions to reach just a few decades ago. In this modern age, cultural, economic and disease boundaries are easily crossed, forcing travelers to be prepared for unplanned emergencies and to protect against illnesses rarely encountered in the developed world. Family members, especially children traveling with their parents, must also prepare for the trip to prevent disease and injury.[2, 3]

Background

Over 750 million tourist arrivals occurred in 2004,[4] with many destinations in remote tropical areas. Travel medicine encompasses a number of disciplines including infectious diseases, tropical medicine, public health, sports medicine, and hyperbaric medicine. Travel medicine consultation is concerned with decreasing the morbidity and mortality associated with travel, by increasing awareness of the risks involved and by educating travelers about preventive measures. The consult involves a detailed assessment of the individual's underlying health, the travel itinerary, the types of activities to be performed, the duration of exposure to the risks in each area visited, and the access to and quality of medical care available. Many recent journals and texts devote sections to comprehensive discussion of travel medicine and risks to different patient groups.[5, 6] This chapter is designed to detail some of the underlying principles involved in travel medicine and should be used in conjunction with actual medical consultation.

Figure 1. It is essential to review travel plans with a specialist before visiting sites such as the one pictured above.

Mortality

Death during overseas travel is most common in people over 45 years of age and is largely due to cardiovascular disease. A second leading cause of deaths abroad is accidents. Data from the Peace Corps reveals that 70% of deaths in volunteers are due to unintentional injury. The risk of death due to injury in male travelers age 25-34 during the years 1975-1984 was greater than 2.5 times the corresponding risk for this group in developed countries.[7] Travel and leisure activities in unfamiliar environments are made more dangerous by unregulated safety standards for motor vehicles and roads. Measures to increase safety during motor vehicle travel, including wearing seat belts and safety devices, avoiding unsafe vehicles, and traveling during daylight hours, would decrease unnecessary deaths during travel. Families traveling with young children should bring their own child car seats. Sixteen percent of all deaths in travelers in the Hargarten study[8] were caused by drowning, presumably from swimming in unfamiliar areas and, in some cases, related to alcohol consumption. Swimming in reputable tourist areas will decrease exposure to dangerous currents and underwater obstacles. Scuba divers traveling abroad need to make themselves aware of different conditions, including types of marine animal envenomation.[9,10]

Travel-Related Infectious Diseases

Travel-related infectious diseases can be divided into those acquired by enteric routes and those acquired by other routes. Long-term travelers will have difficulty avoiding water-transmitted illnesses since it is nearly impossible to drink only purified water and avoid produce washed in local water. It is difficult to refuse food when invited as a guest to a local person's home, as shared meals are often the first introduction into a

Figure 2. Tributaries of the Mekong delta are known to have schistosomiasis.

region's culture and customs.

While many organisms are acquired by the oral route, a plethora of others are transmitted via the respiratory route, by arthropod bites, or from direct contact with the organism in water or soil. Footwear should always be worn, and contact with freshwater bodies known to harbor the snail that transmits the illness schistosomiasis should be avoided.

Schistosomiasis is becoming an increasing problem in travelers. Cases of schistosomiasis seen at hospitals in Britain have recently increased. In one study, 77 patients (32.4% of the total) reported Lake Malawi, a region of the Rift Valley previously thought to be free of schistosomiasis, as their only fresh water exposure.[11] In another report of four cases of acute schistosomiasis in 1997, patients had exposures to fresh water in Lake Malawi, and an acute illness with severe pulmonary involvement. The concern with this atypical clinical presentation raises the possibility of a new emerging parasite variant.[12] Schistosomiasis is reported to be endemic in large parts of South Africa.[13] At a German clinic, patients with schistosomiasis acquired their infection mostly from Africa and were aware of the risk of schistosomiasis but not knowledgeable in avoiding the infection.[14] Given this information, prevention of disease by avoiding contact with freshwater in Africa is essential given the severity of clinical disease and the emergence of disease in unexpected regions.

Diarrhea

Diarrhea is the most common travel-related illness and is often associated with changes in diet. More often, diarrhea has a microbial etiology and a history of exposure to contaminated water and food. In adults, a two week trip from the developed world to developing countries is associated with a 20-50% risk of travelers' diarrhea.[15] Even travel to low-risk areas such as Northern Europe, Canada, Australia and New Zealand are associated with diarrhea in 8% of travelers. Data on travelers' diarrhea in children is limited and many recommendations are extrapolated from the adult literature. The best study examining a wide range of age groups demonstrated that the highest attack rates and most severe disease occurred in children under three years of age.[16]

The most frequent microbial etiology of travelers' diarrhea is enterotoxigenic *Escherichia coli* (ETEC). In over a third of cases, no pathogen is identified; however the cases are likely to be bacterial since a response to antimicrobials has typically been observed.[17]

Traveler's diarrhea is a marker for fecal contamination of water with pathogens that may have serious consequences. Other organisms capable of causing diarrhea include the bacteria - Salmonella, Campylobacter, Shigella - some viruses, and eukaryotic parasites, particularly *Giardia lamblia, Cryptosporidium parvum* and *Entamoeba histolytica*. Traveler's diarrhea in a healthy adult is usually a minor illness and is self-limited in most cases. The mainstay of therapy is re-hydration with practically any over the counter beverage, together with a source of sodium chloride, such as saltine crackers or potato chips. Treatment with a variety of anti-peristaltic agents or antibiotics can shorten the duration of symptoms. Three days of ofloxacin 300 mg twice daily has been shown to be effective.[18] A single dose of ofloxacin 400mg with the anti-peristaltic medication loperamide has recently been shown to be more effective than ofloxacin alone.[19] The twice-daily regimen is recommended for people with fever, bloody diarrhea and symptoms that confine an individual to bed. Ofloxacin can also serve as a good multi-purpose antibiotic for treatment of other unforeseen illnesses such as skin infections, pneumonia and urinary tract infections. Other antibiotics such as rifaximin, levofloxacin, and azithromycin have been studied recently and allow for choices based on underlying clinical need.[20,21]

Two tablets of bismuth subsalicylate can be taken with meals and at bedtime to prevent diarrhea. The salicylate is absorbed and the medication may cause the tongue and stool to turn black. Antimicrobials should only be taken prophylactically by immunocompromised individuals and individuals traveling for a short time, who are aware of the side effects and risks involved with antimicrobials and are unwilling to tolerate the minor inconvenience of diarrhea. Children are much more likely to become dehydrated without early and prompt therapy. Re-hydration with beverages that have a carbohydrate to sodium ratio approximating 1:1 is the recommended treatment. Excess of carbohydrate adds to the osmotic load in the intestine and can exacerbate diarrhea while soups with sodium may lead to hypernatremia. Oral re-hydrating solutions (ORS) containing fixed ratios of carbohydrate and electrolytes are commercially available. Formula or breast-feeding should be continued during ORS treatment, and may actually shorten the duration of symptoms. Medication therapy of children differs from that of adults, due to safety differences in medications and the fact that ORS, when started early, is effective treatment and prevents dehydration. Treatment with anti-peristaltic agents is controversial. Imodium causes drowsiness in children under two years of age, but has decreased stool volume in the sickest children admitted to hospitals with dehydration requiring intravenous therapy.

Antibiotic therapy is indicated for children with prolonged or dehydrating diarrhea, when high fever is present or when an invasive pathogen is suspected or documented to be present. Antibiotic therapy is limited by the lack of human safety data on pediatric use of quinolone antibiotics, and because of data demonstrating cartilage changes in the growth plate of animals treated with quinolones. Data is accumulating on quinolone use for Pseudomonas infections in children and regulatory agencies are reviewing pediatric indications for this class of antibiotics. Currently therapy with trimethoprim 4 mg/kg and sulfamethoxazole 20mg/kg twice a day for three days can be used for children and infants older than two months of age. Effectiveness of these antibiotics is limited by regions with widespread resistance to sulfa medications. Furazolidine, 5 mg/kg divided in four doses for children older than one month is effective against enteric diarrhea causing bacteria as well as against the protozoan *Giardia lamblia*. Bismuth sub-salicylate administered to infants older than three months of age was shown to decrease the duration of diarrhea, total stool output, and duration of hospitalization, as compared to placebo.[22]

It is unlikely that long-term travelers can avoid contaminated water and food sufficiently to avoid enteric diseases. Studies have shown that even short-term travelers who are knowledgeable about avoiding diarrhea often develop diarrhea over the course of their stay, despite their awareness of the problem.[22] Children traveling with parents for long periods of time in the developing world may have to obtain water from the same stream or spigot as local people. Because children may suffer more severe disease from enteric illnesses, preventing illness from contaminated water may require parents to depend on a greater knowledge of water purification. Water-borne diseases acquired by an enteric route are sometimes vaccine preventable; however, preventing illness from contaminated water may require a more sophisticated system of water purification.

Water Purification

Boiling water for one minute (three minutes at altitudes greater than 6,000 feet) and allowing the water to cool to room temperature is the most reliable method of rendering water pathogen-free. This may not be practical in certain areas; therefore, commercial halogen products are available in stores to chemically disinfect water. Alternatively, water-filters are sold by many companies. Filters must be verified for size of particle filtration in order to eliminate protozoa and bacteria.

Malaria

Malaria is transmitted by infected female *Anopheles spp.* mosquitos (see The Malarias, chapter 9). This

Figure 3. Boiling water from this source is recommended!

parasite is widespread throughout the world, though some efforts to decrease the incidence of malaria have been successful. Control of mosquito populations by insecticide spraying and draining wetlands to eliminate breeding grounds is the most effective means of control. Malaria inflicts devastating morbidity and mortality in young children, with the brunt of disease occurring in sub-Saharan Africa. Malaria is resurgent in many areas of the world because of failures in vector control and insecticide-resistant mosquitoes thriving in parts of the world that had previously achieved some degree of control. *Plasmodium falciparum* have developed resistance to all of the available drugs used to prevent and treat this disease in most parts of the world. Thus, knowledge regarding means of avoiding contact with this pathogen can save many a trip into the emergency room.

Preventing Malaria

Preventing malaria depends upon avoiding contact with Anopheline mosquitoes, which tend to bite between early evening and sunrise, and upon taking prophylactic medications. The risk of infection with malaria depends upon the percentage of infected humans and mosquitoes in a region, the behavior and biting habits of a particular species of anopheline mosquito, and climactic conditions that determine the longevity and breeding of mosquitoes. Estimates of risk to travelers to West Africa not using chemoprophylaxis are 24 cases per 1,000 travelers per month, with a case fatality rate of 2%.[23] Children are especially vulnerable to developing both malaria and complications of severe malaria such as cerebral malaria. Children of missionaries or other long-term travelers may have parents who are reluctant to take prophylactic medications for long periods of time. Many people observe that local populations and many expatriates do not take malaria

prophylactic medications, leading some to stop taking these drugs. This decision may have fatal consequences, since adults native to endemic areas develop variable degrees of immunity by virtue of surviving childhood. In an outbreak of malaria among U.S. embassy personnel in Uganda in 1992, risk was highest in people not using bed nets, insect repellent at night, and proper anti-malaria prophylaxis.[24] In this study, children under 15 years of age had a 60% greater risk than people over 15 years of developing malaria, illustrating the greater difficulty of avoiding malaria in children.

Personal Protection Measures

Avoiding Anopheline mosquito bites requires staying in screened areas after dusk, covering the majority of skin with clothing, and sleeping under mosquito nets. Mosquito nets impregnated with permethrins can provide protection for one year. Clothing can be sprayed with permethrin-containing compounds that improve anti-mosquito measures. Topical mosquito repellents for exposed skin containing 20-30% diethyltoluamide (DEET) need to be used every 3-4 hours to be effective. This compound is safe, although neurologic toxicity has been noted in young children using unusually high concentrations of the insecticide. Insecticides and mosquito nets can be purchased from outdoor camping stores prior to a trip. Anti-mosquito measures should be continued during the day by leaving as little skin as possible uncovered. Certain mosquito species (*Aedes spp.*) bite during the day and can transmit viral illnesses such as yellow fever and dengue.[25] Reported dengue cases in the U.S. doubled in 1996, and no vaccine exists to prevent this illness. Anti-mosquito measures are critical in preventing this illness. Unfortunately, multiple studies have documented inadequate use of personal protection measures in knowledgeable people, who subsequently become sick with arthropod-borne diseases.[26]

Figure 4. A site in the Yucutan peninsula free of malaria.

Malaria Chemoprophylaxis

Anti-malarial drugs do not prevent infection but can reduce or prevent the symptoms of clinical malaria. Chloroquine (5 mg/kg of base/week up to 300 mg/week) was previously the drug of choice for chemoprophylaxis in travelers and for treatment of clinical cases. Due to widespread chloroquine resistance, the drug is only effective in malarious regions of Central America west of the Panama canal zone, Mexico, the Caribbean, and parts of the Middle East. Mefloquine, doxycycline, atovaquone-proguanil, and the combination of chloroquine and proguanil are other drugs available for use in chloroquine-resistant areas. Studies in Africa have shown that mefloquine protects >90% of short-term travelers whereas chloroquine provided no protection. Peace Corps volunteers on long term missions received 94% and 86% better protection from mefloquine as compared to chloroquine alone or combination chloroquine-proguanil, respectively.[27] Travelers have reported neuropsychiatric side effects from mefloquine, and this news has unfortunately been widely disseminated in the lay press. In the Peace Corps study, there were no serious neuropsychiatric side effects; only minor side effects such as strange dreams, nausea, and insomnia occurred, and were in fact more frequent in the chloroquine group than in the mefloquine group. Individuals should therefore use mefloquine in chloroquine-resistant areas due to its safety and superior activity against resistant organisms. Doxycycline can be substituted for mefloquine in adults and children older than eight years of age, in areas where mefloquine resistance exists or for those experiencing toxicity from either chloroquine or mefloquine. Doxycycline causes skin sensitivity to the sun and has gastrointestinal side effects that limit long-term use. Doxycycline is not a causal prophylactic agent and must be continued for four weeks after leaving a malarious region when used for malaria prophylaxis.[28] Malarone (atovaquone-proguanil), is a combination of two medications that are relatively ineffective when used alone but that have marked synergy when used together.[29] Clinical trials of atovaquone-proguanil have demonstrated comparable efficacy to other regimens for treatment of malaria.[30] In an area of Thailand with multi-drug resistant *P. falciparum*, atovaquone-proguanil was superior to mefloquine for acute uncomplicated malaria, with 100% cure rate in 79 patients versus 86% cure rate in 79 mefloquine treated patients (p<0.002).[31] Challenge studies of *P. falciparum* in healthy volunteers demonstrated protection of atovaquone-treated subjects and causal prophylactic activity against exo-erythrocytic stages of the parasite.[32] It appears that atovaquone-proguanil will have a role in prophylaxis and is especially useful in short term travelers since it only needs to be taken for one week after leaving an endemic region.[32-34] It will also be useful for travelers to regions where uncertainty exists surrounding levels of resistance to mefloquine and for travelers that do not tolerate doxycycline or mefloquine.

Standby Medication for Presumptive Treatment

Travelers often request medications to treat malaria in the event of developing clinical symptoms in place of prophylaxis. Many expatriate parents would rather treat their children for malaria than expose them to medications over a long period of time. This method is only recommended for medically knowledgeable travelers visiting areas with low malaria risk for short periods of time. One problem with this method is that, by the time symptoms develop, the number of parasites in the body are 10^7 times higher than parasite levels treated by chemoprophylactic strategies.[35, 36] Malaria can be difficult to differentiate from other febrile illnesses. The best treatment for chloroquine-resistant malaria is quinine or mefloquine. Quinine is best administered in a monitored setting once a definitive diagnosis of malaria is established, since the therapeutic-toxic index is narrow. Mefloquine at treatment doses for adults (1250 mg) has neurologic toxicity including vertigo and is available only in oral preparations, which limits its use to alert patients not suffering from nausea or vomiting.

Fansidar (sulfadoxine and pyrimethamine) and Halofantrine (not available in the U.S.) are two drugs used by some travelers for self-treatment. Fansidar resistance is now widespread, and halofantrine can cause changes in electrocardiogram tracings. Doxycycline is not appropriate for self-treatment because it is not rapidly schizonticidal and hence not effective as monotherapy for high levels of parasitemia. Atovaquone-proguanil can be used as stand by treatment until the sick individual can have a proper evaluation of the cause of fever in a health facility.

Vaccine-Preventable Diseases

Vaccines represent possibly the greatest achievement of modern medicine. Advances in molecular biology will alter future vaccine development. DNA vaccines result in the synthesis of peptide-based antigens in human cells, which elicit MHC Class 1 antigen presentation and cellular immune responses against certain intracellular pathogens that would otherwise escape the surveillance of the immune system.[37] Efforts to sequence the human genome and genes from a variety of infectious agents will lead to selection of cassettes of antigenic determinants in vaccines to prevent a wide range of diseases. Specific immune responses from this type of vaccine may improve safety by avoiding stimulating responses to cross-reacting human tissue antigens. This strategy would be a vast improvement over the multiple injections many travelers currently endure.

New vaccines and vaccination recommendations change rapidly. This chapter will highlight issues and controversy in vaccination. Resources, such as the CDC publication: Health Information for International Travel,[38] Centers for Disease Control and Prevention. Health Information for International Travel 2004-2005. DHHS. Atlanta, GA. Available at: http://www.cdc.gov/ travel/ updated annually, and the Red Book: Report of the Committee on Infectious Diseases, updated every three years, should be consulted.[39] Online resources (Table 1) such as the CDC's National Immunization Program website http://www/cdc/gove/nip should be referred to for the latest guidelines on vaccination. The travel consultation is an opportunity to customize appropriate immunizations for a traveler based on knowledge of new vaccine regimens, changing worldwide disease boundaries, emerging disease outbreaks, and changing international health requirements. Families that travel internationally must maintain an up-to-date record of both their own and their children's vaccine status. The International Certificate of Vaccination (Form PHS731) can be ordered from the U.S. Government Printing Office, Washington, D.C. 20402 or by phone (202) 783-3238. Table 2 lists various vaccines to be considered for a traveler, depending upon the itinerary to be followed. Vaccine manufacturers' package inserts should be read carefully for each vaccine to review administration and potential contraindications to vaccination.

Routine Vaccines

Diphtheria-Tetanus Toxoid

Most cases of tetanus in the U.S. occur in people over 50 years of age who were never vaccinated, received incomplete vaccination, or have waning immunity due to not having received a booster vaccine in over 10 years. Sero-surveys documenting that 9% of travel clinic attendees lack tetanus antibodies should prompt parents to vaccinate young travelers planning a long stay abroad if they have not had a booster within 5 years.[39] One may assume a scratch or cut will occur, making the five-year interval appropriate. The combination vaccine boosts diphtheria immunity that may be useful for travel to countries experiencing epidemics.[41]

Pertussis

Since 1993, cases in the United States and abroad have increased and vaccination has not altered the periodic epidemic cycles, which occur every two to five years.[42] This observation has led to the recognition of the importance of adult bacterial carriage and disease in children. Booster doses of vaccine for adults are under consideration now that acellular vaccines appear safer. A recent review of the pertussis acellular vaccine trials found the three or four component vaccines to be more effective after standardizing the case definition, as compared to single or two-component vaccines.[43] Hospital and childcare personnel should probably be vaccinated with a booster dose of 0.25 mg acellular pertussis vaccine in outbreak situations; however, no formal recommendations exist for booster doses in other situations, including foreign travel.

Table 1. Travel Information Resources

Telephone Resources
Centers for Disease Control Hotline   (404)639-1610
   Recorded health information
Centers for Disease Control   (404)332-4565
   Fax Information Service   Documents on health information can be sent to local fax machines
International SOS Assistance   (800)523-8930
   Organization that provides overseas assistance to companies. Individual coverage with emergency evacuation insurance can be purchased
Travel Assistance International   (800)821-2828
   Reasonable individual health insurance and evacuation coverage

Internet Resources
Centers for Disease Control   http://www.cdc.gov/
   Reliable information but needs to be individualized with a travel medicine specialist
World Health Organisation   http://www.who.org/
   Good travel and outbreak section
U.S. State Department   http://www.travel.state.gov/travel_warnings.html/
   Latest state department travel warnings

Measles/Mumps/Rubella

Measles vaccine booster doses are recommended for children over 10 who received a previous dose at 12 months of age or over. Students are also re-vaccinated in the same manner, because outbreaks of measles have occurred in student populations after contact with people infected during foreign travel or after exposure to children with measles.[44]

Hemophilus influenzae

Hemophilus influenzae vaccination is now routine for children and has decreased invasive disease due to this organism. There are no age recommendations for booster doses, with the exception that some practitioners recommend a booster dose for a child being treated for a malignancy.

Streptococcus pneumoniae

The 23-valent pneumococcal polysaccharide vaccine is recommended for adults and high risk children over two years of age. Conjugate pneumococcal vaccines have proven effective in infants and children in preventing otitis media and invasive pneumococcal disease.[45] Vaccination of travelers depends upon recommendations for specific age groups. Persons with underlying illness may also require different regimens, since colonization and disease occurs in both developed and developing countries.

Influenza Virus

The vaccine is important for healthcare workers and others who may come into contact with populations during seasonal outbreaks of influenza. The vaccine is usually composed of antigenic variants of type A and type B strains of influenza that are projected to predominate in the next year's flu season. Influenza is transmitted year-round in the tropics with two distinct peaks. In the Southern Hemisphere, transmission occurs in April-September. Influenza vaccination must be performed on an annual basis and should be considered for certain travelers, especially health care workers.[46]

Required vaccines

Required and recommended vaccines for individual countries are suggested in Health Information for International Travel published annually by the CDC.[31]

Yellow Fever

Aedes spp. mosquitoes transmit this systemic viral illness predominately in rural areas, though cases now occur in cities with sanitation standards favoring mosquito proliferation.[46] The decision to vaccinate de-

Figure 5. A water source that serves multiple purposes may also be a source of different diseases.

pends upon the risk of acquiring yellow fever, which changes with evolving environmental conditions. The live attenuated virus vaccine is safe for children nine months or older and contraindicated only in persons who are immunosuppressed or who have hypersensitivity to egg products.[47] The decision to immunize an immunosuppressed individual requires consideration of the risk of unavoidable exposure to wild-type yellow fever. Pregnant women should not be vaccinated and trips to endemic areas should be postponed until after the mother and child can be safely vaccinated. There have been reports of illness and death in yellow fever vaccine recipients with no immunocompromising conditions.[48] Risk is apparently highest in the elderly particularly those over 75 years of age.[49] The yellow fever vaccine is the only World Health Organization-regulated vaccine that can be required for entry to a country. Cases of yellow fever occur mostly in equatorial Africa and South America. Occasional cases occur elsewhere (Central America) and are reported in the "Summary of Health Information for International Travel," published bi-weekly by the CDC and posted on the CDC home page (Table 1). Countries without incidence of yellow fever, such as most countries in Asia, may require yellow fever vaccination for people traveling from an endemic zone.

Cholera

Vaccination is no longer required, since there is now agreement that the parenterally administered vaccine has limited and short-lived efficacy. Tourists and people traveling to cities for business purposes are rarely exposed to the conditions of extreme poverty necessary to come in contact with the cholera bacteria. Students working in refugee camps or rural villages are at risk for exposure to contaminated water containing cholera. Outbreaks in travelers occurred in association with the last cholera pandemic that swept through

Latin America in 1992. Notably, passengers on a flight from Latin America to Los Angeles were exposed to contaminated food and became ill.[50] Better-tolerated oral cholera vaccines are available in countries outside of the United States and may be required in the future for travel to countries with a history of periodic outbreaks.[51, 52]

Recommended vaccines

Reliable epidemiologic data on the morbidity and mortality of many vaccine-preventable diseases is limited.

Hepatitis A
Children infected with Hepatitis A generally have subclinical disease; however, the virus is shed in stool and may infect and cause disease in adult family members. The incidence in travelers is highly dependent upon the degree of fecal contamination of drinking water, the length of the trip, and different types of lifestyle activities. The incidence in Swiss tourists staying in luxury hotels in Africa was 1 in 1,000, whereas backpackers in India had a risk of 1 in 50.[53, 54] In a French study of young missionaries working in Central or West Africa, 48% converted their serologies to Hepatitis A, at a rate of 19 per 1,000 missionaries each month.[55] Two Hepatitis A vaccines are available in the U.S. that should afford nearly 100% protection in properly vaccinated individuals.[56, 57] A pediatric formulation is available for use in children 2-18 years of age. Expanded vaccination is recommended for children living in areas of the U.S. with higher rates of Hepatitis A than the national average.[58] The vaccine is well-tolerated, with side effects mostly due to muscle irritation at the injection site. Immune globulin from pooled serum provides short-term protection and can be used in travelers requiring immediate protection and for children under two years of age. Immunoglobulin can be administered simultaneously with the Hepatitis A vaccine. The cost of the Hepatitis A vaccine should not be a deterrent to vaccination since titers induced by the vaccine are higher three weeks after vaccination than they are from immunoglobulin alone. In addition, protection is long-lived from the vaccine versus only a few months with immunoglobulin alone.

Hepatitis B
In Asia and Africa, a high percentage of the population is seropositive to Hepatitis B, largely because of maternal-infant transmission. This poses a high risk to health care workers and sexually active travelers. Ten and a half percent of French missionaries in Af-rica became serologically positive for Hepatitis B. Subgroup analysis demonstrated highest rates in persons not involved with health care activities suggesting that sexual transmission was responsible for the majority of the seroconversions.[59] Transmission of Hepatitis B occurs between young children in areas of the world with high seroprevalence. Infants in the U.S.A. are now routinely vaccinated and it is recommended to vaccinate persons age 18 at routine medical visits.[59] Young adults with plans to stay abroad for extended lengths of time and who had not been previously vaccinated should receive vaccination against Hepatitis B, since sexual transmission is the predominant mode of infection in this age group.

Typhoid Fever
Travelers are roughly 100 times less likely to get sick from typhoid than from enterically-acquired Hepatitis A.[60] In a study of *Salmonella typhi* infections in the U.S. for the years 1975-1984, infection in Mexico contributed the most number of cases, reflecting the popularity of this travel destination. However, rates per 100,000 travelers, which reflects actual risk, were higher for Peru (174), India (119), Pakistan (105), Chile (58), and the Philippines (38), compared to Mexico (20).[61] Risk of disease is highest in long-term travelers intending to visit or work in remote locations in developing countries. There are three vaccines currently available for use in the U.S. (Table 2). The Ty21a oral vaccine or the parenteral ViCPS vaccine should be used in place of the parenteral inactivated vaccine because of a better safety profile. There are theoretical concerns that the efficacy of the Ty21A vaccine may be impaired by simultaneous use of antibiotics, mefloquine or the oral polio vaccine. For this reason, the oral typhoid vaccine should be administered at least 24 hours after a dose of these other agents. The ViCPS vaccine should be used in immunocompromised individuals although the vaccine response may be blunted in comparison to that of a normal host.

Polio
The last case of wild-type polio in the Americas was in Peru in 1991, and this region has been certified to be free of polio by the WHO.[62] Most cases now occurring in the U.S. are vaccine-associated,[63] although imported polio is still a concern in travelers returning from endemic areas of Africa and parts of Asia.[64] India and sub-Saharan Africa are the final major regions with reservoirs of polio. Progress in these regions is evident, as only limited poliovirus type 2 transmission is being reported and eradication may soon follow.[65] However, explosive outbreaks in sub-Saharan Africa highlight the

Table 2. Vaccines available for use in travelers

Vaccine	Initial Schedule*	Efficacy (%)@	Duration&	Issues/Contraindications
Inactivated Bacterial Vaccines				
Cholera				
(WC inactive)	2 doses ID, SC, IM: 0,1mo	30-60	3-6mo	Local reactions common, malaise
(WC-BS)	2 doses PO: 0,7days	80	6mo	Not available in US
(CVD-103HgR)	1 dose PO	80	6mo	Available in Europe
Diptheria (dT) (combined vaccine)	1 booster dose	80	5-10yrs	Safe
Meningococcal	1 dose IM	70-90	1-3mo	Polysaccharide vaccine containing four meningitis serotypes, mild infrequent reactions
Plague	3 doses IM: 0,1,6mo		6mo	Rarely indicated, except for rodent handlers
Pneumococcal				
Polysaccharide	1 dose	good	3-5yrs	Re-vaccinate only once. Efficacy depends upon population vaccinated
Conjugate	3 doses in infants < 11mo 2 doses in 12-23mo child			Limited data; studies ongoing
Tetanus	1 booster dose IM	>99	5-10yrs	Routine booster every 10 years/ 5 years with laceration. Arthus reaction with multiple booster doses
Tuberculosis	1 dose ID			Not recommended for adults
Typhoid fever				
(Ty21a)	4 doses PO:0,2,4,6day	70	5	Safe; rare GI side effects
(heat phenol inactivated)	2 doses IM:0,28day	70	3	Frequent reactions, often systemic
ViCPS	1 dose IM	70	2	Local reactions, better tolerated than heat phenol killed vaccine
Viral Vaccines				
Hepatitis A	2 doses IM: 0,6-12mo	>99	>10yrs	Safe; local reactions. Two vaccines in U.S. market equivalent
Hepatitis B	3 doses IM: 0,1,6mo	90	>5yrs	Safe; protection even after antibody titers decline
Japanese Encephalitis	4 doses IM: 0,7,21,365	90	4yrs	Disease low risk for travelers. Vaccine side effects significant, especially in people of European ancestry
Measles/Mumps/ Rubella	1 dose SC 90	20		Young adults need second dose if only immunized once in childhood
Poliomyelitis				
Salk	1 IM booster dose	>99	5-10	Inactivated vaccine, recommended for health care workers and immunocompromised recipients
Sabin	1 PO booster dose	>99	10	Shed live virus, not for health care workers
Rabies	3 doses IM/ID:0,7,21-28	>99	2	Requires 2 doses if exposure occurs. Side effects more prominent with booster doses (6% with immune complex reactions). Avoid ID route if on chloroquine/ mefloquine
Yellow fever	1 dose SC	>99	10	Live virus vaccine, 5% fever, myalgia. Contraindicated in immunocompromised patients and patients with a hypersensitivity to eggs.

*   Primary vaccination schedules. Time 0 is the first dose. mo=months, yrs=years
@   Consensus from multiple sources. May refer to presence of protective antibody rather than actual effectiveness studied with exposure to disease. Where discrepancies exist, CDC estimates given.
&   Duration is CDC recommendations for booster dose. Depends upon initial schedule. Controversy exists for less effective vaccine.

importance of maintaining high levels of vaccine coverage in populations for long periods of time.[66] Both the live oral vaccine and the killed parenteral vaccine are effective. Many clinicians prefer to use the killed vaccine because it carries a lower risk of vaccine-induced paralysis, and because use of the live vaccine may risk spread of the virus from health care workers to other patients, particularly those who are immunocompromised.

Rabies

Rabies is transmitted by the bites of animals, and rarely by exposure to aerosols of bat feces. The rate of animal bites is estimated to be 200-800 bites per 100,000 population per year. Low levels of vaccination in domestic animals (or none at all) in some areas presents potential for transmission.[67] The human diploid cell inactivated rabies (HDCV) vaccine is a three-dose series given over three weeks that has markedly fewer side effects than previous rabies vaccines. Two additional doses of the vaccine are required if a bite occurs and rabies is suspected or confirmed. Careful cleansing of bite wounds may be as important as the vaccine in preventing disease. Side effects such as a serum-sickness hypersensitivity reaction (type 3) are more frequent and severe after booster doses, which may be necessary every two years. An improved human rabies vaccine prepared in purified chick embryo cell culture (PCEC) appears to be as effective as the HDCV vaccine[68] and has not been reported to cause hypersensitivity reactions when booster doses are used.[69] Response to rabies vaccine given intradermally has been blunted by simultaneous use of chloroquine.[70] The intramuscular route should be used in travelers taking chloroquine or related compounds.

Meningococcal Meningitis

Outbreaks of meningitis have occurred in many places including during treks in Nepal, sub-Saharan Africa and in people making the annual pilgrimage to Mecca. New recommendations for vaccination in travelers are only for those traveling to the meningitis belt of sub-Saharan Africa.[71] The quadrivalent polysaccharide vaccine induces immunity to groups A, C, Y, and W-135, thus providing protection to the epidemic A strain usually encountered abroad.[72, 73]

Japanese Encephalitis

Japanese encephalitis (JE) is transmitted by Culex mosquitos in rural areas of Asia and the Indian subcontinent. Most cases of infection are subclinical. In patients with apparent disease, there is approximately a 25% fatality rate, with neurologic sequelae in 30% of

survivors.[74] Fear of this illness frequently causes travelers to request the JE vaccine, despite the fact that there have been only three cases reported among U.S. non-military travelers. Three doses of the vaccine are administered over one month.[75] Side effects are being reported with increasing frequency, and include serum sickness-like reactions, neurologic complications and angioedema.[76, 77] Many countries in Asia, including China and Japan, offer routine vaccination against Japanese B encephalitis. Children planning to live for prolonged periods of time in rural areas known to have JE transmission should be considered for the vaccine.

Simultaneous Administration of Vaccines

It is generally felt that inactivated viral or bacterial vaccines can be administered simultaneously without interference of individual vaccine responses. Combination vaccines providing protection against multiple diseases and decrease the number of injections appear to be safe. Some studies have documented lower immune responses to Hib vaccine after combination vaccination.

Yellow fever vaccine response may be decreased by live oral cholera vaccine (CVD 103 HgR) alone and in the combination live cholera-oral Ty21a typhoid vaccine.[78] In general, live virus vaccines should be administered either simultaneously or at least one month apart. Immune globulin should not be administered at the same time as Measles/Mumps/Rubella vaccine. The oral typhoid vaccine should not be administered while taking antibiotics, and preferably not with antimalarials.

Sex, Sexually-Transmitted Diseases, and HIV

Many sexually active people are aware that HIV is a sexually-transmitted disease. In many African cities, approximately a third of pregnant women are infected with HIV, and in Thailand, AIDS is a leading cause of death. Adults studying or traveling abroad are often willing to experiment sexually and may not be inclined toward monogamy. Sexual activity in the developing world, whether with sex workers, indigenous populations, or expatriates living abroad, must be considered highly risky.[79] Condom use can decrease the chances that a sexual encounter will transmit HIV or other sexually transmitted diseases. Despite knowledge of this fact, in a study of 757 travelers at the Hospital for Tropical Diseases in London, 66% of travelers having sex abroad with a new partner did not use condoms, 5.7% contracted a sexually transmitted disease, and 2.2% were urine HIV-antibody positive.[80] Knowledge of this data should be all that is needed for travelers to avoid engaging in unprotected sexual encounters abroad.

HIV Infection and Travel Abroad

Travel consultation for HIV-infected patients will employ many of the previously described recommendations, although the HIV-infected traveler may have contraindications to many of the preventive measures and may suffer more severe consequences of infection abroad.[81] Many vaccines are contraindicated, and drug interactions with medications needed for travel are common in HIV-infected travelers. Travelers infected with HIV would be wise to plan far in advance of any trip and to consult a specialist with familiarity both with travel medicine and HIV patient care.[82]

Air Travel and Jet Lag

Jet lag may manifest as a variety of physical and psychological symptoms including fatigue, anxiousness, anorexia and insomnia. Resting prior to travel and immediately rescheduling activities to the arriving time zone may benefit some travelers. Sleep-inducing medications and melatonin are used by many travelers to adjust quickly to travel across time zones. Melatonin has not undergone the clinical trial testing associated with other drugs used for sleeping; small studies have demonstrated improved sleep with melatonin and increased wakefulness with caffeine during the day, but efficacy remains largely unknown.[83-85]

Travel Medical Kits

Comprehensive lists of medications to carry while traveling abroad can be found in the texts cited and at the Internet locations provided in Table 1. The lists should be individualized. Travelers working abroad will often have access to hospitals and clinics that provide good medical care. Inquiries prior to travel should help narrow the list of items to carry. The most important items include a complete supply of antimalarials (where appropriate), insect repellents, antibiotics for diarrhea, a topical anti-fungal preparation, antihistamines and contraceptives. Traveling with syringes should be unnecessary if a complete and-up-to date vaccination card is carried within the passport to avoid overzealous vaccination by authorities at border crossings. The one exception is an anaphylaxis kit with a pre-filled epinephrine syringe for medically knowledgeable travelers.

Conclusion

Travel and work abroad can be one of the most rewarding and informative part of a student's curriculum or a scientist's career. Advance preparation is necessary to minimize travel-related morbidity and mortality.

References

1. Edwards M. Genghis Khan: Lord of the Mongols. National Geographic: 190:1-37,1996.
2. Knirsch CA. Travel medicine and health issues for families traveling with children. Adv Pediatr Infect Dis 14:163-89. 1999.
3. Ryan ET Kain KC. Health advice and immunizations for travelers. N Engl J Med 342:1716-25. 2000.
4. World Tourism Organisation. Facts and Figures, 2005 data. http://www.world-tourism.org/facts/menu.html (accessed April 2005)
5. Dupont HL. Steffen R (eds). Manual of Travel Medicine and Health. (B.C. Decker Inc. 2004).
6. Spira AM. Preparing the traveler. Lancet. 361:1368-81. 2003.
7. Behrens RL, Steffen R. In Cook GC (ed) Manson's Tropical Diseases (Elsevier 2003), 533-544.
8. Hargarten SW, Baker TD, and Guptill K. Overseas fatalities of United States citizen travellers: an analysis of deaths related to international travel. Ann Emerg Med 20:622-626. 1991.
9. Spira A. Diving and marine medicine review part 1: Diving physics and physiology. J Trav Med 6:32-44. 1999.
10. Fenner PJ. Dangers in the ocean: The traveler and marine en-venomation: Marine vertebrates. J Trav Med 5:213-216. 1998.
11. Day JH. Grant AD. et al. Schistosomiasis in travelers returning from sub-Saharan Africa. BMJ 313:268-269. 1996.
12. Cooke GS. Lalvani A. Gleeson FV. Conlon CP. Acute pulmonary schistosomiasis in travelers returning from Lake Malawi, sub-Saharan Africa. Clin Infect Dis 29:836-9. 1999.
13. Waner S. Health risks of travelers in South Africa. J Travel Med 6:199-203. 1999.
14. Jelinek T. Nothdurft HD. Loscher T. Schistosomiasis in Travelers and Expatriates. J Travel Med 3:160-164. 1996.
15. Ericsson CD. Dupont HL. Travelers' diarrhea: approaches to prevention and treatment. Clin Infect Dis 16:616-626. 1993.
16. Pitzinger B. Incidence and clinical features of travelers' diarrhea in infants and children. Pediatr Infect Dis J 10: 71-90. 1991.
17. Dupont HL. Ericsson CD. Johnson PC. Cabada FJ. Antimicrobial agents in the prevention of traveler's diarrhea. Rev Infect Dis 8: S167-171.1986.
18. Dupont HL. Ericsson CD. Mathewson JJ. DuPont MW. Five versus three days of Ofloxacin therapy for traveler's diarrhea: a placebo-controlled study. Antimicrob. Agents Chemother. 36: 87-91.1992.
19. Ericsson CD. Dupont HL, Mathewwson JJ. Optimal dosing of ofloxacin with loperamide in the treatment of non-dysenteric travelers' diarrhea. J Travel Med. 2001 Jul-Aug; 8 (4) 207-9.
20. Adachi JA. Ericsson CD. et al. Azithromycin found to be comparable to levofloxacin for the treatment of US travelers with acute diarrhea acquired in Mexico. Clin Infect Dis 37:1165-71. 2003.

21. Ericsson CD. DuPont HL. Rifaximin in the treatment of infectious diarrhea. Chemotherapy. 51 Suppl 1:73-80. 2005.

22. Kozicki M. Steffen R. Scar M. boil it. cook it. peel it or forget it: Does this rule prevent travellers' diarrhea? Internat J Epidemiol 14:169-172. 1985.

23. Steffen R. Fuchs E. et al. Mefloquine compared with other malaria chemoprophylactic regimens in tourists visiting East Africa. Lancet 341:1299-303. 1993.

24. Centers for Disease Control. Malaria in U.S. embassy personnel- Uganda 1992. MMWR; 42:289-96. 1993.

25. Centers for Disease Control: Dengue fever at the U.S.-Mexico border. 1995-1996. MMWR 45:841-844. 1996.

26. Lobel HO. Phillips-Howard PA. et al. Malaria incidence and prevention among European and North American travelers to Kenya. Bull World Health Organ 68:209-215. 1990.

27. Lobel HO, Miani M, Eng T, et al. Long term malaria prophylaxis with weekly mefloquine. Lancet 341:848-51. 1993.

28. Shmuklarsky MJ. Boudreau EF. et al. Failure of doxycycline as a causal prophylactic agent against *Plasmodium falciparum* malaria in healthy non-immune volunteers. Ann Intern Med. 120:294-299. 1994.

29. Canfield CJ. Pudney M. Gutteridege WE. Interaction of atovaquone with other anti-malarial drugs against *Plasmodium falciparum* in vitro. Exp Parasitol 80:373-381. 1995.

30. Looareesuwan S. Chulay JD. Canfield CJ. Hutchinson. DBA. Malarone (atovaquone and proguanil hydrochloride): A review of its clinical development for treatment of malaria. Am J Trop Med Hyg 60:533-541. 1999.

31. Looareesuwan S. Wilairatana P. et al. Efficacy and safety of atovaquone/proguanil compared with mefloquine for treatment of acute *Plasmodium falciparum* malaria in Thailand. Am J Trop Med Hyg. 60:526-532. 1999.

32. Shapiro TA. Ranasinha CD. Kumar N. Barditch-Crovo P. Prophylactic activity of atovaquone against *Plasmodium falciparum* in humans. Am J Trop Med Hyg 60:831-6. 1999.

33. Shanks GD, Kremser PG, Sukwa, et al. Atovaquone and proguanil hydrochloride for prophylaxis of malaria. J Travel Med 6:(Suppl 1): S21-27. 1999.

34. Shanks GD. New options for the prevention and treatment of malaria: Focus on the role of atovaquone and proguanil hydrochloride. J Travel Med 6:(Suppl 1):S1. 1999.

35. Shanks GD. Possible options for malaria chemoprophylaxis on the horizon. J Travel Med 6:(Suppl 1):S31-S32. 1999.

36. White NJ, Krishna S. Treatment of malaria: some considerations and limitations of the current methods of assessment. Trans R Soc Trop Med Hyg 83:767-777.1989.

37. McDonnell WM. Askari FK. Immunization. JAMA 278:2000-2007. 1997.

38. Centers for Disease Control and Prevention. Health Information for International Travel 1999-2000. DHHS. Atlanta, GA. http://www.cdc.gov/travel/(accessed April 20, 2005)

39. American Academy of Pediatrics. In: Peter G (ed.) 1997 Red Book: Report of the Committee on Infectious Diseases. 24th ed. Elk Grove Village, Il. 1997.

40. Hilton E. Singer C. et al. Status of immunity to tetanus, measles, mumps, rubella, and polio among US travelers. Ann Intern Med 115:32-33. 1991.

41. Hardy IR. Dittman S. and Sutter RW. Current situation and control strategies for resurgence of diptheria in newly-independent states of the former Soviet Union. Lancet 347:1739-44. 1996.

42. Black S. Epidemiology of pertussis. Pediatr Infect Dis J 16:85S- 89S. 1997.

43. Cherry JD. Comparative efficacy of acellular pertussis vaccines: An analysis of recent trials. Pediatr Infect Dis J 16:590-596. 1997.

44. Markowitz LE. Preblud SR. et al. Patterns of transmission in measles outbreaks in the United States, 1985-1986. N Engl J Med 320:75-81. 1989.

45. Shinefield HR. Black S. et al. Safety and immunogenicity of heptavalent pneumococcal CRM197 conjugate vaccine in infants and toddlers. Pediatric Infectious Disease Journal. 18:757-763. 1999.

46. Centers for Disease Control. Prevention and control of influenza. MMWR 45 (No. RR-5):1-24. 1996. Yellow fever in 1987. Bull WHO 67:451-453. 1989.

47. CDC. Yellow fever vaccine. Recommendations of the Immunization Practices Advisory Committee (ACIP). MMWR. 39:1-6. 1990.

48. Chan RC. Penney DJ. et al. Hepatitis and death following vaccination with 17D-204 yellow fever vaccine. Lancet. 358:121-2. 2001.

49. Martin M. Weld LH. et al. Yellow Fever Working Group. Advanced age a risk factor for illness temporally associated with yellow fever vaccination. Emerg Infect Dis. 7:945-51. 2001.

50. Mahon BE. Mintz ED. et al. Reported cholera in the United States. 1992-1994: a reflection of global changes in cholera epidemiology. JAMA 276:307-12. 1996.

51. Ryan ET. Calderwood SB. Cholera vaccines. J Travel Med. 8:82-91. 2001.

52. Holmgren J. Czerkinsky C. Mucosal immunity and vaccines. Nature Medicine11: S45-53. 2005.

53. Steffen R. Kane MA. et al. Epidemiology and prevention of Hepatitis A in travelers. JAMA. 272:885-889. 1994.

54. Steffen R. Hepatitis A and hepatitis B: risks compared with other vaccine preventable diseases and immunization recommendations. Vaccine 11:518-20. 1993.

55. Larouze B. Gaudebout C. et al. infection with hepatitis A and B viruses in French volunteers working in tropical Africa. Am J Epidemiol 126:31-37. 1987.

56. Werzberger A. Mensch B. et al. A controlled trial of a formalin-inactivated Hepatitis A vaccine in healthy children. N Engl J Med 327:453-7. 1992.

57. Anonymous. Hepatitis vaccine. Med Lett Drugs Ther 37:51-2. 1995.

58. CDC. Prevention of hepatitis A through active or passive immunization: Recommendations of the Advisory Committee on Immunization Practices (ACIP). MMWR. 48:1-37. 1999.

59. CDC. Update: recommendations to prevent hepatitis B virus transmission–United States. MMWR. 1999 Jan 22;48(2):33-4.

60. Steffen R. Richenbach M. et al. Health problems after travel to developing countries. J Infect Dis 156:84-91. 1987.

61. Ryan CA. Hargrett-Bean NT. Blake PA. *Salmonella typhi* infections in the United States. 1975-1984: increasing role of foreign travel. Rev Infect Dis 11:1-8. 1989.

62. Centers for Disease Control. Certification of poliomyelitis eradication-the Americas. MMWR 1994;43:720-2.

63. Nkowane BM. Wassilak SGF. et al. Vaccine-associated paralytic poliomyelitis-United states: 1973 through 1984. JAMA 257:1335-1340. 1987.

64. Kubli D. Steffen R. Schar M. Importation of poliomyelitis to industrialized nations between 1975 and 1984: evaluation and conclusions for vaccination recommendations. BMJ 295:169-171. 1987.

65. CDC. Progress toward the global interruption of wild poliovirus type 2 transmission. 1999. MMWR;48(33):736-8.747.

66. Centers for Disease Control and Prevention (CDC). Progress toward interruption of wild poliovirus transmission – worldwide, January 2004-March 2005. MMWR 54:408-12. 2005.

67. CDC. Compendium of Animal Rabies Control. 1999. National Association of State Public Health Veterinarians. Inc. MMWR. 48:1-9. 1999.

68. Dreesen DW. A global review of rabies vaccines for human use. Vaccine 15 Suppl:S2-6. 1997.

69. Anonymous. A new rabies vaccine. Med Lett Drugs Ther 40: 64- 65. 1998.

70. Pappaioanou M. Fishbein DB. et al. Antibody response to pre-exposure human-diploid cell rabies vaccine given concurrently with chloroquine. N Engl J Med 314:280-284. 1986.

71. CDC. Change in recommendation for meningococcal vaccine for travelers. MMWR. 48(5):104. 1999.

72. Centers for Disease Control: Epidemic meningococcal disease-Kenya and Tanzania: Recommendations for travelers. MMWR. 39:13-14. 1990.

73. Advisory Committee on Immunization Practices: Meningococcal vaccines. MMWR 34:341-2. 1985.

74. Advisory Committee on Immunization Practices: Inactivated Japanese Encephalitis virus vaccine. MMWR 42:1-15. 1993.

75. Poland JD. Cropp CB. et al. Evaluation of the potency and safety of inactivated Japanese encephalitis vaccine in US inhabitants. J Infect Dis 161:878-882. 1990.

76. Plesner A. Arlien-Soborg P. Herning M. Neurologic complications and Japanese encephalitis vaccination. (Letter) Lancet 348: 202. 1996.

77. Bonington A. Harbord M. et al. (Letter) Immunization against Japanese Encephalitis. Lancet 345:1445. 1995.

78. Wiederman G. Que JU. et al. Safety and immunogenicity of live oral cholera and typhoid vaccines administered alone or in combination with antimalarials, oral polio vaccines, or yellow fever. Fifth International Conference on Travel Medicine. Geneva. Switzerland. 1997.

79. Wang CC. Celum CL. Global risk of sexually transmitted diseases. Medical clinics of North America 83:975-995. 1999.

80. Hawkes S. Hart GJ. et al. Risk behavior and HIV prevalence in international travelers. AIDS 8:247-252. 1994.

81. Karp CL. Neva FA. Tropical infectious diseases in human immunodeficiency virus-infected patients. Clin Infect Dis 28:947-965. 1999.

82. Wilson ME. von Reyn CF. Fineberg HV. Infections in HIV-infected travelers: risks and prevention. Ann Intern Med 114:582-592. 1991.

83. Beaumont M. Batejat D. et al. Caffeine or melatonin effects on sleep and sleepiness after rapid eastward transmeridian travel. J Appl Physiol. 96:50-8. 2004.

84. Sack RL, Lewy AJ, Hughes RL. Use of melatonin for sleep and circadian rhythm disorders. Ann Med 30:115-121. 1998.

85. Brzezinski A. Melatonin in humans. N Engl J Med 336:186-95. 1997.

XI: Mode of Action of Anti-Parasitic Drugs

The Millennium Development Goals are targets that can only be achieved through access and proper use of medicines involved in treating many parasitic infections.[1] The greatest burden of disease due to parasitic infections, particularly those that are vector-borne, rests squarely on the shoulders of the developing world. In contrast, travel and immunosuppression create conditions for a different set of parasites causing unique clinical syndromes in the developed world. Food-borne illnesses due to Trichinella, Giardia, Entamoeba, and Cryptosporidium cause similar disease syndromes in both worlds, while Toxoplasma is found everywhere but causes a diversity of clinical syndromes that depends on age of acquisition of infection and the immune status of the host. This chapter will review the major classes of anti-parasitic drugs and review current knowledge on the mechanism of action of those drugs. An appreciation of parasite life cycles is required, since most drugs have specific activities directed at a distinct aspect of a given parasitic stage. Recommendations on dosage, side effects and use of drugs for specific infections are covered in the chapters devoted to individual organisms.

Anti-parasitic drugs can be grouped according to their activity against certain kinds of parasites. Very often, drugs are active either against protozoa or helminths. Some drugs (e.g., albendazole) have activity against both groups. Traditional herbal medicines have been successfully used to treat protozoan infections for centuries, and many modern drugs are based on these compounds. Modifications to some of the parent compounds have improved the activity and reduced their side effects. The development of in vitro culture of protozoans, either axenically or with mono-layers of permissive cell types, has facilitated research on mechanisms of drug action and drug resistance. In contrast, drugs used to treat helminth infections have often emerged from discovery efforts in treating helminths in livestock animals. The discussion of parasitic drugs in this chapter will focus on major drug classes and the activities observed in cell systems, animal models and the information learned when a parasite develops resistance. Drugs used to treat protozoa are discussed first followed by a discussion of anthelminthic drugs.

Anti-Protozoal Drugs

Malaria was and remains arguably the most important infectious organism to devastate human populations. The mechanism of action of most anti-malarial drugs is incompletely understood. However, progress in understanding unique biochemical pathways of Plasmodia may result in identifying useful targets for inhibitors that have proven successful in treating other infectious organisms.[2] Table 1 summarizes drugs used for the treatment of malaria. Several plants have been used both for treatment and for refinements and chemical modifications to improve upon the natural products.

Table 1. Anti-malarial compounds

Plant Derivatives	Dye Derivatives
Cinchona alkaloids	4-Aminoquinolines
Quinine	*Chloroquine*
Quinidine	*Amodiaquine*
Qinghaosu and derivatives	8-Aminoquinolines
Artemether	*Primaquine*
Arteether	4-Quinoline methanols
Artesumate	*Mefloquine*
Artemisinin	9-Phenanthrene methanols
	Halofantrine

Folate Antagonists	Antibiotics
Pyrimethamine	Tetracyclines
Proguanil	Clindamycin
Cycloguanil	Macrolides
Trimethoprim	
Sulfonamides	

Qinghaosu

The wormwood shrub *Artemisia annua* has been used in Chinese herbal medicine for treating malaria for nearly 2 millennia. Artemisinin was isolated in 1972 from this plant and found to be relatively insoluble.[3] Chemical modifications have improved upon the base compound's pharmacokinetic profile (Fig. 1). The artemisinins have been particularly useful for treating multi-drug resistant *P. falciparum* infections in Southeast Asia. The compounds rapidly clear the blood of parasites with activity against late ring forms and trophozoites, but not against liver forms.[4] Artemisinin derivatives accumulate in a variety of parasite membranes.[5] Killing is thought to involve free radical oxygen intermediates[6,7] after activation by heme.[8,9] The alkylating effects of the intermediates then appear to react with specific parasite proteins, including membranes in the merozoite digestive vacuole, limiting membranes and mitochondrion.[10,11] The site of action has recently been further localized to the sarco/endoplasmic reticulum Ca^{2+}-ATPase (SERCA) of *P. falciparum*.[12] The requirement for activation by heme has been recently debated[13,14] emphasizing the need for further research given resistance to artemisinins will likely soon emerge given the need to replace other classes of drugs due to widespread resistance to aminoquinolines.

The methyl derivative artemether is now recognized to have activity against schistosomes although the exact mode of action is not known.[15]

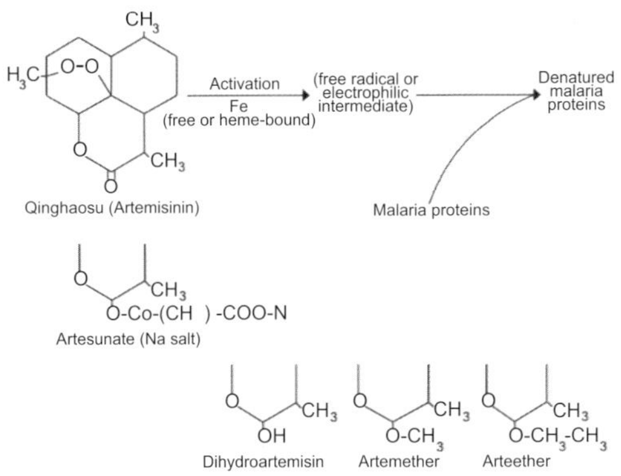

Figure 1. Artemisinin derivatives

Quinine

The bark of the cinchona tree, used since the 1600's in Peru, was imported to Europe for the treatment of periodic fevers. In 1820, quinine was isolated from cinchona bark by Pelletier and Caventou,[16] and today remains the most important first line therapy for severe malaria caused by *P. falciparum*. The laboratory synthesis of quinine is difficult, therefore both quinine and quinidine are still isolated from natural sources for human use (Fig. 2). Quinidine is used to treat cardiac arrhythmias and has replaced quinine in the United States for treatment of severe malaria because quinine is no longer available. Quinidine is more active than quinine against *P. falciparum*, but may have greater cardiac toxicity, and is generally used in the United States in settings where cardiac monitoring is available. The two isomers have no activity against the exo-erythrocytic stages of the parasite. Rather, they exert their action on mature erythrocytic forms.[17] Quinine does not have activity against the gametocytes of *P. falciparum*, so patients recovering from acute malaria treatment remain infectious for mosquitoes as long as the gametocytes remain in the circulation. Quinine is effective and acts rapidly against ring forms and prevents the growth of trophozoites. Quinine causes accumulation of malaria pigments and competes for the chloroquine binding site and binds even when chloroquine resistance is present.[18] Docking of antimalarial molecules with their targets may be affected by surface electrostatic potential.[19] Chloroquine and quinine bind to double-stranded DNA, and inhibit subsequent replication and transcription.[20] It is uncertain what role this mechanism plays in clearing parasites from the blood of patients but altered DNA repair does seem to be involved with the development of quinine drug resistance.[21]

Mefloquine

Mefloquine has a similar quinoline methanol structure as quinine and was developed at the Walter Reed Army Institute for Medical Research (WRAIR) because of its activity against drug-resistant *P. falciparum*. Mefloquine is active against blood forms, but not against the liver forms of *P. falciparum* or the latent liver form (hypnozoite) of *P. vivax*. The mechanism of action may be similar to quinine. Mefloquine causes swelling of the parasitic food vacuoles, but does not inhibit heme polymerase in contrast to chloroquine.[22] In fact, presence of the resistance mutation PfCRT, determining resistance to chloroquine, is conversely associated with increased susceptibility to mefloquine and quinine.[23] Mefloquine binds to free heme and may form toxic complexes to the parasite membrane, however it is not certain whether this is the primary mode of action of this drug.[24]

Halofantrine

Halofantrine was developed as part of the WRAIR program in the 1960's, when drug resistant *P. falciparum* reached alarming levels in Southeast Asia. Halofantrine has activity against the erythrocytic stages, but not against other forms, limiting its use to treatment of drug resistant malaria. The mechanism of action is uncertain, but it may act similarly to chloroquine, quinine, and mefloquine by concentrating in the parasite food vacuole and forming complexes with ferriprotoporphyrin IX to damage the parasite membranes.

Dyes and Dye Derivatives with Antimalarial Activity

Mepacrine

Mepacrine is a yellow dye that was first used for malaria treatment in the 1930's prior to the synthesis of chloroquine. The compound also has activity against

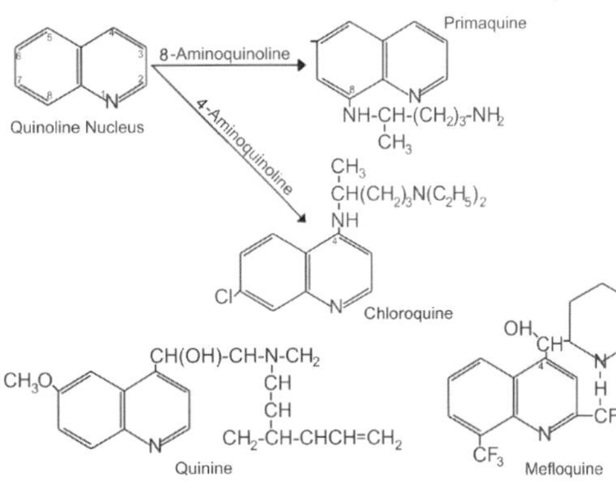

Figure 2. Quinolines

Giardia lamblia and some adult cestodes. Newer drugs with better safety profiles have replaced mepacrine.

Chloroquine

Chloroquine was synthesized in Germany in 1934. It has a quinoline base structure similar to quinine, and an identical side chain as that occurring on the yellow dye mepacrine.[16] Chloroquine has activity against the erythrocytic forms of the four human Plasmodium species, but not against the latent tissue forms (liver hypnozoite) of *P. vivax* or *P. ovale*. Chloroquine is a weak base that needs to be concentrated in the food vacuoles of parasites. The clonal asexual expansion of *P. falciparum* in an infected individual requires energy from hemoglobin utilization. Hemoglobin metabolism occurs in the acid food vacuoles of the malaria parasite where a breakdown product, ferriprotoporphyrin IX is produced and must be converted to a non-toxic substance.[25,26] Accumulation of chloroquine in acidic food vacuoles of *P. falciparum*, causes heme to accumulate instead of being converted to haemazoin (malaria pigment).[27,28] Chloroquine inhibits a substance that was referred to as heme polymerase,[29] however the enzyme has not been found, and other entities involved with dimerizing activity of ferriprotoporphrin have been identified and reviewed recently.[30]

Resistance to Quinolines

Resistance to the quinolines may share many mechanistic properties with multi-drug resistant tumor cells.[31] A p-glycoprotein may be involved with resistance caused by efflux of chloroquine from the malaria parasite.[32,33] Resistance to mefloquine may be mediated via a multi-drug resistance gene in *P. falciparum*. This gene, pfmdr1, is amplified in mefloquine resistant *P. falciparum* and codes for an ATP-binding cassette transporter.[34,35] Pfmdr is a marker for differential activity of all the quinolines and polymorphisms are widespread through out the world.[36] The pfmdr1 gene alone does not cause chloroquine resistance as was originally thought, suggesting that chloroquine resistance may be multi-genic.[37] A chloroquine resistance transporter has been identified (PfCRT) that is tightly linked in epidemiologic studies to chloroquine resistance.[38] Resistant *P. falciparum* has reduced levels of chloroquine accumulation that is reversed in vitro with the addition of calcium channel blockers, and compounds that reverse multi-drug resistance in tumor cells.[39,40] The cg2 gene on *P. falciparum* chromosome 7 mediates chloroquine resistance in isolates from Southeast Asia and South America. The cg2 protein is found at the parasite food vacuole at a site of chloroquine transport. However, it does not appear to be a transporter

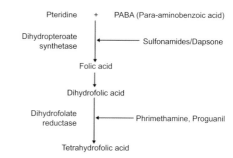

Figure 3. Anti-folates

protein.[41] Further characterization of the molecular basis of quinoline resistance in malaria will likely provide information on novel malaria gene products, thus directing the search for improved inhibitors. Already, phospholipids have received renewed attention as targets of quinoline action, and further studies will provide further insight into the mechanism of action of these drugs.[42]

Primaquine

Methylene blue was observed by Erlich in 1891 to have activity against Plasmodium organisms, and led to the synthesis of a number of 8-aminoquinolines. Primaquine is active against the hypnozoites of *P. vivax* and *P. ovale* both of which cause relapsing malaria. Primaquine also has activity against the *P. falciparum* liver forms and the gametocytes of all four species infecting humans. *P. vivax* cannot be maintained for long times in culture, so it has been difficult to ascertain why primaquine lacks significant activity against erythrocytic forms. The anti-malarial action of primaquine may be mediated by it's effect on oxidation-reduction and disruption of electron transport.[43] Primaquine also has an effect on Golgi apparatus function and inhibits the formation of transport vesicles.[44]

Antibiotics with Anti-malarial Activity

Pyrimethamine, Proguanil, Sulfonamides and Sulfones

The sulfonamides and sulfones are slow-acting agents compared to the quinolines. Nonetheless, they are effective against the erythrocytic stages of all species of Plasmodium. (Fig. 3). They inhibit dihydropteroate synthetase, while pyrimethamine and proguanil inhibit the next step in folic acid synthesis: dihydrofolate-reductase-thymidilate synthase (DHFR). Mammalian cells are able to use preformed, exogenous sources of folates, while *Plasmodium spp.* need to synthesize folates *de novo*. Single step resistant mutants occur via point mutations in the DHFR gene, causing a reduced affinity for the drug.[45] Pyrimethamine and proguanil act on the same enzyme. However, resistance is mediated via different mutations.[46,47]

Tetracyclines

The tetracylcines exert their action against prokaryotic bacteria against the 50s ribosome. Tetracyclines have a slow action against erythrocytic forms of *P. falciparum*, limiting their use to prophylaxis in drug resistant areas, and as an adjunct with quinine for acute treatment in areas with organisms partially resistant to quinine.[48]

Atovaquone

Atovaquone-proguanil is a combination of two medications that are relatively ineffective when used alone to treat malaria, but that have marked synergy when used together.[49] Challenge studies with infections employing non-drug-resistant strains of *P. falciparum* in healthy volunteers demonstrated causal prophylactic activity against exo-erythrocytic stages of the parasite.[50] Atovaquone is also active against *Leishmania donovani*, *Toxoplasma gondii* and the fungus *Pneumocystis carinii*. The mechanism of action is suggested to involve inhibition of electron transport in protozoal mitochondria with cytochrome complex III apparently the target in Plasmodium species.[51]

Other Anti-protozoal Drugs

Nitroimidazoles

Metronidazole and Tinidazole are the prototype drugs used in humans from this class of drugs. They are used to treat anaerobic bacterial infections as well as aerotolerant anaerobic protozoans caused by amoeba, trichomonads, and Giardia. The nitro group is reduced by ferredoxin and it acts as an electron sink.[52] Selective reduction of metronidazole in Giardia and entamoeba is by the enzyme oxidoreductase, an enzyme not present in humans. Nifurtimox is a nitrofuran that is active against bacteria and Trypanosoma cruzi. Similar to the nitroimidazoles, nifurtimox is converted to a reduced intermediate that generates hydrogen peroxide that protozoans are then unable to detoxify, due to the absence of the enzyme catalase.[53]

Antimony

Antimony-containing drugs are sparingly used because of their high degree of toxicity. Originally used for treating schistosomiasis, trypanosomes and leishmaniasis, only the pentavalent antimony, sodium stibogluconate, is still extensively used today for treatment of Leishmania. Antimony interrupts anaerobic pathways of glycolysis and energy production by blocking phosphorylation of fructose-6-phosphate[54] dehydrogenase in amastigotes.[55]

Amphotericin B

Amphotericin B is an anti-fungal agent with potent anti-leishmania activity. Fungi and Leishmania share 24-substituted sterols, hence the drug's activity across two kingdoms. Lipid formulations of Amphotericin B are preferentially taken up by infected mononuclear phagocytes.[56] Liposomal amphotericin B has been used successfully to treat antimony-resistant cases of visceral leishmaniasis.[57]

Melarsoprol

Melarsoprol is an arsenical compound that is used to treat both West and East African trypanosomiasis. Melarsoprol binds to trypanothione,[58] and resistance is mediated by a purine transporter that prevents melarsoprol from concentrating in the trypanomastigote.[59]

Pentamidine

Pentamidine is used to treat West African trypanosomiasis, and as an alternative drug for leishmaniasis. Pentamidine concentrates in the same trypanosome transporter in which melarsoprol concentrates.[60] However, the exact mode of action is unknown. Pentamidine has anti-fungal activity, and is an alternative drug for treating Pneumocystis carinii.

Miltefosine

Miltefosine is a new agent for treating leishmaniasis that was developed initially for use as an anti-tumor agent.[61] The mechanism of action is not fully understood but may be related to the ability of the agent to induce apoptosis of *Leishmania donovani*. [62]

α-difluoromethylornithine (DFMO)

DFMO is a useful drug for treating West African trypanosomiasis, and inhibits ornithine decarboxylase, an enzyme necessary for the production of polyamines.[63] Ultimately, cell differentiation of the protozoa is affected.

Anthelminthic Drugs

The anthelmintic drugs may be classified according to their mechanism of action: some interfere with metabolic pathways, others with steps in reproduction and larval development, while others disrupt the neuromuscular function of helminths.

Metabolic Pathway Inhibitors

Benzimidazoles

This versatile class of drugs has activity against many juvenile cestodes and tissue, and intestinal nematodes. Mebendazole is poorly absorbed and has been most useful in treating intestinal nematode infections. Albendazole is absorbed by humans, and is used for both intestinal and tissue nematodes. Thiabendazole used to be the drug of choice for strongyloidiasis until the safer ivermectin replaced it. The benzimidazoles bind β-tubulin preventing its polymerization with α-tubulin to form microtubules.[64,65] Loss of microtubule function in the nematode intestine[66] blocks glucose uptake, thus preventing ATP synthesis and effectively starving the worm.[67] Human tubulins are not bound by any benzimidazole compound. Resistance to benzimidazoles is associated with mutations in the ben-1 gene. Cross-resistance is present with all drugs in this class.[68] In experimental infection in sheep with the nematode *Haemonchus contortus*, reduction in alleles coding for isotypes of β-tubulin corresponds to benzimidazole resistance.[69] Modelling studies have explored the docking of albendazole with a crystallographic representation of the B-tubulin molecules to explain resistance mutations and species specificity.[70]

Niclosamide

Niclosamide is active against adult cestodes, but not against juvenile forms implicated in cysticercosis or hydatid disease. It is also very active against numerous trematode species, but has been largely replaced by praziquantel. Niclosamide blocks ATP production by uncoupling oxidative phosphorylation to a greater extent in parasites as compared to humans.[71] There is also evidence that host proteolytic enzymes may be able to damage the parasite after niclosamide treatment.[72]

Inhibitors of Neuromuscular Function

Avermectins

Avermectins are naturally occurring substances derived from *Streptomyces avermitilis*. Avermectins have been used to treat infections such as strongyloidiasis and onchocerciasis, as well as having an

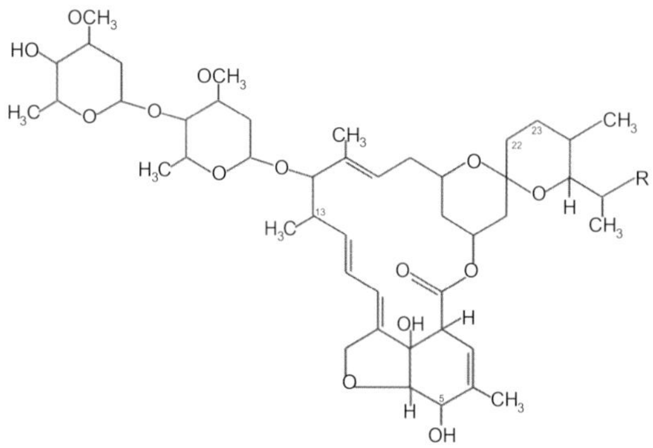

Figure 4. Ivermectin

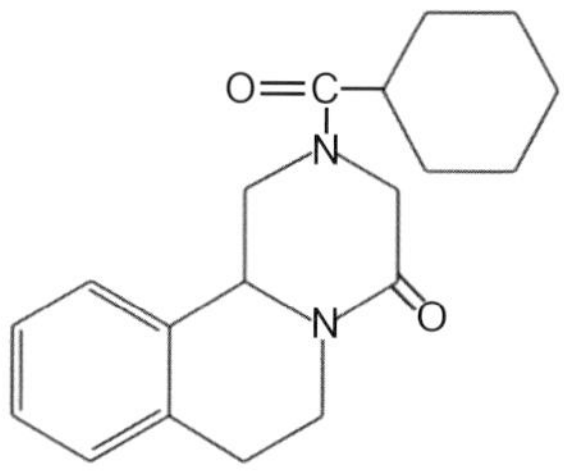

Figure 5. Chemical structure of Praziquantel

extremely important role in treating large and small domestic animals. The action of Ivermectin (a member of the avermectins) at therapeutic concentrations causes paralysis of the musculature of the worm. Avermectins are antagonistic to γ-aminobutyric acid (GABA) receptors in nematodes and arthropods. This may not be the actual anti-parasitic mode of action. Additional studies suggest that the anti-parasitic effect of the avermectins relates to their action on glutamate-gated chloride (GluCl) channels on invertebrate nerve and muscle.[73,74] The GluCl channels are located in the pharyngeal muscles of *Ascaris suum* and other related nematodes.[75] Three parallel genes controlling the GluCl channels in *Caenorhabditis elegans* must be knocked out before resistance to ivermectin is demonstrated.[76] Ivermectin reduces levels of microfilaria of *Onchocerca volvulus* in the skin, but does not kill the adult worms. The drug prevents larval development and release of microfilaria from the uterus of the female adult worm.[77] Ivermectin does not cross the blood brain barrier in humans, thus it is unable to interfere with host GABA receptors (Fig. 4).

Praziquantel

Praziquantel is the drug of choice for infections caused by all species of Schistosoma, and also has broad activity against other trematode and cestode infections. It is ineffective against nematodes (Fig. 5). Praziquantel increases the permeability of the cestode tegument to calcium ions, causing tetanic contractions, and detachment of the worm.[78] Phosphorylation of protein kinase C in the beta subunits of the calcium channels may be important in changes of susceptibility of schistosomes.[79] Praziquantel also has an effect on snail muscle cells similar to caffeine, an effective inhibitor of praziquantel in this system.[80] Praziquantel is active against both sexes of adult schistosomes and the larval forms as well. Spastic paralysis occurs at low doses of drug, and at higher doses, the worm tegument develops blebs and is unmasked, and is now susceptible to immune attack by the host.[81] Praziquantel also has activity against the juvenile forms of *Taenia solium* that cause cysticercosis.

Diethylcarbamazine (DEC)

Diethylcarbamazine is a piperazine derivative that has a pronounced effect in vivo against microfilariae, that is not reproducible in vitro.[73] DEC may have an unmasking effect, exposing surface antigens on the microfilaria to host immune attack. DEC has an effect on prostaglandin synthesis in both host and microfilarial cells, and unmasking may be mediated by prostaglandins.[82]

Pyrantel Pamoate

Pyrantel Pamoate is an example of a drug useful in veterinary medicine that then was developed for treating human intestinal nematode infections, including pinworm, hookworms and Ascaris infection. This compound causes paralysis of intestinal nematodes by binding to cholinergic nicotinic receptors at neuromuscular junctions.[83]

Drugs that Disrupt Reproduction and Larval Development

Oxamniquine

Oxamniquine is an alternate drug to praziquantal for treating *S. mansoni*, and acts against male worms, exposing the worm to a reactive ester that acts as an alkylating agent, that then interacts with parasite DNA.[84] Female worms are not killed, but are unable to produce eggs. Thus, the pathological consequences of infection are reduced after treatment.

Ivermectin

As already mentioned, one of the actions of Ivermectin is to prevent larval development and release of microfilaria from the uterus of the female adult worm.

The Future

Advances in treating and preventing parasitic infections have improved somewhat for malaria, but still lag significantly behind advances in prevention and chemotherapy of diseases caused by bacteria, fungi and viruses. As pointed out at the beginning of this chapter, parasitic diseases affect those living in developing countries most, and reversing this situation can only occur after stable economies in all affected regions of the world are in place. The Millennium Development Goals were developed to set clear milestones for improving human health worldwide, but unfortunately a recent interim report has documented significant shortcomings that may endanger the attainment of the goals by 2015. [85] Implementing health promotion and prevention of parasitic diseases to improve the productivity of its citizens should be the primary goal of all governing bodies in a position to help alleviate the suffering in the developing world. In the future, sequencing the human and selected medically important parasite genomes will undoubtedly serve as an information-rich database, from which drug and vaccine design can proceed. Development of new drugs and vaccines will, however, require large amounts of capital, the experience and good judgement of regulatory agencies, and collaboration with the international pharmaceutical industry. It is essential that politicians, ethicists, entrepreneurs, and scientists alike, collaborate to the fullest to ensure that protozoan and helminth disease control benefits from advances in molecular biology. This may require new paradigms for creating incentives necessary to bring new treatment modalities to the developing world.

References

1. http://www.un.org/millenniumgoals/ (accessed May 22, 2005)
2. Rosenthal PJ. Proteases of malarial parasites: New targets for chemotherapy. Emerging Infectious Diseases;4:49-57;1998.
3. Meshnick SR. Taylor TE. Kamchownwongpaisan S. Artemisinin and the antimalarial endoperoxides: From herbal remedy to targeted chemotherapy. Microbial Rev. 60:301-315,1996.
4. ter Kuile F. White NJ. Holloway P et al. *Plasmodium falciparum*: in vitro studies of the pharmacodynamic properties of drugs used for the treatment of severe malaria. Exp Parasitol. 76: 85- 95,1993.
5. Meshnick SR. The mode of action of antimalarial endoperoxides. Trans R Soc Trop Med Hyg;88 (suppl. 1):S31-S32. 1994.
6. Meshnick SR. Tsang TW.Lin FB et al. Activated oxygen mediates the antimalarial activity of Qinghaosu. Prog Clin Biol Res 313:95-104;1989.
7. Meshnick SR.Yang YZ. Lima V.Kuypers F. Kamchouwongpaisau S.Yuthavong Y. Iron-dependent free radical generation from antimalarial agent artemisinin (Qinghaosu). Antimicrob Agents Chemother 27: 1108-1114;1993.
8. Gabay TM. Krugliak M. Shalmiev G. Ginsburg H. Inhibition by anti-malarial drugs of hemoglobin denaturation and iron release in acidified red blood cell lystes-a possible mechanism of their anti-malarial effect? Parasitology 108: 371-381;1994.
9. Meshnick SR. Thomas A. Ranz A. Xu CM. Pan HZ.Artemisinin (Qinghaosu): The role of intracellular hemin in its mechanism of anti-malarial action. Mol Biochem Parasitol. 49: 181-189; 1991.
10. Ellis DS. Li ZL. Gu HM et al. The chemotherapy of rodent malaria. nn Trop Med Parasitol.79:367-374; 1985.
11. Maeno Y. Toyoshima T. Fujioka. H et al. Morphologic effects of artemisinin in *Plasmodium falciparum*. Am J Trop Med Hyg 49:485-491; 1993.
12. Eckstein-Ludwig U, Webb RJ et al. Artemisinins target the SERCA of *Plasmodium falciparum*. Nature. 2003 Aug 21;424(6951):957-61.

13. Parapini S, Basilico N et al. Evidence that haem iron in the malaria parasite is not needed for the antimalarial effects of artemisinin. FEBS Lett. 2004 Sep 24;575(1-3):91-4.

14. Meshnick SR. Artemisinin and heme.Antimicrob Agents Chemother. 2003 Aug;47(8):2712; author reply 2712-3.

15. Mahmoud MR, Botros SS. Artemether as adjuvant therapy to praziquantel in murine Egyptian schistosomiasis mansoni. J Parasitol. 2005 Feb;91(1):175-8.

16. Tracy JW. Webster LT. In Goodman and Gilman. The Pharmacological Basis of Therapeutics. Chapter 40: 965-1026.1996

17. Skinner TS. Manning LS. Johnston WA. Davis TM. in vitro stage-specific sensitivity of *Plasmodium falciparum* to quinine and artemisinin drugs. Int J Parasitol.26(5):519-25,1996.

18. Frayha GJ. Smyth JD. Gobert JG. Savel J. The mechanisms of action of antiprotozoal and anthelmintic drugs in man. Gen Pharmac 28:273-299; 1997.

19. Portela C, Afonso CM, Pinto MM, Ramos MJ. Receptor-drug association studies in the inhibition of the hematin aggregation process of malaria. FEBS Lett. 2003 Jul 17;547(1-3):217-22

20. Meshnick SR. Cloroquine as intercalator: a hypothesis revived. Parasitol Today 6: 77-79;1990.

21. Trotta RF, Brown ML, Terrell JC, Geyer JA. Defective DNA repair as a potential mechanism for the rapid development of drug resistance in *Plasmodium falciparum*.Biochemistry. 2004 May 4;43(17):4885-91.

22. Jacobs GH. Aikawa M. Milhous WK. et al. An ultrastructural study of the effects of mefloquine on malaria parasite. Am J Trop Med Hyg; 36:9-14;1987.

23. Sidhu AB, Verdier-Pinard D, Fidock DA. Chloroquine resistance in *Plasmodium falciparum* malaria parasites conferred by pfcrt mutations. Science. 2002 Oct 4;298(5591):210-3.

24. Palmer KJ. Holliday SM. Brogden RN. Mefloquine : a review of its antimalarial activity. pharmacokinetic properties and therapeutic efficacy. Drugs; 45:430-475; 1993.

25. Wellems TE. How chloroquine works. Nature; 355: 108-109; 1992.

26. Goldberg DE. Slater AF. Cerami A. Henderson GB. Hemoglobin degradation in the malaria parasite *Plasmodium falciparum*: an ordered process in a unique organelle Proc Natl Acad Sci; 87:2931;1990.

27. Krogstad DJ. Schlesinger PH. Gluzman IY. Antimalarials increase vesicle pH in *Plasmodium falciparum*. J Cell Biol. 101: 2302- 2309, 1985.

28. Krogstad Dj. Schlesinger PH. Acid vesicle function. intracellular pathogens and the action of chloroquine against *Plasmodium falciparum*. New Engl J Med. 317:542-549,1987.

29. Slater AFG. Cerami A. Inhibition by chloroquine of a novel haem polymerase enzyme activity in malaria trophozoites. Nature 355:167-169,1992.

30. Fitch CD. Ferriprotoporphyrin IX, phospholipids, and the antimalarial actions of quinoline drugs. Life Sci. 2004 Mar 5;74(16):1957-72

31. Milhous WK. Kyle DE. Introduction to the modes of action of and mechanisms of resistance to antimalarials. In: Malaria: Parasite Biology. Pathogenesis and Protection (Ed: Sherman IW). ASM Press. Washington DC 1998.

32. Ouellette M. Kundig C. Microbial multidrug resistance. Int J Antimicrob Agents 8:179-187;1997.

33. Krogstad DJ. Gluzman IY. Kyle DE et al. Efflux of chloroquine from *Plasmodium falciparum*: mechanism of chloroquine resistance. Science;238: 1283-1285;1987.

34. Wilson CM. Serrano AE.Wasley A. Bogenschutz MP. Shankar AH. Wirth DF. Amplification of a gene related to mammalian mdr genes in drug-resistant *Plasmodium falciparum*. Science; 244: 1184-1196;1989.

35. Wilson CM. Volkman SK.Thaithong S et al. Amplification of pfmdr 1 associated with mefloquine and halofantrine resistance in *Plasmodium falciparum* from Thailand. Mol Biochem Parasitol; 57: 151-160;1993.

36. Duraisingh MT, Cowman AF. Contribution of the pfmdr1 gene to antimalarial drug-resistance. Acta Trop. 2005 May 2; [Epub ahead of print]

37. Wellems TE. Panton LJ. Gluzman IY et al. Chloroquine resistance not linked to mdr-like genes in a *Plasmodium falciparum* cross. Nature 345:253-255;1990.

38. Bray PG, Martin RE, Tilley L, Ward SA, Kirk K, Fidock DA. Defining the role of PfCRT in *Plasmodium falciparum* chloroquine resistance. Mol Microbiol. 2005 Apr;56(2):323-33.

39. Martin SKJ. Oduola AMJ. Milhous WK. Reversal of chloroquine resistance in *Plasmodium falciparum* by verapamil. Science. 1987; 235:899-901.

40. Kyle DE. Milhous WK. Rossan RN. Reversal of *Plasmodium falciparum* resistance to chloroquine in Panamanian Aotus monkeys. Am J Trop Med Hyg. 48:126-133,1993.

41. Su X. Kirkman LA. Fujioka H. Wellems TE. Complex polymorphisms in an approximately 330-kDa protein are linked to chloroquine resistant *P. falciparum* in Southeast Asia and Africa. Cell; 91:593-603;1997.

42. Porcar I, Codoner A, Gomez CM, Abad C, Campos A. Interaction of quinine with model lipid membranes of different compositions. J Pharm Sci. 2003 Jan;92(1):45-57.

43. Tarlov AR. Brewer GJ. Carson PE. Alving AS. Primaquine sensitivity. Arch Intern Med;109:209-234;1962.

44. Hiebsch RR. Raub TJ. Wattenberg BW. Primaquine blocks transport by inhibiting the formation of functional transport vesicles. J Biol Chem; 266: 20323-20328;1991.

45. Peterson DS.Walliker D. Wellems TE. Evidence that a point mutation in dihydrofolate reductase-thymidylate synthase confers resistance to pyrimethamine in falciparum malaria. Proc Natl Acad Sci USA 85:9114-9118,1988.

46. Peterson DA. Milhous WK. Wellems TE. Molecular basis of differential resistance to cycloguanil and pyrimethamine in *Plasmodium falciparum* malaria. Proc Natl Acad Sci USA 87:3018-3022,1990.

47. Foote SJ.Galatis D. Cowman AF. Aminoacids in the dihydrofolate reductase-thymidylate synthase gene of *Plasmodium falciparum* involved in cycloguanil resistance differ from those involved in pyrimethamine resistance. Proc Natl Acad Sci USA 87:3014-3017,1990.

48. Chongsuphajaisiddhi T. Gilles T. Krogstad DJ et al. Severe and complicated malaria. Trans R Soc Trop Med Hyg; 80 (Suppl: 1-50);1986.

49. Canfield CJ. Pudney M. Gutteridege WE. Interaction of atova-quone with other anti-malarial drugs against *Plasmodium falciparum* in vitro. Exp Parasitol 1995; 80: 373-381.

50. Shapiro TA. Ranasinha CD. Kumar N. Barditch-Crovo P. Pro-phylactic activity of atovaquone against tt in humans. Am J Trop Med Hyg. 60(5):831-6,1999.

51. Fry M. Pudney M. Site of action of the antimalarial hydroxynaph-thoquinone 2-[trans-4(4'-chlorophenyl)cyclohexyl]-3-hydroxyl-1.4-naphthoquinone (566C80). Biochem Pharmacol; 43: 1545- 1553;1992.

52. Muller M. Mode of action of metronidazole on anaerobic bacteria and protozoa. Surgery 93:165-171;1983.

53. Docampo R. Sensitivity of parasites to free radical damage by antiparasitic drugs. Chem-Biol Interactions; 73:1-27;1990.

54. Bueding E. Some biochemical effects of anthelmintic drugs. Bio-chem chemotherapeutic developments in the last 10 years. Clin Infect Dis; 24 :684-703 ; 1997.Pharmac; 18:1541-1545;1969.

55. Berman JD. Chemotherapy for leishmaniasis: biochemical mechanisms. clinical efficacy. and future strategies. Rev Infect Dis; 10:560-586; 1988.

56. Berman JD. Human Leishmaniasis:Clinical. diagnostic. and chemotherapeutic developments in the last 10 years. Clin Infect Dis; 24:684-703; 1997.

57. Torre-Cisneros J. Villanueva JL. Kindelan JM. Jurado R. Sanchez-Guijo P. Succesful treatment of Antimony-resistant visceral leishmaniasis with Liposomal Amphotericin B in patients infected with human immunodeficiency virus. Clin Infect Dis;17: 626-627;1993.

58. Fairlamb AH. Henderson GB. Cerami A. Trypanothione is the primary target for arsenical drugs against African trypanosomes. PNAS 86:2607-2611; 1989.

59. Carter NS. Fairlamb AH. Arsenical-resistant trypanosomes lack an unusual adenosine transporter. Nature 361:173-176; 1993.

60. Fairlamb AH. Carter NS. Cunningham M. Smith K. Characterization of melarsen-resistant *Trypanosoma brucei* brucei with respect to cross-resistance to other drugs and trypanothione metabolism. Mol Biochem Parasitol; 53:213-222;1992.

61. Bhattacharya SK, Jha TK et al..Efficacy and tolerability of miltefosine for childhood visceral leishmaniasis in India. Clin Infect Dis. 2004 Jan 15;38(2):217-21.

62. Verma NK, Dey CS. Possible mechanism of miltefosine-mediated death of *Leishmania donovani.* Antimicrob Agents Chemother. 2004 Aug;48(8):3010-5.

63. McCann PP. Pegg AE. Ornithine decarboxylase as an enzyme target for therapy. Pharmacol Ther; 54:195-215; 1992.

64. Lacey E. The role of cytoskeletal protein tubulin in the mode of action and mechanism of drug resistance to benzimidazoles. Int J Parasotil;18:885-936;1988.

65. Lacey E. Mode of action of benzimidazoles. Parasitol Today 6:112-115;1990.

66. Van den Bossche H. Rochette F. Horig C. Mebendazole and related antihelmintics. Adv Pharmac Chemother 19:67-128; 1982.

67. Martin RJ. Robertson AP. Bjorn H. Target sites of anthelmintics. Parasitology; 114:S111-S124;1997.

68. Le Jambre LF. Molecular biology and anthelmintic resistance in parasitic nematodes. In: Resistance of Parasites to Antiparasitic Drugs(Ed: Boray JC. Martin JC.Rousch RT) MSD Agvet. New Jersey. 1990.

69. Roos MH. The molecular nature of benzimidazole resistance in helminthes. Parasitol Today 6: 125-127; 1990.

70. Robinson MW, McFerran N, Trudgett A, Hoey L, Fairweather I. A possible model of benzimidazole binding to beta-tubulin disclosed by invoking an inter-domain movement. J Mol Graph Model. 2004 Dec;23(3):275-84.

71. Goldsmith R. Drugs for the treatment of helmintic infections. In Tropical Medicine and Parasitology (Ed: Goldsmith R and Heyneman D) Appleton and Lange. E. Norwalk. CT. 1989.

72. Rollo IM. Drugs used in the chemotherapy of helminthiasis. In: The Pharmacologic Basis of Therapeutics (Ed: Goodman LS. Gilman A) MacMillan. London 1970.

73. Martin RJ. Robertson AP. Bjorn H. Target sites of anthelmintics. Parasitology; 114:S111-S124;1997.

74. Cully DF. Vassilatis DK. Liu KK et al. Cloning of an avermectin-sensitive glutamate-gated chloride channel from *Caenorhabditis elegans.* Nature; 371: 707-711; 1994.

75. Martin RJ. An electrophysiologic preparation of *Ascaris suum* pharyngeal muscle reveals a glutamate-gated chloride channel sensitive to the avermectin analogue milbemycin D. Parasitology 112:247-252; 1995.

76. Dent JA, Smith, MM, Vassilatis, DK, Avery L. The genetics of ivermectin resistance in *Caenorhabditis elegans.* PNAS 97: 2674- 2679, 2000.

77. Awadzi K. Dadzie KY. Schulz-Key. H et al. The chemotherapy of onchocerciasis. Ann Trop Med Parasitol;79:63-78;1985.

78. Harnett W. The anthelmintic action of Praziquantel. Parasitol Today; 5: 144-146; 1988.

79. Kohn AB, Roberts-Misterly JM, Anderson PA, Khan N, Greenberg RM. Specific sites in the Beta Interaction Domain of a schistosome Ca2+ channel beta subunit are key to its role in sensitivity to the anti-schistosomal drug praziquantel. Parasitology. 2003 Oct;127(Pt 4):349-56.

80. Gardner DR. Brezden BL. The sites of action of praziquantel in a smooth muscle of *Lymnaea stagnalis.* Canadian Journal of Physiology and Pharmacology; 62: 662-672; 1984.

81. Redman CA. Robertson AP. Fallon PG et al. Praziquantel: An urgent and exciting challenge. Parasitology Today; 12: 14-20;1996.

82. Maizels RM. Denham DA. Diethylcarbamazine (DEC): immunopharmacological interactions of an anti-filarial drug. Parasitology 105: S49-S60;1992.

83. Pinnock RD. Sattelle DB. Gration KAF. Harrow ID. Actions of potent cholinergic anthelmintics (morantel, pyrantel, and levamisole) on an identified insect neurone reveal pharmacological differences between nematode and insect acetylcholine receptors. Neuropharmacology 27: 843-848; 1988.

84. Cioli D. Pica-Mattocia L. Archer S. Drug resistance in schistosomes. Parasitology Today 9: 162-166; 1993.

85. http://www.unmillenniumproject.org/who/index.htm (Accessed May 22, 2005)

Appendix A: Handling of Specimens for the Diagnosis of Parasitic Infections

There is no substitute for a well-trained laboratory diagnostic technician. However, even the best-trained personnel cannot make up for an improper sample delivered to the laboratory in the expectation of securing the diagnosis. Stool, blood, urine and tissue samples must be treated as the most important link between the patient and the correct diagnosis of their parasitic illness. The following advice outlines standard procedure for insuring that the right amount and type of patient specimen is received by the diagnostic laboratory.

Stool Specimens

Proper collection and delivery of stool specimens is the single most important aspect of any diagnostic procedure relying on stool examination. The clinician can control the quality of this aspect, and in doing so, will insure both the reliability and accuracy of any test they recommend, regardless of whether that test is carried out in-house or at a regional diagnostic facility.

1. Fresh, unpreserved feces should be obtained and transported to the laboratory immediately. Fresh specimens are preferred for examinations for trophozoites, and are required when tests for Strongyloides stercoralis larvae are to be performed.
2. Unpreserved feces should be examined within one hour after passage, especially if the stool is loose or watery, and therefore might contain trphozoites of pathogenic Amoebae. Examination of formed stool may be delayed for a short time, but must be completed on the day on which the specimen is received in the laboratory. If prompt examination or proper fixation cannot be carried out, formed specimens may be refrigerated for 1-2 days.
3. If specimens are delayed in reaching the laboratory, or if they cannot be examined promptly (such as those received at night, on weekends, or when no parasitologist is available), portions should be preserved in fixatives such as 8% aqueous formalin or formol-saline, or with polyvinyl alcohol (PVA). Formalin preserves cysts, eggs and larvae for wet-mount examination or for concentration tests. PVA-fixative preserves trophozoites, cysts, and eggs for permanent

staining. A ratio of one part feces to three parts of fixative is recommended. The specimen may be placed in fixatives in the laboratory, or the patient may be provided with fixatives and instructions for collection and preservation of their own specimens.

Stool Examination

Stool specimens may be successfully examined by any one of the three methods listed below. The advantages and limitations of each technique must be recognized.

1. Saline mounts are of value primarily for demonstrating the characteristic motility of Amoebae and flagellates. In addition, seeing red cells inside a trophozoite of an Amoeba is diagnostic for Entamoeba histolytica. These organisms may be found in fresh stools, or occasionally in bloody mucus adhering to the surface of formed stools. Material should be obtained from several parts of the specimen. An iodine stain (a drop of 1% iodine in 2% potassium iodide) mixed with a stool suspension in saline solution facilitates identification of protozoan cysts, but it kills and distorts trophozoites.
2. Concentration techniques, useful for detecting small numbers of cysts and helminth eggs, may be used on unpreserved stool specimens, those preserved in aqueous formalin or formol-saline, or on PVA-fixed material.
3. Stained, thin smears of feces should be made if possible on all specimens obtained fresh or fixed in PVA. If properly prepared, they comprise the single most productive stool examination for protozoa. Smears may be stained with Wheatly-Gomori's Trichrome solution or with iron-hematoxylin (see Appendix B for colors of each). Any outstanding examples of positive specimens should be retained in a permanent file and used for future reference.

Number of Specimens Examined and Appropriate Intervals

1. To detect Amoebae, a minimum of three specimens should be examined; if these samples (obtained preferably at intervals of 2-3 days) are negative and Amoebic infection remains a diagnostic consideration, additional specimens should be examined.
2. With suspected giardiasis, three specimens should initially be examined. If they are negative, additional specimens should be obtained at weekly intervals for three weeks. PCR tests,

antigen capture ELISA, or duodenal aspiration may also be of value for detecting occult infections.

3. A single concentrate from one day's worth of stool is frequently sufficient to detect intestinal helminthic infections of clinical importance. With very light infections due to Schistosoma spp., few or no eggs may be found in the feces or urine. Strongyloides stercoralis may also require concentrating the specimen for diagnosis, but this method is not always reliable; various fecal culture methods or the enteric string test may also be used.

4. Examination after treatment, under most circumstances, should be delayed until one month after completion of therapy (three months after treatment for schistosomiasis or tapeworms).

Examination of Blood

1. Smears for malaria should consist of both thick and thin films. It is important that all involved laboratory personnel be aware of the technique for making thick films as they are useless if improperly made. Smears should be stained with Giemsa solution and a minimum of 100 contiguous microscopic fields examined before a specimen is reported as "negative." If the first specimen is negative, additional thick and thin films should be taken every six hours for the first 24 hours after admission.

2. When examining for filarial infection, the possibility of diurnal or nocturnal periodicity of microfilariae in the peripheral blood must be taken into account, and specimens should be taken every six hours for the first 24 hours after admission, as with malaria. Thick smears or blood concentration methods are most likely to demonstrate infection. Smears should be done in conjunction with the Knott Test (see Appendix B).

Serologic Methods

A variety of immunodiagnostic methods may serve as useful adjuncts to the clinical diagnosis of parasitic infections. In some cases, serologic methods may be the only laboratory recourse for making a diagnosis. Certain serologic tests provide a high degree of diagnostic accuracy; however, mixed infections, cross reacting antigens by related and unrelated parasites, and other diseases or physiologic conditions may interfere with the diagnostic accuracy of a given test.

Western blot analysis and ELISA have come into prominence within the last few years, and these two modalities will undoubtedly continue to offer the clinician sensitive, reliable methods for diagnosing parasitic infections. Positive tests revealing the presence of specific antibodies are indirect evidence of infection, no matter how good the method. Tests employing antibody capture techniques, in which monoclonal antibody are used to select for a single class of immunoglobulin increases the likelihood of a true positive result.

Most serum specimens may be shipped frozen or preserved with thimerosal to a final concentration of 1:10,000 to a state public health laboratory for forwarding to the Centers for Disease Control and Prevention in Atlanta, Georgia. The vial, containing at least 2 ml of serum, should indicate the preservative used.

Polymerase chain reaction (PCR)

The advent of amplifying parasite DNA in stool, blood, and tissue samples by the polymerase chain reaction (PCR) has widened the range of parasite detection methods. Reliable PCR tests have been developed for malaria, most species that cause leishmaniasis, toxoplasmosis, giardiasis, amoebiasis (*Entamoeba histolytica* and *E. dispar*), trypanosomiasis, and many others, as well. Unfortunately, most of these methods have been slow to become adopted by most hospital laboratories, due primarily to the lack of reasonably priced, reliable kits. This deficiency will most likely be corrected within the next few years.

Appendix B: Laboratory Diagnostic Methods

Reliable, practical tests for identifying parasitic protozoa and helminths are outlined here. Part I deals with unpreserved specimens and Part II with preserved specimens. There is no single method that efficiently renders all stages of all parasites available for microscopic identification; several tests must often be performed to obtain optimal results. For reviews of methods, see Garcia and Bruckner,[1] and Garcia.[2]

Unpreserved Stool Specimens

Ideally, stool specimens should be less than one hour old when first examined, although this may not always be possible. Stools that are up to 24 hours old may still be useful for recovering protozoan cysts, larvae and eggs of helminthes, but trophozoites rarely survive that long. A confounding factor when examining specimens left at room temperature for more than 24 hours is that some parasites can grow and develop. Refrigeration helps prevent this problem. Stools should not be frozen, as that would alter the morphology of the organisms examined.

Because of day to day variability in the quantity of various stages of parasite shed by an infected individual, parasites may not be present in a single specimen, particularly when the infection is light. A total of three specimens collected on consecutive days are needed to detect most enteric infections. Some parasites (e.g., the schistosomes and *Giardia lamblia*) often require more specimens for detection.

Barium or mineral oil interferes with identification of parasites. Therefore, patients should not be subjected to radiographic studies involving barium or given laxatives containing mineral oil until the stool specimens have been obtained.

Direct Examination

Gross examination:
1. Observe and record the appearance of the entire specimen, noting the color, consistency, and odor.
2. Examine the specimen for the presence of living parasites.
3. Perform a microscopic examination.
4. Examine a direct smear of the material.

The direct examination is effective for diagnosing living parasites (e.g., *Entamoeba histolytica*, *Giardia lamblia*, *Strongyloides stercoralis*), and should be performed on loose, diarrheic, or purged stool. When motile amoebae are found on a direct smear, a stained preparation should also be examined for the definitive diagnosis. If the Amoeba contains erythrocytes within the cytoplasm, it is *E. histolytica*, and stained specimens are not necessary for further identification.

If the specimen appears negative, as may occur with light infections, the sample should be concentrated.

1. Dip a wooden applicator stick into the specimen to coat the tip of it with stool.
2. Smear the stool onto a clear glass microscope slide on which a drop of normal saline solution has been placed and overlay with a coverslip. Smears must be thin enough to facilitate microscopic observation.

Staining the Direct smear

The Wheatly-Gomori trichrome (WGT) reagent stains the protozoan nuclei red to dark blue, the cytoplasm a lighter blue, and the background material green. Trophozoites and cysts tend to shrink away from the background material and are therefore relatively easy to locate.

The WGT reagent consists of 6.0 g chromotrope 2R, 0.5 g aniline blue CI42755, and 0.25 g dodecatungstophosphoric acid AR in 3 ml glacial acetic acid. WGT stain is applied to a thin smear of stool on a coverslip, and the coverslip is immersed sequentially in the solutions enumerated below for the prescribed lengths of time.

Solution	Time
Schaudinn's fixative	5 minutes at 50+°C, or 1 hour at room temperature
Ethanol-iodine 70%	1 minute
Ethanol 70%	1 minute
Ethanol 70%	1 minute
Trichrome stain	2-8 minutes
Ethanol 90% (acidified)	10-20 seconds

To remove excess stain, briefly dip the coverslip in destaining solution once or twice. Rinse in 90% ethanol to stop the process. Thin smears destain quickly; thicker ones may require three or four dips to obtain optimal differentiation. The process is as follows.

Solution	Time
Ethanol 95% or 100%	Two rinses
Ethanol 100%	1 minute
Xylol	1 minute

Mount the coverslip in an appropriate mounting medium and examine under a microscope.

Concentration Methods

Sedimentation by Centrifugation: Formaldehyde-Ethyl Acetate Method.

Sedimentation by concentration and exposure to formaldehyde-ethyl acetate concentrates cysts and eggs of parasites, but debris and ether-soluble materials localize in the formaldehyde-ether interface or the ether layer in the top of the tube. This process destroys trophozoites, as they disintegrate in ethyl acetate.

1. Mix stool 1:10 with H_2O.
2. Strain through a single layer of gauze into a 15-ml centrifuge tube.
3. Centrifuge the strained stool (1 minute at 2000 rpm) and discard the supernatant.
4. Wash the sediment once with H_2O.
5. Repeat steps 3 and 4.
6. Discard the supernatant and save the sediment.
7. Add 10 ml of 7.5% formaldehyde to the sediment.
8. Let stand 10-30 minutes.
9. Add approximately 3 ml of ethyl acetate, plug the tubes with stoppers, and agitate the mixture vigorously.
10. Remove the stoppers and centrifuge the tubes at 1500 rpm for 1 minute.
11. Gently loosen the debris from the tube wall with an applicator stick, being careful not to disturb the pellet.
12. Discard the supernatant.
13. Examine the sediment microscopically.
14. Add a drop of 70% ethanol-iodine solution (Lugol's solution) and examine again if internal structures of cysts are not recognized on first examination.

Sedimentation by Gravity:

The water sedimentation test is used primarily for the concentration and recovery of *Schistosoma mansoni* and *Schistosoma japonicum* eggs, and it is effective for determining their viability. An entire day's worth of stool should be examined in a single test because schistosome eggs are shed sporadically.

1. Emulsify the entire stool sample in H_2O.
2. Strain the specimen through a single layer of gauze into conical sedimentation flasks.
3. Allow the sediment to settle (approximately 20 minutes) and discard the supernatant.

4. Resuspend the sediment in water.
5. Repeat steps 3 and 4 until the supernatant is clear.
6. Discard final supernatant and save the sediment.
7. Examine the entire sediment microscopically.

The entire water sedimentation procedure should be done within two hours of starting, since prolonged exposure of schistosome eggs to water stimulates them to hatch. If hatching occurs, the empty shells remain in the sediment and the ciliated miracidia can be seen moving about rapidly.

Baerman Sedimentation Method.

This method is extremely useful for concentrating and recovering larvae of *Strongyloides stercoralis*. The test requires a funnel with a piece of rubber tubing attached to it. An adjustable clamp is applied across the tubing, and the entire apparatus is suspended from a ring stand in a 37°C incubator. Larvae concentrate in the sediment that accumulates in the base of the rubber tube connected to the funnel, and the fluid containing them is expressed into a test tube for microscopic identification

1. Emulsify the entire stool sample in H2O.
2. Strain the specimen through a single layer of gauze into conical sedimentation flasks.
3. Allow the sediment to settle (approximately 20 minutes) and discard the supernatant.
4. Resuspend the sediment in water.
5. Repeat steps 3 and 4 until the supernatant is clear.
6. Discard final supernatant and save the sediment.
7. Examine the entire sediment microscopically.

Floatation by Centrifugation:

Floatation methods concentrate various stages of parasites by taking advantage of their specific gravity. The unwanted debris sediments to the bottom of the tube during centrifugation, but the diagnostic forms float to the surface. Cysts and most eggs can be recovered in large quantities by this method, but trophozoites, operculated eggs, and schistosome eggs are either destroyed, or sediment to the bottom of the tube.

Zinc Sulfate Floatation Method

1. Mix 1 part stool in 15 ml H_2O in a 15-ml centrifuge tube.
2. Centrifuge for 1 minute at 2500 rpm; decant the supernatant.

3. Add zinc sulfate solution (specific gravity 1.18) until the tube is half full and resuspend the sediment with a wooden applicator stick.
4. Fill the tube to the top with more zinc sulfate solution.
5. Centrifuge the suspension for 1 minute at 2500 rpm. Do not apply the brake to the centrifuge or jar the tube, as either maneuver causes any eggs or cysts accumulated at the liquid-surface interface to sink.
6. Using a bacteriologic loop, remove two aliquots from the surface and place them on a clean glass slide.
7. Examine microscopically. A small drop of Lugol's iodine solution can be added to provide contrast.

Sugar (Sheather's) Floatation Method.
The recovery of *Cryptosporidium parvum* oocysts is facilitated by this method.
1. Filter stool through three pieces of cheesecloth.
2. Place 2 ml of stool filtrate in a conical tube.
3. Fill the tube to the top with sucrose solution.
4. Place a coverslip on top of the tube.
5. Centrifuge at 1000 rpm for 5 minutes. If the stool sample is watery, no centrifugation is necessary. Let the coverslip rest on the top of sucrose solution for 20 minutes.
6. Examine the coverslip microscopically at 400 X. The focal plane is important, because the oocysts are located on the inner surface of the coverslip, rather than on the slide itself. The oocysts appear slightly pink in color without the addition of any stain. They are ovoid to spherical in shape, range in size from 5 to 6 um in diameter and are usually not sporulated.

Blood (see Smith[3])

Fresh, heparinized, or citrated blood samples are best for examination. Delays reduce the chances of finding the parasites.

Place a drop of blood on a slide, overlay with a coverslip, and examine microscopically for living microfilariae or trypanosomes. Both groups of parasites are motile and can be seen swimming among the formed blood elements. Motility is significantly decreased if the blood sample is refrigerated. If an organism is seen, the smears should be prepared and stained, preferably with Giemsa solution.

Urine

Gross Examination
Observe and record the degree of turbidity and the color of the specimen.

Microscopic Examination
1. Take a drop of urine with a Pasteur pipette, preferably from the bottom of the container, and transfer it to a glass slide.
2. Examine microscopically.
   If *Trichomonas vaginalis* is suspected, the specimen must be fresh (<1 hour old), as the trophozoites quickly lose their characteristic morphology and motility.

Sedimentation by Centrifugation
1. Divide the entire urine specimen into 15-ml conical glass centrifuge tubes.
2. Sediment at 1000 rpm for 5 minutes.
3. Discard the supernatant.
4. Re-suspend the pellets with a Pasteur pipette and examine microscopically.

Sputum

Gross Examination
Observe and record the appearance of the specimen.

Microscopic Examination
1. Transfer a small amount of sputum with a wooden applicator stick to a clean glass slide.
2. Add a drop of normal saline solution.
3. Examine microscopically.

Sedimentation by Centrifugation
1. Mix sputum with equal parts of 3% NaOH.
2. Let stand 5 minutes.
3. Sediment at 1000 rpm for 5 minutes and examine microscopically.

Tissues (see Smith[3])

Place a small piece of tissue between two clean glass slides using forceps, press to flatten, then examine under a microscope.

To examine skin scrapings:
1. Place the scrapings on a clean glass slide.
2. Add a drop of normal saline solution and overlay with a coverslip.
3. Let stand 30 minutes.
4. Press the coverslip gently to break up the skin pieces and then examine microscopically.

Whole tapeworms must be carefully examined for the presence of a scolex. It is located at the narrowest end of the strobila. If only proglottids are available for observation, they must first be preserved in 10% formaldehyde. Then, the central uterus is injected with India ink using a 25-gauge needle. It is then placed between two glass slides, compressed, and examined with the aid of a dissection microscope. With Taenia segments, the lateral branches on one side of the main uterine stem are counted (see *Taenia saginata* and *Taenia solium*).

Arthropods are best identified preserved. The specimen should be placed in 70% ethanol and transferred to a Petri dish for examination when no longer motile.

Aspirated Fluids

Sedimentation by Centrifugation
1. Centrifuge clear fluid aspirates at 1000 rpm for 5 minutes in a conical centrifuge tube.
2. Decant supernatant.
3. Examine the pellet microscopically.
4. Stain by the Wheatly-Gomori trichrome procedure.

Miscellaneous Tests

Tape test for *Enterobius vermicularis* (Pinworm)
Clear tape preparations of various types, available commercially, are routinely used in the diagnosis of pinworm infection. The tape is placed with the sticky side down on the perineum, and eggs or adult worms adhere to it. The tape is then examined microscopically. Adult pinworms are also occasionally found on the surface of formed stool samples. Occasionally, eggs of *Taenia spp.* are seen on sticky tape tests.

Preserved Specimens

Whenever a delay of 24 hours or longer is anticipated, the specimen should be preserved. The preservative to be employed depends on the type of test selected.

Stool: Direct Smear
Merthiolate-iodine-formaldehyde Method (MIF). A solution of merthiolate, iodine, and formaldehyde (MIF) preserves and stains trophozoites and cysts. The organisms develop an orange color, but this stain does not last. Therefore, a permanent stain should also be done on the same stool sample. MIF is not acceptable for other staining procedures, such as the Wheatly-Gomori trichrome stain.

1. Emulsify 1 g of stool sample in 10 ml of MIF solution.
2. Place a drop of stool-MIF-emulsion on a clean glass slide and examine microscopically.

Stools preserved in MIF can be concentrated by sedimentation using the formaldehyde-ethyl acetate method.

Wheatly-Gomori Trichrome Stain for PVA-Preserved Stool
Stool specimens preserved in polyvinyl alcohol (PVA) can be stained by the Wheatly-Gomori trichrome method, which is the same as that for unpreserved stools, except that Schaudinn's fixative is not necessary and the staining time differs.

Solution	Time
Ethanol-iodine 70%	10-20 minutes
Ethanol 70%	3-5 minutes
Ethanol 70%	3-5 minutes
Trichrome stain	8-10 minutes
Ethanol 90% (acidified)	1-10 seconds

Dip the coverslip in the destaining solution once or twice. Rinse in 95% alcohol to stop the process. Thin smears destain quickly; thicker smears require three to five dips.

Solution	Time
Ethanol 95%	Rinse
Ethanol 95%	5 minutes
Xylol	10 minutes

Mount the stained coverslip and examine microscopically.

Blood

Microscopic Examination
A thick smear consists of several drops of blood on a slide, dried in air, and hemolyzed by immersion in a hypotonic solution. This process concentrates the parasites. A thin smear is prepared by making a film of blood analogous to that used for a differential count of the white cells. Giemsa staining is recommended for both preparations.

1. Immerse the slide in 100% ethanol or methanol for 2-3 minutes.
2. Make a solution consisting of 1 drop of concentrated Giemsa stain per 1 ml of distilled water (pH 7.4) and fill a Copeland jar with 50 ml of the mixture.
3. Stain for 10-30 minutes.
4. Wash in distilled H2O.
5. Air dry the slide.
6. Examine microscopically under oil immersion. View 100 contiguous fields of a thin smear.

Concentration by Sedimentation: Knott Test

The Knott technique concentrates and preserves filarial microfilariae, which can be stained by Giemsa solution and identified morphologically.

1. Mix I ml of heparinized blood with 9 ml of 2% formaldehyde.
2. Centrifuge at 2,000 rpm for 10 minutes.
3. Decant the supernatant.
4. Examine the sediment microscopically.

If microfilariae are present, they are stained as follows.

1. Spread the sediment on a clean glass slide.
2. Dry overnight.
3. Stain with Giemsa solution (1 ml of concentrated Giemsa stain in 50 ml of distilled water at pH 7.4).
4. Destain 10-15 minutes in H2O.
5. Air dry.
6. Examine microscopically.

Solutions

Schaudinn's Fixative

- H_gCl_2, saturated aqueous solution: 666 ml (add 80 g H_gCl_2 to 1 liter de-ionized H_2O; stir 3-4 hours and then filter)
- Ethyl alcohol 95%: 333 ml
- Ethanol-iodine solution 70%. Add enough crystalline iodine to 70% ethanol to turn the solution deep amber-brown; filter before using.

Wheatly-Gomori Trichrome Stain

Chromotrope 2R	0.6 g
Light green SF	0.3 g
Phosphotungstic acid	0.7 g

Mix with 1 ml of glacial acetic acid and stir gently for 20 minutes. Add 100 ml of distilled H2O, then store in dark brown bottle.

Buffered Formaldehyde

Formaldehyde solution 37-40%	100 ml
Sodium phosphate (monobasic, 4.0 g anhydrous)	
Sodium phosphate (dibasic, 6.5 g anhydrous)	
H_2O	900 ml

Adjust the pH of the solution to 7.0

Zinc Sulfate

Zinc sulfate	333 g
Water (50°-55°C)	1000 ml

Adjust the specific gravity to 1.18 by adding either more H_2O or more zinc sulfate crystals.

Sugar Solution (Sheather's Method)

Sucrose	500 g
Water	320 ml
Phenol	6.5 g

Merthiolate-Iodine-Formaldehyde Solution

Tincture of Merthiolate No. 99 (Lilly) 1:1000	100 ml
Formaldehyde solution 37-40%	25 ml
Glycerol	5 ml
H_2O	250 ml

Store solution in a dark bottle.

Lugol's Iodine Solution

Iodine	5 g
Potassium iodide	10 g
H_2O	100 ml

Polyvinyl alcohol

Polyvinyl alcohol is available commercially.

Schaudinn's fixative	935 ml
Glycerol	15 ml
Glacial acetic acid	50 ml
Polyvinyl alcohol (powder)	50 g
H_2O	1000 ml

References

1. Garcia LS. Bruckner D. Diagnostic Medical Parasitology. ASM Press, Pubs. pp. 940, 1997.
2. Garcia LS. Practical Guide to Diagnostic Parasitology. ASM Press, Pubs. pp. 320, 1999.
3. Smith JW. et al. Blood and Tissue Parasites. Diagnostic Medical Parasitology. Vol. I. American Society of Clinical Microbiologists. Chicago, Ill. 1976.

Appendix C: Diagnostic Atlas of Parasites

This atlas is intended as a pictorial reference for the diagnostic laboratory. It is important to be reminded that the laboratory obtains the most relevant information regarding a given parasitic infection. The physician must act according to the findings of the laboratory. Pattern recognition is the key to becoming a competent parasitology diagnostic technician. However, space only permits a single example to be shown of each relevant stage of the major parasites infecting the human host. Our atlas can only serve as a guide for a much broader range of variation in both size and shape for any given diagnostic stage. When an object is encountered under the microscope, the parasitic stage usually looks as it is depicted here. However, occasionally, even the most experienced laboratory technician may be unsure of or express some doubt about the identity of some objects. A few commonly encountered artifacts are shown for comparison. Suggested readings to more comprehensive atlases are listed, in case more visual examples are desired for comparison with the object in question. However, there is no shortcut to becoming familiar with each parasite. Only by co-observing patient samples with an accomplished technician can the skills necessary for advancement to the front lines of the diagnostic laboratory be developed.

It is very helpful to have a camera (preferably a digital image capturing device) attached to the diagnostic microscope. Images can then be stored on a computer and recalled on demand. This allows for the accumulation of a permanent record of interesting objects encountered under the microscope throughout the year. Such images are extremely helpful during training sessions for beginning parasitology technicians. Furthermore, digital images can be sent via e-mail, permitting instant consultation with any expert group, such as the Center for Disease Control and Prevention, in Atlanta, Georgia.

The majority of the protozoa depicted here have been stained with either iron-hematoxylin (blue-gray stain) or Wheatly and Gomori's trichrome stain (green and red stain). Helminth eggs are as they appear in unstained, concentrated stool sample. Their yellow-brown tints attest to the fact that they have encountered bile pigments. Microfilariae have all been stained with Giemsa (blue and red stain), as have the malaria parasites. The tissue section of the Nurse cell-parasite complex of *Trichinella spiralis* is stained with hematoxylin and eosin.

Suggested Readings

Garcia LS. Bruckner DA. Diagnostic Medical Parasitology. 3rd. ed. ASM Press, Herndon, Va. pp. 940, 1996.
Ash LR. Orihel TC. Atlas of Human Parasitology. American Society of Clinical Pathologists, Pubs. Chicago, Ill. pp.184, 1980.
Spencer FM. Monroe LS. The Color Atlas of Intestinal Parasites, rev. ed. Charles C. Thomas, Pubs, Springfield, Ill. 1975.
Yamaguchi T. Color Atlas of Clinical Parasitology. Wolfe Medical Publications, Pubs. London. pp. 293, 1980.
Zaman V. Atlas of Medical Parasitology. Lea and Febiger, Pubs. Philadelphia, Pa. pp. 285, 1979.

Anton van Leeuwenhoek, microscopist extraordinaire. Discoverer of the trophozoite of *Giardia lamblia*.

Protozoa

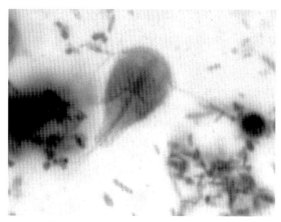

Figure C.1. *Giardia lamblia* trophozoite
15 µm

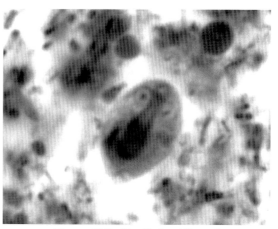

Figure C.2. *Giardia lamblia* cyst
15 µm

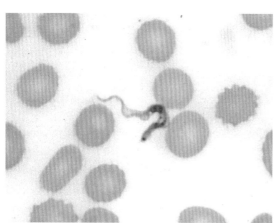

Figure C.3. *Trypanosoma brucei rhodesiense*
25 µm x 3 µm

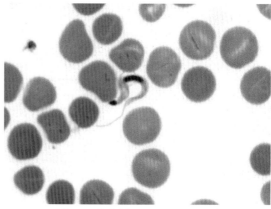

Figure C.4. *Trypanosoma cruzi*
20 µm x 3 µm

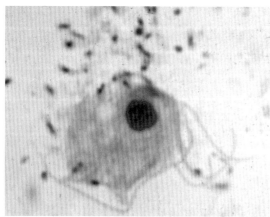

Figure C.5. *Trichomonas vaginalis*
20 µm x 10 µm

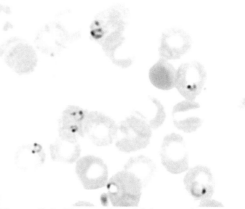

Figure C.6. *Plasmodium falciparum* ring stage

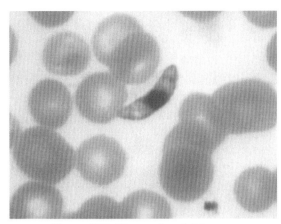

Figure C.7. *Plasmodium falciparum* macrogametocyte

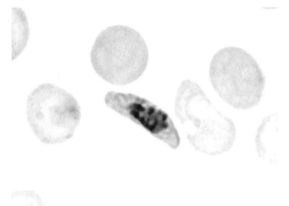

Figure C.8. *Plasmodium falciparum* microgametocyte

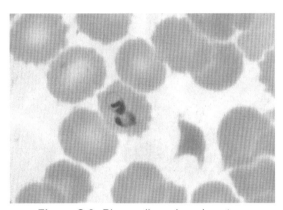

Figure C.9. *Plasmodium vivax* ring stage

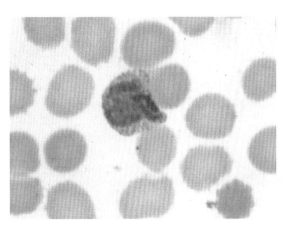

Figure C.10. *Plasmodium vivax* trophozoite

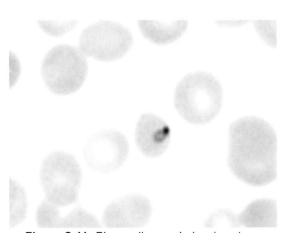

Figure C.11. *Plasmodium malariae* ring stage

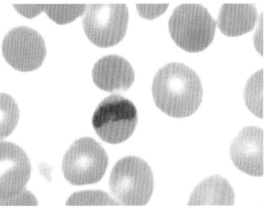

Figure C.12. *Plasmodium malariae* trophozoite

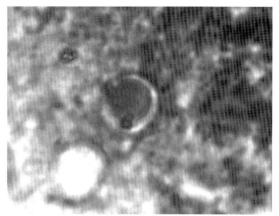

Figure C.13. *Cryptosporidium parvum* oocyst (acid-fast stain), 5 µm

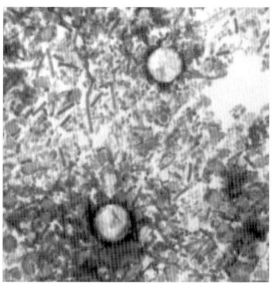

Figure C.14. *Cyclospora cayetanensis*

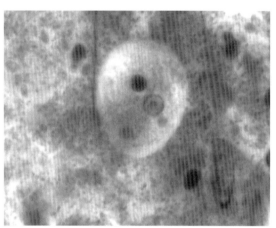

Figure C.15. *Entamoeba histolytica trophozoite* (note red cell in cytoplasm)

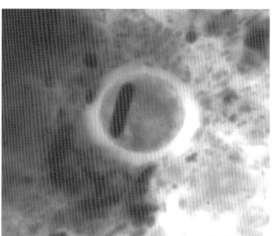

Figure C.16a. *Entamoeba histolytica* cyst
Note smooth-ended chromatoidal bar
15 µm

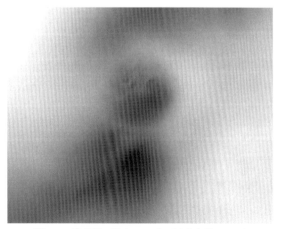

Figure C.16b. *Entamoeba histolytica* cyst
(Through-focus #1):
Note two nuclei
15 µm

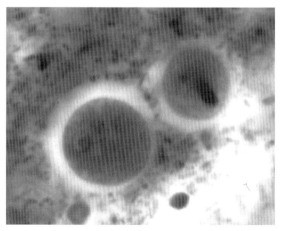

Figure C.16c. *Entamoeba histolytica* cyst
(Through-focus #2):
Note smooth-ended chromatoidal bar

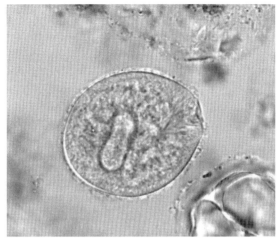

Figure C.17. *Balantidium coli* trophozoite
150 μm x 65 μm (unstained)

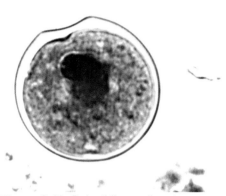

Figure C.18. *Balantidium coli* cyst
65 μm

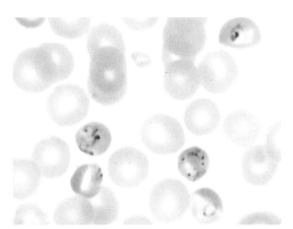

Figure C.19. *Babesia spp.* Bloodsmear

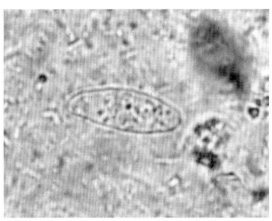

Figure C.20. *Isospora belli* unsporulated oocyst
25 μm x 15 μm

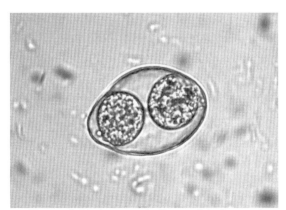

Figure C.21. *Isospora belli* sporulated oocyst
25 μm x 15 μm

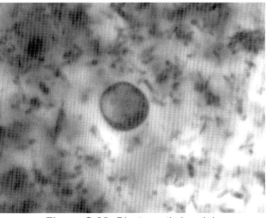

Figure C.22. *Blastocystis hominis*
6 μm

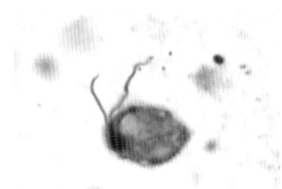

Figure C.23. *Trichomonas hominis*
10 µm x 8 µm

Figure C.24. *Trichomonas tenax*
7 µm x 3 µm

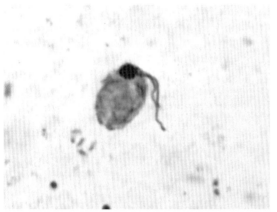

Figure C.25. *Retortamonas hominis*
6 µm x 2 µm

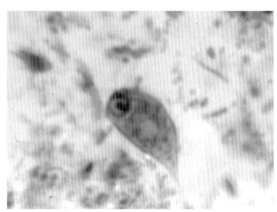

Figure C.26. *Chilomastix mesnili* trophozoite
15 µm x 12 µm

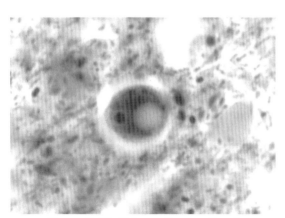

Figure C.27. *Chilomastix mesnili* cyst
8 µm x 5 µm

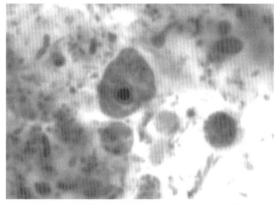

Figure C.28. *Endolimax nana* trophozoite
10 µm x 4 µm

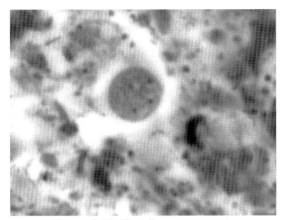

Figure C.29. *Endolimax nana* cysts
Note four nuclei
8 μm x 6 μm

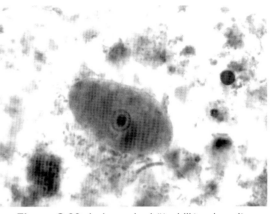

Figure C.30. *Iodamoeba bütschlii* trophozoite
18 μm

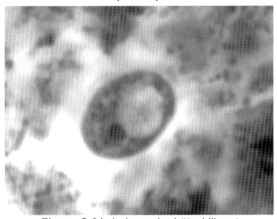

Figure C.31. *Iodamoeba bütschlii* cyst
12 μm x 8 μm

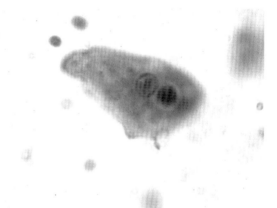

Figure C.32. *Entamoeba gingivalis* trophozoite
30 μm

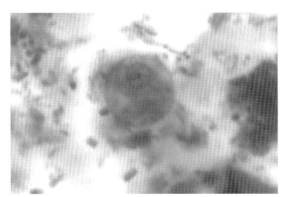

Figure C.33. *Entamoeba hartmanni* trophozoite
10 μm

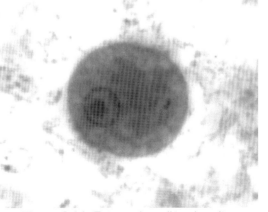

Figure C.34. *Entamoeba coli* trophozoite
35 μm

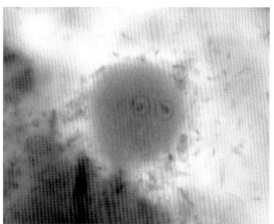

Figure C.35a. *Entamoeba coli* cyst
(Through-focus #1): Two nuclei can be seen
30 μm

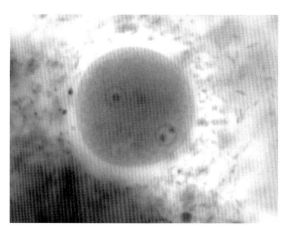

Figure C.35b. *Entamoeba coli* cyst
(Through-focus #2): Two nucleus can be seen

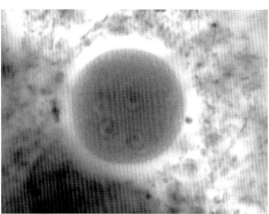

Figure C.35c. *Entamoeba coli* cyst
(Through-focus #3): Three nucleus can be seen

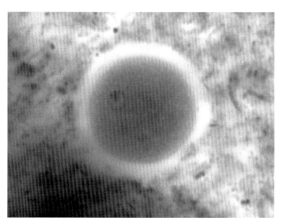

Figure C.35d. *Entamoeba coli* cyst
(Through-focus #4): One nuclei can be seen
A total of eight nuclei are present in the cyst

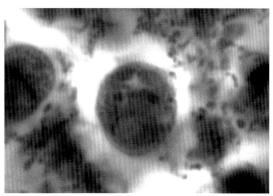

Figure C.36. *Dientamoeba fragilis*
10 μm

Nematodes

Figure C.37. *Enterobius vermicularis*
55 μm x 25 μm

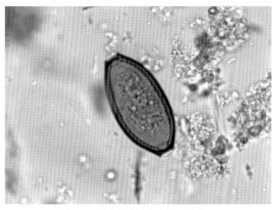

Figure C.38. *Trichuris trichiura*
50 μm x 20 μm

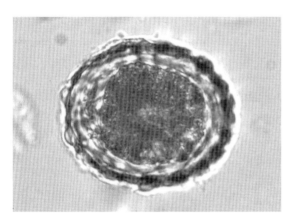

Figure C.39. *Ascaris lumbricoides*
(fertilized)
60 μm x 35 μm

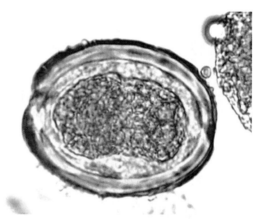

Figure C.40. *Ascaris lumbricoides*
(fertilized, decorticated)
50 μm x 30 μm

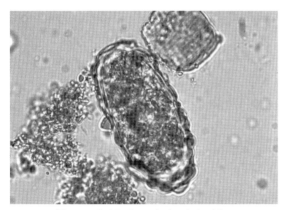

Figure C.41. *Ascaris lumbricoides*
(unfertilized)
Size variable; 70 μm x 30 μm

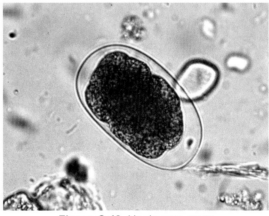

Figure C.42. Hookworm ovum
70 μm x 40 μm

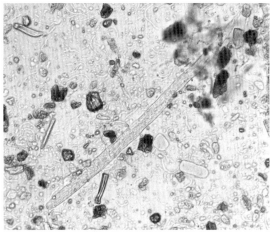

Figure C.43. *Strongyloides stercoralis*
(rhabditiform larvae)
500 µm x 15 µm

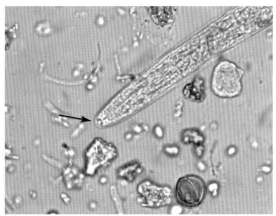

Figure C.44. *Strongyloides stercoralis*
(rhabditiform larvae)
Note short buccal cavity (arrow)

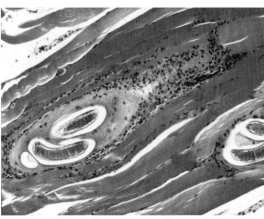

Figure C.45. *Trichinella spiralis*
Larva in muscle

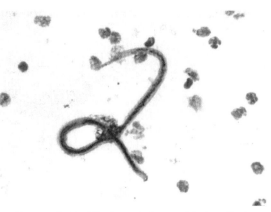

Figure C.46. *Wuchereria bancrofti* microfilaria
260 µm x 9 µm

Figure C.47. *Wuchereria bancrofti* microfilaria
Note sheath and nuclei, which do not extend to end
of tail

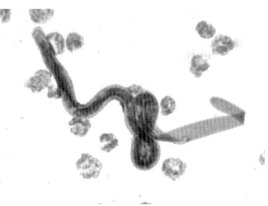

Figure C.48. *Brugia malayi* microfilaria
200 µm x 6 µm

Figure C.49. *Brugia malayi* microfilaria
Note nucleus at tip of tail and sheath

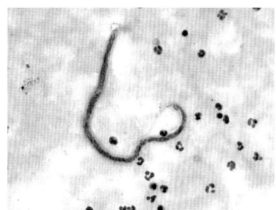

Figure C.50. *Loa loa* microfilaria
Note sheath
35 mm x 40 µm

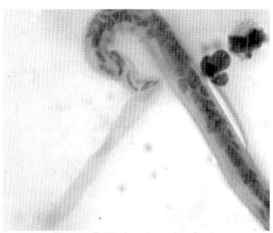

Figure C.51. *Loa loa* microfilaria
Note sheath and nuclei, which extend to end of tail

Figure C.52. *Mansonella ozzardi*
190 µm x 4 µm

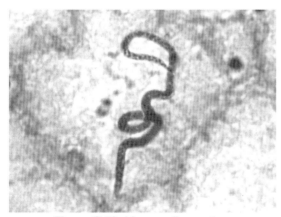

Figure C.53. *Mansonella perstans*
200 µm x 4 µm

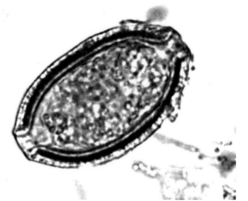

Figure C.54. *Capillaria philippinensis*
40 µm x 20 µm

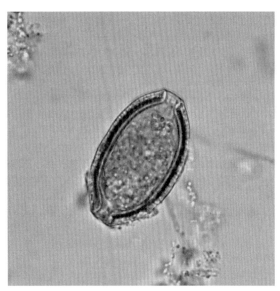

Figure C.55. *Capillaria hepatica*
60 µm x 30 µm

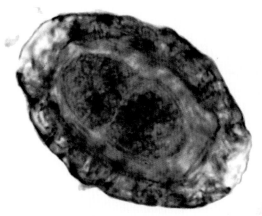

Figure C.56. *Dioctophyma renale*
70 µm x 45 µm

Cestodes

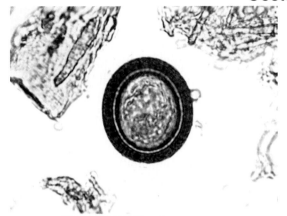

Figure C.57. *Taenia spp.* ovum
40 µm x 30 µm

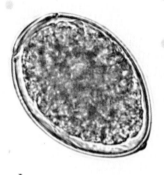

Figure C.58. *Diphyllobothrium latum*
65 µm x 45 µm

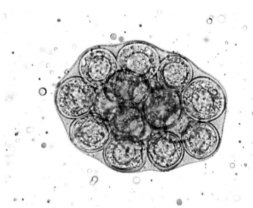

Figure C.59. *Dipylidum caninum* egg cluster
Each egg measures 35 µm

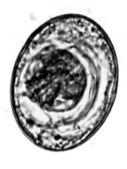

Figure C.60. *Hymenolepis nana*
45 µm x 30 µm

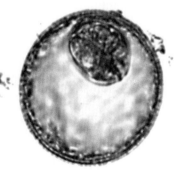

Figure C.61. *Hymenolepis diminuta*
75 µm x 70 µm

Trematodes

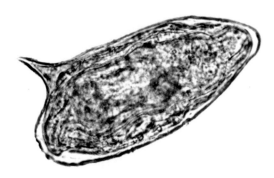

Figure C.62. *Schistosoma mansoni*
160 μm x 60 μm

Figure C.63. *Schistosoma mansoni*
Hatching egg

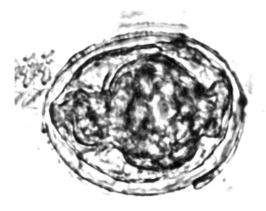

Figure C.64. *Schistosoma japonicum*
85 μm x 60 μm

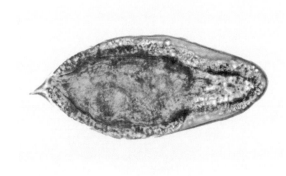

Figure C.65. *Schistosoma haematobium*
170 μm x 60 μm

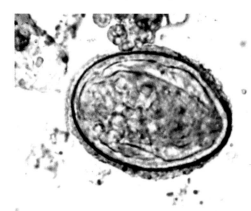

Figure C.66. *Schistosoma mekongi*
60 μm x 45 μm

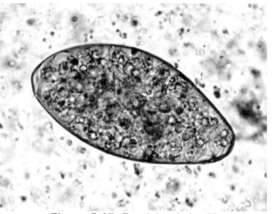

Figure C.67. *Fasciolopsis buski*
135 μm x 80 μm

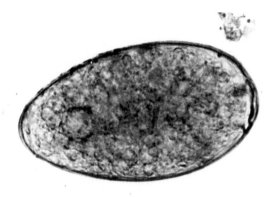

Figure C.68. *Fasciola hepatica*
140 μm x 75 μm

Figure C.69. *Paragonimus westermani*
110 μm x 60 μm

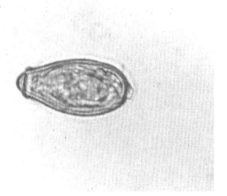

Figure C.70. *Clonorchis sinensis*
30 μm x 16 μm

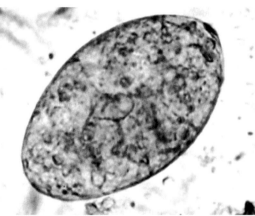

Figure C.71. *Echinostoma ilocanum*
130 μm x 60 μm

Figure C.72. *Heterophyes heterophyes*
20 μm x 15 μm

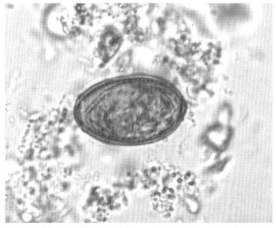

Figure C.73. *Metagonimus yokogawai*
30 μm x 15 μm

Miscellaneous

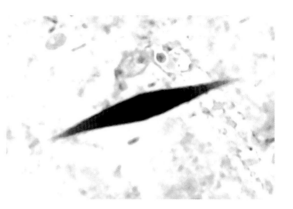

Figure C.74. *Macrocanthorynchus hirudinaceus*
60 μm x 20 μm

Figure C.75. Charcot-Leyden crystal
10 μm x 2 μm

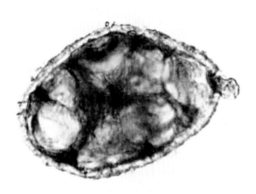

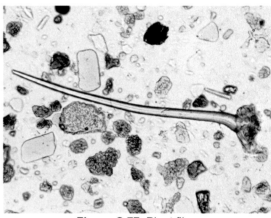

Figure C.76. Digested vegetable matter
(Artifact)

Figure C.77. Plant fiber
(Artifact)

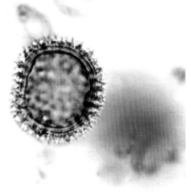

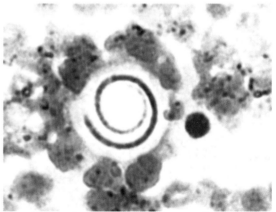

Figure C.78. Pollen grain
(Artifact)

Figure C.79. *Helicosporum spp.* (fungus)
(Artifact)

Reprinted with Special Permission from The Medical Letter

The Medical Letter®

On Drugs and Therapeutics

www.medicalletter.org

Published by The Medical Letter, Inc. • 1000 Main Street, New Rochelle, NY 10801 • A Nonprofit Publication

August 2004

DRUGS FOR PARASITIC INFECTIONS

Parasitic infections are found throughout the world. With increasing travel, immigration, use of immunosuppressive drugs and the spread of AIDS, physicians anywhere may see infections caused by previously unfamiliar parasites. The table below lists first-choice and alternative drugs for most parasitic infections. The brand names and manufacturers of the drugs are listed on page 12.

Infection		Drug	Adult dosage	Pediatric dosage
Acanthamoeba keratitis				
Drug of choice:		See footnote 1		
AMEBIASIS *(Entamoeba histolytica)*				
asymptomatic				
Drug of choice:		Iodoquinol	650 mg tid x 20d	30-40 mg/kg/d (max. 2g) in 3 doses x 20d
	OR	Paromomycin	25-35 mg/kg/d in 3 doses x 7d	25-35 mg/kg/d in 3 doses x 7d
Alternative:		Diloxanide furoate[2]*	500 mg tid x 10d	20 mg/kg/d in 3 doses x 10d
mild to moderate intestinal disease[3]				
Drug of choice:[4]		Metronidazole	500-750 mg tid x 7-10d	35-50 mg/kg/d in 3 doses x 7-10d
	OR	Tinidazole[5]	2 g once daily x 3d	50 mg/kg/d (max. 2g) in 1 dose x 3d.
severe intestinal and extraintestinal disease[3]				
Drug of choice:		Metronidazole	750 mg tid x 7-10d	35-50 mg/kg/d in 3 doses x 7-10d
	OR	Tinidazole[5]	2 g once daily x 5d	50 mg/kg/d (max. 2 g) x 5d
AMEBIC MENINGOENCEPHALITIS, primary and granulomatous				
Naegleria				
Drug of choice:		Amphotericin B[6,7]	1.5 mg/kg/d in 2 doses x 3d, then 1 mg/kg/d x 6d	1.5 mg/kg/d in 2 doses x 3d, then 1 mg/kg/d x 6d
Acanthamoeba				
Drug of choice:		See footnote 8		

* Availability problems. See table on page 12.

1. For treatment of keratitis caused by *Acanthamoeba*, concurrent topical use of 0.1% propamidine isethionate *(Brolene)* plus neomycin-polymyxin B-gramicidin ophthalmic solution has been successful (SL Hargrave et al, Ophthalmology 1999; 106:952). In some European countries, propamidine is not available and hexamidine *(Desmodine)* has been used (DV Seal, Eye 2003; 17:893). In addition, 0.02% topical polyhexamethylene biguanide (PHMB) and/or chlorhexadine has been used successfully in a large number of patients (G Tabin et al, Cornea 2001; 20:757; YS Wysenbeek et al, Cornea 2000; 19:464). PHMB is available from Leiter's Park Avenue Pharmacy, San Jose, CA (800-292-6773; www.leiterrx.com). The combination of chlorhexadine, natamycin (pimaricin) and debridement also has been successful (K Kitagawa et al, Jpn J Ophthalmol 2003; 47:616).

2. The drug is not available commercially, but as a service can be compounded by Panorama Compounding Pharmacy, 6744 Balboa Blvd, Van Nuys, CA 91406 (800-247-9767) or Medical Center Pharmacy, New Haven, CT (203-688-6816).

3. Treatment should be followed by a course of iodoquinol or paromomycin in the dosage used to treat asymptomatic amebiasis.

4. Nitazoxanide is FDA-approved as a pediatric oral suspension for treatment of *Cryptosporidium* in immunocompetent children <12 years old and for *Giardia* (Medical Letter 2003; 45:29). It may also be effective for mild to moderate amebiasis (E Diaz et al, Am J Trop Med Hyg 2003; 68:384). Nitazoxanide is available in 500-mg tablets and an oral suspension; it should be taken with food.

5. A nitro-imidazole similar to metronidazole, tinidazole was recently approved by the FDA and appears to be as effective and better tolerated than metronidazole. It should be taken with food to minimize GI adverse effects. For children and patients unable to take tablets, a pharmacist may crush the tablets and mix them with cherry syrup *(Humco,* and others). The syrup suspension is good for 7 days at room temperature and must be shaken before use. Ornidazole, a similar drug, is also used outside the US.

6. *Naegleria* infection has been treated successfully with intravenous and intrathecal use of both amphotericin B and miconazole plus rifampin and with amphotericin B, rifampin and ornidazole (J Seidel et al, N Engl J Med 1982; 306:346; R Jain et al, Neurol India 2002; 50:470). Other reports of successful therapy are less well documented.

7. An approved drug, but considered investigational for this condition by the FDA.

8. Strains of *Acanthamoeba* isolated from fatal granulomatous amebic encephalitis are usually susceptible *in vitro* to pentamidine, ketoconazole, flucytosine and (less so) to amphotericin B. Chronic *Acanthamoeba* meningitis has been successfully treated in 2 children with a combination of oral trimethoprim/sulfamethoxazole, rifampin and ketoconazole (T Singhal et al, Pediatr Infect Dis J 2001; 20:623) and in an AIDS patient with fluconazole, sulfadiazine and pyrimethamine combined with surgical resection of the CNS lesion (M Seijo Martinez et al, J Clin Microbiol 2000; 38:3892). Disseminated cutaneous infection in an immunocompromised patient has been treated successfully with IV pentamidine isethionate, topical chlorhexidine and 2% ketoconazole cream, followed by oral itraconazole (CA Slater et al, N Engl J Med 1994; 331:85).

EDITOR: **Mark Abramowicz, M.D.** *DEPUTY EDITOR:* **Gianna Zuccotti, M.D., M.PH.**, Weill Medical College of Cornell University *DIRECTOR OF DRUG INFORMATION:* **Jean-Marie Pflomm, Pharm. D.** *CONSULTING EDITOR:* **Martin A. Rizack, M.D., Ph.D.**, Rockefeller University *ADVISORY BOARD:* **Philip D. Hansten, Pharm.D.**, University of Washington; **Jules Hirsch, M.D.**, Rockefeller University; **James D. Kenney, M.D.**, Yale University School of Medicine; **Gerald L. Mandell, M.D.**, University of Virginia School of Medicine; **Hans Meinertz, M.D.**, University Hospital, Copenhagen; **Dan M. Roden, M.D.**, Vanderbilt School of Medicine; **F. Estelle R. Simons, M.D.**, University of Manitoba; **Neal H. Steigbigel, M.D.**, New York University School of Medicine
EDITORIAL FELLOWS: **Monika K. Shah, M.D.**, Columbia University College of Physicians and Surgeons; **Jane Gagliardi, M.D.**, Duke University Medical Center
SENIOR ASSOCIATE EDITORS: **Donna Goodstein, Amy Faucard** *ASSISTANT EDITOR:* **Cynthia Macapagal Covey** *MANAGING EDITOR:* **Susie Wong** *PUBLISHER:* **Doris Peter, Ph.D.**
Founded 1959 by Arthur Kallet and Harold Aaron, M.D. Copyright **2004. (ISSN 0025-732X)**

Infection		Drug	Adult dosage	Pediatric dosage
AMEBIC MENINGOENCEPHALITIS (continued)				
Balamuthia mandrillaris				
Drug of choice:		See footnote 9		
Sappinia diploidea				
Drug of choice:		See footnote 10		
ANCYLOSTOMA caninum (Eosinophilic enterocolitis)				
Drug of choice:		Albendazole[7]	400 mg once	400 mg once
	OR	Mebendazole	100 mg bid x 3d	100 mg bid x 3d
	OR	Pyrantel pamoate[7]	11 mg/kg (max. 1g) x 3d	11 mg/kg (max. 1g) x 3d
	OR	Endoscopic removal		
Ancylostoma duodenale, see HOOKWORM				
ANGIOSTRONGYLIASIS *(Angiostrongylus cantonensis, Angiostrongylus costaricensis)*				
Drug of choice:		See footnote 11		
ANISAKIASIS (*Anisakis* spp.)				
Treatment of choice:[12]		Surgical or endoscopic removal		
ASCARIASIS (*Ascaris lumbricoides,* roundworm)				
Drug of choice:		Albendazole[7]	400 mg once	400 mg once
	OR	Mebendazole	100 mg bid x 3d or 500 mg once	100 mg bid x 3d or 500 mg once
	OR	Ivermectin[7]	150-200 mcg/kg once	150-200 mcg/kg once
BABESIOSIS *(Babesia microti)*				
Drugs of choice:[13]		Clindamycin[7]	1.2 g bid IV or 600 mg tid PO x 7-10d	20-40 mg/kg/d PO in 3 doses x 7-10d
		plus quinine[7]	650 mg tid PO x 7-10d	25 mg/kg/d PO in 3 doses x 7-10d
	OR	Atovaquone[7]	750 mg bid x 7-10d	20 mg/kg bid x 7-10d
		plus azithromycin[7]	600 mg daily x 7-10d	12 mg/kg daily x 7-10d
Balamuthia mandrillaris, see AMEBIC MENINGOENCEPHALITIS, PRIMARY				
BALANTIDIASIS *(Balantidium coli)*				
Drug of choice:		Tetracycline[7, 14]	500 mg qid x 10d	40 mg/kg/d (max. 2 g) in 4 doses x 10d
Alternatives:		Metronidazole[7]	750 mg tid x 5d	35-50 mg/kg/d in 3 doses x 5d
		Iodoquinol[7]	650 mg tid x 20d	40 mg/kg/d in 3 doses x 20d
BAYLISASCARIASIS *(Baylisascaris procyonis)*				
Drug of choice:		See footnote 15		
BLASTOCYSTIS hominis infection				
Drug of choice:		See footnote 16		
CAPILLARIASIS *(Capillaria philippinensis)*				
Drug of choice:		Mebendazole[7]	200 mg bid x 20d	200 mg bid x 20d
Alternatives:		Albendazole[7]	400 mg daily x 10d	400 mg daily x 10d
Chagas' disease, see TRYPANOSOMIASIS				
Clonorchis sinensis, see FLUKE infection				

* Availability problems. See table on page 12.

9. A free-living leptomyxid ameba that causes subacute to fatal granulomatous CNS disease. Several cases of *Balamuthia* encephalitis have been successfully treated with flucytosine, pentamidine, fluconazole and sulfadiazine plus either azithromycin or clarithromycin (phenothiazines were also used) combined with surgical resection of the CNS lesion (TR Deetz et al, Clin Infect Dis 2003; 37:1304; S Jung et al, Arch Pathol Lab Med 2004; 128:466).

10. A free-living ameba not previously known to be pathogenic to humans. It has been successfully treated with azithromycin, IV pentamidine, itraconazole and flucytosine combined with surgical resection of the CNS lesion (BB Gelman et al, J Neuropathol Exp Neurol 2003; 62:990).

11. Most patients have a self-limited course and recover completely. Analgesics, corticosteroids and careful removal of CSF at frequent intervals can relieve symptoms from increased intracranial pressure (V Lo Re III and SJ Gluckman, Am J Med 2003; 114:217). No antihelminthic drug is proven to be effective and some patients have worsened with therapy (TJ Slom et al, N Engl J Med 2002; 346:668). In one report, however, mebendazole and a corticosteroid appeared to shorten the course of infection (H-C Tsai et al, Am J Med 2001; 111:109).

12. A Repiso Ortega et al, Gastroenterol Hepatol 2003; 26:341. Successful treatment of a patient with *Anisakiasis* with albendazole has been reported (DA Moore et al, Lancet 2002; 360:54).

13. Exchange transfusion has been used in severely ill patients and those with high (>10%) parasitemia (JC Hatcher et al, Clin Infect Dis 2001; 32:1117). In patients who were not severely ill, combination therapy with atovaquone and azithromycin was as effective as clindamycin and quinine and may have been better tolerated (PJ Krause et al, N Engl J Med 2000; 343:1454).

14. Use of tetracyclines is contraindicated in pregnancy and in children <8 years old.

15. No drugs have been demonstrated to be effective. Albendazole 25 mg/kg/d x 20d started as soon as possible (up to 3d after possible infection) might prevent clinical disease and is recommended for children with known exposure (ingestion of racoon stool or contaminated soil) (MMWR Morb Mortal Wkly Rep 2002; 50:1153; PJ Gavin and ST Shulman, Pediatr Infect Dis 2003; 22:651). Mebendazole, thiabendazole, levamisole or ivermectin could be tried if albendazole were not available. Steroid therapy may be helpful, especially in eye and CNS infections. Ocular baylisascariasis has been treated successfully using laser photocoagulation therapy to destroy the intraretinal larvae.

16. Clinical significance of these organisms is controversial; metronidazole 750 mg tid x 10d, iodoquinol 650 mg tid x 20d or trimethoprim-sulfamethoxazole 1 DS tab bid x 7d have been reported to be effective (DJ Stenzel and PFL Borenam, Clin Microbiol Rev 1996; 9:563; UZ Ok et al, Am J Gastroenterol 1999; 94:3245). Metronidazole resistance may be common (K Haresh et al, Trop Med Int Health 1999; 4:274). Nitazoxanide has been effective in children (E Diaz et al, Am J Trop Med Hyg 2003; 68:384).

Infection	Drug	Adult dosage	Pediatric dosage
CRYPTOSPORIDIOSIS (*Cryptosporidium*)			
Non-HIV infected			
Drug of choice:	Nitazoxanide[4]	500 mg bid x 3d[7]	1-3yrs: 100 mg bid x 3d
			4-11yrs: 200 mg bid x 3d
HIV infected			
Drug of choice:	See footnote 17		
CUTANEOUS LARVA MIGRANS (creeping eruption, dog and cat hookworm)			
Drug of choice:[18]	Albendazole[7]	400 mg daily x 3d	400 mg daily x 3d
OR	Ivermectin[7]	200 mcg/kg daily x 1-2d	200 mcg/kg daily x 1-2d
Alternative:	Thiabendazole	Topically	Topically
CYCLOSPORIASIS (*Cyclospora cayetanensis*)			
Drug of choice:[19]	Trimethoprim-sulfamethoxazole[7]	TMP 160 mg/SMX 800 mg (1 DS tab) bid x 7-10d	TMP 5 mg/kg, SMX 25 mg/kg bid x 7-10d
CYSTICERCOSIS, see TAPEWORM infection			
DIENTAMOEBA fragilis infection[20]			
Drug of choice:	Iodoquinol	650 mg tid x 20d	30-40 mg/kg/d (max. 2g) in 3 doses x 20d
OR	Paromomycin[7]	25-35 mg/kg/d in 3 doses x 7d	25-35 mg/kg/d in 3 doses x 7d
OR	Tetracycline[7,14]	500 mg qid x 10d	40 mg/kg/d (max. 2g) in 4 doses x 10d
OR	Metronidazole	500-750 mg tid x 10d	20-40 mg/kg/d in 3 doses x 10d
Diphyllobothrium latum, see TAPEWORM infection			
DRACUNCULUS medinensis (guinea worm) infection			
Drug of choice:	See footnote 21		
Echinococcus, see TAPEWORM infection			
Entamoeba histolytica, see AMEBIASIS			
ENTEROBIUS *vermicularis* (pinworm) infection			
Drug of choice:[22]	Pyrantel pamoate	11 mg/kg base once (max. 1 g); repeat in 2wks	11 mg/kg base once (max. 1 g); repeat in 2wks
OR	Mebendazole	100 mg once; repeat in 2wks	100 mg once; repeat in 2wks
OR	Albendazole[7]	400 mg once; repeat in 2wks	400 mg once; repeat in 2wks
Fasciola hepatica, see FLUKE infection			
FILARIASIS[23]			
Wuchereria bancrofti, Brugia malayi, Brugia timori			
Drug of choice:[24]	Diethylcarbamazine*	6 mg/kg in 3 doses x 14d[25]	6 mg/kg in 3 doses x 14d[25]
Loa loa			
Drug of choice:[26]	Diethylcarbamazine*	6 mg/kg in 3 doses x 14d[25]	6 mg/kg in 3 doses x 14d[25]

* Availability problems. See table on page 12.

17. Nitazoxanide has not consistently been shown to be superior to placebo in HIV-infected patients (B Amadi et al, Lancet 2002; 360:1375). A small randomized, double-blind trial in symptomatic HIV-infected patients who were not receiving HAART found paromomycin similar to placebo (RG Hewitt et al, Clin Infect Dis 2000; 31:1084).

18. G Albanese et al, Int J Dermatol 2001; 40:67.

19. HIV-infected patients may need higher dosage and long-term maintenance (A Kansouzidou et al, J Trav Med 2004; 11:61).

20. A Norberg et al, Clin Microbiol Infect 2003; 9:65.

21. Treatment of choice is slow extraction of worm combined with wound care (C Greenaway, CMAJ 2004; 170:495). 10 days' treatment with metronidazole 250 mg tid in adults and 25 mg/kg/d in 3 doses in children is not curative, but decreases inflammation and facilitates removal of the worm. Mebendazole 400-800 mg/d x 6d has been reported to kill the worm directly.

22. Since all family members are usually infected, treatment of the entire household is recommended.

23. Antihistamines or corticosteroids may be required to decrease allergic reactions due to disintegration of microfilariae from treatment of filarial infections, especially those caused by *Loa loa.* Endosymbiotic *Wolbachia* bacteria may have a role in filarial development and host response, and may represent a new target for therapy. Treatment with doxycycline 100 or 200 mg/d x 4-6wks in lymphatic filariasis and onchocerciasis has resulted in substantial loss of *Wolbachia* with subsequent block of microfilariae production and absence of microfilaria when followed for 24 months after treatment (A Hoerauf et al, Med Microbiol Immunol 2003; 192:211; A Hoerauf et al, BMJ 2003; 326:207).

24. Most symptoms caused by adult worm. Single dose combination of albendazole (400 mg) with either ivermectin (200 mcg/kg) or diethylcarbamazine 6 mg/kg is effective for reduction or suppression of *W. bancrofti* microfilaria but does not kill the adult forms (D Addiss et al, Cochrane Database Syst Rev 2004; CD003753).

25. For patients with microfilaria in the blood, Medical Letter consultants would start with a lower dosage and scale up: d1: 50 mg; d2: 50 mg tid; d3: 100 mg tid; d4-14: 6 mg/kg in 3 doses (for *Loa loa* d4-14: 9 mg/kg in 3 doses). Multi-dose regimens have been shown to provide more rapid reduction in microfilaria than single-dose diethylcarbamazine, but microfilaria levels are similar 6-12mos after treatment (LD Andrade et al, Trans R Soc Trop Med Hyg 1995; 89:319; PE Simonsen et al, Am J Trop Med Hyg 1995; 53:267). A single dose of 6 mg/kg is used in endemic areas for mass treatment (J Figueredo-Silva et al, Trans R Soc Trop Med Hyg 1996; 90:192; J Noroes et al, Trans R Soc Trop Med Hyg 1997; 91:78).

26. In heavy infections with *Loa loa*, rapid killing of microfilariae can provoke an encephalopathy. Apheresis has been reported to be effective in lowering microfilarial counts in patients heavily infected with *Loa loa* (EA Ottesen, Infect Dis Clin North Am 1993; 7:619). Albendazole or ivermectin have also been used to reduce microfilaremia; albendazole is preferred because of its slower onset of action and lower risk of encephalopathy (AD Klion et al, J Infect Dis 1993; 168:202; M Kombila et al, Am J Trop Med Hyg 1998; 58:458). Albendazole may be useful for treatment of loiasis when diethylcarbamazine is ineffective or cannot be used, but repeated courses may be necessary (AD Klion et al, Clin Infect Dis 1999; 29:680). Diethylcarbamazine, 300 mg once/wk, has been recommended for prevention of loiasis (TB Nutman et al, N Engl J Med 1988; 319:752).

Infection	Drug	Adult dosage	Pediatric dosage
FILARIASIS (continued)[23]			
Mansonella ozzardi			
Drug of choice:	See footnote 27		
Mansonella perstans			
Drug of choice:	Albendazole[7]	400 mg bid x 10d	400 mg bid x 10d
OR	Mebendazole[7]	100 mg bid x 30d	100 mg bid x 30d
Mansonella streptocerca			
Drug of choice:[28]	Diethylcarba-mazine*	6 mg/kg/d x 14d	6 mg/kg/d x 14d
	Ivermectin[7]	150 mcg/kg once	150 mcg/kg once
Tropical Pulmonary Eosinophilia (TPE)[29]			
Drug of choice:	Diethylcarba-mazine*	6 mg/kg/d in 3 doses x 12-21d	6 mg/kg/d in 3 doses x 12-21d
Onchocerca volvulus (River blindness)			
Drug of choice:	Ivermectin[30]	150 mcg/kg once, repeated every 6-12mos until asymptomatic	150 mcg/kg once, repeated every 6-12mos until asymptomatic
FLUKE, hermaphroditic, infection			
Clonorchis sinensis (Chinese liver fluke)			
Drug of choice:	Praziquantel	75 mg/kg/d in 3 doses x 1d	75 mg/kg/d in 3 doses x 1d
OR	Albendazole[7]	10 mg/kg x 7d	10 mg/kg x 7d
Fasciola hepatica (sheep liver fluke)			
Drug of choice:[31]	Triclabendazole*	10 mg/kg once or twice[32]	10 mg/kg once or twice[32]
Alternative:	Bithionol*	30-50 mg/kg on alternate days x 10-15 doses	30-50 mg/kg on alternate days x 10-15 doses
Fasciolopsis buski, Heterophyes heterophyes, Metagonimus yokogawai (intestinal flukes)			
Drug of choice:	Praziquantel[7]	75 mg/kg/d in 3 doses x 1d	75 mg/kg/d in 3 doses x 1d
Metorchis conjunctus (North American liver fluke)[33]			
Drug of choice:	Praziquantel[7]	75 mg/kg/d in 3 doses x 1d	75 mg/kg/d in 3 doses x 1d
Nanophyetus salmincola			
Drug of choice:	Praziquantel[7]	60 mg/kg/d in 3 doses x 1d	60 mg/kg/d in 3 doses x 1d
Opisthorchis viverrini (Southeast Asian liver fluke)			
Drug of choice:	Praziquantel	75 mg/kg/d in 3 doses x 1d	75 mg/kg/d in 3 doses x 1d
Paragonimus westermani (lung fluke)			
Drug of choice:	Praziquantel[7]	75 mg/kg/d in 3 doses x 2d	75 mg/kg/d in 3 doses x 2d
Alternative:[34]	Bithionol*	30-50 mg/kg on alternate days x 10-15 doses	30-50 mg/kg on alternate days x 10-15 doses
GIARDIASIS (*Giardia duodenalis*)			
Drug of choice:	Metronidazole[7]	250 mg tid x 5d	15 mg/kg in 3 doses x 5d
	Nitazoxanide[4]	500 mg bid x 3d	1-3yrs: 100 mg q12h x 3d
			4-11yrs: 200 mg q12h x 3d
	Tinidazole[5]	2 g once	50 mg/kg once (max. 2 g)
Alternatives:[35]	Paromomycin[7,36]	25-35 mg/kg/d in 3 doses x 7d	25-35 mg/kg/d in 3 doses x 7d
	Furazolidone	100 mg qid x 7-10d	6 mg/kg/d in 4 doses x 7-10d
	Quinacrine[2]	100 mg tid x 5d	2 mg/kg tid x 5d (max. 300 mg/d)
GNATHOSTOMIASIS (*Gnathostoma spinigerum*)			
Treatment of choice:[37]	Albendazole[7]	400 mg bid x 21d	400 mg bid x 21d
OR	Ivermectin[7]	200 mcg/kg/d x 2d	200 mcg/kg/d x 2d
±	Surgical removal		
GONGYLONEMIASIS (*Gongylonema sp.*)[38]			
Treatment of choice:	Surgical removal		
OR	Albendazole[7]	10 mg/kg/d x 3d	10 mg/kg/d x 3d

* Availability problems. See table on page 12.

27. Diethylcarbamazine has no effect. Ivermectin 200 mcg/kg once, has been effective.

28. Diethylcarbamazine is potentially curative due to activity against both adult worms and microfilariae. Ivermectin is only active against microfilariae.

29. Relapse occurs and can be treated with diethylcarbamazine.

30. Annual treatment with ivermectin, 150 mcg/kg, can prevent blindness due to ocular onchocerciasis (D Mabey et al, Ophthalmology 1996; 103:1001). Diethylcarbamazine should not be used for treatment of this disease.

31. Unlike infections with other flukes, *Fasciola hepatica* infections may not respond to praziquantel. Triclabendazole (*Egaten* - Novartis) may be safe and effective but data are limited (CS Graham et al, Clin Infect Dis 2001; 33:1). It is available from Victoria Pharmacy, Zurich, Switzerland (www.pharmaworld.com; 41-1-211-24-32) and should be given with food for better absorption. A single study has found that nitazoxanide has limited efficacy for treating fascioliasis in adults and children (L Favennec et al, Aliment Pharmacol Ther 2003; 17:265).

32. J Richter et al, Curr Treat Option Infect Dis 2002; 4:313.

33. JD MacLean et al, Lancet 1996; 347:154.

34. Triclabendazole may be effective in a dosage of 5 mg/kg once/d x 3d or 10 mg/kg bid x 1d (M Calvopiña et al, Trans R Soc Trop Med Hyg 1998; 92:566). See footnote 31 for availability.

35. Albendazole 400 mg daily x 5d alone or in combination with metronidazole may also be effective (A Hall and Q Nahar, Trans R Soc Trop Med Hyg 1993; 87:84; AK Dutta et al, Indian J Pediatr 1994; 61:689; B Cacopardo et al, Clin Ter 1995; 146:761). Combination treatment with standard doses of metronidazole and quinacrine given for 3wks has been effective for a small number of refractory infections (TE Nash et al, Clin Infect Dis 2001; 33:22). In one study, nitazoxanide was used successfully in high doses to treat a case of *Giardia* resistant to metronidazole and albendazole (P Abboud et al, Clin Infect Dis 2001; 32:1792).

36. Not absorbed; may be useful for treatment of giardiasis in pregnancy.

37. M de Gorgolas et al, J Travel Med 2003; 10:358. All patients should be treated with a medication regardless of whether surgery is attempted.

38. ML Eberhard and C Busillo, Am J Trop Med Hyg 1999; 61:51; ME Wilson et al, Clin Infect Dis 2001; 32:1378.

Infection	Drug	Adult dosage	Pediatric dosage
HOOKWORM infection (*Ancylostoma duodenale, Necator americanus*)			
Drug of choice:	Albendazole[7]	400 mg once	400 mg once
OR	Mebendazole	100 mg bid x 3d or 500 mg once	100 mg bid x 3d or 500 mg once
OR	Pyrantel pamoate[7]	11 mg/kg (max. 1g) x 3d	11 mg/kg (max. 1g) x 3d
Hydatid cyst, see TAPEWORM infection			
Hymenolepis nana, see TAPEWORM infection			
ISOSPORIASIS (*Isospora belli*)			
Drug of choice:[39]	Trimethoprim-sulfamethoxazole[7]	TMP 160 mg/SMX 800 mg (1 DS tab) bid x 10d	TMP 5 mg/kg, SMX 25 mg/kg bid x 10d
LEISHMANIA infection			
Visceral[40]			
Drugs of choice:	Sodium stibo-gluconate*	20 mg Sb/kg/d IV or IM x 28d[41]	20 mg Sb/kg/d IV or IM x 28d[41]
OR	Meglumine antimonate*	20 mg Sb/kg/d IV or IM x 28d[41]	20 mg Sb/kg/d IV or IM x 28d[41]
OR	Amphotericin B[7]	0.5-1 mg/kg IV daily or every second day for up to 8wks	0.5-1 mg/kg IV daily or every second day for up to 8wks
OR	Liposomal amphotericin B[42]	3 mg/kg/d IV (d 1-5) and 3 mg/kg/d d 14 and 21[43]	3 mg/kg/d IV (d 1-5) and 3 mg/kg/d d 14 and 21[43]
Alternative:[44]	Pentamidine[7]	4 mg/kg IV or IM daily or every second day for 15-30 doses	4 mg/kg IV or IM daily or every second day for 15-30 doses
Cutaneous[45]			
Drugs of choice:	Sodium stibo-gluconate*	20 mg Sb/kg/d IV or IM x 20d[41]	20 mg Sb/kg/d IV or IM x 20d[41]
OR	Meglumine antimonate*	20 mg Sb/kg/d IV or IM x 20d[41]	20 mg Sb/kg/d IV or IM x 20d[41]
Alternatives:[46]	Pentamidine[7]	2-3 mg/kg IV or IM daily or every second day x 4-7 doses[47]	2-3 mg/kg IV or IM daily or every second day x 4-7 doses[47]
OR	Paromomycin[7,48]	Topically 2x/d x 10-20d	Topically 2x/d x 10-20d
Mucosal[49]			
Drugs of choice:	Sodium stibo-gluconate*	20 mg Sb/kg/d IV or IM x 28d[41]	20 mg Sb/kg/d IV or IM x 28d[41]
OR	Meglumine antimonate*	20 mg Sb/kg/d IV or IM x 28d[41]	20 mg Sb/kg/d IV or IM x 28d[41]
OR	Amphotericin B[7]	0.5-1 mg/kg IV daily or every second day for up to 8wks	0.5-1 mg/kg IV daily or every second day for up to 8wks

*   Availability problems. See table on page 12.

39. In immunocompetent patients usually a self-limited illness. Immunosuppressed patients may need higher doses, longer duration (TMP/SMX qid x 10d, followed by bid x 3wks) and long-term maintenance. In sulfonamide-sensitive patients, pyrimethamine 50-75 mg daily in divided doses (plus leucovorin 10-25 mg/d) has been effective.

40. Visceral infection is most commonly due to the Old World species *L. donovani* (kala-azar) and *L. infantum* and the New World species *L. chagasi*. Treatment duration may vary based on symptoms, host immune status, species and area of the world where infection was acquired.

41. May be repeated or continued; a longer duration may be needed for some patients (BL Herwaldt, Lancet 1999; 354:1191).

42. Three lipid formulations of amphotericin B have been used for treatment of visceral leishmaniasis. Largely based on clinical trials in patients infected with *L. infantum*, the FDA approved liposomal amphotericin B *(AmBisome)* for treatment of visceral leishmaniasis (A Meyerhoff, Clin Infect Dis 1999; 28:42). Amphotericin B lipid complex *(Abelcet)* and amphotericin B cholesteryl sulfate *(Amphotec)* have also been used with good results but are considered investigational for this condition by the FDA.

43. The FDA-approved dosage regimen for immunocompromised patients (e.g., HIV infected) is 4 mg/kg/d (d 1-5) and 4 mg/kg/d on d 10, 17, 24, 31 and 38. The relapse rate is high; maintenance therapy may be indicated, but there is no consensus as to dosage or duration.

44. For treatment of kala-azar in adults in India, oral miltefosine 100 mg/d (~2.5 mg/kg/d) for 3-4wks was 97% effective after 6mos (TK Jha et al, N Engl J Med 1999; 341:1795; H Sangraula et al, J Assoc Physicians India 2003; 51:686). Gastrointestinal adverse effects are common, and the drug is contraindicated in pregnancy. The dose of miltefosine in an open-label trial in children in India was 2.5 mg/kg/d x 28d (SK Bhattacharya et al, Clin Infect Dis 2004; 38:217). Miltefosine *(Impavido)* is available from the manufacturer (Zentaris – Frankfurt, Germany at Impavido@zentaris.de).

45. Cutaneous infection is most commonly due to the Old World species *L. major* and *L. tropica* and the New World species *L. mexicana, L. (Viannia) braziliensis* and others. Treatment duration may vary based on symptoms, host immune status, species and area of the world where infection was acquired.

46. In a placebo-controlled trial in patients ≥12 years old, oral miltefosine was effective for the treatment of cutaneous leishmaniasis due to *L.(V.) panamensis* in Colombia but not *L.(V.) braziliensis* in Guatemala at a dosage of about 2.5 mg/kg/d for 28d. "Motion sickness," nausea, headache and increased creatinine were the most frequent adverse effects (J Soto et al, Clin Infect Dis 2004; 38:1266). See footnote 44 regarding miltefosine availability. For treatment of *L. major* cutaneous lesions, a study in Saudi Arabia found that oral fluconazole, 200 mg once/d x 6wks, appeared to speed healing (AA Alrajhi et al, N Engl J Med 2002; 346:891).

47. At this dosage pentamidine has been effective against leishmaniasis in Colombia where the likely organism was *L. (V.) panamensis* (J Soto-Mancipe et al, Clin Infect Dis 1993; 16:417; J Soto et al, Am J Trop Med Hyg 1994; 50:107); its effect against other species is not well established.

48. Topical paromomycin should be used only in geographic regions where cutaneous leishmaniasis species have low potential for mucosal spread. A formulation of 15% paromomycin/12% methylbenzethonium chloride *(Leshcutan)* in soft white paraffin for topical use has been reported to be partially effective in some patients against cutaneous leishmaniasis due to *L. major* in Israel and against *L. mexicana* and *L. (V.) braziliensis* in Guatemala, where mucosal spread is very rare (BA Arana et al, Am J Trop Med Hyg 2001; 65:466). The methylbenzethonium is irritating to the skin; lesions may worsen before they improve.

49. Mucosal infection is most commonly due to the New World species *L. (V.) braziliensis, L. (V.) panamensis,* or *L. (V.) guyanensis*. Treatment duration may vary based on symptoms, host immune status, species and area of the world where infection was acquired.

Infection		Drug	Adult dosage	Pediatric dosage
LICE infestation *(Pediculus humanus, P. capitis, Phthirus pubis)*[50]				
Drug of choice:		0.5% Malathion[51]	Topically	Topically
	OR	1% Permethrin[52]	Topically	Topically
Alternative:		Pyrethrins with piperonyl butoxide[52]	Topically	Topically
	OR	Ivermectin[7, 53]	200 mcg/kg x 3, d 1, 2 and 10	200 mcg/kg x 3, d 1, 2 and 10

Loa loa, see FILARIASIS

MALARIA, Treatment of *(Plasmodium falciparum, P. ovale, P. vivax, and P. malariae)*

P. falciparum[54] acquired in areas of **chloroquine-resistance**

ORAL[55]

Drugs of choice:		Atovaquone/ proguanil[56]	2 adult tabs bid[58] or 4 adult tabs once daily x 3d	<5kg: not indicated 5-8kg: 2 peds tabs once/d x 3d 9-10kg: 3 peds tabs once/d x 3d 11-20kg: 1 adult tab once/d x 3d 21-30kg: 2 adult tabs once/d x 3d 31-40kg: 3 adult tabs once/d x 3d >40kg: 4 adult tabs once/d x 3d
	OR	Quinine sulfate **plus**	650 mg q8h x 3-7d[57]	30 mg/kg/d in 3 doses x 3-7d[57]
		doxycycline[7,14] **or plus**	100 mg bid x 7d	4 mg/kg/d in 2 doses x 7d
		tetracycline[7,14] **or plus**	250 mg qid x 7d	6.25 mg/kg qid x 7d
		clindamycin[7,59]	20 mg/kg/d in 3 doses x 7d[60]	20 mg/kg/d in 3 doses x 7d
Alternatives:		Mefloquine[61]	750 mg followed 12 hrs later by 500 mg	15 mg/kg followed 12 hrs later by 10 mg/kg
		Artesunate[62]* **plus**	4 mg/kg/d x 3d	4 mg/kg/d x 3d
		mefloquine[61]	750 mg followed 12 hrs later by 500 mg	15 mg/kg followed 12 hrs later by 10 mg/kg

* Availability problems. See table on page 12.

50. For infestation of eyelashes with *P. pubis* lice, use petrolatum; TMP/SMX has also been used (TL Meinking, Curr Probl Dermatol 1996; 24:157). For pubic lice, treat with 5% permethrin or ivermectin as for scabies (see page 9). TMP/SMX has also been effective together with permethrin for head lice (RB Hipolito et al, Pediatrics 2001; 107:E30).

51. KS Yoon et al, Arch Dermatol 2003; 139:994.

52. A second application is recommended one week later to kill hatching progeny. Some lice are resistant to pyrethrins and permethrin (TL Meinking et al, Arch Dermatol 2002; 138:220).

53. Ivermectin is effective against adult lice but has no effect on nits (KN Jones and JC English III, Clin Infect Dis 2003; 36:1355).

54. Chloroquine-resistant *P. falciparum* occurs in all malarious areas except Central America west of the Panama Canal Zone, Mexico, Haiti, the Dominican Republic, and most of the Middle East (chloroquine resistance has been reported in Yemen, Oman, Saudi Arabia and Iran). For treatment of multiple-drug-resistant *P. falciparum* in Southeast Asia, especially Thailand, where resistance to mefloquine is frequent, atovaquone/proguanil, artesunate plus mefloquine or artemether plus mefloquine may be used (JC Luxemburger et al, Trans R Soc Trop Med Hyg 1994; 88:213; J Karbwang et al, Trans R Soc Trop Med Hyg 1995; 89:296).

55. Uncomplicated or mild malaria may be treated with oral drugs.

56. Atovaquone plus proguanil is available as a fixed-dose combination tablet: adult tablets (*Malarone*; 250 mg atovaquone/100 mg proguanil) and pediatric tablets (*Malarone Pediatric*; 62.5 mg atovaquone/25 mg proguanil). To enhance absorption, it should be taken with food or a milky drink. Atovaquone/proguanil should not be given to pregnant women or patients with severe renal impairment (creatinine clearance <30mL/min). There have been several isolated reports of resistance in *P. falciparum* in Africa (E Schwartz et al, Clin Infect Dis 2003; 37:450; A Farnert et al, BMJ 2003; 326:628).

57. In Southeast Asia, relative resistance to quinine has increased and treatment should be continued for 7d.

58. Although approved for once daily dosing, Medical Letter consultants usually divide the dose in two to decrease nausea and vomiting.

59. For use in pregnancy.

60. B Lell and PG Kremsner, Antimicrob Agents Chemother 2002; 46:2315.

61. At this dosage, adverse effects including nausea, vomiting, diarrhea, dizziness, disturbed sense of balance, toxic psychosis and seizures can occur. Mefloquine should not be used for treatment of malaria in pregnancy unless there is no other treatment option because of increased risk for stillbirth (F Nosten et al, Clin Infect Dis 1999; 28:808). It should be avoided for treatment of malaria in persons with active depression or with a history of psychosis or seizures and should be used with caution in persons with psychiatric illness. Mefloquine can be given to patients taking β-blockers if they do not have an underlying arrhythmia; it should not be used in patients with conduction abnormalities. Mefloquine should not be given together with quinine, quinidine or halofantrine, and caution is required in using quinine, quinidine or halofantrine to treat patients with malaria who have taken mefloquine for prophylaxis. Resistance to mefloquine has been reported in some areas, such as the Thailand-Myanmar and Thailand-Cambodia borders and in the Amazon basin, where 25 mg/kg should be used. In the US, a 250-mg tablet of mefloquine contains 228 mg mefloquine base. Outside the US, each 275-mg tablet contains 250 mg base.

62. F Nosten et al, Lancet 2000; 356:297; M van Vugt, Clin Infect Dis 2002; 35:1498.

Infection	Drug	Adult dosage	Pediatric dosage
MALARIA, Treatment of (continued)			
P. vivax[63] acquired in areas of **chloroquine-resistance**			
ORAL[55]			
Drug of choice:	Quinine sulfate **plus**	650 mg q8h x 3-7d[57]	30 mg/kg/d in 3 doses x 3-7d[57]
	doxycycline[7,14]	100 mg bid x 7d	4 mg/kg/d in 2 doses x 7d
OR	Mefloquine[61]	750 mg followed 12 hrs later by 500 mg	15 mg/kg followed 12 hrs later by 10 mg/kg
Alternatives:	Chloroquine **plus**	25 mg base/kg in 3 doses over 48 hrs	25 mg base/kg in 3 doses over 48 hrs
	primaquine[64]	30 mg base daily x 14d	0.6 mg/kg/d x 14d
All *Plasmodium* except **Chloroquine-resistant *P. falciparum***[54] and **Chloroquine-resistant *P. vivax***[63]			
ORAL[55]			
Drug of choice:	Chloroquine phosphate[65]	1 g (600 mg base), then 500 mg (300 mg base) 6 hrs later, then 500 mg (300 mg base) at 24 and 48 hrs	10 mg base/kg (max. 600 mg base), then 5 mg base/kg 6 hrs later, then 5 mg base/kg at 24 and 48 hrs
All *Plasmodium*			
PARENTERAL			
Drug of choice:[66]	Quinidine gluconate[67]	10 mg/kg loading dose (max. 600 mg) in normal saline over 1-2 hrs, followed by continuous infusion of 0.02 mg/kg/min until PO therapy can be started	10 mg/kg loading dose (max. 600 mg) in normal saline over 1-2 hrs, followed by continuous infusion of 0.02 mg/kg/min until PO therapy can be started
OR	Quinine dihydro-chloride[67]*	20 mg/kg loading dose in 5% dextrose over 4 hrs, followed by 10 mg/kg over 2-4 hrs q8h (max. 1800 mg/d) until PO therapy can be started	20 mg/kg loading dose in 5% dextrose over 4 hrs, followed by 10 mg/kg over 2-4 hrs q8h (max. 1800 mg/d) until PO therapy can be started
Alternative:	Artemether[68]*	3.2 mg/kg IM, then 1.6 mg/kg daily x 5-7d	3.2 mg/kg IM, then 1.6 mg/kg daily x 5-7d
Prevention of relapses: *P. vivax* and *P. ovale* only			
Drug of choice:	Primaquine phosphate[64]	30 mg base/d x 14d	0.6 mg base/kg/d x 14d
MALARIA, Prevention of[69]			
Chloroquine-sensitive areas[54]			
Drug of choice:	Chloroquine phosphate[70,71]	500 mg (300 mg base), once/wk[72]	5 mg/kg base once/wk, up to adult dose of 300 mg base[72]

* Availability problems. See table on page 12.

63. *P. vivax* with decreased susceptibility to chloroquine is a significant problem in Papua New Guinea and Indonesia. There are also a few reports of resistance from Myanmar, India, the Solomon Islands, Vanuatu, Guyana, Brazil, Colombia and Peru.

64. Primaquine phosphate can cause hemolytic anemia, especially in patients whose red cells are deficient in glucose-6-phosphate dehydrogenase. This deficiency is most common in African, Asian and Mediterranean peoples. Patients should be screened for G-6-PD deficiency before treatment. Primaquine should not be used during pregnancy.

65. If chloroquine phosphate is not available, hydroxychloroquine sulfate is as effective; 400 mg of hydroxychloroquine sulfate is equivalent to 500 mg of chloroquine phosphate.

66. Exchange transfusion has been helpful for some patients with high-density (>10%) parasitemia, altered mental status, pulmonary edema or renal complications (KD Miller et al, N Engl J Med 1989; 321:65).

67. Continuous EKG, blood pressure and glucose monitoring are recommended, especially in pregnant women and young children. For problems with quinidine availability, call the manufacturer (Eli Lilly, 800-545-5979) or the CDC Malaria Hotline (770-488-7788). Quinidine may have greater antimalarial activity than quinine. The loading dose should be decreased or omitted in those patients who have received quinine or mefloquine. If more than 48 hours of parenteral treatment is required, the quinine or quinidine dose should be reduced by 30-50%.

68. Limited studies of efficacy except with *P. falciparum*; not FDA-approved or available in the US (Artemether-Quinine Meta-Analysis Study Group, Trans R Soc Trop Med Hyg 2001; 95:637; K Marsh, East Afr Med J 2002; 79:619).

69. No drug regimen guarantees protection against malaria. If fever develops within a year (particularly within the first two months) after travel to malarious areas, travelers should be advised to seek medical attention. Insect repellents, insecticide-impregnated bed nets and proper clothing are important adjuncts for malaria prophylaxis (Medical Letter 2003; 45:41). Malaria in pregnancy is particularly serious for both mother and fetus; therefore, prophylaxis is indicated if exposure can not be avoided.

70. In pregnancy, chloroquine prophylaxis has been used extensively and safely.

71. For prevention of attack after departure from areas where *P. vivax* and *P. ovale* are endemic, which includes almost all areas where malaria is found (except Haiti), some experts prescribe in addition primaquine phosphate 30 mg base/d or, for children, 0.6 mg base/kg/d during the last 2wks of prophylaxis. Others prefer to avoid the toxicity of primaquine and rely on surveillance to detect cases when they occur, particularly when exposure was limited or doubtful. See also footnote 64.

72. Beginning 1-2wks before travel and continuing weekly for the duration of stay and for 4wks after leaving.

73. Beginning 1-2d before travel and continuing for the duration of stay and for 1wk after leaving. In one study of malaria prophylaxis, atovaquone/proguanil was better tolerated than mefloquine in nonimmune travelers (D Overbosch et al, Clin Infect Dis 2001; 33:1015).

Infection	Drug	Adult dosage	Pediatric dosage
MALARIA, Prevention of (continued)			
Chloroquine-resistant areas[54]			
Drug of choice:	Atovaquone/ proguanil[56,71]	1 adult tab/d[73]	11-20kg: 1 peds tab/d[56,73] 21-30kg: 2 peds tabs/d[56,73] 31-40kg: 3 peds tabs/d[56,73] >40kg: 1 adult tab/d[56,73]
OR	Mefloquine[61,71,74]	250 mg once/wk[72]	5-10kg: 1/8 tab once/wk[72] 11-20kg: 1/4 tab once/wk[72] 21-30kg: 1/2 tab once/wk[72] 31-45kg: 3/4 tab once/wk[72] >45kg: 1 tab once/wk[72]
OR	Doxycycline[7,71]	100 mg daily[75]	2 mg/kg/d, up to 100 mg/d[75]
Alternatives:	Primaquine[7,64]	30 mg base daily[76]	0.6 mg/kg base daily
	Chloroquine phosphate	500 mg (300 mg base) once/wk[72]	5 mg/kg base once/wk, up to 300 mg base[72]
	plus proguanil[77]	200 mg once/d	<2yrs: 50 mg once/d 2-6yrs: 100 mg once/d 7-10yrs: 150 mg once/d >10yrs: 200 mg once/d
MALARIA, Self-Presumptive Treatment[78]			
Drug of Choice:	Atovaquone/ proguanil[7,56]	4 adult tabs daily x 3d	<5kg: not indicated 5-8kg: 2 peds tabs once/d x 3d 9-10kg: 3 peds tabs once/d x 3d 11-20kg: 1 adult tab once/d x 3d 21-30kg: 2 adult tabs once/d x 3d 31-40kg: 3 adult tabs once/d x 3d >40kg: 4 adult tabs once/d x 3d
OR	Quinine sulfate **plus**	650 mg q8h x 3-7d[57]	30 mg/kg/d in 3 doses x 3-7d[57]
	doxycycline[7,14]	100 mg bid x 7d	4 mg/kg/d in 2 doses x 7d
OR	Mefloquine[61]	750 mg followed 12 hrs later by 500 mg	15 mg/kg followed 12 hrs later by 10 mg/kg

MICROSPORIDIOSIS

Ocular (*Encephalitozoon hellem, Encephalitozoon cuniculi, Vittaforma corneae [Nosema corneum]*)

Drug of choice:	Albendazole[7] **plus** fumagillin[79]*	400 mg bid	

Intestinal (*Enterocytozoon bieneusi, Encephalitozoon [Septata] intestinalis*)

E. bieneusi[80]

Drug of choice:	Fumagillin*	60 mg/d PO x 14d	

E. intestinalis

Drug of choice:	Albendazole[7]	400 mg bid x 21d	

Disseminated (*E. hellem, E. cuniculi, E. intestinalis, Pleistophora sp., Trachipleistophora sp.* and *Brachiola vesicularum*)

Drug of choice:[81]	Albendazole[7]	400 mg bid	

Mites, see SCABIES

MONILIFORMIS *moniliformis* infection

Drug of choice:	Pyrantel pamoate[7]	11 mg/kg once, repeat twice, 2wks apart	11 mg/kg once, repeat twice, 2wks apart

*   Availability problems. See table on page 12.

74. Mefloquine has not been approved for use during pregnancy. However, it has been reported to be safe for prophylactic use during the second or third trimester of pregnancy and possibly during early pregnancy as well (CDC Health Information for International Travel, 2003-2004, page 111; BL Smoak et al, J Infect Dis 1997; 176:831). For pediatric doses <1/2 tablet, it is advisable to have a pharmacist crush the tablet, estimate doses by weighing, and package them in gelatin capsules. There is no data for use in children <5 kg, but based on dosages in other weight groups, a dose of 5 mg/kg can be used. Mefloquine is not recommended for patients with cardiac conduction abnormalities, and patients with a history of depression, seizures, psychosis or psychiatric disorders should avoid mefloquine prophylaxis. Resistance to mefloquine has been reported in some areas, such as the Thailand-Myanmar and Thailand-Cambodia borders; in these areas, atovaquone/ proguanil or doxycycline should be used for prophylaxis.

75. Beginning 1-2d before travel and continuing for the duration of stay and for 4wks after leaving. Use of tetracyclines is contraindicated in pregnancy and in children <8 years old. Doxycycline can cause gastrointestinal disturbances, vaginal moniliasis and photosensitivity reactions.

76. Studies have shown that daily primaquine beginning 1d before departure and continued until 3-7d after leaving the malaria area provides effective prophylaxis against chloroquine-resistant *P. falciparum* (JK Baird et al, Clin Infect Dis 2003; 37:1659). Some studies have shown less efficacy against *P. vivax*. Nausea and abdominal pain can be diminished by taking with food.

77. Proguanil (*Paludrine* – Wyeth Ayerst, Canada; AstraZeneca, United Kingdom), which is not available alone in the US but is widely available in Canada and Europe, is recommended mainly for use in Africa south of the Sahara. Prophylaxis is recommended during exposure and for 4wks afterwards. Proguanil has been used in pregnancy without evidence of toxicity (PA Phillips-Howard and D Wood, Drug Saf 1996; 14:131).

78. A traveler can be given a course of atovaquone/proguanil, mefloquine or quinine plus doxycycline for presumptive self-treatment of febrile illness. The drug given for self-treatment should be different from that used for prophylaxis. This approach should be used only in very rare circumstances when a traveler can not promptly get to medical care.

79. Ocular lesions due to *E. hellem* in HIV-infected patients have responded to fumagillin eyedrops prepared from *Fumidil-B*, (bicyclohexyl ammonium fumagillin) used to control a microsporidial disease of honey bees (MC Diesenhouse, Am J Ophthalmol 1993; 115:293), available from Leiter's Park Avenue Pharmacy (see footnote 1). For lesions due to *V. corneae*, topical therapy is generally not effective and keratoplasty may be required (RM Davis et al, Ophthalmology 1990; 97:953).

80. Oral fumagillin (Sanofi Recherche, Gentilly, France) has been effective in treating *E. bieneusi* (J-M Molina et al, N Engl J Med 2002; 346:1963), but has been associated with thrombocytopenia. Highly active antiretroviral therapy (HAART) may lead to microbiologic and clinical response in HIV-infected patients with microsporidial diarrhea (USPHS/IDSA Guidelines for the Treatment of Opportunistic Infections in Adults and Adolescents with HIV, 2004; In press). Octreotide (*Sandostatin*) has provided symptomatic relief in some patients with large-volume diarrhea.

81. J-M Molina et al, J Infect Dis 1995; 171:245. There is no established treatment for *Pleistophora*. For disseminated disease due to *Trachipleistophora* or *Brachiola*, itraconazole 400 mg PO once/d plus albendazole may also be tried (CM Coyle et al, N Engl J Med 2004; 351:42).

Infection		Drug	Adult dosage	Pediatric dosage
***Naegleria* species**, see AMEBIC MENINGOENCEPHALITIS, PRIMARY				
Necator americanus, see HOOKWORM infection				
OESOPHAGOSTOMUM *bifurcum*				
Drug of choice:		See footnote 82		
Onchocerca volvulus, see FILARIASIS				
Opisthorchis viverrini, see FLUKE infection				
Paragonimus westermani, see FLUKE infection				
Pediculus capitis, humanus, Phthirus pubis, see LICE				
Pinworm, see ENTEROBIUS				
PNEUMOCYSTIS JIROVECI (formerly *carinii*) pneumonia (PCP)[83]				
Drug of choice:		Trimethoprim-sulfamethoxazole	TMP 15 mg/kg/d, SMX 75 mg/kg/d, PO or IV in 3 or 4 doses x 14-21d	TMP 15 mg/kg/d, SMX 75 mg/kg/d, PO or IV in 3 or 4 doses x 14-21d
Alternatives:		Primaquine[7,64]	30 mg base PO daily x 21d	
		plus clindamycin[7]	600 mg IV q6h x 21d, or 300-450 mg PO q6h x 21d	
	OR	Trimethoprim[7]	5 mg/kg tid x 21d	
		plus dapsone[7]	100 mg daily x 21d	
	OR	Pentamidine	3-4 mg/kg IV daily x 14-21d	3-4 mg/kg IV daily x 14-21d
	OR	Atovaquone	750 mg bid x 21d	1-3mos: 30 mg/kg/d
				4-24mos: 45 mg/kg/d
				>24mos: 30 mg/d
Primary and secondary prophylaxis[84]				
Drug of Choice:		Trimethoprim-sulfamethoxazole	1 tab (single or double strength) daily	TMP 150 mg/m^2, SMX 750 mg/m^2 in 2 doses on 3 consecutive days per wk
Alternatives:[85]		Dapsone[7]	50 mg bid, or 100 mg daily	2 mg/kg/d (max. 100 mg) or 4 mg/kg (max. 200 mg) each wk
	OR	Dapsone[7]	50 mg daily or 200 mg each wk	
		plus pyrimethamine[86]	50 mg or 75 mg each wk	
	OR	Pentamidine aerosol	300 mg inhaled monthly via *Respirgard II* nebulizer	≥5yrs: 300 mg inhaled monthly via *Respirgard II* nebulizer
	OR	Atovaquone[7]	1500 mg daily	1-3mos: 30 mg/kg/d
				4-24mos: 45 mg/kg/d
				>24mos: 30 mg/kg/d
Roundworm, see ASCARIASIS				
Sappinia Diploidea, See AMEBIC MENINGOENCEPHALITIS, PRIMARY				
SCABIES *(Sarcoptes scabiei)*				
Drug of choice:		5% Permethrin	Topically[87]	Topically[87]
Alternatives:[88]		Ivermectin[7,89]	200 mcg/kg once[87]	200 mcg/kg once[87]
		10% Crotamiton	Topically once/daily x 2	Topically once/daily x 2
SCHISTOSOMIASIS *(Bilharziasis)*				
S. haematobium				
Drug of choice:		Praziquantel	40 mg/kg/d in 2 doses x 1d	40 mg/kg/d in 2 doses x 1d
S. japonicum				
Drug of choice:		Praziquantel	60 mg/kg/d in 3 doses x 1d	60 mg/kg/d in 3 doses x 1d
S. mansoni				
Drug of choice:		Praziquantel	40 mg/kg/d in 2 doses x 1d	40 mg/kg/d in 2 doses x 1d
Alternative:		Oxamniquine[90]*	15 mg/kg once[91]	20 mg/kg/d in 2 doses x 1d[91]
S. mekongi				
Drug of choice:		Praziquantel	60 mg/kg/d in 3 doses x 1d	60 mg/kg/d in 3 doses x 1d

*   Availability problems. See table on page 12.
82. Albendazole or pyrantel pamoate may be effective (JB Ziem et al, Ann Trop Med Parasitol 2004; 98:385).
83. Pneumocystis has been reclassified as a fungus. In severe disease with room air PO$_2$ ≤ 70 mmHg or Aa gradient ≥ 35 mmHg, prednisone should also be used (S Gagnon et al, N Engl J Med 1990; 323:1444; E Caumes et al, Clin Infect Dis 1994; 18:319).
84. Primary/secondary prophylaxis in patients with HIV can be discontinued after CD4 count increases to >200 x 10^6/L for >3mos.
85. An alternative trimethoprim/sulfamethoxazole regimen is one DS tab 3x/wk. Weekly therapy with sulfadoxine 500 mg/pyrimethamine 25 mg/leucovorin 25 mg was effective PCP prophylaxis in liver transplant patients (J Torre-Cisneros et al, Clin Infect Dis 1999; 29:771).
86. Plus leucovorin 25 mg with each dose of pyrimethamine.
87. In some cases, treatment may need to be repeated in 10-14 days.
88. Lindane (γ-benzene hexachloride; *Kwell*) should be reserved as a second-line agent. The FDA has recommended it should not be used for immunocompromised patients, young children, the elderly, and patients <50 kg.
89. Ivermectin, either alone or in combination with a topical scabicide, is the drug of choice for crusted scabies in immunocompromised patients (P del Giudice, Curr Opin Infect Dis 2004; 15:123). The safety of oral ivermectin in pregnancy and young children has not been established.
90. Oxamniquine has been effective in some areas in which praziquantel is less effective (FF Stelma et al, J Infect Dis 1997; 176:304). Oxamniquine is contraindicated in pregnancy.
91. In East Africa, the dose should be increased to 30 mg/kg, and in Egypt and South Africa to 30 mg/kg/d x 2d. Some experts recommend 40-60 mg/kg over 2-3d in all of Africa (KC Shekhar, Drugs 1991; 42:379).

Infection	Drug	Adult dosage	Pediatric dosage
Sleeping sickness, see TRYPANOSOMIASIS			
STRONGYLOIDIASIS (*Strongyloides stercoralis*)			
Drug of choice:[92]	Ivermectin	200 mcg/kg/d x 2d	200 mcg/kg/d x 2d
Alternative:	Albendazole[7]	400 mg bid x 7d	400 mg bid x 7d
OR	Thiabendazole	50 mg/kg/d in 2 doses x 2d (max 3g/d)[93]	50 mg/kg/d in 2 doses x 2d (max 3g/d)[93]
TAPEWORM infection			
— **Adult** (intestinal stage)			
Diphyllobothrium latum (fish), *Taenia saginata* (beef), *Taenia solium* (pork), *Dipylidium caninum* (dog)			
Drug of choice:	Praziquantel[7]	5-10 mg/kg once	5-10 mg/kg once
Alternative:	Niclosamide*	2 g once	50 mg/kg once
Hymenolepis nana (dwarf tapeworm)			
Drug of choice:	Praziquantel[7]	25 mg/kg once	25 mg/kg once
Alternative:	Nitazoxanide[4,7]	500 mg x 3d[94]	1-3yrs: 100 mg bid x 3d[94] 4-11yrs: 200 mg bid x 3d[94]
— **Larval** (tissue stage)			
Echinococcus granulosus (hydatid cyst)			
Drug of choice:[95]	Albendazole	400 mg bid x 1-6mos	15 mg/kg/d (max. 800 mg) x 1-6mos
Echinococcus multilocularis			
Treatment of choice:	See footnote 96		
Taenia solium (Cysticercosis)			
Treatment of choice:	See footnote 97		
Alternative:	Albendazole	400 mg bid x 8-30d; can be repeated as necessary	15 mg/kg/d (max. 800 mg) in 2 doses x 8-30d; can be repeated as necessary
OR	Praziquantel[7]	50-100 mg/kg/d in 3 doses x 30d	50-100 mg/kg/d in 3 doses x 30d
Toxocariasis, see VISCERAL LARVA MIGRANS			
TOXOPLASMOSIS (*Toxoplasma gondii*)[98]			
Drugs of choice:[99,100]	Pyrimethamine[101]	25-100 mg/d x 3-4wks	2 mg/kg/d x 3d, then 1 mg/kg/d (max. 25 mg/d) x 4wks[102]
	plus		
	sulfadiazine	1-1.5 g qid 3-4wks	100-200 mg/kg/d x 3-4wks
TRICHINELLOSIS (*Trichinella spiralis*)			
Drugs of choice:	Steroids for severe symptoms		
	plus		
	mebendazole[7]	200-400 mg tid x 3d, then 400-500 mg tid x 10d	200-400 mg tid x 3d, then 400-500 mg tid x 10d
Alternative:	Albendazole[7]	400 mg bid x 8-14d	400 mg bid x 8-14d
TRICHOMONIASIS (*Trichomonas vaginalis*)			
Drug of choice:[103]	Metronidazole	2 g once or 500 mg bid x 7d	15 mg/kg/d orally in 3 doses x 7d
OR	Tinidazole[5]	2 g once	50 mg/kg once (max. 2 g)

* Availability problems. See table on page 12.

92. In immunocompromised patients or disseminated disease, it may be necessary to prolong or repeat therapy, or to use other agents. Veterinary parenteral and enema formulations of ivermectin have been used in severely ill patients unable to take oral medications (PL Chiodini et al, Lancet 2000; 355:43; J Orem et al, Clin Infect Dis 2003; 37:152; PE Tarr Am J Trop Med Hyg 2003; 68:453).

93. This dosage is likely to be toxic and may have to be decreased.

94. JO Juan et al, Trans R Soc Trop Med Hyg 2002; 96:193.

95. Patients may benefit from surgical resection or percutaneous drainage of cysts. Praziquantel is useful preoperatively or in case of spillage of cyst contents during surgery. Percutaneous aspiration-injection-reaspiration (PAIR) with ultrasound guidance plus albendazole therapy has been effective for management of hepatic hydatid cyst disease (RA Smego, Jr., et al, Clin Infect Dis 2003; 37:1073).

96. Surgical excision is the only reliable means of cure. Reports have suggested that in nonresectable cases use of albendazole or mebendazole can stabilize and sometimes cure infection (P Craig, Curr Opin Infect Dis 2003; 16:437).

97. Initial therapy for patients with inflammed parenchymal cysticercosis should focus on symptomatic treatment with anti-seizure medication. Treatment of parenchymal cysticerci with albendazole or praziquantel is controversial (JM Maguire, N Engl J Med 2004; 350:215). Patients with live parenchymal cysts who have seizures should be treated with albendazole together with steroids (6 mg dexamethasone or 40-60 mg prednisone daily) and an anti-seizure medication (HH Garcia et al, N Engl J Med 2004; 350:249). Patients with subarachnoid cysts or giant cysts in the fissures should be treated for at least 30d (JV Proaño et al, N Engl J Med 2001; 345:879). Surgical intervention or CSF diversion is indicated for obstructive hydocephalus; prednisone 40 mg/d may be given with surgery. Arachnoiditis, vasculitis or cerebral edema is treated with prednisone 60 mg/d or dexamethasone 4-6 mg/d together with albendazole or praziquantel (AC White, Jr., Annu Rev Med 2000; 51:187). Any cysticercocidal drug may cause irreparable damage when used to treat ocular or spinal cysts, even when corticosteroids are used. An ophthalmic exam should always precede treatment to rule out intraocular cysts.

98. In ocular toxoplasmosis with macular involvement, corticosteroids are recommended in addition to antiparasitic therapy for an anti-inflammatory effect.

99. To treat CNS toxoplasmosis in HIV-infected patients, some clinicians have used pyrimethamine 50-100 mg/d (after a loading dose of 200 mg) with sulfadiazine and, when sulfonamide sensitivity developed, have given clindamycin 1.8-2.4 g/d in divided doses instead of the sulfonamide. Atovaquone plus pyrimethamine appears to be an effective alternative in sulfa-intolerant patients (K Chirgwin et al, Clin Infect Dis 2002; 34:1243). Treatment is followed by chronic suppression with lower dosage regimens of the same drugs. For primary prophylaxis in HIV patients with <100 x 10⁶/L CD4 cells, either trimethoprim-sulfamethoxazole, pyrimethamine with dapsone, or atovaquone with or without pyrimethamine can be used. Primary or secondary prophylaxis may be discontinued when the CD4 count increases to >200 x 10⁶/L for more than 3 months (USPHS/IDSA Guidelines for the Treatment of Opportunistic Infections in Adults and Adolescents with HIV, 2004; In press).

100. Women who develop toxoplasmosis during the first trimester of pregnancy can be treated with spiramycin (3-4 g/d). After the first trimester, if there is no documented transmission to the fetus, spiramycin can be continued until term. If transmission has occurred *in utero*, therapy with pyrimethamine and sulfadiazine should be started (JG Montoya and O Liesenfeld, Lancet 2004; 363:1965). Pyrimethamine is a potential teratogen and should be used only after the first trimester.

101. Plus leucovorin 10-25 mg with each dose of pyrimethamine.

102. Congenitally infected newborns should be treated with pyrimethamine every 2 or 3 days and a sulfonamide daily for about one year (JS Remington and G Desmonts in JS Remington and JO Klein, eds, Infectious Disease of the Fetus and Newborn Infant, 5th ed, Philadelphia:Saunders, 2001, page 290).

103. Sexual partners should be treated simultaneously. Metronidazole-resistant strains have been reported and can be treated with higher doses of metronidazole (2-4 g/d x 7-14d) or with tinidazole (WD Hager, Sex Transm Dis 2004; 31:343).

Infection	Drug	Adult dosage	Pediatric dosage
TRICHOSTRONGYLUS infection			
Drug of choice:	Pyrantel pamoate[7]	11 mg/kg base once (max. 1 g)	11 mg/kg once (max. 1 g)
Alternative:	Mebendazole[7]	100 mg bid x 3d	100 mg bid x 3d
OR	Albendazole[7]	400 mg once	400 mg once
TRICHURIASIS (*Trichuris trichiura*, whipworm)			
Drug of choice:	Mebendazole	100 mg bid x 3d or 500 mg once	100 mg bid x 3d or 500 mg once
Alternative:	Albendazole[7]	400 mg x 3d	400 mg x 3d
	Ivermectin[7]	200 mcg/kg daily x 3d	200 mcg/kg daily x 3d
TRYPANOSOMIASIS[104]			
T. cruzi (American trypanosomiasis, Chagas' disease)			
Drug of choice:	Benznidazole*	5-7 mg/kg/d in 2 divided doses x 30-90d	≤12yrs: 10 mg/kg/d in 2 doses x 30-90d
OR	Nifurtimox[105]*	8-10 mg/kg/d in 3-4 doses x 90-120d	1-10yrs: 15-20 mg/kg/d in 4 doses x 90d 11-16yrs: 12.5-15 mg/kg/d in 4 doses x 90d
T. brucei gambiense (West African trypanosomiasis, sleeping sickness) **hemolymphatic stage**			
Drug of choice:[106]	Pentamidine isethionate[7]	4 mg/kg/d IM x 10d	4 mg/kg/d IM x 10d
Alternative:	Suramin*	100-200 mg (test dose) IV, then 1 g IV on days 1,3,7,14 and 21	20 mg/kg on days 1,3,7,14 and 21
Late disease with CNS involvement			
Drug of Choice:	Melarsoprol[107]	2.2 mg/kg/d x 10d	2.2 mg/kg/d x 10d
OR	Eflornithine[108]*	400 mg/kg/d in 4 doses x 14d	400 mg/kg/d in 4 doses x 14d
T. b. rhodesiense (East African trypanosomiasis, sleeping sickness) **hemolymphatic stage**			
Drug of choice:	Suramin*	100-200 mg (test dose) IV, then 1 g IV on days 1,3,7,14 and 21	20 mg/kg on days 1,3,7,14 and 21
Late disease with CNS involvement			
Drug of choice:	Melarsoprol[107]	2-3.6 mg/kg/d x 3d; after 7d 3.6 mg/kg/d x 3d; repeat again after 7d	2-3.6 mg/kg/d x 3d; after 7d 3.6 mg/kg/d x 3d; repeat again after 7d
VISCERAL LARVA MIGRANS[109] (*Toxocariasis*)			
Drug of choice:	Albendazole[7]	400 mg bid x 5d	400 mg bid x 5d
	Mebendazole[7]	100-200 mg bid x 5d	100-200 mg bid x 5d
Whipworm, see TRICHURIASIS			
Wuchereria bancrofti, see FILARIASIS			

* Availability problems. See table on page 12.
104. MP Barrett et al, Lancet 2003; 362:1469.
105. The addition of gamma interferon to nifurtimox for 20d in experimental animals and in a limited number of patients appears to shorten the acute phase of Chagas' disease (RE McCabe et al, J Infect Dis 1991; 163:912).
106. For treatment of *T.b. gambiense*, pentamidine and suramin have equal efficacy but pentamidine is better tolerated.
107. In frail patients, begin with as little as 18 mg and increase the dose progressively. Pretreatment with suramin has been advocated for debilitated patients. Corticosteroids have been used to prevent arsenical encephalopathy (J Pepin et al, Trans R Soc Trop Med Hyg 1995; 89:92). Up to 20% of patients with *T.b. gambiense* fail to respond to melarsoprol (MP Barrett, Lancet 1999; 353:1113).
108. Eflornithine is highly effective in *T.b. gambiense* but not against *T.b. rhodesiense* infections. It is available in limited supply only from the WHO and the CDC.
109. Optimum duration of therapy is not known; some Medical Letter consultants would treat for 20d. For severe symptoms or eye involvement, corticosteroids can be used in addition.

MANUFACTURERS OF DRUGS USED TO TREAT PARASITIC INFECTIONS

albendazole – *Albenza* (GlaxoSmithKline)
Albenza (GlaxoSmithKline) – albendazole
Alinia (Romark) – nitazoxanide
amphotericin – *Fungizone* (Apothecon), others
Ancobon (ICN) – flucytosine
§ *Antiminth* (Pfizer) – pyrantel pamoate
• *Aralen* (Sanofi) – chloroquine HCl and chloroquine
   phosphate
§ artemether – *Artenam* (Arenco, Belgium)
§ *Artenam* (Arenco, Belgium) – artemether
§ artesunate – (Guilin No. 1 Factory, People's Republic
   of China)
atovaquone – *Mepron* (GlaxoSmithKline)
atovaquone/proguanil – *Malarone* (GlaxoSmithKline)
azithromycin – *Zithromax* (Pfizer)
• *Bactrim* (Roche) – TMP/Sulfa
§ benznidazole – *Rochagan* (Roche, Brazil)
Biaxin (Abbott) – clarithromycin
§ *Biltricide* (Bayer) – praziquantel
† bithionol – *Bitin* (Tanabe, Japan)
† *Bitin* (Tanabe, Japan) – bithionol
§ *Brolene* (Aventis, Canada) – propamidine isethionate
chloroquine HCl and chloroquine phosphate – *Aralen*
   (Sanofi), others
clarithromycin – *Biaxin* (Abbott)
• *Cleocin* (Pfizer) – clindamycin
clindamycin – *Cleocin* (Pfizer), others
crotamiton – *Eurax* (Westwood-Squibb)
dapsone – (Jacobus)
Daraprim (GlaxoSmithKline) – pyrimethamine USP
† diethylcarbamazine citrate USP – *Hetrazan*
Diflucan (Roerig) – fluconazole
§ diloxanide furoate – *Furamide* (Boots, United Kingdom)
doxycycline – *Vibramycin* (Pfizer), others
† eflornithine (Difluoromethylornithine, DFMO) – *Ornidyl*
   (Aventis)
§ *Egaten* (Novartis) – triclabendazole
Elimite (Allergan) – permethrin
Ergamisol (Janssen) – levamisole
Eurax (Westwood-Squibb) – crotamiton
fluconazole – *Diflucan* (Roerig)
• *Flagyl* (Searle) – metronidazole
flucytosine – *Ancobon* (ICN)
• *Fungizone* (Apothecon) – amphotericin
§ *Furamide* (Boots, United Kingdom) – diloxanide furoate
§ furazolidone – *Furozone* (Roberts)
§ *Furozone* (Roberts) – furazolidone
† *Germanin* (Bayer, Germany) – suramin sodium
§ *Glucantime* (Aventis, France) – meglumine antimonate
† *Hetrazan* – diethylcarbamazine citrate USP
Humatin (Monarch) – paromomycin
§ *Impavido* (Zentaris, Germany) – miltefosine
iodoquinol – *Yodoxin* (Glenwood), others
itraconazole – *Sporanox* (Janssen-Ortho)
ivermectin – *Stromectol* (Merck)
ketoconazole – *Nizoral* (Janssen), others
† *Lampit* (Bayer, Germany) – nifurtimox
Lariam (Roche) – mefloquine
§ *Leshcutan* (Teva, Israel) – topical paromomycin
levamisole – *Ergamisol* (Janssen)
Malarone (GlaxoSmithKline) – atovaquone/proguanil
malathion – *Ovide* (Medicis)
mebendazole – *Vermox* (McNeil)
mefloquine – *Lariam* (Roche)

§ meglumine antimonate – *Glucantime* (Aventis, France)
† melarsoprol – *Mel-B* (Specia)
† *Mel-B* (Specia) – melarsoprol
Mepron (GlaxoSmithKline) – atovaquone
metronidazole – *Flagyl* (Searle), others
§ miltefosine – *Impavido* (Zentaris, Germany)
NebuPent (Fujisawa) – pentamidine isethionate
Neutrexin (US Bioscience) – trimetrexate
§ niclosamide – *Yomesan* (Bayer, Germany)
† nifurtimox – *Lampit* (Bayer, Germany)
nitazoxanide – *Alinia* (Romark)
• *Nizoral* (Janssen) – ketoconazole
Nix (GlaxoSmithKline) – permethrin
§ ornidazole – *Tiberal* (Roche, France)
† *Ornidyl* (Aventis) – eflornithine
   (Difluoromethylornithine, DFMO)
Ovide (Medicis) – malathion
§ oxamniquine – *Vansil* (Pfizer)
§ *Paludrine* (Wyeth Ayerst, Canada; AstraZeneca,
   United Kingdom) – proguanil
paromomycin – *Humatin* (Monarch); *Leshcutan* (Teva,
   Israel; (topical formulation not available in US)
Pentam 300 (Fujisawa) – pentamidine isethionate
pentamidine isethionate – *Pentam 300* (Fujisawa),
   NebuPent (Fujisawa)
† *Pentostam* (GlaxoSmithKline, United Kingdom) – sodium
   stibogluconate
permethrin – *Nix* (GlaxoSmithKline), *Elimite* (Allergan)
§ praziquantel – *Biltricide* (Bayer)
primaquine phosphate USP
§ proguanil – *Paludrine* (Wyeth Ayerst, Canada; AstraZeneca,
   United Kingdom)
proguanil/atovaquone – *Malarone* (GlaxoSmithKline)
§ propamidine isethionate – *Brolene* (Aventis, Canada)
§ pyrantel pamoate – *Antiminth* (Pfizer)
pyrethrins and piperonyl butoxide – *RID* (Pfizer), others
pyrimethamine USP – *Daraprim* (GlaxoSmithKline)
* quinidine gluconate (Eli Lilly)
§ quinine dihydrochloride
quinine sulfate – many manufacturers
• *RID* (Pfizer) – pyrethrins and piperonyl butoxide
• *Rifadin* (Aventis) – rifampin
rifampin – *Rifadin* (Aventis), others
§ *Rochagan* (Roche, Brazil) – benznidazole
* *Rovamycine* (Aventis) – spiramycin
† sodium stibogluconate – *Pentostam* (GlaxoSmithKline,
   United Kingdom)
* spiramycin – *Rovamycine* (Aventis)
Sporanox (Janssen-Ortho) – itraconazole
Stromectol (Merck) – ivermectin
sulfadiazine
† suramin sodium – *Germanin* (Bayer, Germany)
§ *Tiberal* (Roche, France) – ornidazole
Tindamax (Presutti) – tinidazole
tinidazole – *Tindamax* (Presutti)
TMP/Sulfa – *Bactrim* (Roche), others
§ triclabendazole – *Egaten* (Novartis)
trimetrexate – *Neutrexin* (US Bioscience)
§ *Vansil* (Pfizer) – oxamniquine
Vermox (McNeil) – mebendazole
• *Vibramycin* (Pfizer) – doxycycline
• *Yodoxin* (Glenwood) – iodoquinol
§ *Yomesan* (Bayer, Germany) – niclosamide
Zithromax (Pfizer) – azithromycin

---

* Available in the US only from the manufacturer.
§ Not available in the US; may be available through a compounding pharmacy
† Available under an Investigational New Drug (IND) protocol from the CDC Drug Service, Centers for Disease Control and Prevention,
   Atlanta, Georgia 30333; 404-639-3670 (evenings, weekends, or holidays: 404-639-2888).
• Also available generically.

Web Sites of General Interest

1. American Society for Tropical Medicine and Hygiene – www.astmh.org/404.cfm
2. American Society for Parasitologists – asp.unl.edu/medical/
3. The Centers or Disease Control and Prevention – www.cdc.gov
4. Foreign Consular Offices in the United States – www.state.gov/s/cpr/rls/fco/
5. World Health Organization – www.who.org
6. Royal Society of Tropical Medicine and Hygiene – www.rstmh.org/
7. British Society for Parasitology – www.gla.ac.uk/departments/ibls/II/parasitology/bsp/public_html/
8. Infectious Disease Society of America – www.idsociety.org
9. International Federation for Tropical Medicine – www.iftm.org
10. American Society for Tropical Medicine and Hygiene Travel Clinic Directory – www.astmh.org/clinicians/clinics.cfm
11. London School of Hygiene and Tropical Medicine – www.lshtm.ac.uk
12. Medical Ecology – www.medicalecology.org
13. Karolinsk Institute – www.micf.mic.ki.se/Diseases/C03.html

Web Sites of Specific Interest

1. The Trichinella Page – www.trichinella.org
2. Lymphatic filarisis – www.filariasis.org/index.pl
3. Malaria – www.malaria.org
4. Emerging infections – www.fas.org/promed/
5. Laboratory diagnosis and images of parasites – www.dpd.cdc.gov/dpdx/

Journals of Interest

1. American Journal of Tropical Medicine and Hygiene
2. American Journal of Parasitology
3. Transactions of the Royal Society for Tropical Medicine and Hygiene
4. Bulletin of The WHO
5. Molecular and Biochemical Parasitology
6. Parasitology Today
7. Journal of Tropical Pediatrics

Index

d=drawings, t=table, *italics*=figure